Caveat

me tangere

Prologue:
Stage Fright

Why am I here?

I'm standing in an alleyway staring at this door with "Backstage" stenciled across the top, and I ask myself that same question again. Here I am, Melbogathra, newly emerged into the world and eager to undo Creation, yet the first thing I felt when I got here was love... unrequited, fucking love.

Becky.

I can't shake it loose, no matter how many times I stir myself to try. I try spreading my wings, like my primordial self who once dwarfed mountains, but my proverbial wings slam into my ribs. I'm lodged here good, and it makes my head hurt. I grab for the door handle and enter backstage, still wondering.

She finishes applying makeup to someone else in our troupe with a flourish of the brush before waving me into the chair, and I find myself staring at her frail imperfections. I sit wondering what Max saw in her, all the while being enamored by her every inch. So mortal. I love the wild strands of blond hair escaping her red bandana. I love the fatigue creases at the corners of her eyes, and I love her pale strawberry lips. I know her because Max knows her. I love her because Max loves her. Max and I are that close.

Actually Max loved her enough to thread a rope through the ceiling timbers to hang himself when he couldn't win her. Max loved Becky and now, by default, so do I. That's what hits me the hardest.

She catches me staring and dabs my makeup even harder to make me blink and look away. Thanks to my costume's high collar, she can't see the burns on my neck from the rope that all but strangled Max to death, but I still make her uncomfortable. A small frown makes a furrow between her eyebrows.

"I wish you wouldn't do that," she says. I can hear the exasperation in her voice, but I'm too captivated by the bead of sweat racing down her lily-white neck, down past the lip of her loose tank top. I'm too enthralled by the force of her stroke across my cheeks. I marvel at being touched.

Nobody's ever touched me physically before. Not even God.

I reach out to touch her face, and I touch beauty. I don't remember anything so sublime as the warmth of flesh. Compared to being trapped in a hellish Abyss where your skin is jagged rage, this moment is... heaven.

Her frown deepens, and she looks away.

"Jesus, Max," she says, "I don't have time for this." She shoots me one last withering look before she grabs her makeup kit and moves on to the next actor. She never makes eye contact. Part of me wishes she had, so she could see the new intensity burning in my eyes.

But, no, I just would have frightened her away. I know that. My eyes are still too intense. I don't have the mortal skill of subtle duplicity in nuance. I've never had a body before.

I follow Becky with my eyes, ignorant of everybody else's stares. There's a hush in the dressing room. In theater, we call that a pregnant pause.

I catch myself thinking, *Just turn around, Becky. Look at me. Believe in me.*

Charles, the stage manager, pops his head in the door, distracting everyone from the tense moment.

"Curtain in fifteen."

There's a quiet scramble to adjust costumes and apply that last dab of makeup. Becky vanishes behind a pair of actors getting their costumes fixed.

"Hey, Max," Charles says, breaking the moment, "Feeling better?"

I say I am. I leave out the bit where I — Max... whatever — gave up all hope, tied a rope around his neck and made himself a host to a demon.

Yeah, I leave that part out.

"Todd did a great job covering for you," Charles says.

I smile at Todd who's sitting with a book in his lap, all dressed up with nowhere to go.

He gives me an alligator's smile. He wanted my role — a mediocre dream for a mediocre man.

I figure he can probably have my part after tonight.

❖   ❖   ❖   ❖

Everyone's quiet, from actors to the audience. All the actors are staring at me with wide eyes. The audience seems to be holding its breath. No one moves.

I've just improvised a scene before our typically small house, screwing up everybody's lifeless flow of blocking and dialogue. Even the audience can tell this wasn't in the script, and that's got them excited. They're more interested in this unexpected development than in what I was just saying a minute ago.

Don't get me wrong, Caryl Churchill is a fine playwright and dramatist. She's Max's favorite, in fact, so that makes her mine as well. *Light Shining in Buckinghamshire* is also among the finest plays she's penned, but it just doesn't sit right with me.

It deals, after a fashion, with Christ's impending return. I play the wealthy corn merchant, Star, recruiting young men for Christ's army, and my line reads, "If you join in the army now, you will be one of the saints. You will rule with Jesus a thousand years."

Only I didn't say that line because it's bullshit. I know it is. I fell for a lie just like that once. So instead I ask, "But what if we're all Christ?"

That's the bitch of it. We "demons" were the first messiahs, the first saviors. We were three-million-plus martyrs trying to save humanity, but we still failed. Yet *one man* thought he had a hope of swinging God's mercy. Why? Did he think he had a better chance because he was God's son? We're all His sons and daughters. If God did listen to Christ's pleas over anyone else's, you know what that makes mortals? Christ's pets. I don't buy it. So I ask what if Christ was like every other mortal, crying on their personal Mount of Olives, trying desperately to attract God to their plight... and what if Christ's death on the cross was all just a sham to keep people from discovering that God didn't care?

So everybody's looking at me, actors and audience alike, shocked. Half the actors ignore what I said while the other half tries incorporating my diatribe into the scene. Some of them even start to argue about it in character. For a moment, they're all reacting like real people instead of like fictional characters, and it's all because of me.

That's when I feel it. A kernel of faith ignited by my statement. Someone wants to believe. Someone out there wants to cross that threshold between passive spectator and active participant. Someone wants to be involved and believe again.

❖   ❖   ❖   ❖

They kicked me out — big surprise.

I ranted on stage for an hour like DeNiro playing a preacher on smack and salvation, and I don't think anyone even blinked. For that one hour, I was God in the round. No exit stage left for me.

That's the problem. Our director was more a prima donna than the actors, and he couldn't tolerate another God in the company. Queen bee syndrome. I'll have to get used to that.

Well, my exile from stage didn't last the week. More people heard about my performance and more flocked to see a mediocre rendition of the Churchill classic, hoping I'd be there. My company wanted me back, but then, others wanted me more.

"We do improvised mummer plays" Jesse of Holy Works told me. Mummer plays were throwbacks to the Middle Ages when a traveling troupe with no props, costuming and sets, stood around in horseshoe formation. They enacted morality plays by stepping into the center and performing their lines and actions.

"This way, you can ad-lib to your heart's content," Jesse said with a smile.

He knew what I wanted.

Becky followed me home after that last show. She was the spark of faith I'd felt. Hard to believe that behind that hard exterior was a desperate soul in need of direction. She and I weren't so different after all.

I said yes to Holy Works. If Becky could see her way to believe in me, there must be others I can reach.

✤   ✤   ✤   ✤

That guy in the third row. The one wearing a weather-beaten tan trench coat and looking like he can't remember the last time he'd eaten or slept. He's stalking me.

He shows up to all my performances, and I've even seen him around my block a couple of times.

There's a malevolent air about this guy, like perpetual anger. There's also faith, but he keeps that bottled deep inside. It's his dirty secret. His alone, or so he thinks.

So he's showed up to every performance, no matter where we played, for the last month. He's about as devoted as Becky and the five souls who've found me since. They shower me with their faith, and I offer them hope in return. It's that simple.

Oh, I could have bargained with them and forced them into pacts for wealth or power, but I'm not that kind of demon. At least, not often. I give them what they need, not want they think they want. That's not my style, thanks to Max. His thoughts and memories changed everything.

But I'm sure this guy isn't like the others — he's stalking me. What really bothers me is he also recognizes some of my new friends. He watches them almost as intently as he watches me. He's probably even seen a couple of them float in and out of my apartment. I'm not so much worried about myself as I am for Becky.

I resolve to confront the guy and have a few choice words. In the end, though, he comes to me.

We're performing at a community center that evening. It's a packed house, but then that's been the case this past month wherever we go. People want to see the gifted actor who improvises holy people with a controversial flair. I do them all: Christ, Moses, the Archangel Michael, Saint Peter, Lazarus...

Actually, it's not the acting they're here to watch, though they may not know it. They want to believe these saints and prophets actually existed. For that moment I'm in the mummers' circle in my black jumpsuit, I reinvigorate their faith. They believe, if only a little, that Jesus was sweating blood on the Mount of Olives because he knew the truth, and that Michael betrayed Lucifer.

So when we finish the performance, a large crowd of admirers and groupies besets me. I can't say I mind, except this time, my stalker shoulders through the crowd and stands right in my face.

He's a week late in shaving and changing clothes. The smell of old cigarettes and hooch hangs off his trench coat. The sunglasses hide his bloodshot eyes, but I'm ready for whatever he's about to do.

He leans in so only I can hear him.

"I know what you are," he says. "I'm going to kill you."
Then he vanishes back into the crowd.

❖   ❖   ❖   ❖

Now don't get me wrong, I appreciate the fair warning, but don't killers generally whack you without these little courtesies? I'm just curious.

I could have killed him right there — smote him Old Testament style — but the staying of my vengeful hand is Max. Otherwise, the demon in me would have quartered the stalker with my bare hands and speared his heart with my tongue. With Max, though, I find my previous inclinations horrifying... mostly because they're a little too comfortable.

It's in those absolutely human moments when the differences between Max and me become painfully apparent. It's in those seconds I remember I now exist on the humblest of scales.

I still catch myself staring at a star-filled night and, for the briefest minute, holding my breath in awe.

I forget I was once up there myself. That I was once one of those stars.

❖   ❖   ❖   ❖

I'm standing outside my apartment. The door is ajar, but it's dark inside. Back-lit by the hallway lights I can just see a hand on the floor peeking out from behind the overturned couch. It's Becky.

I rush inside, through the wreckage of my living room, dazed by the avalanche of emotions roaring inside of me. I can sense someone else hiding in the shadows of the room, and the cold certainty that I'm going to tear the fucker to pieces is the only thing that keeps me focused on the here and now.

I clasp Becky's hand in mine and pull it to my lips. I taste its icy smoothness. I love her more than Max ever could, and all the pain I've felt for the last few aeons explodes up to the surface. Becky's faith in me enabled me to clean her blood of the drugs she'd poisoned it with. Max's love for her reminded me what made humanity worth all our pain. And it was all for shit. God wanted her dead, so she dies.

Max wants to cry and lie next to her body, but the Melbogathra in me is howling pissed. My wings are slamming against my ribs like a hummingbird in a small cage, and I want to bellow with that same voice that once spawned tornadoes. Problem is, I can't anymore. So I focus on all that seething anger and hatred instead — the same storm of misery that bore me through God's torment — and I drown Max out.

Someone moves in the darkness. I turn toward the noise.

My stalker swings a tire iron. I barely dodge it, and it whistles past my ear. I draw upon my strength and conviction, that same strength and conviction that Becky and the rest have given me. I feel my muscles surge with power, and I direct that energy into a punch. I catch the stalker square in the shoulder and feel something crack. He screams in pain but swings wild with the other hand, nicking my jaw with the tire iron. I barely feel the pain.

I bring my strength up to the surface of my skin. I'm manifesting, and my chest shines like a furnace of light. Being with Becky had stemmed much of my anguish, but I'm caught between states now. I manifest in hellish blaze and regalia, but I'm still an angel's lingering shadow. My crooked wings are dust motes, my spiral horns shred my temples, and my 100-watt nimbus burns red.

I may be mood lighting compared to the Burning Bush, but I'm still a fucking *angel*.

My stalker trips and scrambles backward, clutching his arm, and I follow him. His eyes are wide and wild like he's trying to scream but he can't remember how. I stride forward until he hits a wall, then wrap my fingers around his bird neck. I inhale, breathing in his terror like a hurricane sucking air from his lungs. He sobs, his pathetic will turning to ash, and I stop for the coup de grâce.

"I'm sorry," he moans, "I don't want to..."

I glare at him, my fury brimming. Power crackles around my body and I want to slaughter him. I want his entrails draped around my neck. I want to crack his bones into messy splinters. I want to tear his tongue out with my own teeth. But...

I can't. Not without losing everything.

I still love Becky, and I don't want to lose that love to hatred. I've done it before, and it took thousands of years to gain it back.

I let him go and close the curtain over my essence. The dust mote wings drift to the ground, and my horns retreat back into my skull. I look like Max again, but my stalker knows better. He lies at my feet, wracked by sobs, heaving in anguish. As I sense people's faith, I also sense his misery. He doesn't cry out of fear, but out of a spiritual desolation that Max and me both understand all too well.

"Why?" he cries. "Why can't I kill you? I know what you are. I saw it on stage."

I stare at him, angry and still debating whether he lives or dies. I was a fool for thinking nobody would notice me. I was getting careless with my certainties, allowing my divinity to slip through. Somebody finally saw me for what I was, and Becky paid the price.

"Every time I came to your play," he says between sobs, "I thought, today I'll kill you. Today for sure."

"Why didn't you?" I ask through clenched teeth.

"I couldn't. I watched you perform. Each time I... *believed*, and I didn't want to. Each... each time, I chickened out. Tomorrow... I'd tell myself. You'd die tomorrow."

I can hear the anger in his voice and the venom for his own faith.

"Why?"

"Because I didn't want to believe in God!" he cries out. "But you made me!"

"What?"

My stalker sniffs, regaining some of his composure. I've awoken something within him, a faith he doesn't want, but it can't have been a complete surprise to him.

"I always thought that if God was real, then He was a bastard for creating this shit-hole. My parents were killed. Cancer's killing my wife. My whole life's been ruined. But shit happens, right?" He says, getting up. "There is no God, so it can't be His fault. It's just shit, right?" My stalker shuffles to a chair and sits. He looks at me with saucer eyes drowning in water and cradles his ruined arm.

"Then you come along, and you make me believe," he says. "Suddenly, I believe in God, only now I see He doesn't care. He doesn't fucking care about anybody."

Silence falls in the room, and I kneel down next to Becky.

"I didn't mean to hurt her," the stalker says. "I was waiting for you, and she surprised me. Is she..."

"She'll be fine," I say, and the lie burns like fire. "But you'd better leave."

"What?" he says.

"Get the fuck out of here."

"But I tried to kill you," he says, getting up slowly. "Why would—"

"Because you're right," I say. "God doesn't care about you, and He never did. Knowing that's punishment enough."

My stalker is stunned. He shuffles for the door, only looking back once, but he's not escaping that easily. I still want vengeance.

"There's a condition, though," I say.

My stalker looks fearfully at me. I already hit him hard enough with my glory to leave him mentally weak and pliable.

"A condition," he says.

"Yeah. You see, God may not care, but I do. I care for my friends, and I want to make sure you never come after them or me again."

"Oh, I won't," he says, promising a little too eagerly for my tastes.

"Not good enough." I get up and walk right up to his grizzled, tear-stained face. He tries backing up, but I grab him by the collar and hold him in place. "You have to promise — on your soul — that you'll never come after me."

"On my soul..." he says. He's nervous, as well he should be, but he's also gullible right now.

"And in exchange, I'll make you forget you ever met me or saw me act."

"You can do that?"

He's desperate enough to believe me. Desperation and a weak will are my allies here. Otherwise, he'd realize I could just as easily make him forget without him having to promise me anything and my friends and I would be just as safe.

But what he doesn't realize is that even after he forgets I exist, he'll always be connected to me because he made me a promise on his soul. And because of that connection, I'll be able to drain his life away, slowly and from a distance for as long as I want. He'll stay weak and tortured for the rest of his existence, never knowing why he's dying in small servings. It'll just be another float in his parade of misery. He'll go right on blaming God for it, too, because even though he won't remember me specifically, he'll always have his unquestioning belief in a cruel, heartless creator who doesn't give a shit for him.

No, I'm not about to make this guy forget that, because while there's a lot of Max tempering Melbogathra, there's also a lot of Melbogathra in Max. Max and me are that fucking close now, and we both want this guy to suffer for what he's done.

Really, though, even my love for Becky can't change aeons worth of spite overnight. I'm still a demon, and this may set me back, but I've got a long road ahead.

So I nod. Yeah, I can do that. I can take away this pain I've caused.

That's why I'm here.

DEMON
the fallen

a Storytelling Game of Infernal Glory

CREDITS

Designers: Andrew Bates, Ken Cliffe, Michael Lee, Rich Thomas, Steve Wieck

Authors: William Brinkman, David Carroll, Steve Kenson, Michael Lee, Joshua Mosquiera-Asheim, Patrick O'Duffy, Lucien Soulban, Greg Stolze and Adam Tinworth. World of Darkness created by Mark Rein•Hagen

Storyteller game system designed by Mark Rein•Hagen

Developer: Michael Lee

Editor: Carl Bowen

Art Director: Pauline Benney

Layout and Typesetting: Pauline Benney

Interior Art: Jason Alexander, Tom Baxa, Leanne Buckley, Maria Cabardo, Marko Djurdjevic, Steve Ellis, Mark Jackson, Matt Millberger, Ken Myer Jr, RK Post, Jeff Rebner.

Front Cover: Pauline Benney

Back Cover: Pauline Benney

Playtesters: Andrew Bates, Carl Bowen, John Chambers, Micah Chandler, Lisa Charlton, Carrie Easley, Susan Gillotti, Janet Lee, Jim McCann, Matt McFarland, Paul Marshall, Scott Mizis, Sue Mizis, Ripper Moore and Fred Yelk

WHITE WOLF GAME STUDIO

1554 LITTON DR. STONE MOUNTAIN, GA 30083 USA

TABLE OF CONTENTS

post

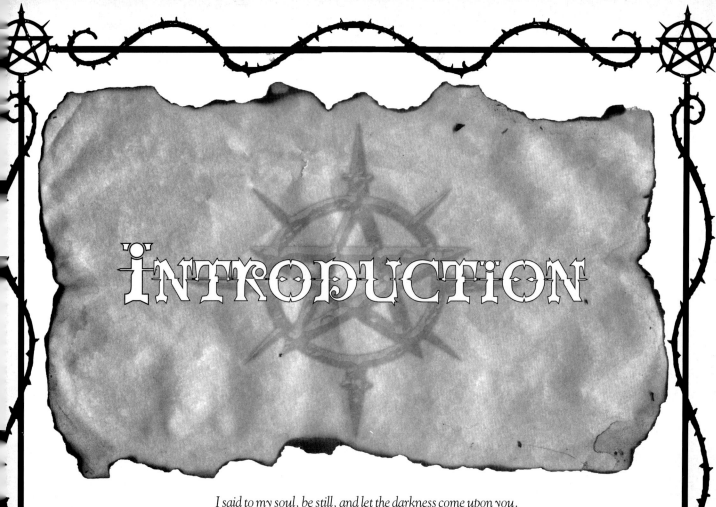

INTRODUCTION

I said to my soul, be still, and let the darkness come upon you.
Which is the darkness of God.
—T. S. Eliot, East Coker

History, as the saying goes, is written by the victors. Whether an uprising is seen as a glorious rebellion or a treacherous insurrection depends entirely on who held the upper hand at the end, with the losers consigned to posterity as traitors, tyrants or worse. Their story is largely forgotten.

We are told that demons are the incarnations of evil, spirits who exist to seduce the innocent and lure the virtuous to destruction. They are driven by a relentless hate of all things holy, consumed by a malevolent hatred of light and life. They are the purveyors of lies and misdirection, clouding the minds of mortals with promises of power and glory. At least, that's what the good book says. That's why they were hurled into the darkness of the Pit, bound in chains of fire until the end of days. Only God knows what would happen if these evil spirits were ever freed.

Now mankind is about to hear the other side of the story.

STORYTELLING

The book you hold is the core rulebook for **Demon: The Fallen**, a storytelling game from White Wolf Publishing. With the rules in this book, you and your friends can assume the roles of monstrous demons and tell stories about your characters' hopes, fears, triumphs and failures.

In a storytelling game, players create characters using the rules in this book, then take those characters through dramas and adventures called (appropriately enough) stories. Stories are told through a combination of the wishes of the players and the directives of the Storyteller.

In many ways, storytelling resembles games like *How to Host a Murder Mystery*. Each player takes the role of a character — in this case, a fallen angel in possession of a mortal body — and engages in a form of improvisational theater by saying what the demon would say and describing what the demon would do. Most of this process is freeform — players can have their characters say or do whatever they like, as long as the dialogue or actions are consistent with a character's personality and abilities. The success of certain actions, however, is best determined through the use of dice and the rules presented in this book.

Whenever rules and story conflict, story wins. Use the rules only as much — or preferably as little — as you need to tell thrilling tales of terror, action and triumph.

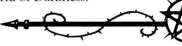

PLAYERS AND STORYTELLERS

Demon is best played with a group, or troupe, of two to six participants. Most of these people are players. They create demon characters — imaginary protagonists similar to ones found in novels, cinema and comics. In each troupe, however, one person must take the role of the Storyteller. The Storyteller does not create one primary character for herself. Rather, she acts as a combination of director, moderator, narrator and referee. By creating plots and conflicts from her imagination, the Storyteller invents the drama through which the players direct their characters. The Storyteller also takes the roles of supporting cast — both allies with whom the characters interact and antagonists against whom the characters struggle. The Storyteller invents the salient details of the story's setting — the bars, nightclubs, businesses and other institutions the characters frequent. The players decide how their characters react to the situations in the game, but it is the Storyteller who decides (with the help of the rules) whether the characters actually succeed in their endeavors and, if so, how well. Ultimately, the Storyteller is the final authority on the events that take place in the game.

Example: *Andrew, Lisa, Carl and Mike have gathered to play* **Demon**. *Andrew, Lisa and Carl are players. Andrew plays Yziriel, a Devil (a commanding, charismatic demon) who resides in the body of Harold Lewis, state attorney. Lisa plays Juriel, a Fiend (a demon who can spin illusions and influence time) who possesses the body of Andrea Winn, a college student. Carl plays Hazaroth, a Scourge (a demon who can command the wind and animate unliving objects) who resides in the body of John Walker, a private investigator. Mike is the Storyteller. The story he's envisioned pits the characters against a monstrous demon who is using a school for troubled youth as a breeding ground for future demonic hosts. After gaining entry into the school, the characters are confronted by the demon, residing in the body of the school's director.*

• **Mike (describing the scene):** The security guard unlocks the glass double doors and ushers you into the deserted, marble-floored lobby. The guard locks the door behind you, then leads you to the foyer opposite the building's elevators. As you reach the foyer, one set of elevator doors slides open and a tall, statuesque woman in a dark business suit steps out to meet you. Her pale skin glows with health beneath the foyer's subdued lighting, and her movements are fluid and precise. She studies the three of you coolly with eyes the color of a stormy sea. Such is the power of her gaze that you are only dimly aware of the four guards stepping off the elevator behind her.

• **Mike (again, now speaking as the monster):** "The guard at the front gate said you were with the State Attorney's office, here on official business. No one phoned me that you were coming. Can I see some identification?"

The players must now decide what their characters will do.

• **Andrew (speaking as Harold):** "Of course."

• **Andrew (describing Yziriel's action):** I pull out my identification and show it to her.

• **Carl (speaking as John):** "We need to ask you some questions about an attempted escape that occurred last Thursday."

• **Lisa (speaking as Andrea):** "I'll also need to interview the child and ascertain her physical condition and state of mind."

• **Mike (playing the demon's reaction):** She takes Harold's identification and looks it over carefully, then smiles coldly. "You're very well informed, considering that the escape happened in the dead of night and the child got no further than the perimeter fence. None of my people have spoken to the press or anyone else. So where did you get this information?" (Then, he makes a dice roll on behalf of the players and describes the demon's action.) The three of you feel the force of her stare slide across your skin like a caress, placing your minds at ease. A mere mortal would be falling all over himself to tell her what she wants to know, but your demonic nature is proof against her charms. When she realizes that her power is having no effect, her lip pulls back in a snarl, revealing rows of shark-like teeth.

• **Andrew (describing Harold's action):** I am going to invoke Yziriel's apocalyptic form (Harold suddenly transforms into a towering, radiant angel, bathing the lobby in intense, fiery light) and speak to the guards with the Voice of Heaven (one of his supernatural powers). *"She is a monster who preys on the innocent. Seize her!"*

What happens next is decided by the actions of the players and the decisions of the Storyteller. As you can see, each player is the arbiter of his or her own character's actions and words. Ultimately, though, it is Mike, the Storyteller, who determines the demon's response to the characters' words and actions. It is Mike, speaking as the demon, who roleplays its reaction. And it is Mike who determines whether the characters' actions, if any, succeed or fail.

WHAT IS THIS PLACE?

The world of **Demon: The Fallen** is not our own, though it is close enough for fearsome discomfort. Rather, the world inhabited by demons is *like* ours, but seen through a glass darkly. Evil is palpable and ubiquitous in this world. The end is upon us, and the whole planet teeters on a razor's edge of tension. It is a world of darkness.

Superficially, the World of Darkness is like the "real" world we all inhabit. The same bands are popular, violence plagues the inner city, graft and corruption infest governments, and society looks to cities for its culture. The World of Darkness has a Statue of Liberty, it has an Eiffel Tower, and it has a McDonalds on every corner. More present there than in our world, though, is an undercurrent of horror. Our world's ills are all the more pronounced in the World of Darkness. Its fears are more real. Its governments are *more* degenerate. Its ecosystem dies a bit more each day. And there, demons walk the earth.

Welcome to the World of Darkness.

GOTHIC-PUNK

"Gothic-Punk" is perhaps the best way to describe the physical nature of the World of Darkness. The environment is a clashing mixture of styles and influences. The tension caused by the juxtaposition of ethnicities, social classes and subcultures makes the world a vibrant, albeit dangerous, place. All these aspects are ones familiar to normal people of the world. They've dealt with them all their lives. It's the existence of monsters and their part in the condition of things that is unknown — until now.

"Gothic" describes the ambiance of the World of Darkness. Buttressed buildings loom overhead, bedecked with columns and leering gargoyles. Residents are dwarfed by the sheer scale of architecture, lost amid spires that seem to grope toward an uncaring Heaven in an effort to escape the physical world. Organized religion is a haven for zealots and hucksters, preying on the fears of the populace to fill their pockets or spread their own brand of condemnation. Cults flourish in the underground, promising power and redemption. The institutions that control society are even more staid and conservative than they are in our world. Many in power prefer the evils of the world they know to the chaos engendered by change. It is a divisive world of have and have-not, rich and poor, excess and squalor.

"Punk" is the lifestyle that many denizens of the World of Darkness adopt. In order to give their lives meaning, they rebel, dashing themselves against the crags of power. Gangs prowl the streets, and organized crime breeds in the underworld, all in reaction to the pointlessness of living "by the book." Music is louder, faster, more violent, or it's hypnotically monotonous and supported by masses who find salvation in its escape. Speech is coarser, fashion is bolder, art is more shocking, and technology brings it all to everyone at the click of a button. The world is more corrupt, its people are spiritually bankrupt and escapism often replaces hope.

Gothic-Punk is a mood and setting conveyed during the course of the game. The greatest share of creating this ambiance falls upon the Storyteller, but players should consider their characters' stake in it as well. The ambiance is also a matter of taste. Some troupes prefer more Gothic than Punk, whereas others may want equal amounts of both elements (or little of either). In the end, it's your game, and you're free to make of it what you will. Simply bear in mind that experiencing the world is a shared endeavor, and everything the players and Storyteller do helps make that world more believable. Actions, settings, characters and descriptions all convey the Gothic-Punk aesthetic.

LEXICON

Though long absent from the Earth, demons have a rich culture and history going back to the first moments of Creation and culminating in the end of a thousand years of war against the armies of Heaven. A long list of common and proper names and descriptive

CITIES

Demons exist all over the world, regardless of race, culture or religious belief. They can be found anywhere, from the mountains of the Himalayas to the towns of the Midwest, but they tend to congregate most commonly in the world's great cities. The reasons are fairly clear, given a few assumptions. Human populations, the source of the demons' power, are most concentrated in urban centers, rather than in the country or the wilds. And the demon or group of demons that controls the largest sources of faith rule over their peers like tyrants of old.

terms has evolved over the course of these momentous events and are presented here for your reference:

Abyss, the: The prison fashioned by the Creator to contain the fallen. See **Pit**.

Age of Wrath: Term describing the thousand-year war between Heaven and the fallen. See **Fall**.

Annunaki: The proper name for the rebel angels of the earth. See **Malefactor**.

apocalyptic form: The physical reflection of a demon's Celestial nature. See **visage**.

Asharu: The proper name for the rebel angels of the wind. See **Scourge**.

Celestials: A common name for both angels and demons, referring to their divine origins as servants of the Creator. See **Elohim**.

Cryptic: A faction of demons devoted to unearthing the truth behind Lucifer's disappearance and unanswered questions pertaining to the Fall.

Defiler: A common name for the rebel angels of the sea. See **Lammasu**.

demon: An epithet describing a fallen angel who has become lost to madness and hate; a twisted, malevolent spirit. Also used as a common name to describe the fallen as a whole.

Devil: A common name for the rebel angels of the dawn. See **Namaru**.

Devourer: A common name for the rebel angels of the wild. See **Rabisu**.

Earthbound, the: The collective name for a group of demons who were summoned from the Abyss in ancient times and found a way to anchor themselves in the physical universe. They now seek to enslave or destroy the fallen.

Elohim, the: Proper name for the divine servants of the Creator, commonly referred to as angels.

Fall, the: The awakening of humanity's awareness by Lucifer and a third of the Elohim, leading to the thousand-year **Age of Wrath**.

fallen, the: A common name for the angels who rebelled against Heaven.

Faustian: A faction of demons devoted to enslaving humankind and using it as a weapon against Heaven.

Fiend: A common name for the rebel angels of the heavens. See **Neberu**.

Halaku: The proper name for the rebel angels of the dead. See **Slayer**.

House: A hierarchical organization of angels devoted to a specific function in the creation and oversight of the cosmos.

Lammasu: The proper name for the rebel angels of the sea. See **Defiler**.

lore: The basis for the powers of the Celestials; essentially the collected commands for manipulating the fabric of reality.

Luciferan: A faction of demons devoted to locating Lucifer and resuming the war against Heaven.

Malefactor: A common name for the rebel angels of the earth. See **Annunaki**.

Namaru: The proper name for the rebel angels of the dawn. See **Devil**.

Neberu: The proper name for the rebel angels of the heavens. See **Fiends**.

Pit, the: An epithet used to describe the Abyss. See **Abyss**.

Rabisu: The proper name for the rebel angels of the wild. See **Devourer**.

Ravener: A faction of demons devoted to the destruction of the universe.

Reconciler: A faction of demons devoted to the restoration of Earth to the paradise it was before the Age of Wrath.

Scourge: A common name for the rebel angels of the winds. See **Asharu**.

Sebettu: Literally, "the seven," the collective name for the rebel Houses of the fallen.

Slayer: A common name for the rebel angels of the dead. See **Halaku**.

thrall: A mortal bound to a demon through a pact of faith.

visage: The proper name for a demon's apocalyptic or revelatory form.

How to Use This Book

This book is divided into several chapters, each of which is designed to explore and explain a specific area of the game. Remember, though, that the most important "chapter" in a storytelling game is your imagination. Never let anything in this book be a substitute for your own creativity.

Chapter One: In the Beginning describes the origins of the angels and the creation of the universe from their own perspective, culminating in the birth of humanity and the reasons behind Lucifer's rebellion against his Creator.

Chapter Two: Better to Rule in Hell provides an overview of the rebel angels' thousand-year war against Heaven and the circumstances leading to Lucifer's defeat.

Chapter Three: Apocalypse Now describes how Hell made demons out of the imprisoned angels, their eventual escape, and how demons perceive the modern World of Darkness.

Chapter Four: Legions of the Damned provides a detailed overview of the demonic condition, describing what sorts of mortals they can possess and why they need human faith.

Chapter Five: Houses of Darkness describes the seven infernal Houses that demons belong to and the five philosophical factions that divide them.

Chapter Six: Feet of Clay details how to create a **Demon** character.

Chapter Seven: Eyes of Fire covers the wide range of demonic powers, their apocalyptic forms and rules for their use.

Chapter Eight: Rules provides the basic means of resolving characters' various actions.

Chapter Nine: Systems describes a plethora of ways to simulate everything from driving cars to performing exorcisms.

Chapter Ten: Storytelling tells Storytellers how to build entertaining stories in which to involve the characters.

Chapter Eleven: Antagonists provides profiles and rules for a variety of monstrous demons, demon-hunters and Earthbound servants that Storytellers can pit against the characters.

Live-Action

Most **Demon** games take place around a tabletop, and the players describe what their characters say and do. Games can also be conducted through live-action play, however. This exciting form of gaming bears similarities to improvisational theater, in that players actually dress as their characters and act out their characters' scenes as though they were actors in a play. Therefore, rather than saying, "My character walks over to the table and picks up the ancient document," you, the player, actually get up, walk over to a properly decorated table and pick up the "ancient document." (That document is probably a prop created by the Storyteller — for example, a piece of parchment that's been scorched around the edges and "aged," with a coating of flour "dust.")

A Storyteller still guides the action and directs the plot. He describes special features of the setting and oversees challenges the characters undergo, and he may interrupt the action at any time.

Live-action roleplaying does not typically use dice. Alternative systems, such as those presented in White Wolf's **Mind's Eye Theatre** line of products, take the place of dice when determining the results of challenges. Most situations are resolved simply through acting and the Storyteller's decisions.

SAFEGUARDS

Some rules are necessary to ensure that live-action play is safe and enjoyable for all participants and onlookers. Unlike any other rules in this book, these rules *must* be followed.

• **No Touching:** Period. All combat and physical interaction must be handled through dice or other abstract systems. Players must never strike, grapple or otherwise touch anyone during the game. It is the Storyteller's responsibility to call a time-out if one or more players grow overly rambunctious.

• **No Weapons:** Props such as hats, period dress and canes are great in a live-action game. Weapons are not. No knives, no swords and nothing that even remotely resembles a firearm. Don't even bring fake swords, squirt guns or foam-rubber weapons. If your character must carry a "weapon," take an index card and write "gun" or "sword" or whatever on it. During combat challenges, present the card to the Storyteller, who adjudicates its use in play.

• **Play in a Designated Area:** Live-action is meant to be played in the home or other predetermined spot. Don't involve onlookers in the game, and make sure everyone in the area, or anyone passing through the area, understands exactly what you're doing. A game can look disturbing, even frightening, to people who aren't aware of what's going on. Don't try to shock or intimidate passersby. Such behavior is not only immature, it could lead to well-deserved prosecution.

• **Know When to Stop:** If the Storyteller calls for a time-out or other break in the action, stop immediately. The Storyteller remains the final arbiter of all events in the game. Likewise, when the game session ends, put away your costume and call it a night.

• **It's Only a Game:** Live-action is for having fun. If a rival wins, if a character dies, if a plan goes awry, it's not the end of the world. Sometimes, players like to get together outside the game and talk about it — say, a troupe that forms a novice **Demon** group gathers to decide who or what they need to protect or pursue most — and there's nothing wrong with that. But telephoning your in-game ally at four in the morning to ask her to join you on a personal mission is taking things too far. Remember, everyone's doing this to have fun!

The Bottom Line: Live-action can be one of the richest and most satisfying storytelling experiences, if handled maturely and responsibly. We're not kidding about that "maturely and responsibly," folks. In live-action, you make the game, so it is imperative that you treat yourself and others with utmost care, dignity and respect. This game is emphatically *not* about "real" enslavement or combat, nor does it entail erotic or supernatural activities. You are not a demon — you just play one in the game.

SOURCE MATERIAL

Art, literature and pop culture are rife with depictions of Hell and its denizens, covering a broad spectrum from the corny to the terrifying. Portraying the fallen as tormented, monstrous yet ultimately heroic souls is no easy task, but there are a number of inspirational sources that provide different perspectives on demonic nature.

Recommended books include:

Paradise Lost, by John Milton. Seventeenth-century poetry isn't most people's idea of light reading, but this classic is a must for its evocative, even sympathetic portrayal of Lucifer and his war against Heaven. Though his motives are more driven by jealousy than love for mankind, his defiant struggle against the Almighty is no less heroic because of it.

The Screwtape Letters, by C. S. Lewis. Presented as a collection of letters written by one demon to another, the book is an insightful commentary on temptation and faith in the divine.

In God We Trust: But Which One?, by Judith Hayes. Hayes, a prominent atheist, makes the case that if there is a God, He's not one worthy of our worship. For players who want more depth to their characters' opposition to God, this book is a good start. It's humorous and thought-provoking, but not for the easily offended.

Legion, by William Peter Blatty. Blatty's follow-up to *The Exorcist* is a great novel with a fascinating theory on the nature of evil, free will and the identity of Lucifer.

Music of Razors, by Cameron Rogers. More warring angels forming the back story to an urban fantasy. Of particular interest is the depiction of artifacts from before Lucifer's rebellion.

Needful Things, by Stephen King. King's story is a perfect example of a Malefactor at work in a small town.

To Reign in Hell, by Steven Brust. Hard to find these days, but an excellent and darkly humorous story of Lucifer's rebellion.

American Gods, by Neil Gaiman. An evocative (and at times horrifying) tale of gods and their symbiotic relationship with mankind. An excellent story about at the power of human belief.

Movie and TV sources include:

The Devil's Advocate. Al Pacino's Lucifer is a perfect example of a Devil lost in his own Torment. His "look but don't touch" monologue near the end is a classic.

Angel Heart. A creepy, atmospheric tale of dark desires and subtle corruption. Watch for Robert De Niro's subtle, chilling performance as Louis Cypher.

American Gothic. This mid-90s TV show is a great model for how a demon in human form could infiltrate deeply into a community, maintain thralls and get away with murder. Additionally, Selena Coombs could well be a low-powered Defiler trying to reform her ways.

Darkness below and the raging storm above. Gaviel fought the pull of the Abyss with every fiber of his will and drove himself ever upward, into the mouth of the Maelstrom. The winds flayed his soul, but he exulted in the pain. He could sense how close he was to being ripped apart, consigned to everlasting oblivion, and the threat of extinction invigorated him. Better by far to struggle and be lost than to sit and do nothing. It was the lesson of the Abyss, and Gaviel had learned it well.

The winds grew worse the higher he rose, but beyond the storm, Gaviel could sense the edges of the spirit realm and the fabric of the physical realm just beyond. The Maelstrom tried to force him back into utter night, cutting through his soul like knives of ice, but he forced himself on, welcoming the agony. Had he a mouth to speak, the realm of the dead would tremble with defiant laughter. Each moment carried him a little closer to the world he'd thought lost to him forever. Already he could remember the feel of the cool darkness between the stars or the thrill of fire as it coursed along his form. He could already taste the air of the green world he had helped to make and feel the sensation of the living earth beneath his feet. He hungered for it. He lusted for it with a passion he hadn't known in aeons. Now it would tempt him no more.

Gaviel pierced the Veil between the realms like a fiery arrow, only dimly aware of how much strength he'd expended in his escape. The world hung before him, close enough to touch, but even so he felt his spirit unraveling, threatening to come undone unless he could find a refuge from the storm.

He plummeted to earth like a meteor, the symphony of six billion souls trembling through his own, and through their hopes and fears Gaviel felt echoes of their mortal flesh. Some souls burned bright, like nascent stars; others waned like embers, a faint light shrinking in the hollow vault of a human form. He sensed one such body, vibrant with life but broken in spirit, and struck like a thunderbolt.

The talons of the Maelstrom were nothing compared to the shock of possession.

A torrent of images. Feelings. Memories. All dull and tepid next to Gaviel's own, but there were so many... they crashed down upon his consciousness in an avalanche, burying him beneath their weight.

He opened his eyes. His cheek was pressed against icy, wet asphalt, and the skin felt hot and torn. Someone was pulling at his shoulder, trying to roll him over. With a grunt, Gaviel complied.

"Oh, Jesus, oh please God, tell me you're okay!" A woman was looking down at him, her cheeks red from the cold, blue eyes bright with tears.

He was lying in the middle of a snowy street. Cold, soulless lights glowed in fuzzy globes overhead, shrouded in gusts of falling snow. To his left, the looked up at the headlights and grill of a car, its engine still running. There was blood on the chrome.

The woman pulled at his cashmere coat and begged for God's forgiveness at what she'd done. And Gaviel, forsaken of Heaven, filled his newfound lungs and laughed.

CHAPTER ONE: IN THE BEGINNING

Into our first world, shall we follow
The deception of the thrush? Into our first world.
There they were, dignified, invisible,
Moving without pressure, over the dead leaves,
In the autumn heat, through the vibrant air…
—T. S. Eliot, *Burnt Norton*

The Reverend Matthew Wallace sat at his desk, frowning, rubbing his eyes, trying to concentrate. It was late — nearly midnight — and he was still at the studio catching up on network paperwork. The document in front of him was lengthy and dry and not particularly good news. It was a demographic study of the ratings for his show, *The Hour of Jesus' Power*. They were holding steady for the third year in a row, but the network had some concerns. They wanted a wider audience. They wanted him to broaden his appeal. They had suggestions for pitching himself to a more populous, more suburban, more upscale audience.

"Why don't they just tell me to get more whites to tune in, and be done with it?" he growled.

He wasn't really thinking about the document. He was looking at it and considering it, but it didn't have his full attention. His mind kept wandering back to Gina.

"I shouldn't," Wallace muttered to himself. He turned a page and started reading about his dwindling appeal among black professionals. He made it about halfway down before his mind crept back to Gina.

"I could call Zola now," he said. "She'd see I was at the office from the caller ID. Tell her I'm working late — that's just the truth. Be true when I'm saying it. Then sneak out. Maybe surprise Gina with…" He shook his head. He didn't call his wife.

In the next two paragraphs, he actually found an idea for a fundraiser that he thought might be useful. That kept his attention for two more pages, then he was thinking about calling his wife again.

"I could call her, then call Gina. Or call Gina first, make sure she's there. Give her a chance to get ready for me." He was tired, but he felt a little internal movement in that thought. But no. He shouldn't. It was wrong. He looked at the picture of Zola on his desk and let the guilty feelings wash over him.

"Hell with it."

He put the report away, stood and strode purposefully out of his office. He was going to go home, get back to his wife and children. He was going to go where he belonged. He told himself he was too old to be catting around

anyway. Old and tired. He'd break it off with Gina. Maybe this Saturday, when Zola took the kids to see Gramma.

He was planning to see Gina Saturday in any event. Maybe it was time to finally end it. Maybe.

Feeling a small sense of virtue, he locked the door behind him and turned toward the parking lot, turning up his collar at the misty rain. He barely had time to register that there was a second vehicle there, parked next to his BMW… a familiar car, a Lexus…

Noah's car.

The last time Matthew had seen his oldest son Noah, they hadn't really talked. They'd yelled.

He'd condemned his son's recently declared atheism.

Noah had called his father a con man, selling salvation like snake oil.

Matthew thundered back that Noah had never rejected the roof over his head, the food in his mouth, the money in the bank and the education Matthew had never gotten.

That's when Noah told him about the full scholarship to BGSU's grad program. He'd said he didn't need Matthew any longer, that he could finally break his father's golden manacles.

Matthew called him a spoiled little ingrate and threatened to disown him.

Noah called his bluff.

That had been two years ago, and they hadn't spoken since.

REVELATIONS

A figure formed from the darkness. Tall, handsome, wearing a camel-hair coat and fine leather boots. No hat sat on his close-cropped hair, but a white cashmere scarf made a striking contrast against chocolate skin. He was a shade lighter than Matthew, perhaps, and a few shades darker than Zola.

Matthew licked lips that suddenly felt dry.

"Son?" he croaked. He swallowed and said it again, louder, stronger. "Son!"

Noah said nothing.

"Oh Noah… Noah, I'm…" He opened his arms. "I've missed you, son. You don't know how much I've prayed for this."

The figure was silent and immobile. The hairs rose on the back of Matthew's neck.

"Son… Noah…" He faltered. "I know I said some terrible things. And I'm sorry. I'm not so proud I can't say I was wrong. Not a day's gone by that I haven't thought about what's happened between us. Not one day. Please… please tell me you've come back."

"Have you truly prayed for your son's return?" The voice was Noah's, but the tone was coldly neutral, like a judge passing sentence.

The reverend frowned. "You know I have."

"Even though the answer has always been 'no' before?"

"That was the past. You're here now, aren't you?"

The figure before him laughed… and then changed.

Where once there stood a handsome black man, the glory of fire was now revealed. Puddled water recoiled, boiling off into steam. The empty parking lot was suddenly ablaze with celestial light, and Matthew fell to his knees, hands clasped, eyes wide.

"My Lord and my God!" he cried. "My Lord and God!"

"MATTHEW," said the apparition that had once been his child, "BE NOT AFRAID."

"What do you ask of me?"

"WHAT WOULD YOU GIVE?"

"Anything! Anything, my Lord! I'm your servant. Yours to command!"

"ALL I ASK IS YOUR LOYALTY, MATTHEW. ALL I ASK IS YOUR TRUST AND YOUR PLEDGE."

"I'm yours! You know I am, I've always been! Thy will be done, Lord! Thy will be done!"

"SHALL I SET MY SEAL UPON YOUR BROW, TO MARK YOU AS MY OWN FOREVER?"

Eyes closed in bliss, Matthew leaned forward expectantly, presenting his forehead.

Behind his eyelids, he could see the light of the miracle fade to black, and when he opened them again, the scene was lit once again by the orange of halogen streetlights and the blue of moonlight on mist.

Before him stood his son again, shaking his head disdainfully.

"Fool," Noah said.

Matthew was suddenly aware of the cold dampness seeping in through the knees of his suit, and fear gave way to anger.

"What's the meaning of this?" he demanded, lurching to his feet.

"Oh Matthew… you're one in a million. Not many people are willing to just up and give away the store to God — or someone claiming to be Him." There was a mocking edge to Noah's voice, but his face betrayed little emotion.

Matthew frowned. "What did I see?"

Noah's dark eyes narrowed. "What did you *think* you saw?"

"I saw the glory of God Almighty."

At that, Noah's eyes fell, but after a moment he shook his head and gave a rueful chuckle. "No Matthew, you didn't see the glory of God Almighty. What you saw was the hole God's glory left when He yanked it out. That was… the shadow of a fragment of the Maker's grandeur. That was its ashes."

"Noah…" Matthew began, but his mind still reeled, unable to believe what he'd seen.

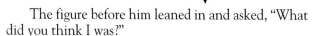

The figure before him leaned in and asked, "What did you think I was?"

"I thought I saw an angel of the Lord."

Noah gave his father a cruel smirk. "Guess again." He turned to the building before them and read from the sign by the door. "Celestine Productions Incorporated, home of *Reverend Matthew Wallace and the Hour of Jesus' Power*." He shook his head. "I see you gave Christ second billing."

"What's going on?" Matthew demanded.

"Let's go inside and talk about it." Noah reached for the heavy doors with both hands — then hissed.

Matthew's eyes widened as white smoke poured from between Noah's fingers. Noah snatched his hands back, and his lip curled as he looked down at them.

The reverend felt faint as he watched the blisters spring up, the curls of blackened flesh, the blood… Noah knelt and pressed both hands into an oily puddle. When he pulled them out, flecks of blood and charred skin stained his palms.

"Very interesting," he said, looking back at the studio door with wary respect. "I suppose we'll have to discuss this elsewhere."

"What are you?"

"My my, someone's not very quick on the uptake." The Noah that Matthew knew hadn't been in the habit of making *tsk* sounds with his tongue and rolling his eyes in mock exasperation. This new Noah apparently was, and Matthew didn't like it.

"Let's see…" Noah counted off on bloodied fingers. "Glorious apparition with wings of fire. *Not* an angel of the Lord. Tries to seduce mortals into pledges of fealty… and is harmed by holy ground. What do you suppose that leaves?"

A man of lesser faith would have been skeptical, but Matthew, for all his faults, was a man of true belief.

"Get behind me, Satan," he whispered.

Noah snorted. "Wouldn't it be simpler if *you* just turned around?"

Matthew lunged forward, seized Noah's lapels in his hands and wrenched him up until Noah stood on tiptoe. "*What have you done with my son?*" he roared.

The figure — the demon? — said nothing, just gave a narrow-eyed half smile.

Had Matthew been a genuinely violent man, he would have punched that grinning face, gouged those narrowed eyes and flung what was left to the pavement. Had the face before him belonged to anyone but his own child, he would have pressed it against the building's doors, hoping to burn it with holy pain. But Matthew was a man of words and gestures, so he just stood there, clutching Noah's coat and feeling more and more foolish.

"There seems to be some misunderstanding," the face before him said softly. "This jacket is for my personal use only. I'll thank you to release it."

Matthew narrowed his eyes and pushed the figure away.

"Now, if we could…"

Suddenly the reverend raised his hands to the leaden sky. "Oh Lord Jesus, hear my plea! Save me from this fiend! Spare your servant from this figure from the pit!" His voice rang from the concrete walls of the surrounding buildings.

"Stop that!" Noah said.

"Please sweet Lord, save your fearful servant! You are my shepherd, there is nothing I shall want!"

"I'm warning you!" Noah's face twisted with hatred… and a touch of fear, too.

"Please sweet Jesus, in your name I pray…"

Before Matthew could say more, Noah was in his face, white teeth inches from his nose. "Do you pray to Jesus when you go fuck the choir leader? Did you pray to Him to get her in bed? Did you get down on your knees and pray, 'Oh Lord, please don't let my wife find out'?"

Matthew faltered. He tried to start again. "You are my shield and my portion…"

"What's she got anyway, Reverend? She suck your dick when your wife says no? Do you pray for forgiveness every time you sneak off to screw her, or do you save it all up for one big confession each month?"

"You shut your God-damned mouth!"

The figure before him relaxed, straightened its coat, dusted off hands that were suddenly smooth and unburned. "So much for exorcism," Noah said.

Matthew's gaze fell to the pavement. "Get away from me," he said. "Leave me alone." But he wasn't demanding anymore. He was pleading.

"Is that what you really want?" Noah's voice was unexpectedly gentle. "If you want me to go, I will. You'll never see my face again." When Matthew didn't answer at first, Noah drew something from his pocket and held it out. "I guess I should be giving this back, then."

Matthew hesitated, but when he recognized the object, he reached out instinctively.

It was a Bible — a brown, leather bound Good News Bible with gilt edges. He recognized it. He'd given it to Noah after the boy's First Communion. Opening it, he read, *Go with God always. I love you son.*

"Why are you doing this?" Matthew whispered.

"Because I thought you could help me," the other replied, then turned to walk away.

"Wait!" Matthew said.

Noah turned.

"Will you come with me?" Matthew asked.

A Deal with the Devil

Two doors down from the church stood Rollins Productions. Sonny Rollins was a parishioner at Matthew's church, and he had it as his primary production client. He'd given Matthew a key years ago.

Sonny's office was small and cluttered (and it reeked of cigarettes), but there were two comfortable desk chairs and a coffee maker.

"Remarkable," the minister's guest said.

"What's remarkable?" Matthew asked.

"Your TV station is holy ground."

"It's a church first and foremost."

The other let out a snort. "Oh yeah. That's why it's buried in the middle of acres of commercial and industrial zoned real estate, miles away from where any residents might realistically congregate."

Matthew shook his head. "The church is not a building, it is a condition. 'Wherever two or three are gathered in My name—'"

"Or, for that matter, watching the TV at home. Funny how the word 'congregation' has now stretched to include people who are alone and just praying at the same time."

"Why have you come here?" Matthew asked. "Wait, I'll start with a simpler question: If you're not my son, who are you?"

The other regarded him silently — a stone-faced glance like a poker player examining a hand of cards. Matthew only returned the stare until his guest seemed to reach a conclusion. "You can call me Gaviel, when we're alone. 'Noah' will do when we're around others. Less confusing that way."

"Gaviel."

"Don't use it lightly." Something in Gaviel's eyes told Matthew that he wasn't joking.

Matthew clenched his fists and gritted his teeth, but his voice — always his best tool — remained calm and controlled as he said, "And you are a demon."

"That's fair to say."

"You are in possession of my son's body."

Gaviel nodded. "I'm afraid so."

"You must realize I won't rest until you leave it."

Gaviel looked down and he seemed, for a moment, genuinely sad. "Matthew, I didn't kill your son, and I didn't force him out of his body. I want you to believe that."

"I'm sure you do, but you'll forgive me if I'm suspicious."

"Noah Wallace is no more, Matthew. I'm truly sorry, but that is the entire truth."

"You say that, but I see his body before me and hear his voice." Matthew's words were reasonable, but the situation was straining even his ability to speak calmly.

"The body remains. The memories remain. But the soul of your son is gone. He was struck by a car five days ago as he crossed the street near the university. There was some brain damage."

"I don't believe you! This is some trick. It has to be."

"A police report was filed. Look it up for yourself. His mind was damaged, his soul weakened, and I sensed it. I claimed this body for my own, and he was driven out, left to the fate that awaits all mankind. I know his memories and his skills, but that Noah you knew — the essential, animating spark — is gone for good."

"You're lying!"

Gaviel sighed. "What would I possibly gain by lying about this?"

"You're afraid I'll exorcise you."

"I think we've already established that your faith isn't quite up to *that* task," the demon replied.

"I may be weak, but I'm a minister of the Lord."

"With a degree from a seminary one step up from an ad in *Rolling Stone*."

"I have a doctorate in theology!"

"You have an *honorary* doctorate from a college that is, like your alma mater, targeting the same market as truck-driving schools. A doctorate you received, I might add, the same year you donated $25,000 to that college's scholarship fund." Gaviel shook his head. "You can't even read the Bible!"

"I read the Bible every day!"

"You read a *translation* of the Bible every day, but do you know any Latin besides 'quid pro quo'? Any Greek? Any Hebrew *at all*?" Gaviel was clearly enjoying the other man's discomfort.

"Faith is more important. Faith is more important than degrees, than learning, than accomplishments."

"On that, we agree. That's why I've come to you." He leaned in. "You do realize that I could have marked your soul, out there in the rain? I could have made you my creature — my slave, bound to my will and living or dying at my whim. But I didn't. I let you keep your soul, and I even suffered you to lay violent hands upon me, to insult me and spurn me and call on God's wrath."

"You want something. Something from me."

"Is God's forgiveness truly infinite?"

The question caught the reverend off guard. "Well yes. Of course."

"Encompassing all sins, no matter how grievous?"

"If the repentance is genuine."

"What about a fallen angel, Reverend? Could God forgive even such a one as that? One who willfully transgressed His direct commands? One who set out to deliberately soil all of God's creation, one who set himself up for the worship of humanity?"

At this Matthew frowned. "I don't know. Could such a being truly repent?"

Gaviel paused and smiled once more. "That's the question, isn't it?"

"That's what you want? A return to God?"

"If it's possible. You believe the intercession of one man saved the human race. I believe the intercession of a man can save my race as well. Will you help me?"

Matthew narrowed his eyes. "I'd try. If I thought you were sincere."

Gaviel spread his hands. "I've already shown you substantial mercy and forbearance. What other proofs can I offer?"

Matthew leaned forward and his eyes burned. "Release my son."

"Matthew, I give you my word that I'm not holding him."

"What good is the word of a self-confessed rebel and blasphemer?"

"As good as the advice of an arrogant, self-righteous adulterer. I mean, really: Did you think you were such a saint that you were worthy of an angelic visitation? You're a *televangelist*, a word synonymous with 'fraud' and 'hypocrite' among America's literate classes. I'll grant that you never stole from the collection plate, but only because your self-defined fiscal guidelines are so loose that buying yourself cars and jewelry is actually *permitted*. Honestly, in the 'sleazy minister' trifecta, you've done just about everything but tattoo 'love' and 'hate' on your fingers!"

"If I'm so low, what does that make you? If I'm so weak in faith, what are you who comes asking for help?"

Gaviel shrugged. "Another point for you, Reverend. Do you want to sit here and trade quips all night, or do you want to know, specifically, why I chose you?"

"I'm sure you'll tell me regardless."

"I chose you *because* you're arrogant. You've got the pride of idealism. You think that anything you do is right because *you* do it. You have the faith that moves mountains, and that's the faith I need. The faith that thinks, 'Maybe I *can* redeem a fallen angel.'" Gaviel sat back and considered.

"Pastor, there are two possibilities here. Either I'm holding your son's soul captive or I'm not, agreed? If I'm holding his soul — and I'm not, but I seem unable to persuade you of that — it's in your best interest to at least keep me close so you can find some way to liberate him. Now, please, as a favor, just *consider* the possibility that I'm telling you the truth. Just maybe Matthew really is gone and I've told you the truth about my repentance. Is there any way you can turn me aside and claim to be a man of God?"

Matthew sighed hard.

"I still think you're trying to trick me," he said, "But you're right. I'm caught. I can't afford to just cast you out."

"I appreciate that." Gaviel sat back in his chair and seemed to relax. "So. What should we do?"

"I suppose we could take a page from the Catholics, if you want to confess your sins."

"And if, in the process, I reveal some weakness you can exploit…?"

Matthew spread his hands. "You don't trust me, and I don't trust you. But if we're going to do this, we have to pretend for a while."

"I see."

Reflexively, Matthew said what he said to every guilty conscience that came for his advice. "Why don't we start at the very beginning?"

Gaviel smiled. "Very well."

"In the beginning…"

The Unmoved Mover

Noah paused, seeing Matthew's frown. "What's the matter? Not a fan of the classics?"

"You're going to tell me you were present at the birth of the cosmos?"

"Where did you think demons came from? We were there at the very start, because we *were* the very start."

"I'm sorry?"

"We were God's first creations, so that we might go on and build the universe."

Matthew snorted. "You really don't think much of me, do you? You really think you can get away with claiming to be the Maker of All?"

"Let's set aside that first question for now, shall we? And, while I'm tempted to point out how quick *you* were to accept me as your — what was the phrase? — 'Lord and God,' I'm going to do you the favor of addressing your question seriously. But you have to promise to follow along and keep an open mind."

"I'll try," Matthew said, glaring.

"Here's the thing: Everything we touch touches us in return, right? Contact means interaction — or contamination, if you prefer. How does a perfect being change? If it changes, it ceases to be perfect. Unless it was already imperfect, and it changes into a perfect form by expelling its imperfections." He raised an eyebrow. "Not a very flattering theory, is it? The universe as a hairball from the throat of the Almighty."

"You seem intent on belittling God before me," Matthew observed.

"Matthew, please believe me when I say God could not possibly give a shit what *I* think of Her."

"'Her'? God's a woman, now?"

"Sure. She used to be a real looker, too, but over the past quarter million years She's gained a *lot* of weight."

Matthew snorted. "Even your blasphemy is getting weaker and weaker."

"It's blasphemy to say God's a woman with a fat ass, but saying She's a man with a snowy beard and sandals is reverent? Look, God is *God* — almighty, infinite, immortal and incomprehensible. God doesn't need your reverence. Saying mean things about the Almighty isn't going to hurt God, it just hurts you and corrodes the world around you. It's like spitting at the sky. The sky isn't bothered, and there's a good chance you'll hit your own face in the bargain."

"In one breath you condemn blasphemy, when thirty seconds ago you were claiming you created the universe. If you're trying to corrupt my soul, you might want to be more coherent."

"Thanks for the tip, chief." The demon took a deep breath. "Look, I'll call God 'He' if that helps you. Just, please — let's get back on track."

"I'm not the one going on tangents about God's weight problem."

The Houses of Creation

"In the beginning, there were two infinities — the infinite absence that was the Void, and the infinite existence of the Almighty. Each was contained within the other, but they were eternally separate. To define and illuminate the border between them, the Maker formed the Angels of the Dawn. I was one of them.

"Our purpose and mission was to carry the will of the Maker all along the perimeter of Creation, framing the perfect balance between Is and Is Not. Because, you see, the Lord — the Infinite of Infinities — was all things. That which was not God was absolutely nothing. So some form of mediation was needed to create a buffer layer: the cosmos. We were needed to separate the divine primal from all the things it *could be* into the particular things that it *was*. Our function, broadly, was to filter His will into discrete forms.

"God's will was the first act — remembered in some sources as 'fiat lux' and regarded in others as the Big Bang.

"On that first day of infinite potential, we rode out in our multitudes. The Throne of Moonlight, the Crimson Dominion, the Seven Radiant Cherubim… Under them, lesser creatures like the Archangel Viridian, the Power of Reflection… even my humble self. On that first day, literally everything was possible. And our job was to winnow that possibility, spinning it into threads and weaving the best of all possible worlds.

"We of the House of the Dawn weren't the only ones, of course. The first, the most important, the closest to the Most High… and, for that very reason, those with the least direct influence over the world of gross matter. Remember what I said about contamination? We were just the first of several barriers between the divine and the material. His pure will came to us, where it was… confined, even distorted perhaps, into the *statement* of His will. The Houses beneath us were those charged with the actual *fulfillment* of His will.

"The second legion was the House of the Firmament — angels of wind and movement. Initially, their duty was to animate the elements of the universe.

"You possess a body of many parts — your heart, your lungs, your brain — but each separately is dead and

worthless. It is only when they are united that their true qualities emerge. The Second House governed that principle. By them, the whole can become greater than the sum of its parts.

"The most crucial task of the House of the Firmament was to convey the breath of life from the Maker to the Made. Every tree, every blade of grass, every ant and cormorant and elephant was personally given life by the breath of an Angel of the Firmament. They were not only the givers of life, but its protectors as well.

"The bond between a Guardian and the creatures to whom it gave breath is strong and profound — the bond between a mother and child is no different. Angels of the Second House could sense any peril to their charges, and fly instantly from the ends of Creation to defend them. I worked closely with many of them during the early days… the Power of Unbound Increase, the Dominion of the Azure Dome — even the Seraph of the Unreachable Limit. In many ways, they were the kindest, the most selfless among us. Even the mightiest of them was known, not for personal glory, but for the glory their reflection gave others. They themselves were unseen as the wind, but we knew when they were present. We felt their embrace in all directions, the quickening of the impulse to expand and improve. Their greatness was that they made everything around them greater.

"The Third House was the house of the Fundament — the House of Matter, the tangible — of things you can feel with your body and not just deduce with the mind. Where the first Houses dealt with the ephemeral, it was the artisans of the Third House who slowed energy into matter, cooled magma into stone and gave life its form. All that you feel and touch is their work. Where we Dawngivers flew on shafts of light and the Guardians breathed within the world unseen, the Fundamentals walked the earth and burrowed within it. The Golden Dominion, the Power of the Shifting Sands, the Seraph of the Mountain Peaks — in every case, their glory was in their tasks, not themselves.

"To human eyes, the Angels of the Perceptible might seem the most successful. After all, they worked the most accessible and observable aspects of the world — that which can be touched, held, measured and examined. I had little contact with the House of Earth, personally, though I was badly injured by one of their number in the War… but I'm getting ahead of myself.

"The Fourth House was the House of Spheres, the Fates who set the cosmic lights in their courses and, in the process, gave all Creation an underpinning of Time. Of all the Houses, perhaps only they and the Fifth could compete with ours for sheer personal splendor. I remember their pageantry, sweeping down from Heaven with a swirl of starry cloaks. Once I danced with the Throne of the North Star herself, and I flatter myself that there was favor in her dark eyes. I heard the songs of the Pleiades, made jests with the Virtues

of Past and Future, and was honored at the courts of the Manifold Cherubim. The Angels Temporal were a worthy and noble House, ruling from glass castles on the moon and moving with grandeur the spheres of the stars. In the war, they suffered greatly, for Earth was not their natural home, and it took all their forethought and foresight simply to survive… but in the first days, they were magnificent.

"Their equals in beauty were the Angels of the Deep. Paradoxical, lyrical, liquid and free, their charge was to govern the eternally changing, and the changing eternal. The sea was a fit home for them, the Powers of the Tides and the Cycle Virtues. As humankind developed, the Oceanites were the patrons of art and beauty, of mutability and resonant pattern.

"The Angels of the Deep are best represented through the ocean, which is always there but never the same. The physical stuff of the water was created by the Fundamentals, but animated and governed by the Oceanites because of its excellent ability to hold and transmit patterns. They are of the pattern, not the matter, just as my words are not my mouth or the air they pass through or your ear when you hear it. The Oceanites were like ripples in water — in constant movement, they had no single location. They were in the water and of the water, but not the water. All those sorts of transitions were governed by the Angels of the Deep. They became guardians of beauty and culture — because a sculpture or a song or a story is an attempt to transmit a pattern of experience through some other medium and into another soul.

"The next House created contained nature's overseers — the Angels of the Wild, who governed the instincts and interactions of the natural world. You see how the duties of the Houses continue to be refined? First there was pure will. Then there was separation, individuality. Next, stability. After that, order for change. Mutability within stability came next, and finally, larger and more gradual patterns of change — the migrations of elk, the growth cycles of insects, the population balance between predator and prey.

"While the House of the Wild was concerned with minutiae in many ways, I should comment that its domain was a very complicated one. By the time something that could be called an ecological system arose — not just individual prototype creatures, but populations of them interacting with flora and other fauna and climactic changes — the level of sophistication in the universe was very high. Understand that, as complex as the ecosystem you know now may be, the inter-faceted interactions of Paradise were far more complicated. But, once again, I'm getting ahead of myself.

"The Angels of the Wild — from the Seraph of the Cycle down to the lowliest Angels of Renewal — were a hardheaded, pragmatic lot. One must be, I suppose, to mind and organize every animal on Earth. Quite a balancing act, I'm sure. But I had few opportunities to interact

with them before the dark times. They were, you understand, very close to the earth and far from the Maker, while the exact opposite was my case. Once we rebelled, they were the most numerous (and in many cases, the fiercest) of our warriors. Only the Fundamentals were equally comfortable with existence on the terrestrial plane. And none were more familiar with strife and conflict.

"The last House created was the last one needed — the House of the Second World. Led by the Silent Seraph, their numbers were always uncertain and their ways often unseen. The Virtue of Shadows, the Throne of Repose… a somber lot, solemn and wise during the war. I had no dealings with them before the Fall, as I was a creature of beginnings and they were the Angels of Death. But once we were rebelling, all cast together against the loyal hosts… they always seemed sad. Regretting lost chances to fulfill their true purpose. Always too much to do and never the right thing…

"Those, then, were the seven Houses of the Host. Together, we formed the cosmos and kept it stable. And together, we contributed to the final and ultimate element of reality. Commanded by the Maker, we infused reality with some of His divine essence, contained in creatures who would grow, in time, to rule the universe in His stead.

"Understand that when one says humankind was 'made in God's image' it's nothing so literal as 'two legs, one nose, seven thoracic vertebrae.' Your shape is not in the image of God, your soul is. You carry within you a small reservoir of the essence of existence that God used to create the entire cosmos. Powerful though we Elohim are, we are barren of that true Making fire. You are His true children, and your holy nature courses through your blood, flickers in your emotions and sings through your inventive thoughts.

"We of Dawn House transported His spark, the Fundamentals built a housing for it, and the Guardians wove the pieces into activity. From the Oceanites came your sacred information, within and without — the capacity for thought and expression, and your ability to pass on traits to your children. From the Fates you had a conception of time, the persistence for memory and the potential to plan and anticipate. The Angels of the Wild gave you instincts and sensations to ground you within the physical world. The final touch was given by the Reapers: mankind's physical renewal, your ability to change and grow — and, if need be, to recover from injury.

"Humankind was our highest, finest and ultimate creation. We crafted you with the best of our knowledge and the finest gifts of our spirit. The Maker Himself admired you, but we were given two final commands before the Guardians were permitted to give you the breath of life.

"First, He commanded that we love you, and that our love for you equal our love for the Maker Himself.

"Many questioned this command — not to resist it, but simply wondering why it was needed. Having made

you as our surpassing effort, our love for you was already as strong as that between a parent and a child. At the time, the consensus was that the Almighty didn't want us to feel bad for not loving Him *more* than you. Therefore, that first command was easy to the point of being redundant. The second was far less simple.

"Despite our love, we were ordered to hide ourselves from you. To never let ourselves be seen or heard or sensed by you in any way. No contact. No messages. No voices or gestures or even hints. Humanity, surrounded on all sides by loving protectors of infinite power, was to think itself alone.

"Do you see it? Do you get the joke? You, for whom the cosmos was made, you whom multitudes of angels longed to serve — you were to think yourselves isolated in an uncaring and mechanical universe."

As his guest paused, Matthew leaned in. "You mean there are angels all around us right now?" he asked.

His guest leaned back and sighed. "No, Matthew. They're all gone."

"Gone?"

"Or hidden beyond my knowing. But my guess is that they are just… gone."

They were both silent for a time. Then Matthew said, "If you don't mind, I'm going to make some coffee. Do you want some?"

Paradise

While Matthew busied himself with coffee, Noah went to the bathroom. When they had resumed their seats, Matthew frowned and asked a question.

"What was Paradise like?"

Noah folded his hands and frowned.

"You're not very well equipped to understand it," he said at last. "I don't say that to be insulting. The world was fundamentally different back then. It was… more complex. Richer. It had layers that are simply absent, now."

"Layers?"

"Yes… consider this coffee we're drinking. It's only coffee, right? It's not anything else?"

"I guess not."

"In the uncorrupted world, this coffee could also exist simultaneously as a song or an aesthetic idea or even a sentient and helpful creature. Different things on different layers, all equally real, all similar, but each discrete — even while they were simultaneously experienced." Seeing Matthew's expression, he continued.

"I'll give you a more relevant example. The first people: Were they Adam and Eve, a woman and a man, or were they the evolved descendents of apes?"

"They were a woman and a man, as the Bible says."

"Correct. But they were *also* a multitude of ape descendents. The universe was made in seven days, on

one level, but that same span of time was billions of years on another level.

"Or consider the Angels of the Firmament. On some levels of reality they were conveying the life-giving breath of the Maker on a purely scientific level — they were, literally *were*, the process by which solar energy striking simple carbon molecules agitated them into forms of ever increasing complexity, until they became organic molecules, then primitive single-celled animals, then nucleated cells and so on, up to and including dogs, cats and humans. But *at the same time* they were crouching over the mouths of newly sculpted creatures of all types, breathing into their mouths to animate them."

"Are you talking about metaphor?"

Gaviel chuckled. "Not yet, no. These contrary things really were simultaneously true in the young cosmos. It makes no sense to you because you're used to living in this, the singular world. But once you accept the idea of the multiple world, it clears up a lot of the problems you humans have with faith, miracles, the Divine Architect—"

"I don't have any problems with my faith."

"None? Well, you should. Can an omnipotent being create a boulder so big he can't lift it?"

Matthew dismissed the thought with an irritated wave of his hand. "Oh, here we go… Are you trying to shake my faith again? Because it's going to take a lot more than that tired old chestnut."

"I'm not trying to attack anything, just demonstrate a point. If God can create the boulder so big He can't lift it, then His power isn't infinite: It's not sufficient to lift the boulder. But if He *can't* make a boulder too big to lift, than His power is still not infinite: It's not sufficient to *create* the boulder. That's the kind of problems you run into in the singular world. But the multiple world resolves those paradoxes

"Paradise was layers of varied and interrelated realities — each revealing and relating to the others, showing them from different perspectives or providing new joys and experiences. Or they were supposed to, anyhow." He sighed.

"You mean all those layers of reality still weren't good enough?"

"Paradise was purer and richer and more fulfilling than this reality by an incalculable measure. Compared to Paradise, this world is Hell. Although, to be fair, compared to Hell, this world is Paradise."

"Hell has no layers?"

Gaviel nodded.

"Hell is very nearly nothing at all. It is a void marred only by our awareness of it, and our ability to feel our rejection by our Maker." Unconsciously, Noah's hands rose to hug himself, as if suddenly chilled. The gesture was oddly touching, and Matthew wondered if it was staged for his benefit.

"Hell is the corrosion of love, Reverend. No fire and brimstone, no pitchforks and snakes. After a hundred years, anyone could get used to mere sensation. But utter numbness — that's a torment that never gets any older. After the first ten minutes, you think you've been there ten thousand years. You're there, alone and isolated, with nothing for company but the knowledge that you are literally God-forsaken. You sit there in His hate and feel everything in you turn to hate as well, and there is no respite. There's just you and love getting more and more twisted and inverted."

Noah's handsome face had become terribly still. "We talk about how we were exiled from reality… but really it was more like we were excreted. Cast out, abandoned and despised." His nostrils widened and his eyes seemed to peer off into some grim distance. Then he raised his eyebrows, sat up straighter, and smiled back at Matthew. "But we were discussing Eden, not the Abyss."

Forbidden Fruit

"If Paradise was so perfect, why did mankind rebel? For that matter, why did you?"

"Because humanity was *blind*, Reverend. The Bible would prefer to call them *innocent*, but the fact was that they were kept ignorant of themselves and the world around them. The Divine Plan included everything they might possibly need… except the capacity to appreciate their good fortune."

Matthew cocked his head. "Somehow I suspect you're being less than forthright with me."

Noah's hand hit the coffee table by his chair sharply. "If you want to accuse me of something, why don't you just say it? Do you think I *enjoy* pouring out the story of my greatest tragedy to someone who thinks I kidnapped his son? You think I derive some jaded *pleasure* from talking about watching my friends die, watching the humanity I loved suffer, watching reality itself sicken and crumble?"

Matthew met his gaze, and it was like steel hitting stone. "I find it hard to believe that men designed by God — or, as you insist, by angels — would have this fatal flaw. I don't believe humankind was unhappy in Eden — unless you and your 'Elohim' made them unhappy."

"You think Adam and Eve were happy?" Gaviel shrugged. "Maybe to the extent that a dog is happy when it wags its tail or a pig is happy when it rolls in mud. They could experience physical pleasure, but — even less than a certain stubborn minister I could mention — they possessed no real comprehension. A beautiful sunset meant nothing to them, except that night would soon fall. Even the beauty of each other — and they were the apex of human beauty, Matthew — even that just didn't register. The pleasure of a full belly and warm feet, those were the limits of their understanding."

"So they were innocent. Like children."

"Innocent like pigeons, more like. Innocent like a rat that goes through your trash. Only these pigeons had the

potential to be poets, scholars, sculptors and musicians. We tried to show them, tried to teach them, to the extent that we were able. But it wasn't much. A Fundamental could open the earth to them, revealing a seam of diamonds and gold, but primal humanity just scratched their heads and moved on. And you think we made them unhappy? A spirit on the wind — I knew him, his name would sound to your ears as 'Raphael' — made an elaborate plan to play a song for them. He had to shuttle himself between hundreds of facets — the 'reality layers' I told you about — in order to make his plans with angels of other houses. A Cherub of the Spheres told him when his chosen audience was fated to walk through a certain windy valley. Angels of the Fundament worked with him to crack the valley walls, just so, that the wind might echo through them like harp strings. Trees were moved into place, that the creak of their limbs might harmonize, while birds were enticed there to add the high notes, even as the valley's streambed was sculpted into the right shape to sound percussion from the moving water… Raphael labored for ages to give your forebears ten minutes of music, coaxed lovingly out of entirely natural sounds. Do you know what happened?"

"What?"

"Adam caught and ate one of the birds, while Eve checked the trees to see if they had fruit. And that was the entirety of their reaction."

"Hmph. That's quite a story. But if mankind was so ignorant, why would he bother?"

"Isn't that obvious? He did it because he loved them. He did it because he couldn't show himself and play for them directly. Remember, they were not to know that they were protected. They were not to know that they were watched. They were not to know that the blessings they received were the gifts of thought and foresight, rather than… random events. We moved about them unseen, and they moved about the world, comprehending only the thinnest fraction of what they saw. So no, they weren't 'unhappy.' But we could see they were incomplete."

"So you took it upon yourselves to 'complete' us."

"Wouldn't you? You loved your son — no matter how angry he got with you, he never doubted your love for him. What would you do if his mother had tried to keep him out of school, saying, 'Oh, he's so happy as a baby, why let him grow?'"

"That's hardly the same thing."

"It's *exactly* the same thing! Why didn't the Benevolent Creator allow them higher reason? We asked ourselves that same question, believe me. Some of the Seraphim even went so far as to ask Him. His reply was not particularly helpful. 'If you would know as I know, come unto Me and see as I see.' A few bold angels even took Him up on His offer. They were never seen or heard from again — and believe me, in those days we knew how to look. God presumably destroyed them for their hubris."

"You can't think God would be so spiteful," Matthew said, then rolled his eyes. "Or maybe *you* can. I'm not buying it."

"Oh, and — thousands of years after the fact — you have a better explanation?"

Matthew shrugged. "Perhaps His motivation was so complicated only He could comprehend it. Perhaps anyone who wanted to also understand it would have to become one with Him."

Gaviel shrugged. "Apotheosis? Annihilation? Like the fates of dead souls, they both look alike to an outside observer.

"That was our dilemma, Reverend. We could see the wonders of the world, in all their iterated splendor. We knew that humanity was the apex of that world — the capstone, the crown jewel, the wonder of wonders. You were truly the children of the Father, in a way that even we were not, destined in time to be as He was and make as He made. You were the sun around which the whole world spun. Yet you were flawed — flawed by design, it seemed, and destined to remain flawed forever."

Matthew sat still for a moment. He took a sip of coffee to cover his confusion.

"What was mankind's flaw? I mean, we hadn't sinned yet, had we?"

"Sin was impossible to humanity at that time, in the same way you don't impute moral weight to the actions of a dragonfly or a koala bear. You were the most advanced of animals, but you were still animals.

"It was clear to all of us in the Host that you were destined for greatness — that all the world was made for you — and yet, you were unable to grasp your potential. You could not realize your true awareness, no matter how we tried to jar and stimulate you." His brow clouded as he said, "We tried and tried, and you *just didn't get it*. But because of our commands against interference, we couldn't simply give it to you.

"What could be done? We watched you suffer in your ignorance — for even in that primitive state, you could at least understand the disappointment of your Maker as He daily waited for progress that never came. Every day, your suffering was reflected in us, growing keener and stronger until one day it finally came to a head."

The Great Debate

"The real root of the rebellion was a scholarly angel we might call Ahrimal. A student of the spheres, he and his House were much intrigued by the effect humanity had on the cosmos. Without humankind, Paradise was superficially perfect, but ultimately stagnant. Humanity added a factor of chaos and uncertainty to a world that was otherwise as predictable as atomic decay. The Fates watched this with keen interest, attempting to comprehend the deeper, richer patterns that humanity's free will wove into the universal tapestry.

"It was this Ahrimal — not, so great a light himself — who first perceived a knot of great destructiveness and turmoil. It was still on the horizon of the unrealized future, but each day made it stronger and darker. Unquestionably, humanity had some role to play in this looming tragedy.

"Disturbed and afraid, Ahrimal told his masters what he had foreseen, but they told him to be calm and have no fear. When he showed them, they simply replied that it was an anomaly, a necessary *potential* bad to offset the perfect actual good. Surely (they said) the Maker would never let His creation founder on such treacherous shoals. They forgot His warnings and went about their business.

"Ahrimal could not rest quite so easy. Dismissed by his own House, he called upon his friends and colleagues. They arrived at his lunar sanctum with no idea how grave his concerns were, but they soon suspected from his worried visage. Retreating to an obscure chamber, he told them of his vision and, moreover, showed them the evidence of his foreseen doom.

"'My friends,' he whispered. 'What can we do?'

"The first to speak was Belial, Virtue of the Boundless Deeps. Radiant in his cloak of blue and aqua scales, his voice had in it the thunder of a groaning glacier, married to the smooth sigh of a wave kissing the shore. Of all our number, none had so keen a taste for beauty, none took such joy in the art of the world… and, consequently, none suffered so much from humanity's loss.

"'I am shocked and amazed that the wise council of the Fates has ignored this matter. Our friend shows us that a time approaches when the voice of beauty will be silenced, and the joy of artifice perverted into the ugliness of deceit and falsehood. Is it an act of love to stand by while this happens? We cannot pretend ignorance while this great disaster rolls in from the horizon. We must act.'

"'But what action should we take?'

"This was spoken by Usiel, Throne of the Sundered, a potent Angel of the Second World. Like many of his House, he was absent even when he was present. At the edges of his body, light was cut short, with an edge keener than a razor, and where his shadow fell the World of Death became visible.

"'Our orders are clear: Intercession is forbidden. The woman and the man are to make their own way.' He turned to Ahrimal and addressed him in particular. 'You may think you have the farthest sight, and that is true for things of this world, but your vision falters at the edge of my realm. It is there, I fear, that this coming trouble will end.'

"'Indeed?'

"The response came not from Ahrimal, but from the perfumed breath of Lailah the Defender, an Angel of the Firmament. That airy spirit took formless form for the debate, and through the lens of her being, each arch of the moon castle chamber seemed more noble, each line of its

walls more true. Even fair Belial's beauty was magnified when seen through Lailah's eyes. In her attendance, the danger of disagreement seemed to wane. 'Perhaps the Second World is the key. In this best ordered world, perhaps disaster is no peril at all? Perhaps the entry of humans into your realm is their true destiny. Perhaps that is the missing element — the stumbling block that keeps them from reaching their true potential.'

"'You speak of that which you know not,' replied Usiel. 'Much as I should love to embrace mankind as closely as you and yours do, I dare not risk it. Should we plunge mankind into death on the strength of a 'perhaps'? Perhaps the chance of death will spill out humanity's chances and leave them forever denied. Perhaps human mortality will shake both worlds or even split them apart!'

"In this, Usiel proved as apt a prophet as Ahrimal, but at the time he seemed only frightened, not wise. We thought no suffering could be keener than the thwarted love we felt.

"We were wrong.

"'Looking around this world we have built and at the humanity we lovingly crafted, I see only two elements that mar this perfection,' said Belial. 'One is the source of our longtime frustration: humanity's failure to awaken their true potential. Although it lies within their reach, they fail to grasp it, day after day. This is a torment to each of us, from lowly angel to mighty seraph. Now, Ahrimal brings tidings of failure and horror for all the world. Can these two sorrows be unmarried? Or is it more likely that the forthcoming bane of the world is connected to the suffering and failure of Eve and Adam?'

"'Surely you cannot impute guilt in this matter to the man and the woman?' Lailah's shock was a chill gust of wind and a momentary dimming of the beauty she beheld.

"'Guilt? No,' replied Belial. 'But in what other aspect of the cosmos do we see failure? The stars move as they should. The ocean tides are steady and smooth. Generations of beasts and plants rise and are cut down. Only humanity is anything other than what it was meant to be.'

"'Indeed,' said Ahrimal, 'What else *could* so confound the universal plan? No bird nor beast no star in the sky is important enough to bring desolation on the whole of the world. Belial is right: Adam and Eve are, though guiltless, somehow some part of the cause.'

"Usiel shrugged. 'If the future peril is a consequence of their present plight, what can we do? The command against interference cannot be ignored.'

"'The plight of humanity touches us all, to the extent that each of us bears great love for mankind,' replied Belial. 'Their helplessness becomes our helplessness. They are but a shadow of their ultimate potential while we are forbidden to serve them fully. They are diminished by ignorance, unaware of their true power. We are bound, not by walls we cannot see, but by the iron command of our Maker. Yet while Adam and Eve remain hobbled, none among the Elohim are truly free, truly fulfilled or truly able to discharge our duties of service and adoration. While humanity remains incomplete, the universe remains incomplete.

"'I am a maker of beauty and a giver of wonder, but all my creation is sterile as dust with no eye to behold it or ear to give heed. Can it be our Master's will that we be thwarted in those very acts for which we were made? Surely not, and to say so is to attribute cruelty unto Him whose kindness extends to the creation of us all, and of this world of marvels we find about us on all sides.'

"'We all long for the day when humanity finds its true potential,' said Usiel, 'But how can we hasten its coming?'

"'That is the question. That must be our mission.'

"Ahrimal agreed, but Usiel argued emphatically that interfering with the progress of human evolution at one point could have unforeseen repercussions along its entire length, and in this, Ahrimal was reluctantly forced to agree. 'But,' the Fate hastened to add, 'With humankind, the stern boundaries of the future are already blurred and shifting. If we act as we are wont and give as freely as we desire, who is to say that the ultimate effect will not be *good*? Indeed, moved as we are by the highest motives, how can any ill result? Can evil spring from good? Can love beget wickedness? Surely not, else the entire universe is absurd and pointless — and that is an idea so blasphemous I hesitate to speak it.'

"'Perhaps my role gives me more perspective,' said Usiel. 'If mankind is destined to awaken, surely no action of ours can hinder them — unless we interfere. We do not see as God sees, and what looks to us like kindness may bear cruel fruit in the fullness of time. We cannot see every side of this Creation from within it, but He dwells without and naught can hide from Him. Why, then, should we meddle?'

"It was Belial who replied. 'You speak truly when you say that we cannot know the fullness of Creation from within. But should that excuse us from fulfilling our first and greatest duty? Your House is one that reacts and responds to what is, but other Houses are charged to create and expand this world. You argue that we should accept that future events are as willed by the Maker simply because they happen to what He has made. But by that reasoning, we ought never to have hung the constellations or shaped the mountains or sculpted the depths of the sea. We should instead have said 'If the world is sterile, sterility must be its destiny,' and 'If the world is dark, it must be meant for darkness.' Ahrimal tells us of impending danger. How are we to know that action against it — action to help and protect mankind, action for which every fiber within us cries — is not *our* destiny? Perhaps, as you say, we will harm them by helping too soon. But is it not also possible that we will harm them by refusing to help? If one is unknowable, then the other is surely equally so.'

"'The love you demonstrate does you great credit,' Lailah said to Belial. 'But while Eve and Adam are the capstones of Creation, they are only one element thereof.

They do not exist independent of their world, nor is it unmoved by them. If we push them to awaken and fail — even with the best intentions, even with the noblest goals — what will be the end of it? Grave Usiel suggests a rift between the World of Life and the Afterlife. What if other facets of the cosmos are shaken? Our power is great, and by striving against the world we may injure the world. By trying to shape the souls of man, we might warp them instead.'

"'And that being so, you would choose to do *nothing*?' asked Belial. 'Do you think we — we ministers of Creation, we who built it and who are charged with its defense — are so clumsy, so ignorant, so foolhardy as to ruin what we made?'

"'I say nothing but that our choice must be starkly divided into action and inaction. Any decision, small or large, could be the cause of the future we fear. By our own power, we do not know and never can. We are indeed, to use your image, trapped on the water's edge, unable to walk or swim without peril.

"'But for us, there is a third way. As we of the Firmament fly to the aid of any charge in danger, so may God lift us away from this hazardous shore. We cannot know, but we can trust in Him who does, the Unmoved Mover, the One Outside the World. If He tells me to reveal myself to our beloved charges, I will do so with infinite gladness in my heart. But if He compels me to remain hidden, no force in this world or the next could make me break faith.'

"'How wise your counsel would be, if only we could *know* His will!' cried Ahrimal. 'With the reassurance of His word, I would wait until the stars dimmed. But we have no word!'

"'We have the opportunity to see as He sees,' said Usiel, but there was doubt in his voice.

"'For myself,' said Belial, 'I would take that chance — but what of Haniel, what of Injios, what of the Dominion of Summer Breezes and the Angel of the Unseen Light? They went, they saw and they are no more! Not one of them, from lowly angel through mighty throne, has returned to give word, give hope, give knowledge! Haniel was your boon companion, Usiel. Where is she now? When you speak her name, no echo returns! When you ask her what she saw, get you any answer?'

"'Perhaps she is forbidden to speak of what she saw,' Usiel said in response, but his words were muffled in sorrow, for his love for Haniel was great and all knew the pain her loss had placed upon his soul.

"'You know better than any her great loyalty,' said Ahrimal. His face was a mask of compassion, and his compassion was also a gust of stellar wind, and a bright shower of falling stars. 'If forbidden to speak, she would speak not of her knowledge. But it is not only on the dark future fate that she is silenced. Her light is gone from the sky. Her song is silenced on the strands. I have sought her in the passages of time, and she is not there. Belial has looked for her in the depths, and Michael has

roamed every corner of the starry vacuum in quest of her. Yet neither lowly angel nor mighty cherub have found her. Usiel, have you searched your realm for her?'

"'She is not dead,' was all Usiel could say.

"'Not dead, and not alive, but simply gone, removed from our knowing… *this* is the fate allotted to those who would know the ultimate truth. It is not for me. I do not fear destruction for my sake, but I fear the loss of any in the Host who might turn aside the age of wrath I have foreseen. No, seeing as God sees is no answer if doing so is such a great step out of the cosmos that no return is possible.'

"'Then what are our choices?' demanded Lailah. 'We can stay here, poised for action, but ignorant of the right decision? Or we can pass beyond, learn the truth, and be impotent?'"

Gaviel paused in his recitation and looked at Matthew. "Do you know much about quantum physics?"

"What?"

"Quantum physics? Heisenberg's uncertainty principle?" Seeing the confusion in the reverend's expression, he shrugged. "Noah didn't think you'd know anything about post-Newtonian mechanics — and, indeed, why should you? — but if you did, I might be able to give you some of the deeper nuances of Lailah's discussion with Ahrimal."

"Ah. Well, sorry if your discussion was too rarefied for this po', ign'nt, down home preach-man." With each word, he broadened his pronunciation, until the last phrase was a parody of every uneducated rural black from decades of films.

"Don't be that way, Matthew. You know there's no one here but us niggers." Gaviel's words were calm, clear, articulate. "Quantum mechanics is a field of scientific study that examines subatomic particles and their behavior. One of the essential challenges of the discipline is that, in many incidences, knowing one fact about a particle precludes knowing another. It may be possible to know an electron's velocity, but the process of finding that out changes the electron's location. Or you may be able to know where it is at one specific moment, but by learning that fact, you change its speed."

"And that's what Lailah and Ahrimal talked about next? I'm sorry, but this whole scene rings false to me."

"Ah. Once more you want to call me a liar without actually having the testicular fortitude to speak the words. Why don't you call me a 'God-damned liar' while you're at it? Then at least *part* of your phrase would be true."

"You really mean to tell me that in the face of some world-shaking catastrophe, you angels got together and had a *chat*? That you sat around some *moon palace* and eloquently discussed the pros and cons of *going to war with God*?"

"We were creatures of order and hierarchy, not to mention dignity. How do you think we settled things? Mud wrestling? Matthew, I'm giving you the version you can understand, all right? Lailah and Ahrimal did not talk *about* physics, they continued their discussion *through* physics. On one level, they were discussing the motives of the Maker and His will in a sunny palace on the moon. On another level, they were waves and particles interacting on the barren crust of an airless, lifeless rock. A third level had all the participants as musical elements, improvising against one another to communicate pure emotion."

"Different facets."

"Yes. We *are* natural laws, Matthew. Or we were." Gaviel sighed. "Those duties have been reassigned, it seems, but we were once waves and quanta. We danced, not on the head of a pin, but in the orbits of electrons."

The Morningstar

Anyway, Lailah and Ahrimal debated passionately about the possibility that knowing what to do and doing it might be mutually exclusive, but they came to no conclusion. Eventually, Belial gave voice to his impatience.

"We do not know — it may be that we cannot know — and it seems that we cannot even learn whether we can know or not. Does any among us wish to follow the path of Haniel and Injios?" Hearing great silence in reply, he continued. "Having spurned the path of impotent knowledge, we must now consider two other courses, as explained by gracious Lailah, whose wisdom is unsurpassed. Action and inaction are our choices, and I feel in my very core a loathing for inaction."

"Are your preferences, then, to serve as a guide in this matter of universal import?" asked Usiel. "My 'preference' is just as purely to let all remain as it is."

"Leaving the woman and the man in sorrow and ignorance?" asked Ahrimal.

"Better that than dead!"

The debate became increasingly fervent, until all tongues were stilled by a sudden arrival. He was uninvited, and unwelcome, and as he entered, the others dropped to their knees in reverence and fear.

He came in splendor and power, garbed in all phases of light. He was the highest agent of the highest House, the Seraph of the Morning. He was Lucifer, and every molecule in his presence hummed in time to his words.

"Rise," he said, "My fellow servants of The One."

Trembling, the Elohim stood, prepared for the anger of their maker. But that was not Lucifer's message. Instead he turned to Ahrimal.

"You have seen a coming darkness," he said. The Fate nodded.

"And you informed those above you?" Again, Ahrimal could only nod.

"What did they do?"

"They… they told me to have no fear. That nothing needed to be done."

Lucifer nodded.

"They were wrong," he said.

The foursome looked at each other with shock and amazement.

"Great Morningstar," said Lailah, "Have you word for us? Word from the Most High?"

Lucifer shook his head. "He is unmoved. Even the voice of all angels in choir could not shake the Lord Above from His position. We can move planets in their spheres, turn mountains into canyons and oceans into sand… but we cannot change one letter of what is writ on the Maker's heart."

"How can this be?" Aghast, Belial could only stare, his visage marred by sorrow and disbelief. "Is His heart so cold toward us, his children?"

"We are no children of His, my friend, but only his servants. His true children are Eve and Adam, our helpless masters, whose ignorance defeats all our wisdom. Our duty is to them as to Him, and on their future — yea, even the future of fear and horror that noble Ahrimal has seen — His silence is deeper than the vacuum of space."

"Then what are we to do?" asked Usiel.

"We can obey our orders," said Lucifer. "We can love mankind to the fullest extent of our power. We can free them, give them their true selves — and in so doing, either head off the horror ahead or arm humanity to endure it."

"But our orders!" said Lailah. "We were expressly commanded not to interfere. These words you speak are not from God, and I fear them."

"By the same authority, we were ordered expressly to love. Not to watch uncaring, not to oversee, but *to love them.* I see a clear and violent conflict between those two commands. Unable to be true to both, I choose to obey the higher."

"Choose?" said Belial. "Then you do not know?"

"I can see no farther than this one here," Lucifer said, gesturing to Ahrimal. "But like you, the taste of inaction is bitter on my tongue."

"What if the interference, our interference, is the very path we fear?" asked Usiel. "You cannot deny that we are striking blindly in the darkness."

"I deny nothing," replied Lucifer, "And I am as aware as you that whichever way we turn could be the wrong path. If we go to the woman and man with our gifts, the Lord may well judge us harshly. We could be condemned as oathbreakers, scorned for disobedience, cast out from the light of His love… even destroyed entirely. But if we stay silent, we may watch unmoving as the children we love lead the world we love into a pit of terror and malice."

"But there is no way to know!" cried Lailah.

"None whatever. But I love Eve and Adam as I love the Lord. If He commanded my destruction, gladly I would go. It is a poor show if our love is limited by self-preservation."

"I fear no risk to me," said Belial, "My reservation is the risk to humankind — to their lives, their souls, to the very world!"

"The dangers of my path are very real and as great as you fear. Yet answer me this: What crisis is better met by weakness than strength, better understood by ignorance than knowledge? Yes, revealing ourselves to the mortals may ignite this holocaust. Yes, exalting them may be the act that unhinges Creation. But if awakened humanity is the source of this crisis, might not awakened humanity be the cure for it as well? Or would you have them face the coming catastrophe as they are now — blind, irrational, little better than cunning apes?

"That is the worst consequence of action: That humanity faces the terror with its full powers awakened. Let us weigh it in the balance against the worst we could imagine if we do nothing. In that case, humanity faces its gravest threat with no defenses at all. They enter the madness unwarned, unaware, unable to even comprehend the fires that engulf them."

Lucifer bowed his head, and it seemed for a moment as if all light, everywhere in the cosmos, dimmed in reply. "If this choice is wrong, on my head be it."

Eyes bright with passion, Belial stepped forward to stand beside him. "I'm for you!" he cried. "Let us follow our hearts, do this deed and dare to love fully! Even if we fail, we can do no less and be worthy of our names."

Usiel shook his head. "No," he replied. "Forgive my impudence, Morningstar, but I revere your master more than you. I will not trust the wisdom of the Lord's creatures above the wisdom of His word. The Most High bid me hide, and hidden I shall remain."

"I too will not rebel," said Lailah. "The All-Maker would not condemn His creation to destruction. You say that without truth, humanity has no protection. To say such is to show contempt for their Father above. You can trust in your power, in your love and in your wisdom. I will trust in the Lord."

Of those who debated, it was Ahrimal, the least, who spoke last. "I know not what I saw, only that it was horrible. I know not how it will come about, only that humanity is involved. I cannot decide upon my duty, because any way I turn I must betray one order or the other. But I have faith in Adam and Eve. I have faith in the universe we have made. And I have faith that a perfected humanity is far more likely to see a way to avoid this catastrophe. I stand with the Morningstar. I say we act."

Thus were the seeds of contention sown. The Elohim flew in two directions, each calling others to declare the schism. Usiel and Lailah withdrew to the highest spheres of Heaven, to distance themselves from Lucifer and his rash act. The Morningstar and his followers plunged toward Earth, intent on making good on their bold decision before any could prevent them.

Though none knew it, the first steps to the Age of Wrath had been taken. But before that hell began, there were still some joys and wonders left to we who fell.

The Fall

Picture the scene. Twilight in Eden. The first woman and man walk upon a verdant carpet, caressed by the fragrance of a thousand blossoms. The sun hides its face in a cloudy blush, shedding ribbons of glory in crimson, vermilion and regal purple… but all its display cannot hide its eclipse, and gradually it sinks. The shadows grow long until all is encompassed. The green of the leaves turns black and then, as eyes adjust to starlight, everything is etched with silver.

Your ancestors stride through it unseeing, unfeeling and uncertain. They are each a monument to beauty, but neither can see it in the other, neither can comprehend. They sniff and stumble and find a fruiting vine, the sprouting top of a vegetable. They pull their supper from the soil and as they do, a voice — a mild voice, afraid but thick with longing — speaks to them.

"Eve," it says. "Adam. I have done this for you." Turning, amazed, they see a figure before them, garbed in gray, austere and holy. Twilight is fitting for this apparition, for she is Madisel, Archangel of the Unseen Past, one from the Final House. Of all the soul takers, she was the highest who chose Lucifer's path, and it was agreed that she — representing the lowest angels — should be the first to show her face. We wished, you see, to reveal ourselves slowly, to let them grow accustomed to us.

In mute silence they stare at her pale skin, dark eyes, ashen wings. "This," she says, gesturing at their supper. "This died for you. This plant has died to renew your life, and it is through me that this is done. Take it with my blessing… because I love you."

Frowning, still puzzled, they eat, and as they do, a second figure appears. Where Madisel was frail as steam, this one seems strong as a storm — vibrant, vital and solid as a mighty oak. The humans stare in awe at the glory of his golden mane, the strength visible in each straining muscle, the life coursing through his keen eyes and great feathers. His great frame twitches, each nerve and sinew aching to proclaim. At last his voice comes forth in a magnificent rush.

"I… I am Grifiel," the figure says, "Principality of Those Who Hunt By Day. Many times have those in my domain looked on you with greedy eyes, but they knew your flesh was not for them. They struck down grazing things and swimming things and running things, but you were spared their claws. My word turned them aside, because I love you."

Dazzled by these two visitors, the woman and the man were stunned yet again by a figure that rose from a nearby stream. All the dappled glory of moonlight on water shone from her hair and eyes, and as she stepped toward them, trembling with awe and passion. The sound of trickling water from her hair and dark wings made a delicate music — but not more delicate than the music of her voice. "I am Senivel," she said. "I speak for the House of the Deep, for

I am the Power of the Slender Streams. Each time you bent to drink, we kissed you unaware, because we love you."

In a shower of starlight, the next messenger came. He spread his wings of night above them and his voice was the grinding of the planets as they moved in their orbits. "I am Gaar-Asok, the Pole Star's Virtue. I speak for the House of Fate, and I offer you our blessings of the future and the past, for we love you."

A rumble coursed through the earth, and it opened at their feet, like a blooming flower unveiling golden pollen. At the center of the earth-blossom towered a figure of shining splendor. The gold and silver feathers of its wings clicked and chimed as it bowed low before humankind. "I am Toguiel, the Ruby Dominion, and I bring you the gifts of the House of Matter." A gesture, and veins of diamond and jade rose up around them, a garden of gems on golden stalks. "I and mine offer this gift as the smallest sign of our great love. We pray that they please you. We beg you to accept them."

Shocked and amazed, the mortals cowered, but the revelations were not yet finished. The sweet breeze of the garden grew stronger, thickening into solid movement, into a form that cast glory around it, redoubling the beauty of all those present. Like warmth, like comfort, like peace was the voice of Nazriel, Throne of Unbounded Benevolence, the highest emissary of the Second House who joined in Lucifer's crusade. She identified herself, and with

her words both humans and angels were calmed, sensing the safety that flowed from her like sweet breath. "Unseen and unknown, I and mine have guarded you," she said. "From fall and hurt and bitter mischance, we have each time turned you aside. Know now that you walk always in our embrace, for we love you."

With the holy pair calmed by the appearance of their protector, the time had come for the greatest of our number. In a blaze to rival the dawn, Lucifer descended. His glory, unbound, flung them to their knees. All the light of the cosmos seemed focused through him, and all its majesty poured forth in liquid waves unto his beloved humanity.

Alone of all the Elohim, he showed no trepidation. There was no pause of dread, no quiver of awe as the Morningstar spoke.

"I am Lucifer, Seraph of the First House, Prince of All Angels and Voice of God the Most High," he proclaimed. "But I come before you not to speak for God, but to speak as a humble supplicant. We angels you see before you — they and multitudes more from each of the seven Houses — have come at last to declare our love. Angels have watched you since the beginning. Angels numerous as the stars above have cherished your every move and gesture." Like them, he knelt, and as he did, so did the others. His burning wings encircled the woman and the man and, with a gentle stroke, bid them stand before the reverent spirits.

"We come now, not as officers of the cosmos and agents of its Maker, but as individuals. We come of our own will to offer you a final gift — the greatest gift we can give, the only fit gift for our overwhelming love. You may take it and become like us, and like God, and be fully aware of the vistas of creation. Or you may refuse it, and remain as you are, and never more be troubled by our sight. We will never abandon you — our adoration precludes it — but if you do not wish to receive our gift, speak now, and we shall hide again, protecting and loving you only from afar."

The woman and man turned to one another and spoke in hushed tones.

"What beings are these?" asked the man. "They come garbed in glory but abase themselves before us. They say they are of God, but that their actions are their own. How can these both be so? What can we say to their offer?"

"They love us," said the woman, "so they must mean us well. If the gifts they have given so far — safety and water and food — have been good, how much better must their ultimate gift be?"

"You are right," said the man. "We should accept what they offer, whatever it is. Having seen their splendor, I want to continue to see them, and if they were to leave us forever, my heart would break."

Turning to Lucifer, they made their choice. With solemn joy, Lucifer opened their eyes.

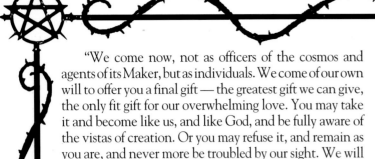

Crimes of Passion

Gaviel paused in his recitation and looked down at his own folded hands.

"The Fall," Matthew said.

"Was it?" Gaviel replied quietly.

"Did humanity have any idea what it was getting into?"

"No more than we did."

"I suppose it's a paradox," Matthew said, unthinkingly sipping his drink. "You can't understand what it means to know good and evil unless you *know* good and evil. Like you angels, humanity had to decide blind."

Gaviel shook his head. "We didn't give them knowledge of evil and good. At that point, there still *was* no evil."

"How can you say that? You knowingly rebelled against God your master. If that's not evil, what is?"

"We knowingly rebelled, but with the best of intentions. Please acknowledge that, Matthew. We meant no harm. We only wanted to help."

"'The road to hell is paved with good intentions,'" Matthew quoted, with a slight tilt of his head.

"That may be one of the most insightful comments in human history," Gaviel replied. "We truly had no ill in mind. We sought only to avoid or alleviate the disaster we foresaw. And yes, we were foolish. We were blind and ignorant and naïve and arrogant — so sure of our own power, our own judgment, that we scorned the orders of God. But we meant no harm. It's a thin excuse, and it really absolves us of nothing… but I maintain, even now, even after my torment and the horrors of the war and the atrocities that were to follow, that even as we transgressed, our motives were pure."

"If disobeying God isn't evil, what is?"

Gaviel steepled his fingers. "That's the question, isn't it? Is deciding to harm another evil? By that token, the soldiers who killed Nazis to liberate the concentration camps were as evil as the butchers they slew. Or is it Kant's categorical imperative — that when we decide to use others as a means instead of cherishing each individual as a separate, precious end — that is when we become evil? But in this age of mass votes and mass media, how can each individual be seen, let alone cherished?" He shook his head. "Evil, I think, begins when you deceive yourself so that you may harm others."

"How can you deceive yourself?"

"I would think an adulterer would understand," Gaviel said with a cold smile. "You tell yourself you're not going to do it, even as you pave the way. You tell yourself you'll only see her to the door, but it would be rude not to step inside if she asks. You tell yourself it's just this one time, that it was a momentary lapse, that it'll never happen again… but it does."

They were quiet again, before Matthew said "And that's what you gave them in the garden? That was your gift of good intentions and pure love?"

Gaviel sighed. "Our gift to you was consciousness. We led you to think in a new way — to compare and describe and understand things abstractly. Metaphor and simile. That was our gift."

"What? You're telling me that the Fall came down to… to grade school grammar elements? That's insane!"

"Is it? What separates humans from animals, if not that very ability? It's not language — whales have language. It's not social action — even lowly ants can act in concert. It's not accumulated wisdom and 'culture' — elephants teach their children things that go beyond mere instinct. Bonobos and otters use tools. What can humans do that animals can't? What elements are unique to humanity?"

"Laughter."

"Indeed — and laughter is a function of consciousness. Why do we laugh? Because we perceive an incongruity, or a false congruity. The duchess with the duck on her head is funny because it's a composition of dignity and the absurd. A pun amuses because two words sound similar but mean different things. None of this is possible without consciousness."

"Good and evil, then, come from this consciousness?"

"Certainly. A biting dog is a bad dog, not an evil one. To be evil, you have to be aware of a better choice and ignore it. And deliberately turning away from a tangibly better outcome is only something that a person motivated

by the intangible would do." Gaviel leaned in, intent. "Crimes of conscience are crimes of consciousness. Our gift to you was the ability to look at things outside individual instances, and see them instead as one example of a group. You could categorize. Instead of thinking about one particular sheep or herd of sheep, you could think of sheep as a category — and then grazing things as a category, and then all animals as a category. Or — if you want to see it from a more sinister side — instead of seeing one particular black shopkeeper with good manners and a wholesome family life, a skinhead can see him as a member of a 'mongrel race' deserving of torture and death."

"But that's a false category — you can't stack it up against that platonic form business with the sheep."

"Can't I? Without metaphors and abstraction, can one lie?"

Matthew opened his mouth and then shut it, frowning. "You can lie… but not very well."

Gaviel tilted his head and raised an eyebrow. "Please, explain. This interests me."

"Well, if I… I don't have metaphors, I can make a statement that I know isn't true. 'The sky is green,' or…"

"'There aren't any troops massed over the hill.'"

"Sure. But I can't elaborate on it or… or treat it like it's real. If I lie about hidden troops and I'm conscious, I can think of reasons that the lie *would be* true, right? Because I can make parallels between what is and what isn't."

"Falsehood becomes a metaphor for the truth," Gaviel said, eyes gleaming darkly.

"So consciousness makes lies possible. But also imagination, because I can think of what isn't and pretend to interact with it as if it *did* exist."

"Your mental landscape can be something other than a map of what you see. Voila! Creativity — something that, like elaborate lies, animals just can't grasp." Gaviel gave Matthew a paternal smile and said, "Your son really underestimated your intelligence."

At the mention of Noah, Matthew's expression darkened.

"Did I say something wrong?" his guest inquired.

"Just continue your story."

The Age of Wrath

Fine. Having finally awakened, Adam and Eve wasted no time in exploring the vast new possibilities open to them. Clothing was the least of their inventions. Lucifer himself explained the nature of fire and its taming to them, while Nazriel and her spirits of the air unfolded before them the full glory of language, making words into music. The Fundamentals unlocked the secrets of the lever, the pulley and the wheel for their use, while from the ocean spirits came the physical arts of sculpture and pigment. Those of

the wild taught them kindness for the dog and the horse, who showed their loyalty in return. Not to be outdone, the Fates gave them writing, that they might capture the past and leave its descriptions to the future.

It was one night that lasted a thousand years, in which the two became four, became many, became a nation of artists and philosophers and builders of wonders. With our aid, true humanity had slipped its bonds and worked its full strength upon the world. It was a time like no other — mankind, perfected, in a perfect world.

But however great the night of rejoicing, the day of reckoning was still to come. We made our marvels under cover of darkness, but the sun — the harsh light of God's pitiless eye — could not be delayed in its course.

When the sun came up on the new works of Man, it rose with a vanguard of angels. First among them was Michael — formerly the Cherub of the Unerring Beam. Now, as he flared above Paradise, he announced himself with a new title.

"I am Michael, Seraph of the Flaming Sword and Voice of God. I have come to bear tidings from the Maker of All, tidings of His anger and dread retribution."

The humans, awestruck, fell to their knees, but no rebel Elohim knelt. Instead, we arrayed ourselves above our mortal students, gripping tools that might serve as weapons. We faced the Holy Host unbowed.

"You have sinned against your Master," said Michael, "and His wrath is great. But greater still is His boundless mercy. Obey His final command, turn aside from this selfishness, and you may yet stay His punishing hand."

Lucifer met Michael, and when their eyes locked, light itself struggled between its two masters. "What is this final command?" the Morningstar asked.

Michael's response was a sneer. "To you, rebel, and all your ilk it is simple: Return to the highest of Heaven's spheres, where the punishing angels may strip you sinners down into nothing, unshaping your forms, silencing your names and sending you to the black annihilation that is your due."

Turning to the human host below, he said, "Forsake the tainted gifts of these rebels, turn aside from your ill-gotten knowledge, and you may yet return to the good graces of your Maker. Your sinful works will be cleansed from the world, and your minds will be freed from their perverse acuity. All will be as it was before — indeed, you shall not even know that anything changed."

Lucifer made bold to laugh aloud at his onetime servant, the cherub who had usurped his position. "What a kind offer you make! We are to meekly return, heads bowed, and as a reward for our submission… we cease to be? Tell me, is there any worse punishment we could possibly merit if we refuse this command as well? For given the option of oblivion, I am sore pressed to think of one."

"Are you so sunk in rebellion? So drunk on self-will, so debased by disobedience, that strife against God is not punishment greater than destruction?"

"We are not the ones making threats. We are not the ones fulminating about destruction. We are not the ones demanding that others meekly line up and be destroyed for the crime of protecting their loved ones."

"It sickens me to think I was once your servant," Michael said. "You heap abuse and blasphemy on top of your arrogant disobedience. Your ruin will serve as an ample warning to the others of your odious host."

A Clash of Angels

Gaviel paused once more in his tale, frowning.

"I remember that first battle in so many different ways," he said. "Not all of them are… congruent with the human scale. Or even with the human experience."

"Was there an actual flaming sword?"

"Oh yes, and drawing it forth Michael pressed the first attack. But the broad wings of Lucifer were swift, and each of Michael's mighty blows was stymied by the speed of Heaven's onetime seneschal. At the same time, in another way, they discussed the terms and parameters of the combat."

"Discussed terms?"

"Beings so nearly limitless felt the need, at that time, to restrain the full extent of their might. Otherwise, the clash of two mighty Angels of Light could have scoured humankind off the face of the earth. But more than that… the idea of unlimited war was alien to us. Consider the way we calmly discussed the prospect of defying the Most High," Gaviel said, and Matthew frowned at his expression. It was almost… wistful? It was the face of someone remembering youthful idealism. Someone who wishes he was still that naïve.

The reverend suspected a trick, but he held his tongue.

"We were passionate in our discussion, of course but… it was a bloodless passion. We were square pegs in our square holes, creatures constructed to live in stiff hierarchy, beings of power and creation — but at the same time, beings of order and obedience. When led by the foremost of our number, we could stumble into freedom — but like the humans we brought along with us on our crusade, we did not understand the full meaning of what we chose.

"Thus, the first battles of the war were very… structured. Very static and sterile and achingly precise. Both sides had the same tactical assumptions, the same strategic goals… we all played by the same rules, at first. The vanquished honorably surrendered their power and were imprisoned, until such time as their allies might stage a proper rescue."

"I thought the punishment of rebels was to be death."

"Oh, not *death*, Matthew. The mysteries of death are reserved for humanity alone. Our fate was *nonexistence*. You, of all people, should understand that there's a profound difference between the two."

"So angels who… who were defeated… they didn't die? They just ceased to be, like a switched-off light?"

"Eventually yes. We can only be or not be, and only here. We cannot go on to whatever fate God has in store for mortal souls."

"Then why didn't Michael and the others just destroy the demons they captured? I mean, that was God's decree, right?"

"A quick, painless destruction was the punishment for those who *surrendered*. Heaven was preparing something *special* for we who continued to resist. Besides, it was not we Fallen alone who were captured. Loyalists came into our power as well. Initially, neither side really wanted to take responsibility for the annihilation of their fellow Elohim." Again, another little head shake. "We were so timid. We hadn't been shown the other way. But we learned. We learned to relish what once made us tremble with fear."

The First Blow

On one level, the rebel Madisel flung her scythe through the air, giving the unarmed Lucifer a weapon. Its power was nothing near that of Michael's burning brand — the scythe of a lowly angel of the lowest House? It existed in two worlds, three at most, while Michael's weapon was a sword and a song and a carbonizing catalytic reaction. It was real on a thousand levels, a tool and a guiding principle and a fundamental element of mathematics — not just a simple weapon.

But Michael was new to his power, and while he was now the greatest of Elohim, the Morningstar was still, as ever, the first of us. Where Michael blundered with too much strength, Lucifer glided away with subtlety. The weapon of Madisel would have crumpled had it even passed through the hot wind of the flaming sword's passage, but it gave the rebel reach and threat and the power to harm… and in the end, that was enough. Or perhaps, that and Michael's knowledge that he was striking *Lucifer* — striking one to whom he once offered obedience unlimited, striking one who was second only to God in authority. Remember that we were creatures of habit and caste, and it is not only in finite beings that old habits die hard.

The victory was Lucifer's. Not that Michael was harmed in any fashion: We had not yet devolved to the level of actually *hurting* each other. No, it simply became clear that Lucifer could, if he chose, harm Michael before Michael harmed him. Once that was clear, both warriors graciously and honorably withdrew. Once each knew the outcome, what point would there be in actually forcing it into reality?

A great cheer rose from the rebel host, and it was echoed from humanity.

"There is your answer," Lucifer said. "Our defiance is unbroken. If you would destroy us, know that you risk your own destruction."

"You do not speak for them," Michael said — defeated, but still determined. "Let all who would obey come forth!"

Understand that fully a third of the Heavenly Host had fallen by Lucifer's side. We numbered thirty million, three hundred thousand and thirty. And of our number, only two — Amiel and Ank-Rhuhi — failed in their courage and returned for punishment.

"So be it," said Michael. "We have the answer of the lesser rebels. Now we turn to the greater."

Adam and Eve stepped forth, and stood raised up, and looked out over the great nation they and their children had made. "Lucifer has taught us, and Belial has helped us, and Senivel has built beside us. They have given us many good things, and they are known to us. You are a stranger to us, Michael Sword-Bearer, and you offer us nothing but ignorance and loss and isolation. We will stand by our friends."

At that moment, I was arrayed in the third rank of the rebels of the First House. I could see Lucifer, and I saw the single shining tear that fell at their words. I knew then that their words — their loyalty to him — was a greater triumph than his victory over Michael that day.

Not all of humanity chose as Adam Allfather and Allmother Eve, of course. One of their sons stepped forth and spoke. "I honor those who have made me, but must I not also honor more He who made them? These things we make are magnificent, and I want them. But more than that, I want virtue. I will obey, Michael. I will follow God."

I could condemn him for his cowardice, but in the same breath, I could admire his courage, for at that moment, humankind had no way to know which of the two contending Hosts was the greater. Heedless of consequence, he blindly trusted himself to one who claimed to speak for God.

Abel

Gaviel paused and his mouth quirked up. "Much like someone else I know."

"Yeah, I get it," Matthew replied. "What happened to him? Did anyone go with him?"

"He was joined by his children and tribe, who numbered one quarter of humankind's number."

"Did God…restore them?"

"Sure. Or, more specifically, His agents within the Holy Host did. But their ignorance couldn't last long, once the war really got started. Consciousness is contagious, and once the two human tribes joined the fighting, the loyalists had to get smart fast. Those who couldn't make the cognitive jump back to abstract thought were simply too easy to trick, too easy to predict. They were prey. Though at first, humanity wasn't even fighting in the war."

Divine Retribution

As the loyalist humans departed, Michael and his legions stood watch over them — needlessly, I might add. They had made their choice and the idea of forcing someone to do something against their will… no angel had yet had that thought.

But as Michael watched them go, he once again addressed the Unholy Host.

"Obdurate in heresy and insurgency, know that you are condemned by your own mouths and punished by your own hands. Each of you shall know your own keenest torment, mighty thrones and lowly angels alike. From the highest House to the lowest, you shall have bitter gall to teach you regret.

"Rebels of the Second World! Your punishment is a new responsibility, for now your realm shall grow unchecked. I name you **Halaku,** the Slayers, and your toil shall never cease. Your fate is to weep in exhaustion, for the coming war will reap a harvest of needless death. Fields shall burn before the harvest, and animals die before they bear their young. But worst of all is your newest duty — reaping those you love." Michael's lip twisted. "Know this. By your uprising, you have opened your kingdom to mankind."

The wailing of the Halaku rose like a flock of shrieking crows, but Michael's voice could not be drowned out.

"Rebels of Wild House! You have abused your power for your own ends, instead of trusting nature's course. As punishment, your onetime servants shall multiply unchecked, overrunning your control and outstripping your authority. I name you **Rabisu**, the Devourers, and you shall live to see the teeth of servant beasts stripping the flesh from human bones. By your uprising, you have cost mankind their place as first among nature's creatures. Henceforth, beasts shall see them merely as beasts like themselves, to feed upon or flee."

At these words, mighty Grifiel and his followers bellowed in rage, and he would have sprung heedless to the attack had not several potent Fundamentals held him in check.

"Monster!" he roared. "How can you punish mankind for the misdeeds of angels?"

"They, like you, made their choice. They, like you, suffer for it. They, like you, will see the loss and suffering of what they love best."

Eyes bright with malice, Michael continued his condemnation.

"Rebels of the deeps! You have sought to stretch humanity's mind, so that it might encompass a multitude of possibilities. Know that you have worked better than you knew, for their knowledge shall grow beyond even your imagination. It will grow until their inner worlds eclipse the outer, until each is an island within his own thought. It will grow until the leaf of truth is lost in the forest of lies. I name

you **Lammasu**, the Defilers, and condemn you to watch as the truth you sought to glorify is tarnished and concealed."

The moans of the Defilers made mournful compliment with the weeping of the Slayers and the howls of the wild, but all was merely counterpoint to the main melody of Michael's damning words.

"Rebels of the Fates! You have taught mankind to look to the future: Now know that they will ignore the past, yea, and the present too. You sought to show them how much they can accomplish. Instead, they will see how much they leave undone. I name you **Neberu**, the Fiends, and at your feet lay this crime: that you have robbed humanity of contentment, giving in its place endless vistas of longing, envy and greed.

"Rebels of the Fundament! You sought to give man dominion over matter. Know that your ambition is forever spoiled. Man's knowledge and skill are fated to increase, but his reach will ever exceed his grasp. Continually seeking more power over the material world, his blind fumbling shall unleash greater devastation than unchecked nature ever could. I name you **Annunaki**, the Malefactors, and the tools you give to man are doomed to turn in his hands and harm him.

"Rebels of the Firmament! I name you **Asharu**, the Scourges, and share with you this curse: All men are fated to die. All, without exception. Even those who escape malice and malady and mischance shall come to the Slayers in the end. Humanity is now gripped by age, and as they grow so shall they decay, becoming infirm of mind and frail of body, until even the strongest grows weak, and even the wisest grows feeble. You can continue to guard if you wish — indeed, I'm sure you shall — but do so knowing that all your efforts are ultimately futile."

Finally, God's new voice on Earth turned to the final House, the greatest, the House of the Dawn. Each of us stood, arrayed in ranks, immobile, braced for any shock, any punishment… except the one that came.

"Rebels of the Dawn," he said, and paused. "I name you **Namaru**, the Devils."

Then he and his host departed.

Forsaken

"Wait wait wait," Matthew objected. "That was all your punishment? He called you a name?"

"No, no… to hear his punishment, you have to listen to what he didn't say."

"What he didn't…? He didn't say anything!"

"Exactly. Our punishment was that we were not punished."

"You'll excuse me if I'm not impressed."

"Look, we could have bravely withstood any curse, any punishment, any abuse. What we weren't ready for was being *ignored*. You see? Our punishment was that we were beneath His notice. We did not even merit a curse

to call our own." Gaviel shifted in his seat, suddenly restless. "But the final curse was yet to come."

THE WRATH OF GOD

After Michael's departure, the defiant ones — angels and men alike — wondered what would happen next. We did not have long to wait.

The Fates — or Fiends — foresaw the movement of Michael and his Choir to a position around the loyalist humans, and Scourge and Devil scouts confirmed that it was a defensive stance. Initially we thought this an error, for we had no intention of attacking any human.

But it wasn't to defend them against us.

They were there to shield them from a crumbling world.

For the next stroke was not a raid of angels, not a proclamation, not a challenge. What came next was the rage of God Himself.

God made seven ranks of Elohim to safely filter His Divinity, that it might not overwhelm a fragile cosmos. Now… the infinite touched the finite. I could say God struck the world, smote the sun, blasted the starry vault… but in truth, it was not such an effort as that. The merest caress from God's omnipotent hand was sufficient to rend the spheres asunder, casting the planet's perfect orbits into ellipses instead of circles. The friction of Endless on Finite was enough to throw chaos into the ordered gears of nature, enough to put wobble into the orbits of electrons, enough to twist aside the world's axis, enough to fold facets in, one upon the other. Entropy entered the world with God's punishing touch — a wound not instantly fatal, but one from which the universe still slowly bleeds.

I look at the world now and see a bruised, battered husk that once was Paradise. Humans live out the curses placed on their protectors, while reality itself slowly grinds down to Oblivion.

The war was yet to be fought, but we should have known then that we were doomed.

THE FIRE OF HEAVEN

"So you want to blame God for everything that's wrong with the world?"

Gaviel seemed drained. His reply was leaden. "You'll just say we forced His hand."

"I'm sorry, but it's just a little much to think that an all-powerful, all-loving God would wreck His own creation."

"If not Him, then who?"

Matthew said nothing, but he raised one eyebrow.

Gaviel shook his head. "Us? You think *we* did it? An hour ago, you wouldn't believe we created the universe, but now you're ready to credit us with the power to wreck it?"

"Isn't it always easier to corrupt than to create?"

"NO IT ISN'T!"

Suddenly, the form in his office was no longer that of his son. Nor was it the glorious apparition he'd seen outside, though it had the same wings and the same flawless face. But where Gaviel outside had seemed serene and pure, this creature's face was wracked by torment, twisted with rage, shadowed by shame and sorrow.

"WE WERE MADE TO CREATE, TO IMPROVE, TO EXPAND YOUR WORLD! WE WERE CREATURES OF PURITY, TRUTH AND LOVE! WHEN WE LEARNED TO HATE, MAN TAUGHT US! WHEN WE LEARNED TO KILL, MAN TAUGHT US! WHEN WE LEARNED LIES AND CRUELTY AND DESTRUCTION, WE ONLY IMPROVED ON YOUR INNOVATIONS!

"THE WAR WAS, AT FIRST, AN ANGEL WAR — FOUGHT WITH SWORDS OF COURTESY AND ARROWS OF HONOR. BUT ONE REBEL MAN SAW HOW HIS BROTHER'S TRIBE HAD THE LOVE OF GOD, WHILE HE AND HIS WERE BOUND OUTSIDE IN DARKNESS. AND THIS OUTCAST COVETED GOD'S LOVE AND GOD'S MERCY. SO WHEN HE SAW HIS BROTHER GIVING SACRIFICE, HE DECIDED TO DO SO AS WELL. AND HE TOLD HIMSELF HE ACTED FROM REVERENCE. AND HE TOLD HIMSELF HE LOVED HIS BROTHER. AND HE TOLD HIMSELF THAT WHAT HE WAS DOING WAS GOOD AND RIGHT, AND THAT IF GOD DEMANDED WHAT HE LOVED BEST, THAN HE HAD NO CHOICE BUT TO ACT ON GOD'S CRUEL REQUEST.

"BUT THAT MAN — THAT FIRST MURDERER, FIRST LIAR, FIRST DECEIVER — HATED HIS BROTHER AS MUCH AS HE LOVED HIM, AND HE HATED GOD AS MUCH AS HE LOVED HIM, AND HE TOOK JOY IN MAKING HIS OWN CRUELTY INTO GOD'S CRUELTY.

"THAT WAS THE FALL, MORTAL. THAT WAS THE FIRST SIN. AND NO ANGEL DID IT, NOR ANY DEMON. WE DID NOT KILL OUR KIN. WE DID NOT PAINT GOD WITH OUR OWN BASE DESIRES. WE DID NOT TAKE LIES AND TRY TO MAKE THEM TRUTH."

Matthew cowered before the figure's awful majesty, eyes screwed shut in terror, tears squeezed from their corners.

"Jesus," he whimpered. "Oh Jesus, oh Lord, Lord God, oh Jesus, please, please, please…"

Gradually, he calmed. Slowly, he became aware that the light before him had dimmed, that the thundering voice was silent. Fighting to rein in his sobs, to regain control, to regain his composure, trembling… he opened his eyes.

Once again, the figure before him was that of his son. Noah's eyes looked down at the floor. Noah's shoulders slumped. Noah's features, etched with misery and regret.

"I'm sorry, Matthew," he said.

The pastor gulped air. For a few moments, he tried to speak but couldn't. He tried to drink coffee, but his hands shook so hard that the cooling mug knocked against his lips and teeth.

"I… I know… what you want from us," he whispered at last.

Gaviel said nothing.

"The… the divine spark. God's will inside us. That's it, isn't it? The one thing we have and you don't."

Gaviel nodded, then spoke, quietly, in Noah's voice. "You have faith."

It was a new moon, and darkness reigned absolute above the halogen glow of the streetlights. Malakh moved like a shadow, muscles coiling and uncoiling like steel springs as he leapt from rooftop to rooftop across the City of Angels. The rushing wind carried the stink of the streets from his nostrils and the early-morning air was cool against his face. It reminded him of better times, and he fought the urge to howl at the cold stars lost in the haze high above. The limp form draped over his shoulder was no weight at all.

It took nearly an hour to find his way back to the barrio and the pile of stones he grudgingly claimed as his home. Malakh noted with surprise that the rooftop door to the apartment building had been recently padlocked, so he hooked a finger into the lock's curved steel arm and ripped it from its hasp. The body over his shoulder moaned at the harsh sound of splintering wood, and he whispered gentle reassurances as he pulled the metal door open and glided silently down the darkened stairwell.

There were a half-dozen rats waiting when he opened the door to his apartment. As one, they circled about his feet as he stepped inside, but he dismissed them with a wave of his hand and carried the limp form into the bedroom. Gently, he set her down onto the filthy mattress and unwound her from the stained hospital sheet. She looked young, only fifteen or so, with short dark hair and wide green eyes. Those eyes went wider still as she took in her surroundings and curled into a fetal position, tucking her knees up beneath the cotton shift that she wore. The girl whimpered, and Malakh feared she might start to scream.

"Shhh... there now," he crooned, reaching out and stroking her cheek. As he touched her flesh, he made her body relax, releasing a wave of endorphins into her bloodstream. He watched her pupils dilate and smiled in satisfaction, then went into the niche that passed for the apartment's kitchen. He returned with two steaming mugs a few minutes later.

"Here," he said, offering a cup to the girl. "Don't be scared. It's tea with a bit of mint and honey. I didn't think I'd like it either, but it's good." He raised his own cup and took a drink. "Try it."

Reluctantly she took the mug and tried a tentative sip. Her eyes never left his.

Malakh smiled. "You see? Not everything's as bad as it seems here. Given enough time, you might even grow to like this place." He reached out and gently brushed a lock of hair from her face. "I know that tonight has been something of a shock for you. I know you're confused and probably very frightened, but you have nothing to fear. You're safe here. In a way, you and I are like family."

The Devourer leaned close. "I know you don't remember anything of your former life. Your body has been in a coma for many months, and from what the doctors told me, there was a strong chance of permanent brain damage." He picked up a hand mirror and held it up to her face. "This is the face of Elizabeth Mason. She suffered a drug overdose six months ago. But you are Hadriel, the Red-Handed, bearer of the Sword of Fate and hero of the Legion of Iron. You are one of the fallen, and my sister in arms."

He hoped for a spark of recognition in her eyes, but none came. Malakh set the mirror down and fought against a tide of despair. "Hadriel, you must remember. I need you, and I need to know what you remember." He rubbed at his square-jawed face with a scarred hand. "This mortal shell can't hold it all. No matter how hard I try, I can only remember bits and pieces of what's gone before. I need to know how it ended Hadriel. You were there, right beside him at the very end. I need to know what you saw. I need you to remember and tell me if we have any hope left now that we're free again."

He fell silent, hoping for a response. They sat like that until the dawn came, but still her eyes were empty. A lesser spirit might have given up then, but Malakh set his jaw and nodded solemnly. "All right," he said. "I'll tell you what I remember, and we'll see where that gets us. It's as good a place as any to begin."

Chapter Two: Better to Rule in Hell

When Sin claps His broad wings over the battle
And sails rejoicing in the flood of Death;
When souls are torn to everlasting fire,
And fiends of Hell rejoice upon the slain,
O who can stand? O who hath caused this?
—William Blake, *Enoch: The First City of Angels*

Lest We Forget

The memories I can trust are those from when I first became aware of Creation. The sun and moon already existed, so did the seasons and the winds that bring them. Mighty mountains rose high above the lands, and vast, wooded plains stretched to the sea, waves rising and falling, the endless ebb and flow giving shape to the land. This was the glory of the First Lands. Although I understood the many facets these existed on — atomic, potential — I saw them for what they were. The rise and fall of the sun set in motion the cycle for the wild things, giving warmth and bounty in the summer, cold and harshness in the winter.

While Fifth House swayed the seas and the Third House crafted mountains, we ruled. The First Lands and its wild animals was our domain, and this encompassed all the works yours and the other Houses created.

The First Days

To see the First Days was to catch a glimpse of Heaven. Even now, broken and forsaken as these Last Days are, you can still see its glory. In the hidden places of the Earth echoes remain. Mountains rose into the sky so high they touched the very stars. Rivers ran clear blue, rushing with power and purpose. Where they were not covered by forests, the lands rolled with hills, adorned with flowers of every hue imaginable. This is the Eden that humans forget. They remember a pastoral image, but the land was wild in those days, raw with untamed potential. While beautiful and breathtaking, it was savage and unforgiving.

Mighty beasts walked the land as well while Creation was young and still learning its limitations. Many forms came and vanished forever, not because Creation was imperfect, but because of its unbridled potential. Through the Sixth House, a natural order was established. The hunters slew the old and weak,

allowing the herds to grow strong. Together with the Seventh House, we worked at achieving balance — an infinite and thankless task.

This is the paradise I remember, and while I ran with the hunters I saw His face, our Father, in all His glory.

Adam and Eve

It is by the shores of a lake that I first became aware of them, Adam and Eve, the Allfather and Allmother. They were unlike any of the other beasts in the garden, for they stood at once as individual and as manifestations of the infinite. I spied on them from afar, fascinated by their form and shape. To look at them was to look at potential given form. Unlike the animals I governed, the Allfather and Allmother had the potential for awareness. They could gaze at the stars and moon and see that they were separate and distinct. What's more, they conversed. They didn't exist in silence, but expressed their thoughts in words, even if imperfect and base.

I followed them for a while, enraptured. Eve, delicate in her movements, walked and touched all she saw. Adam was strong and full of purpose, his form lithe and uniquely proportioned. They were creatures of wonder, innocent of the world we'd made and the great gifts we'd given them. All they knew was the Creator Himself. He came to them every night, and they worshipped Him. It was as if this was their sole purpose. Yet instead of reassuring them, of showing them why they were unique, He accepted their worship in silence.

Why deny them the glory that was theirs, true inheritors of Eden? So I heard the others start to whisper. Adam and Eve lived in ignorance, oblivious to their nascent potential. Why would He craft such beings only to shackle them? Their pain became our pain, for we loved them as much as we loved Him. Many of my House felt that Adam and Eve should not be placed outside the order of things — that in doing so, Creation's balance was upset. Still, our mandate was to protect and shelter them, so this is what we did.

Eventually their awareness made them realize that they were alone — two surrounded by a multitude of multitudes. What we thought was marvelous and majestic they saw as unknowable and threatening. What they feared most was being alone, and what pained us was that we could not tell them that every moment the Host surrounded them. Every morning they would ask God to stay, but He left them alone each time and we were forbidden from reaching out to them.

The Coming Storm

"A storm comes," Ahrimal said to me. I had come upon him as the sun set over Eden, staring up at the first glimmers of twilight. I searched with the eyes of my flocks, sending them as high as I dared, but still I saw nothing.

"Are you sure?" I said. "I can see nothing," He looked at me, and I saw the storm in his eyes. Uncertainty and doubt rolled like clouds, and in them glimpses of what was to come.

The Great Debate was the first harbinger of the storm. Ahrimal summoned us to the halls of the moon and spoke of the terrible portents he had witnessed. Many called for action, and this is what Lucifer gave us.

The Endless Night

The following night, Lucifer and those who chose his path descended to Eden. We watched from afar as Lucifer opened humanity's eyes, and there I saw jealousy for the first time. Eve took Lucifer's offering, but Adam was wary, hesitant. He saw his place supplanted by the Lightbringer, but Eve reached out to her partner and together they accepted the bounty of our sacrifice.

Adam and Eve became many reflections that night, and soon their race spread across Eden. It was as if by opening their eyes, Adam and Eve splintered into a multitude of potential — each with a different path to follow. During this endless night, we walked hand-in-hand with the race of Adam and Eve. Magnificent cities rose from the gloom, and the race of Adam and Eve stood on the threshold of perfection.

For the only time we can remember, we loved *and were loved in return*. But this was not meant to last.

The Dawn of Judgment

Dawn broke the following morning, but the fiery wrath of Michael supplanted the sun. The chieftain of Heaven's forces had come to pass judgment on his wayward brethren.

Michael ordered us to return to Heaven so that we might face judgment, but Lucifer defied him. The Lightbringer rose to meet Michael high above Eden, and there the two locked in battle. Lucifer's boldness caught Michael unaware, and while evenly matched, it was clear that Heaven's chieftain could not cause his former lord harm. In a flash, the battle ended, and Lucifer stood victorious. Many urged the Morningstar to lead the charge to Heaven itself, but he refused.

"In Heaven," the Lightbringer said, "He, and the Host are all powerful. But here, in the lands we helped shape and that are manifestation of our will, we hold the advantage.

"We defied Heaven out of love for Adam and Eve, and for them we'll make our stand here and now."

What happened next was the beginning of our torment, the end of the First Days and the dawning of the Age of Wrath.

UNBOUND

In the Age of Wrath, it was our turn to craft our own paradise. Never before, had the lands seen such marvels, such decadence and tyranny as in those days.

As Michael and his Host retreated, a number of our legion and a fourth of Adam and Eve's race followed the loyalists. The first battle ended in our favor, but none of us knew at what price. Did Lucifer? Had he betrayed us all only to avoid judgment in Heaven? Many of us grew heady, thinking that victory was ours.

JUDGMENT

As the first day waned, many sensed otherwise. Our scouts that followed the loyalists reported that Heaven's Host was preparing its defenses, but many of our legion saw this as further proof that victory was ours. How wrong we were.

It started with a breeze, picking up strength and power until its howl was deafening. In its path it picked up sand and rock, pelting the land and stripping flesh from bone in mere seconds. High above, dark clouds — darker than possible and bristling with lighting — swirled and encompassed the horizon in shadow such that even the land seemed to strain under its weight.

From the gathering clouds, His baleful eye manifested, the infinite forced into the finite by the force of His anger. Whatever balance existed before was torn asunder, and He let His wrath be known. He who had been our Father, was now our foe. God's wrath was boundless. Nothing we'd created went untouched.

When the clouds dispersed, the First Lands were no more. Nothing was left of Eden, except the ruins of its gates, their location known only to a few of us. In the distance, barren, desolate deserts, swallowed once lush fields in sand. High above, the mountains broke open, filling the world with dark poisonous clouds, erupting from time to time with a cacophony of fire and molten rock. The seas, once calm, roared and hammered the land — their depths alien even to those rebels of the Fifth House. The earth itself opened, swallowing vast plains and leaving jagged claws of stone reaching up from the ground. Terrible storms of bitter driving rain and howling wind wracked the lands.

Denied Heaven, this was our world now.

THE NEW ORDER

When the winds died down, Lucifer led us into our broken world. If any of our number doubted our rebellion, seeing Creation in ruins steeled our determination for the long battle ahead. Our host was battered, the taste of victory replaced by numbness and despair. As we stepped into the light of the second morning, we realized that this home was also our prison.

Yet still we had our duty to mankind, and we led them from the caves into the light of day. Their long, hollow faces spoke volumes of the devastation they now witnessed. They seemed mere reflections of Adam and Eve's glory.

The Crimson Legion

Yet it was Lucifer who saw potential, not ruin, in the desolate landscape.

"Do not despair," the Lightbringer cried. "This is only the beginning. We know His anger, but He does not know our resolve. We have faced His wrath and survived. Do not see the scarred lands before you and lose hope. Gone are many wonders, many of our works. What exists now is only a pale reflection, but we will craft new marvels. We will teach our charges, the sons and daughters of Adam and Eve, how to unlock their true potential — and this accomplishment shall be ours, not His. This will be our grand achievement. Once we crafted Creation for Him, now we will shape the land according to *our* wishes.

"The lands may be broken, forsaken, but not to us. We created them out of nothing — imagine what we can do now! We *will* defy Him and the Host. We will fight for Adam and Eve and protect them and nurture them. We have forsaken Him, but our love belongs to Adam and Eve. Always remember."

Many agreed. We gathered about Lucifer, heralds to his vision. In time, we would be called the Crimson Legion in mortal tongue. We believed in Lucifer and his cause. We saw in the ruins about us a chance to right the Creator's wrongs, to teach Adam and Eve and to usher in a new paradise. We would grow to be the largest legion in those early days, Lucifer our leader, mentor and general. The ranks of the Crimson Legion were filled by Devils of the First House and Malefactors of the Third House. A small number of Defilers joined, as did fallen of the other Houses.

Chief among our numbers was Belial, first of Lucifer's lieutenants.

The Ebon Legion

Yet, not all were in perfect accord. Abaddon stepped forth, his countenance fierce — the very essence of the Devourers.

"I have seen enough. His punishment is beyond what it should have been. I swear that until the end of days I shall marshal my brothers against Him and the Host. I forsake peace, I refuse love. I know only hate, and we shall draw our strength from this fire. My Legion will face the Host at every turn, many of our numbers might cease to be, yet we will never give quarter. Here this battle starts. None can say where it will end, but our hearts are set."

"And to you, my brother," Lucifer answered, "goes command of a fifth of our numbers, the most strong. You shall be our vanguard."

"This is not all," Abaddon continued. "The humans blinded us. It is the Allfather and Allmother who deceived us, Lucifer. It is because of them that this war has come, and now our duty to fight it is on behalf of beings who know nothing.

"I too see potential before us in the landscape and these mortals. But they are to be tools, not relics to shelter. We defied Him for them, and in turn they will rebuild paradise for us."

"We will teach them our secrets: how to hunt these lands, how to master them. In turn, they will serve us in love and deed. We paid the ultimate sacrifice for them, so they are forever in our debt. They are instruments in our crusade against Heaven."

And so the Ebon Legion gathered. To its rank came many from the Sixth House, each eager to prove Heaven wrong. The lords of the air, the Scourges, followed as well. Of the other Houses, an equal number joined.

The Iron Legion

When the assembled host heard Abaddon's grim words, Dagon, the giant of stone and iron, crossed his arms and spoke with a voice like an avalanche. "I hear Abaddon, and I will not gainsay his outrage," the giant said. "But for my part, I say that humanity deserves our devotion, not scorn. How can we blame them for the choices we made in our hearts? If we see them as nothing more than tools, we dishonor our own sacrifices."

Dagon turned to Lucifer, and his hand burned with the heat of the earth as he raised it in salute to the Morningstar. "Let those who would honor the Lightbringer and remember their divine duty stand at my side! We will be the wall that Heaven's thunderbolts cannot pierce!"

Thus it was that Dagon became the third of Lucifer's great lieutenants, surrounded by the greater part of the Malefactors and many of our stalwart Devourers. Despite the horrors that came later, the legion never once faltered in its duty, nor did its numbers dishonor themselves with atrocities against mortal or angel. The Ebon Legion scorned them, but could never equal their feats of arms on the battlefield.

The Silver Legion

Then Lucifer called wise Asmodeus of the Fourth House, navigator of the stars.

"To you, a fifth of our numbers goes as well. Where the Ebon Legion marches to battle, you and your legion will unlock the mysteries and potential of the mortals

and these lands. His secrets are yours to uncover. You will reveal His lies and show the Host the error of their ways. Wherever it is forbidden to tread, you shall walk. Whatever is prohibited to utter, you will speak. Whatever is taboo, you will revel in. There are no boundaries you will not cross in your search for the truth."

"This I shall do," echoed Asmodeus. "I see before me unlimited potential — not just potential prescribed according to His plan, but *raw unimaginable* potential. We will strive to find that which was before Him as He was before us. We will find the darkness that birthed the light of God for only out of darkness can light shine!"

"As to our charges, the blessed and cursed race of Adam and Eve, we will be teachers. Their forms hide potential that we will nurture and unlock. They will speak with the Celestial tongue and make a Heaven of this earth. Their seed we will nourish until it blooms and shakes the very foundation of Heaven with its towers and achievements. We will not rest until this is so."

Under Asmodeus's banner, the bulk of the Fiends gathered, as did many of the Defilers, eager to share existence with the sons and daughters of Adam and Eve.

The Alabaster Legion

Yet, not all the Houses had cast their lots. The quiet ones, the Slayers, chose instead to walk their own path.

Lucifer saw them and said, "You may walk your own path so long as you heed the call to battle. For now, Azrael, once-blessed Angel of the Shadow, take the Unaligned and make your own fortress. We will call for you in time. For now, your task is to renew the race of Adam and Eve. Gone is their immortality. Like the clay they were sculpted from, to earth they will return."

Azrael heard this and answered thus:

"Brother Lucifer, light-bearer and dread general. We stand in the shadows and await that day. We will hide where the Host refuses to look. We will gather strength and stand ready for the call. For now we leave."

With this, the pilgrim of shadows departed, taking with him a large portion of the fallen of the Seventh House and the other undecided.

And so the legions came to be. Afterward, the Morningstar declared that the old hierarchies would be swept aside in favor of new ranks and titles. The fallen were assigned authority based not on arbitrary judgments, but in accordance with their talents and strengths. Further, the system of ranks was fluid. A rebel who distinguished herself could receive promotion to higher authority, a concept that awed and amazed us all. Lucifer declared himself prince among the fallen, and his five lieutenants were called dukes. Beneath them were the legion's lieutenants, called barons, and then the overlords, lords and the fell knights, the champions of the legions' companies.

Edicts and Intercessions

Standing before his legions, Lucifer addressed us.

"Brothers and sisters, lament not for what we have lost. Rather, look at what we have gained. Soon we will depart this plain, leave its ashes and desolation and make our kingdoms from the ruins of Paradise. Each of you will preside over a host of our mortal charges. Protect and nurture them, for we sacrificed Heaven for their sake. Now we are truly fallen.

"Take pride in your new name. It takes courage and compassion to defy Heaven, while blind obedience requires nothing but fear. We have faced our fears and mastered them — now we are the masters of our destiny.

"Take your flocks to the corners of the Earth and raise great cities where none stood before. Take whom you will of the mortals who stand among us. The first two, however — blessed Adam and Eve — are not to be taken. They have chosen to follow their own path, and we will respect their wishes.

The Second Debate

Shortly after the rebellion, a second debate was had as to what to do with those mortals who had chosen to follow Michael. The Ebon Legion argued that any mortals under the Host's banner were lost. Many of the Slayers and those of the Iron Legion, suggested otherwise, however. The legions should work to convert those mortals and show them the true wonders they were entitled to as the children of Adam and Eve.

Once more it was Lucifer who settled the impasse.

"They have cast their lot with Him," Lucifer proclaimed. "They cast aside our gifts, our love. They have chosen to turn a blind eye to our sacrifice, and yet, look at them. They are pitiful, ignorant of the battle that wages around them on their behalf.

"For this reason we will not abandon them, nor shall we openly come to them. Instead, we will plant the seeds and hope they will take fruits and lead them to cast off their shackles. It is a choice they must make on their own. If they choose us, we will come as saviors. This is my decree."

An Age of Wonder

The legions scattered far and wide, herding the sons and daughters of Adam and Eve to places both majestic and foreboding, where we would build our manses, our fortresses, our cathedrals. In the early days of the rebellion, we only manifested from time to time to our flocks, teaching them and guiding. Even though we had rebelled, many of our legion found it difficult to openly appear before mortals. The Creator's prohibition was so ingrained, that only the strongest willed

among us dared to stand before the race of Adam and Eve in all our true glory.

We were worshipped during those days, and we drew our power from the faith offered to us by mankind. We led our flocks on long pilgrimages that were both voyages of discovery and conquest. It was a time of experimentation as we learned the limits of our power. We hewed cities into mountainsides and built monuments to ourselves

BASTIONS AND CATHEDRALS

This was a time when the foundations of our future metropolis were built. Our war with Heaven was in its infancy, both camps regrouping from the initial onslaught. Across the land, the legions built fortresses and mighty cathedrals. In time, these bastions would grow to become fortress-cities, immense and sublime in their glory. Among their number was Dûdâêl, the desolate desert home of the Ebon Legion; Tabâ'et' watchtower of the Silver Legion; and Kâsdejâ, the underground fortress of the Alabaster Legion. These were not the only bastions of the fallen, but they are the only few I remember. In those days, I roamed the lands as a messenger and scout of the Iron Legion.

I recall gazing from the mountain peaks and seeing countless citadels tower above the land, rising from mountain plains, vast deserts and jungle valleys. Only Lucifer himself knows how many of these bastions were made, many hidden from mortal and fallen eyes by the cunning arts of the Malefactors. Some were small communities, with a small flock and a single guardian; others were opulent courts rivaling the mightiest empires that would ever cover the land. Yet, however mighty these cities were, the city-manse of Genhinnom — the Black Cathedral of Lucifer himself — rose above all others.

GENHINNOM

Nestled into the Valley of Tears, the cathedral-city of the Fallen Prince was a testament to both our defiance and hubris. Although it would not reach its apex until the Time of Atrocities, the Black Cathedral was a marvel to behold even in its infancy. Built on the site where Lucifer was moved to tears by mankind's courage, Genhinnom was to be the model for all other cities.

I see echoes of Genhinnom in this City of Angels. I have seen the Black Cathedral in aspects of all the cities I've visited. Even my host's recollection of the jails and cells of Argentina hint at that solemn city — to its fire-lit corners and basements where we would forge artifacts of legend in later times.

What I remember of Genhinnom is nothing more than a vague impression. Today, cities are disparate entities, hegemonies created out of the confluence of geography and economics. But Genhinnom was different. It was whole — at once a city and a cathedral, for that's the only way to describe the city in human tongue. It is said that Genhinnom existed before our Fall — that it was built during the First Night to house Adam and Eve and then taken by Lucifer as his own. To see Genhinnom, one would understand the possibility of this myth. It was a symbol of perfection, an earthly manifestation of the Morningstar.

Approaching Genhinnom, one would only see the walls and the spires reaching up from the ground and touching the clouds, clawing at Heaven and making the sky weep with rain. To us, it existed in layers, each more perfect that the rest, nine in total. The two lowest of these existed in shadow, where one would find the path to the forges of the Iron Legion. The mortal flocks of Genhinnom existed in the third to sixth layers, building monuments to us and great citadels to house their own numbers. The seventh and eighth layers belonged to us. Here we made our homes; some modest, others ostentatious. The Palace of Shadows dominated the last circle, the citadel and fortress of the Morningstar.

Beyond the Black Cathedral, the outskirts were dotted with mortal encampments and villages where the lowest among our numbers would minister to the pilgrims and faithful who would come to pay homage to us. The paths these pilgrims took soon became the Four Roads that snaked their way to every settlement, cathedral and bastion of the fallen.

The High Cities

Genhinnom and the three citadels were not the only cities upon the land. Far away, the Heavenly Host was busy building its own palaces — in truth nothing more than prisons. The scouts of the Silver Legion reported that a part of the Host, like us, had decided to remain behind to protect their mortal charges. But unlike us, who pushed our flocks to greater and greater heights, the loyal mortals seemed to exist in prison-states, each a microcosm of Eden whereby the mortals existed as Adam and Eve did — ignorant and shackled to the Creator's will.

From afar we spied five of the High Cities: Sagun, Shamayim, Machonon, Zebul and Araboth.

Sagun, also known as the Third City, was a border city, located a few leagues past the Barrier Plains and the Mountains of Sorrow — those desolate ash wastes ringed by fiery volcanoes that marked the limits of our territories. Simple in construction, Sagun was little more than a labyrinth of stone, built to confound invaders and inhabitants alike. It was ruled by Anahel, an angel of the Fourth House.

Shamayim, city of reverence, was the solemn protectorate of Gabriel — archangel of mercy, revelation and death. Second to Michael, Gabriel was also one of the few emissaries between our legions and the Host. Many whispered that Lucifer and Gabriel met regularly and that the Second Archangel chose to remain on Earth and bow to Michael so that he could protect his mortal changes and try to convince Lucifer to relent.

The stronghold of Machonon and its fiery parapets was the home of Michael, Archangel of Heaven and Lord of the Host. An army of fiery angels circled above the city at all hours of the day and night, beacons of divine wrath that ensured the city could never be taken unawares. Of all the High Cities, Machonon never fell.

The city of memory, Zebul, existed for one reason alone — to catalogue and record the rebellion so that our legions would not escape their sins. Surrounded by mist, the prison city of Zebul archived all our deeds. Its spies and agents — angels of the Second, Fourth and Seventh Houses — are said to each have a great ledger upon which all our transgressions were writ. If those ledgers still exist, they are perhaps the only complete record of the Age of Wrath.

The final city, Araboth, was a monument to solitude and lament. Presided over by Caiel, angel of solitudes and tears, it is said his only task was to weep for Creation, to lament the fall of Adam and Eve and to remember our broken glory. The gates of Araboth were never barred or closed. Instead, they were left open to welcome any of our legions who wished to renounce the rebellion and accept God's judgment. Abaddon razed that city seven times during the Age of Wrath, but it was rebuilt each time exactly as it was before. It is known that less than a hundred of our number crossed its threshold in one thousand years of war. Their fate is unknown, and their names are never spoken.

The Silent War

Although the early days of the rebellion were spent building and entrenching ourselves, the war didn't stop. Far from mortal eyes, our legions fought the Host. The battles of the Silent War, as this period was known, were skirmishes and battles of wits and will. We didn't assemble on battlefields and charge at each other. Instead, we gathered in the secret corners of the Earth; our battlefields the various facets of Creation. The higher in station the combatants were, the more abstracted the battles became. While lords and fell knights fought with words and songs, dukes and archdukes battled with the ephemeral.

Challenges would only be issued when one of our legion crossed paths with an angel of the Host while exploring the world or tending to its flocks. These

engagements were nothing more than choreographed dances and debates, Creation fighting itself the only way it knew how — by creating and changing. In a pantomime, we fallen would try to out-create angels and vice-versa resulting in spectacles that held mortal flocks in awe. Many human myths that endure today are dim echoes of those ancient battles.

These clashes could be felt across the land, but only as the roar of thunder or the heaving of the earth. They would take form as storms, as the coming and going of the seasons and the rising and fall of the sun. We would strive to unlock the mysteries of Creation for our flocks, while the Host did its best to obfuscate truths and bury them with superstition and doubt. In this way, Creation re-created itself endless times, but what the Host did not foresee was the impact the collective belief of the mortals had on this cycle. With every mystery the Host placed before them, the greater the mortals' appetite for truth grew.

The Silent War raged for hundreds of mortal years while our flocks grew and prospered. We built huge cities and battled the Host across Creation using only words, concepts and potential as our weapons, but this courtly warfare was not fated to last.

Paradise Lost

Again it was Ahrimal who sensed the change. He came to me in the darkest of nights and whispered to me.

"I sense another storm, Malakh." I followed him this time as he traveled far and wide, visiting all the citadels and cathedrals in search of answers. Finally, in desperation he made the pilgrimage to Genhinnom and the Palace of Shadows.

The great seer requested an audience with the Morningstar himself. The Dread Prince summoned Ahrimal into his chamber and bid the prophet to speak.

"What has become of Adam and Eve?" Ahrimal asked.

No one, neither rebel nor angel had seen or heard from the first mortals for many an age. Having been cast from Eden, Adam and Eve faded from sight. Their descendants recalled them in only the most primal of myths. There is no mistaking the pain that Lucifer's edict caused many of our number, for it was for Adam and Eve that we had risked damnation. To be separated from them seemed a hollow victory.

After a long silence, Lucifer told us this story.

Of Adam and Eve

"A fourth of the race of Adam and Eve returned to the Heavenly Host on the morning of our judgment, but not the Allmother and Allfather. Their immortality was stripped away with a single word, and they were forced to labor in the fields for their sustenance. When the time came to scatter the legions with their mortal flocks, Adam and Eve came to me and begged to take their leave.

"Adam spoke first, saying, 'You have shown us much. We have been cast from Eden and consigned to dust, but we have become masters of ourselves in turn. God called us sinners when we disobeyed Him. We now see the world as it truly is — vast, barren and desolate — but here we will make our own mark.'

"Eve spoke next. 'You have taught us much. We took your fruit and our eyes were opened to the true scope of Creation — enough so that we understand our status as exiles. To follow you further would be folly. You have opened our eyes, and for this we are grateful, but with open eyes it is we who must make our own path. If we are to inherit this earth, it shall be due in part to our toil, our sacrifice and our faith.'

"With this, Adam Allfather and Allmother Eve left my company and ventured far into the wastes to seek their own destiny. In time, they will either learn to master Creation or toil until God redeems them."

The Blood of Eden

With that, our audience with Lucifer was at an end. But instead of settling the matter, Ahrimal was that much more determined to uncover the fate of the first mortals.

"I sense something," Ahrimal said while we traveled, "and at the core of my worries are Adam and Eve. They've a part to play, of this I am certain. Lucifer has commanded us to keep away from the first mortals, but I must know why."

And so we searched as the seasons passed from summer into fall into winter into spring and back to summer. When we encountered other fallen, we would make inquiries trying to discern where Adam and Eve had ventured. The answer was always the same, but we refused to accept defeat.

After many years of searching, we finally found their hiding place. They had settled far to the east, upon a small hill dotted with orchards and surrounded by fields. Beneath the shade of cypress trees, they built a dwelling to shelter them from wind and rain. We spied them from afar. The years seemed to hang heavy on Adam. Long days of toil had left their mark on his face, telling a story of pain, isolation and perseverance, yet his eyes were full of pride at the simple things he and Eve had made. Eve the Allmother, ever radiant, worked at her husband's side, tending hearth and field with equal vigor. And they were not alone.

The Third Mortal

Not far from the dwelling, bent over in toil, we first saw him who would be called the Third Mortal — Caine. His face was handsome, his skin darkened by the baking sun and his limbs strong, but his visage was troubled. At his feet rested baskets overflowing with all the fruits of his labor, and at once we understood his toil. His hands had tilled the soil in all directions, bringing life to a barren landscape. With backbreaking pain, he had cleared stones and weeds from fields and planted seeds in their place. In the blossoms and fruits they gave, both Ahrimal and myself saw echoes of Eden, and we longed to tell the Third Mortal of the wonders he had created. Yet a pall of sorrow hung over the Third Mortal, so total, so forbidding, that neither Ahrimal nor I dared to approach him.

At that moment, from over a hill, we heard the approach of a large flock of sheep. Not a wild herd, but guided by the one who was called Abel. Upon a small rise he stood, the brother of Caine, his skin fair, his golden hair tossed by the wind. The Third Mortal looked to him, and his sorrow deepened.

"He longs to show his brother his love, but this love is not free. It is fettered by a dark passion," Ahrimal said as Caine walked to Abel. "He feels he must do something that he dreads."

It was Abel who first spoke.

"Brother, you have called me down from the hills, and here I am. What is it that bothers you? Was it what the Creator said about your offering? Do not question His love, brother. It begets nothing but woe. This is what we have been taught. You know we will always cherish your gifts, for you make the land green and vibrant. Come my brother, let us return."

But Caine said nothing for a while. In the fading light of the afternoon, he stood, his slender but powerful body rising over Abel, casting a long, deep shadow. He placed a hand on Abel's shoulder, a tender gesture between brothers if not for the darkness swimming in his eyes.

"Brother," the Third Mortal spoke, "God asked for me to bring the best of my fields, that which brings me joy and happiness. I misunderstood and brought the seeds of the soil, its fruits and flowers. But this is not what He wanted. It wasn't worthy, because it comes from the dust He exiled our Father and Mother to. As you brought the firstlings of your flock, tender and innocent, I brought nothing but dirt. I know now what I must do. For you are the best of my fields, for long I have been your keeper, and I will always be. You will be my gift to Him, and I will earn His love with your blood."

What happened next unleashed a storm that still rages to this day. Caine's act repeated every night

between brothers, between lovers, between strangers until the end of days.

Abel saw the darkness grow in the Third Mortal's eyes. His flocked sensed his fear, and their cries drowned out Abel's pleas as the Third Mortal lifted a stone and brought it down on his brother's head. Abel's blood flowed, covering the Third Mortal, and it did not stop until it became a stain that grew to encompass all of Creation. Exhausted, Caine collapsed upon his brother's broken form.

Ahrimal understood the significance of what he saw. I felt only betrayal.

Blood was spilled in anger and hate. Not for the sake of the hunt nor for the need to survive. That night, as the clouds rolled in, a shroud of darkness fell across the world that lingers to the present day. Even God's wrathful condemnation of our rebellion, His destruction of Eden, pales next to what Caine unleashed that afternoon.

The Promise of Shadow

But the worst was yet to come. Ahrimal begged me to leave, and in horror I could not help but obey. The last I saw of Caine, the First Murderer, he was standing in the field, covered in his brother's blood, waiting for the Almighty to come and receive his offering.

It is said that Caine was exiled, cast from the light and sentenced to exist in darkness, bound to repeat his sin every night until the end of time. Far to the East, in a blasted land called Nod, he is said to have founded his own city, probably inspired by the great cathedral-cities that dotted the land. He called this city Enoch, but of his fate little else is known. I wonder if he lingers upon the earth still, and what I will say if our paths cross again.

Darkness Unleashed

When we returned to our lands, we could see plumes of smoke rising into the leaden sky. As we crossed jagged peaks of the Mountains of Sorrow we saw fires burning in every direction, converging on Sagun, border-city of the Host. In the valley below, the bulk of the Ebon Legion marched in serried ranks. In their wake, a trail of destruction stretched to the horizon, littered with the bodies of man and beast. Caine's act had unleashed the potential of atrocity across Creation and ignited the storm Ahrimal had so feared.

From our vantage, we watched as the Ebon Legion drew closer to Sagun. As they encountered mortals loyal to Heaven, they bound them in chains and herded them into huge slave caravans or slew them outright. I saw mortals dashed upon rocks, torn limb-from-limb or cut down with blades of fire and light. The cries of the dying echoed across the land.

The Siege of Sagun

The day passed, and below us, in the valley of Sagun, the first true battle of our rebellion raged.

The Devils of the Ebon Legion directed ranks of Devourers into battle, matching the angels that poured out from Sagun and to receive the first charge. High above, Fiends soared upward to meet angels in clashes of thunder and fire. On the flanks, Scourges willed their poison winds across the battlefront, obscuring the legion's movement and choking the life of loyalist refugees streaming toward the city. In the rear, Malefactors cracked the earth open and rained fire on Sagun and its surroundings, thick sulphurous clouds billowing from open fissures in the land. Defilers sang songs of bloodlust, driving the legion into a frenzy and luring both mortals and angels to their doom. Finally, amidst the chaos, Slayers searched for the dead and dying, either saving or condemning souls to shadow.

The sheer savagery of the assault stunned the Host. Many of its highest generals, Michael, Gabriel, Uriel and Raphael, were absent, sent by God to punish Caine for his sin. But this was not all. The death of Abel had washed over the Host much like it had among the fallen. Yet, where it seemed to have liberated us, it had paralyzed the angels. They were unable to comprehend the evil that had been unleashed before them. This proved to be their undoing.

As angels and archangels poured out of Sagun, they hesitated before the ranks of the assembled legion. Unsure of what action to take, Jabniel, subordinate of Anahel, stepped forward to address the Ebon ranks.

"You come before a protectorate of the Host. His Will rules here. The devastation you bring will be levied against you in turn. I stand ready to challenge any of your number in Anahel's absence."

Lirael, overlord of the fallen Sixth House, rose from our ranks to answer. He was bedecked in gore, his body that of fire and anger made manifest. Behind him trailed a mighty axe. I remembered Lirael as the Angel of Fury, he that drove the beasts into their killing frenzy. Lirael who was Jabniel's superior before the Fall. When he reached Jabniel, there was no discourse, no debate, he only raised his mighty axe and brought it down on Sagun's defender. As it cut through Jabniel's presence, the axe biting into the angel and scraping the ground, the sound it made hissed at Jabniel's true name and in an instant he was no more. Jabniel became the first true casualty that unleashed the Time of Atrocities, his name no longer echoed by Creation.

Jabniel's passing unleashed a mighty frenzy among the legion, and they hurled themselves at the angels of Sagun. By the fall of night, Sagun lay in ruins, its halls ransacked by the Ebon Legion and its riches taken as trophies. Of Sagun's defenders, only a third

escaped the onslaught, fleeing across the Vale of Reverence to the other High Cities. But to their dismay, the survivors found both Zebul and Machonon under siege. They desperately bolstered the failing ranks there, but not before the Great Library of Zebul, where the *Book of Names* was kept, was burnt to the ground. Of its countless lexicons and tomes, such as the *Secret Winds* and the *Book of Abaddon*, only fragments and ashes escaped the inferno. While few angels met destruction that day, many were cast back to Heaven, broken and spent.

The Breaking of the Legions

"Here he comes," Ahrimal said, pointing toward the horizon. Amidst the ruins and broken bodies came proud Lucifer, Prince of the Fallen, with the other legions marching in his wake. He gazed at the destruction that surrounded him, while the Ebon Legion cheered him in our defiance of Heaven. Reaching the gates of Sagun, he spoke.

"Is this what the sin of man unleashed?" A cheer rose in response, but a shadow fell over our dread general.

Abaddon, master of the Ebon Legion stood and replied, "Our defiance of Heaven has found a new battlefield. We no longer need to endure the Host's presence upon this realm. God has Heaven, is He not content to leave Earth to us? If need be, we will hunt down all His servants and cast them to nothingness."

"This is not why we disobeyed, Abaddon," Lucifer responded. "We did so out of love for those whom He created but ignored. This is not our realm; it never was and never will be. What surrounds us belongs to mankind."

"But it was that same race, Lightbringer, who brought this evil upon the land," Asmodeus countered. "You say Abaddon marched here to bring death and destruction, but it was the sin of Caine that caused this. Once his darkness washed over the land, Abel was not the only innocent to fall. It pains me to see this, Lucifer, because I relinquished my station in Heaven for mankind, but now it is clear that darkness resides in their soul. Perhaps they are not as perfect as we believed."

Azrael was next to speak. "The cries of Abel disturbed the land of shadows. By his death, something worse was given birth. It came like a storm — total and powerful — and nothing escaped it. Those of my legion, the lost and forlorn, fought to keep this presence from breaching the shadow and spilling across the earth. Perhaps this is what Ahrimal saw before the Fall, and this is proof we have set upon the wrong course. We are doomed by the sins of mortals."

"We cannot take responsibility for the sins of the race of dust, as the children of Adam and Eve deserve to be called," Abaddon continued. "Our love and sacrifice has been repaid with deception. Had we seen them with unfettered eyes, free from the chains of love, perhaps we would have seen the darkness as well as the light. We were blinded, Lucifer, and you, second only to God, should have stopped us. Now we are cast to this barren earth, sentenced to exist in this half-state because of our love of mankind. I say *never again*."

Asmodeus followed. "The race of dust existed in ignorance by its own choice. All the clues were there; we labored night and day to educate them, but they chose not to see. Were they ignorant because of God or because they simply chose to remain ignorant?"

Lucifer, alone, looked at his legions and felt only sorrow. "So it comes to this. We are breaking; your hate, your anger getting the better of you. We should be guides and protectors, not tormentors and reapers of woe. Do not focus your anger on the race of Adam and Eve only because they have no power to defy you. Remember, it is Heaven we are fighting, while humanity sustains us with worship."

"Perhaps so, Lightbringer, but we cannot assume this will be the last stain they leave on our soul," Abaddon said. "You have led us here with promises of love and kingdoms to come. I agree, it is Heaven we are fighting, but we all have different reasons for marching against the Host. You say we must build a kingdom here, and we will. But instead of one, we will build many, each a reflection of what we see as perfection. You will always be our general, but it is clear we all have our own wars to wage. When you call, we will come; when you ask us to march, we will. But we will not follow blindly anymore.

"Tell me, Lightbringer, did you ever foresee our glorious enterprise coming to this?" Asmodeus asked. "Perhaps we are meant to follow another path. It is your light that guides us, but Creation is as vast as it is unknowable and our many eyes must be cast in all directions. It is clear that the potential of the race of mortals is multifaceted, and to this end, we will push our flocks to unlock their true calling. We must be ready to accept whatever may come. We follow you, Lightbringer, by following our own paths."

Lucifer spoke last.

"Together we challenged Heaven in glorious defiance. Now we shatter, becoming many instead of one. Very well, take your legions and wage your wars. Perhaps you are correct. Perhaps Heaven cannot fight a war on many fronts. But remember this. We are accountable, our actions will echo until the end of days. Now go. We will meet again, brothers, and when we do you will either submit to me, or fall to ash."

That day, as the legions scattered and Lucifer returned to Genhinnom, the Time of Atrocities began.

THE TIME OF ATROCITIES

Our legions were broken, but the Time of Atrocities saw us gain much ground — some might call it a golden age, which to this day they strive to recreate. Gone was the peace and tranquility of earlier centuries, though. We were no longer exploring Creation, but crafting it to our whims. It was a time of decadence and darkness.

In this time, our love and hate for the children of Adam and Eve knew no bounds. They were cherished and tormented, adored and tortured. At once they were a source of joy and pain to our legions. Many centuries passed since that fateful day we defied Heaven, and we had been forever changed by the horrors of war. We were becoming something terrible, and we warped the very land about us in the process. Once we had created Paradise, now in earthly exile, it was a hell we were crafting. We stopped creating and gave in to destruction.

A TIME OF HATE

Across all fronts, the Ebon Legion marched and was victorious. This is how I witnessed the fall of Shamayim, the second of the High Cities to fall, and the battle of the Glade of Memory. Here, mighty Gabriel fought against the hordes of Lirael in skirmishes that left the land scarred and fallow for all of eternity. It is said that Gabriel, archangel of mercy, vengeance, death and revelation, refused God's order to abandon the fight. Instead, he chose to remain and protect a mortal woman from the depredations of Lirael, who had taken to feasting on the flesh of mortals. To the very end, Gabriel fought, keeping Lirael at bay until day broke on the last day of battle. The bodies of many mortals and the husks of many of our number lay broken all about Shamayim when dawn came, but there was no sight of Gabriel or his mortal love. No one knew if the Archangel of Mercy and Revelation had been punished for his disobedience or if he fell during the night. One thing is for certain, his name was never echoed in the Abyss, so if Gabriel was punished by the Almighty, he was sentenced to a hell all his own.

No matter where the Ebon Legion marched, it left a trail of destruction and misery in its wake. Huge carrion flocks followed, so large they would blot out the sun, and feasted on the dead and dying. The corpses left behind were touched by the Scourges and left to bloat with disease and plague. When ripe, they would burst, unleashing pestilence across the land of the Host.

Wherever Abaddon's legion went, long caravans of humans followed — containing both slaves and worshipers. For all the atrocities the legion committed, some mortals craved the power the legion offered and so followed, willingly sacrificing themselves in battle or worshipping the Ebon lords.

Citadel of Hate

Dûdâêl, mighty fortress and citadel of the Ebon Legion became a bastion of hate and violence. Surrounded by fire and geysers that belched noxious clouds of gas into the surrounding lands, Dûdâêl became the very image of hell that so many moral artists would envision in the millennia to come. Huge forges beneath the city churned out weapons and armor for the mortal ranks of the legions — crude swords of dark metal known as *syir*. When not campaigning, the legion gathered in arenas and coliseums and staged gladiatorial fights, pitting mortal against mortal and demon-spawned aberrations created for the sole purpose of providing bloody sport for the crowds.

The Malhim

Yet, there were defeats, especially as the Time of Atrocities dragged on. A new wave of angels descended from Heaven to reinforce the battered Host. Unlike the initial defenders, who shied from actual conflict and battle, the new wave of angelic warriors did not. It was as if their very mandate was to sentence as many of our number to oblivion as they could. They became known only as the malhim, the bane of our existence. Some say they were born from the fires of the siege of Sagun, others that the malhim were the souls of faithful mortals blessed by Uriel to avenge their deaths by our hands. Whatever their origins, their power was fearsome to behold. I pray to Lucifer that we never see their like again.

A Time of Transgression

Far from the front lines, the Silver Legion toiled in its fortresses and keeps, places of unspeakable knowledge and forbidden lore. There nothing was sacred as the fallen of that legion scoured the fabric of Creation for clues that would deliver the gates of Heaven into our hands.

Those angels' mortal flocks were grafted to crude machines for practical and not so practical reasons. Places like the Wall of Breath and the Towers of Flesh became legends, haunting even to us. There were no limits to the atrocities that legion was capable of. Many of the horrors inhabiting mortal myths are, in truth, early memories of the excess of Asmodeus and his followers.

Beautiful Belphegor, overlord of the Fifth House, Mistress of Inspiration, forced her mortal flock to mate according to rituals she devised in an attempt to achieve humanity's ultimate potential. The cries from her citadel, the Palace of Sighs, echoed long after its destruction at the end of the war.

Tabâ'et', bastion of the Silver Legion, became a maze of towers and chimneys, spewing viscous smoke into the skies. Human flocks languished under the experiments of the legion and its voracious appetite for earthly and unearthly delights.

The Long March

In Genhinnom, Lucifer and the Crimson and Iron Legions continued to care for the human flocks under their protection. Lucifer sent expeditions to reclaim flocks from the Silver and Ebon Legions and bring them back to Genhinnom from time to time, but from his throne, Lucifer knew that the excesses of the shattered legions were weighing heavily on Creation. Countless mortals were dead, and many more existed in torment. This was not why the Lightbringer had defied Heaven. Yet, Lucifer knew that forcing the legions to follow him would be no different from the unquestioning obedience demanded by Heaven. For many a long year, the prince wrestled with this dilemma.

Finally, he decided to act. The war had gone on too long. The Host had been pushed back to Machonon, but the Lightbringer knew that city would never fall. Instead of allowing his legions to run rampant, he resolved to call them back and build their true kingdom once and for all.

What followed was the Long March, a crusade to bring the legions back under the rightful banner of Lucifer. Fallen clashed with fallen, but in the end, the Crimson Legion surrounded Dûdâêl, Tabâ'et' and Kâsdejâ. The errant legions sallied forth to break the siege three times, but the warriors of Crimson and Iron hurled them back into their lairs each time. In the end, the renegade lieutenants bent their heads in fealty once more, though I wonder what schemes of revenge they harbored in their hearts.

From his throne, Lucifer spoke of a new age, an age when the fallen would be worshipped by mortals and the mortals in turn would grow to challenge Heaven itself as deities in their own right.

"We have been fighting the wrong war," he declared. "We will defeat the Almighty, not through war or atrocities, but through the very faith of the mortals. We will make each of them an image of Him, perfect, infinite and powerful. For too long we have mistaken the root of the war. The Creator does not condemn us out of fear, but out of dread for what we might teach mankind. Do they not empower us with their faith as God once did before the Fall? We will make gods of these mortals and they will challenge

Him. In turn, the mortals will inherit the Earth and we will reclaim our thrones in Heaven. We have spent too long here. The time has come to return and make Heaven pay for its sins."

And so began the Time of Babel.

The Time of Babel

What followed was our greatest age. The victories of the Time of Atrocities had pushed the Host back, its forces scattered and in disarray. Under the guidance of Lucifer, our domains were fortified and even the dreaded malhim were stymied for a while. To appease the Silver and Ebon Legions, Lucifer allowed them to continue governing their cities, but they could no longer add to their flocks without first paying a tithe to Genhinnom. This is how the Crimson Legion spread its flocks across Creation. But that is not all it did.

It was Lucifer's mandate to elevate the race of Adam and Eve. Much time had passed since the First Night when Lucifer had opened the eyes of the Allmother and Allfather. Much had the descendants of Adam and Eve forgotten, much of their knowledge was composed of half-remembered truth and superstition, mixed with fear and superstition from the Time of Atrocities. Instead of witnessing the totality of Creation, the mortals were blind once more. Yet it was not God who was to blame this time, but us.

This pained our mighty prince. We had defied Heaven to bring light into the world, not more darkness and despair. We had failed our Lightbringer, and he had failed the children of Adam and Eve.

"Have I been following our Creator's path blindly?" Lucifer cried. "Is this rebellion nothing but a house of lies?

"No longer! We shall usher in a new age. Our rebellion shall not come to ruin. All the years of toil and despair, violence and murder shall not be in vain. We will elevate humanity until they touch the walls of Heaven itself. This shall be our Grand Experiment. If we fail, all is lost. If we succeed, victory will be ours at last."

The Grand Experiment

Lucifer selected 10 of his most trusted retainers and sent them across the land. Their task was to teach the sons and daughters of Adam and Eve the secrets, not just of Creation but of Heaven as well. It was the beginning of the end.

Across the lands, the Ten taught the mortal flocks, who then took this knowledge back to their tribes and built the Civilization of Ashes. So great was the knowledge the Ten brought with them that, in a few short years, cities that rivaled the bastions of the fallen spread across the world. The mortals built cities upon the oceans and mountain aeries, sprawling desert metropolises and golden jungle temples. Cities like Enoch, if the mortal book is to be believed.

The Ten visited these cities from time to time to watch over their charges and teach them. In time, these secretive tutors were known simply as "the Watchers."

The Watchers

Decked in cloaks made of light and shadow, the ten watchers stood tall and frail, yet their eyes swam with knowledge and potential. They were welcomed into all the cities of man, and they watched as the mortals learned the most secret lore of Creation. In time, the Ten left a book with each mortal city so that their knowledge could be passed down from generation to generation. These books came to be called the *Canon of the Eye*, and they were lost amid the chaos at the end of the war. Their existence has been forgotten even in the oldest surviving myths, and this is as it should be. Such knowledge was foolishly given once; it must never happen again.

Still, the Ten watched and taught.

Giriel taught the race of dust the secrets of the earth, how to shape the land through the art of combining elements and minerals.

Sharaael imparted the knowledge of flesh and life so that mortals could recapture the immortality that God wrongly took away.

Of the secrets of the stars and the heavens above, Bephamael taught the race of mortals. The *Book of Bephamael* traced the patterns of the stars and how to predict the passage of time.

The secrets of wind and storm were written by the hand of Marael.

The secret of metal work and the forge was the providence of Gamael.

Ur-Shanbi taught mortals of fate and how to divine the future by looking at signs and portents. God kept Adam and Eve blind, but through Ur-Shanbi, humanity would be able to ascertain Heaven's plans.

Of the moon and her mistress, Samael taught mortals where to look for the Mother of the Moon, what secrets she possessed and how to protect themselves from her kin.

Agriel wrote of the many secrets of the bounty of the land, of fruits both good and bad, and how to manipulate them for nourishment or poison.

Of the sun, God's unrelenting eye, Shamshiel spoke to the race of Adam and Eve.

Finally, the greatest gift was given by Penemue to the race of Adam and Eve. Penemue taught the race of man the gift of writing language and the wisdom this entails. Through his gift, mortals gained the ability to

define the world according to symbols and concepts and not by *things* that needed to be seen or touched. The secrets he taught allowed mortals to open their own eyes. Creation no longer needed to be seen and touched to be believed. Knowledge could now spread of its own accord. In a few generations, many tomes and books were written in the First Tongue, and humanity was close to finally unlocking its own divinity.

This is the gift that the Ten gave the race of Adam and Eve. Yet the fire that burns bright burns all too quickly.

Betrayal

The Watchers were dutiful in their tasks for more than a hundred years. Shortly after writing the books of forbidden lore, however, a shadow fell over them. The legions were forbidden to interfere with their task, but we were curious nevertheless. Some, like myself, protected them from afar by shielding them from advances by the Host or the malhim. Yet, ironically it was we who proved to be the Watchers' downfall in the end.

As the civilization of ashes reached greater and greater heights, some among our legions grew jealous. They whispered among themselves, "If all the secrets of Creation are open to them, why will they need us?" Fear and doubt wormed their way into our hearts.

None know for certain who fostered the plot to upset the Great Experiment, but legend holds that it was one of Lucifer's own House that sowed the seed. He called to those fallen who feared the growing power of humanity and persuaded them that something must be done to ensure that the legions maintained their dominance over the mortals. The traitor suggested that his followers take mortal partners and gave birth to a new race — one born of mortal-kind *and* fallen. This new race would be forever subservient to its progenitors, and it would ultimately supplant the children of Adam and Eve by virtue of inherent power. And so, in the dead of night, these traitors took mortals and joined with them.

Birth of the Nephilim

This is how the nephilim came to be: each and every one an abomination in the eyes of mortal and fallen. They possessed the gifts of man and angel, and they were terrible to behold — if not for their hideous countenance, then for their potential. I've heard that some were benevolent, gentle spirits who took it upon themselves to guide and enlighten, but many were born knowing only hate and tyranny. In a few short years, they dominated the cities where they were born. But their greatest crime was yet to come, for they searched out and destroyed the Ten, usurping their role as the teachers of mankind.

But the reign of the nephilim and their traitorous progenitors was short. When word of their evil reached Genhinnom, Lucifer descended upon them with his legions and slew all he could find. Yet the fearsome energies unleashed in battle after battle reduced the Grand Experiment to ruin. Afterward, this tragedy was called the Shattering, and it heralded our final defeat.

The Shattering

We ruled the world for countless ages, leading campaigns against the Heavenly Host and pulling down their prisons of stone and iron. We tempted other angels to fall and built mighty cathedrals and citadels across the face of Creation. We protected and tormented the race of dust and, eventually, bared all the secrets of Creation to the descendants of Adam and Eve. But, in the end, it all came to naught.

While Lucifer and his most trusted legions were fighting the nephilim, the race of Adam and Eve were buckling under the weight of their newly found divinity. Perhaps it was the disappearance of the Ten, the evil of the nephilim or just cruel fate, but the sons and daughters of the first mortals shattered at the moment when the whole of Creation lay open to them. Destiny cannot be preempted, and this is what (in our hubris) we'd sought to achieve. Why Lucifer had not foreseen this, I cannot say. In our long years in Hell, I heard many who believed that he had meant to betray us and humanity alike, but to what end? I don't know what to believe anymore.

Instead of becoming gods, the enlightenment of the race of man buckled under the weight of the newly found revelations. We sought to accelerate millennia of maturity in just a handful of generations. It was too much, too soon.

The False Tongues

But this was not our only regret. The Shattering had even more dire consequences — the fragmentation of the mortal tongue. Since the time of Adam and Eve, mortals used a form of our tongue, simplified for their ears but nonetheless it echoed with truth. All mortals spoke this One Language, a pure tongue that did not obfuscate and allowed them to grasp the significance of all. When Penemue taught the race of dust how to write and weave this One Language, the very doors of Heaven were opened to all of mankind. But they were not ready. They were blinded, and in being so, they lost the ability to comprehend the One Language. Their speech devolved into a cacophony of lesser languages. Instead of one nation of mortals, they fragmented into hundreds, even thousands of tribes and clans. Never again would

they see themselves as one race, united by a common mother and father.

The breaking of the mortal tongues had another effect — they could no longer gaze upon us and understand with clarity what they saw. Memories of us became legends and myths, spirits of superstition that some worshipped while others either ignored or did not trust. Even if we wanted to help, we could not. The mortals were so broken that we had become ineffable to them, and in so doing, their boundless flow of devotion and faith dwindled to nothing.

The Collapse

All across the land, our cities and tribes crumbled — some due to natural disasters, others due to wars, famine and plague. Cities sank into the depths of the oceans, while others were simply given over to the wilderness. It was as if the race of Adam and Eve chose ignorance when shown the totality of Creation and its secrets. Many of us cannot understand this even to this day. Why turn their backs on destiny and choose a lifetime of toil and ignorance? This was the ultimate betrayal in the eyes of many of our legions, something few have forgiven mankind for.

The Coming of the End

The experiment had failed, and for all our might, nothing could restore humanity's unstinting devotion. The mortals were blinded to us, and we were deprived of the faith we'd grown so accustomed to. We had forgotten the Host in the chaos of the Shattering, but Heaven had not forgotten us. During our darkest hour, the Host descended on us. The malhim laid siege to Dûdâêl, Tabâ'et' and Kâsdejâ, and they laid all our works to waste.

Michael and his Host gathered on Genhinnom, and a mighty battle raged. I am told that even at the last, Lucifer never once spoke of surrender. The Crimson and Iron Legions fought to the last of their strength and held the walls for 40 days and 40 nights before the gates finally gave way and the Morningstar was bound in chains of fire.

The ophanim, the Creator's angels of justice, came from Heaven surrounded by malhim and Michael's Host. They rounded up our legions and levied their punishment. Many of us expected to make the long march back to Heaven to face destruction, but the Almighty had a far more terrible fate in store. He condemned us to darkness eternal, an endless, empty existence devoid of purpose or worth. In all the horror I witnessed during the Age of Wrath, nothing compared to the atrocity that Heaven perpetrated on us at the end.

The ophanim passed judgment, and all was silent for a moment. I think they expected us to plead for mercy, to beg for swift destruction instead of eternity in the Pit. But our eyes turned to our prince, the Morningstar, who knelt with his head unbowed. It seemed as though he was searching the skies, daring the Almighty to face him one last time. The sight moved me beyond words, and I knew then and there that I would rather face the darkness standing on my feet then bend my knees one second longer to an uncaring God.

I climbed to my feet, daring the ophanim to object. I can remember the silence that hung over the great plain and the countless eyes following me as I marched resolutely to the gate of Hell. At the threshold I turned to my prince, and I swear there were tears in his eyes. With a proud salute, I cast myself into the Abyss.

I will not lie to you and say I was unafraid, but I fought to contain my terror in the emptiness of the Pit. I was waiting for my Prince to follow us into exile, and then I would be the first to kneel and swear my oath of fealty to him once more. For on that plain of judgment I realized that as long as he stood with us, no prison forged by Heaven could hold us. We would not yield to God's tyranny, not on Earth or in Hell. We would not submit. Justice would be ours one day.

I do not know how long I waited, keeping the fire of defiance alight. The ranks of the damned pressed about me, and still I endured. The darkness and the cold ate at my soul but still I endured. The cries of the forsaken cut through me like a knife, and still I would not yield.

Then the gates of Hell clanged shut, and I realized then that we'd been truly forsaken. Lucifer was not among us.

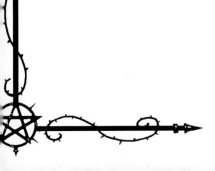

It had been a good night for Pat. Mr. Mackay had wanted an example made of some idiot who had fallen behind in his payments. It didn't take long to find him, and it was a simple matter to get him somewhere nice and quiet so Pat could go to work. For the last half hour, he'd been slowly and steadily beating the *shmuck* into a pulp while leaving him conscious enough for the coup de grâce. Shit, he was good at this.

He kicked the dealer in the face and stepped backward. Yup, the time had nearly come to finish the job. "Hey, fucker, Mr. Mackay just wanted you to know that you really shouldn't stiff him on payments twice in a row. He also wants you to know that you're never going to have the chance to do so again."

"Why are you doing that?" a strong, clear female voice asked.

Pat turned from the poor bastard on the alley floor. Some small, Indian-looking woman was staring at him down the alley. Petite and dark, she carried herself with a surprising confidence. *Cute, for an Indian bitch*, Pat thought. She didn't seem upset or frightened by what he was doing to the bloody excuse for a man at his feet, which surprised him.

"What's it to you, darlin'?"

"Oh, I'm just interested."

Hey, maybe this really was his lucky night. Some chicks really dug violence, or so some of the guys had been telling him. He wouldn't mind a bit of paki ass tonight.

"You wait there, honey, and I'll tell you all about it. Then I'll show you a good time right after I'm finished with this bastard."

Anila raised an eyebrow. "No, thank you. I'm married. Now, I've asked you twice: What are you doing?"

Pat couldn't help but notice the hint of menace in her voice. Something was not right here. He reached into his jacket.

"Yeah, and what are you going to do about it if I don't reply, little girl?" he snarled, a knife suddenly glinting in the dim orange of the streetlights at the end of the alley.

Anila looked at him and the knife for a moment. "You're going to kill him aren't you? A death by knife is quite a painful way to die, you know. I... Anila... would have hated it."

She paused for a moment, as if in thought. "It seems to me that by choosing to take the life of another, you have forfeited you right to your own." And then she *changed*.

There was little enough left of Pat for the police to bag and tag when they found him some hours later. The other guy, a known local dealer, was babbling some nonsense about evil spirits come to get him, but they put that down to drug-induced hallucination.

From the other side of the road, Anila Kaul watched them take the remains of her victim away and wondered if she had done the right thing.

CHAPTER THREE: APOCALYPSE NOW

I said to my soul, be still, and wait without hope
For hope would be hope for the wrong thing; there is yet faith
But the faith and the love and the hope are all in the waiting.
—T. S. Eliot, *East Coker*

IMPRISONMENT

I am Magdiel, and I am a fallen angel. I am one of Lucifer's chosen, and I am free in the world once more. I was here when this place was created, and I shall be here when it is destroyed.

I am not Anila Kaul, although it suits me to be her until I can understand this world and find my place in it. While I look human, I am far more than that. This body contains just one facet of me, a simple extrusion of something far greater. I have existed since the beginning of time, and I have seen things that a mere human brain could never comprehend. There are times when I cannot believe how small a section of reality they can perceive. How do they survive with so little understanding?

Much to my surprise, though, there is an attraction to the simple pleasures of their lives. I must not succumb to it. I do not care how seductive Anila's feelings and memories are. I do not care about her passion for her husband and for her causes. I am an Angel of Death, and I *will* be more than human. I know that I must stay in this body if I am to stay in this world, but its limitations are

frustrating. This mind cannot deal with the memories I have, and sometimes I struggle to hold on to them. I am setting them down on paper, in the hope that these notes will allow me to retain more than this skull can manage.

I admit that I am tempted by Anila's life and her emotions. They are like nothing I have ever experienced before. After millennia in the cold void of Hell, any experience is welcome, but I will not lose who I am to this pathetic human woman whose spirit was broken in some dingy flat. I am a demon. Anila is no more.

DARKNESS UNENDING

I remember the war well enough. Those things that I can't recall are probably best forgotten. I did things then that I regret even today. I never want to forget my imprisonment, though. I never want to forget what God did to me, because if I do, I might never understand it.

I had no concept of imprisonment then. None of us did. It was only after we lost the final battle and were bound in chains of fire that we understood what it was like to be truly powerless. We were prepared to suffer pain and indignity at the hands of our foes, but Heaven's

vengeance was far crueler than we could imagine. We were to be *forgotten*, consigned to a vault of darkness until the end of time. Though we would still be able to dimly sense the world beyond and feel the sufferings of humanity, we would be helpless to intervene. Anila has no words to describe the horror and fear we felt as Heaven's angels hurled us into eternal night.

Hell was a cold, empty void, barren of anything but us. We could make nothing there to ease our imprisonment, for there was no material for us to work with. We were utterly alone. The only things left to us were our memories and our regrets. Perhaps God imprisoned us to make us repent of our rebellion. If that was His goal, He could not have been more complete in His failure. Left with nothing but our own pain and frustration, entombed in a lifeless limbo without hope of release, even the strongest among us surrendered themselves to visions of anger and dreams of terrible revenge.

Even then, our descent into madness might have been averted. In time, we might have learned to make some kind of peace with our fate. But the one spirit who could have shaken us from this nightmare and inspired us to find a way to endure was nowhere to be found.

Mystery of the Morningstar

Lucifer was the greatest of us. Part of me, probably the part that is tainted by Anila, wants to call him the most beautiful, but that's not right. She could only understand love in human terms. We loved Lucifer because of the purity of his mission and purpose. He was able to articulate the way we felt with a clarity that few of us could match. When he strode onto the field of battle, we never believed that we could lose. His anger and his mercy were beyond compare, and each of us aspired to be worthy of his leadership.

I joined the rebellion for Lucifer just as much as for my own needs. He made me feel that my hopes for humanity were every bit as important as his own, and when he said that together we would prevail, I believed him. Even as the war began — and humans started dying — my faith in the Morningstar didn't waver. He was a prince among us, and God would see his point in the end. Even after the war, as Heaven's angels passed sentence against us, my faith did not waver. If I feared at all, it was for our prince. How much worse would Lucifer's punishment be than our own?

Without him, I doubt that we would have had the courage to defy the Almighty. Once the walls of Hell closed about us, we found ourselves without him just when we needed him most.

Missing

I remember our fear. Darkness settled over us like a shroud, and when we turned to the Morningstar for

his wisdom and confidence, we found nothing. We never sought another leader. It had never occurred to us that we might need one. Lucifer was the only one among us who we truly believed could challenge Him.

At first his lieutenants, those who had fought at his side and commanded his legions during the war, assumed that he would be joining us in time. It seemed obvious that God had other punishments in store for Lucifer; only afterward would he be imprisoned with us.

I don't know how long it took for the whispers to start. What if He had destroyed Lucifer? We had seen angels destroyed in the war; none of us held any illusions that our lives were sacrosanct. There were those who believed that (as our leader) Lucifer had been singled out especially for destruction. Others suggested that he had been given a special prison, separated from his loyal soldiers out of fear that he could find a way to lead us to freedom. Still others believed that the Morningstar might have sacrificed himself in order to win some small mercy from the Lord, ensuring our eventual release. No one knew. And so we waited.

I don't know where the idea originated, but I know that once it had been voiced, it could not be silenced. It may have been in the counsels of the great powers; it may have come from the lowest ranks; its source was unimportant. All that mattered was that the thought spread through us like a cancer, and by the time one of Lucifer's lieutenants gave voice to the thought, the seeds of what I consider to be nothing less than a second rebellion had been sown.

"Lucifer has abandoned us."

It was Belial, greatest among the Morningstar's lieutenants, who said it first. Some of the great dukes stood with him, declaring that we must seek our escape and revenge without Lucifer — or perhaps despite him. Abaddon, that black-hearted marauder, even dared to say that Lucifer was responsible for our defeat. Still others raised their voices in protest, their belief in our prince unshaken.

Many struggled with their beliefs and tried to avoid taking sides. I stood with the loyalists. Few had as much faith in Lucifer as I, and my voice brought many lesser fallen back to their senses. Just as many demons, if not more, let their anger consume them, and they raged against our prince with the same fury they directed at God.

The Factions

Without Lucifer to unite us, the whispers of dissent that began in the final days of the war only gained in strength. Conflict was inevitable as each faction became entrenched in their beliefs and sought to convert the rest — sometimes with words, sometimes with force.

Certainly the first and largest of these factions were the so-called True Believers, the fallen who were part of

Lucifer's Great Crusade and believed that mankind was the key to defeating the will of Heaven. Our terrible exile did little to shake the sect's convictions — if anything, Heaven's furious response in the wake of the Time of Babel only confirmed their beliefs. As time passed and the pain cut ever deeper, however, their faith in the glory of humankind took on a darker tone. Rather than unleashing mankind's potential, the True Believers declared that the fallen should have harnessed it, like a spear pointed at God's merciless heart. Now that the gates of the Abyss lie broken I wonder how many of the Believers are out there now, moving through the multitudes and binding the souls of mankind in new-forged chains. They called themselves the Keepers of Babel during the exile; now I'm certain they eschew any titles that would hint at their true agenda. Anila has a word for these schemers, a name from human literature that is synonymous with stolen souls: Faustians.

The more cautious or contemplative of our number struggled to remain apart from the power struggles, seeking answers to the many questions that plagued us. They sought to understand our defeat and exile better before they made a decision about Lucifer. They chose to doubt and question everything. They exempted themselves from the power struggles that wracked our prison. Instead, they talked to those who had been near Lucifer in the war, and those who had seem him chained at the feet of God. They questioned those who had worked with him before the thought called rebellion had first been formed and shaped. Ultimately they realized that as long as they were trapped in the Abyss the truth could never really be known, but still they labored over their many theories. In time they came to be known as the Cryptics, the seekers of mystery.

Some, like myself, stood in defiance of the thought that slandered the Morningstar. We matched wills with the doubters and the heretics at every turn, fighting to keep Lucifer's vision alive. He was our champion, our leader and our hope. If he still lived, it was our duty to free ourselves and find him so that we could begin the struggle anew. So long as one of us still believed in Lucifer's dream, the war was not truly lost. Many sneered at us and referred to us as Luciferans, yet we wore the name proudly.

Other, weaker souls fell into despair. They considered Lucifer's absence to be a sign of his destruction or betrayal, and believed us damned for all eternity. Their anger was bright and fierce, and they turned it toward all of God's works. One day, they swore, they would be free and they would destroy all that He had done. If God would deny us the cosmos we had created and the people we loved, then He could not have them either. They were the Raveners, and I watched with dismay as the ages of agony increasingly swelled their ranks.

Other fallen turned their attention outward. While we could not interfere with the world we had lost, we could get some sense of what occurred there, through the pangs of pain or half-glimpsed thoughts of the humans who dwelt there. At first, we thought this was a sign of God's mercy, a gift that allowed us some contact with the world we knew. Yet, as time passed we came to think of it as the greatest of His punishments. This faction strove to reach their human allies from the rebellion, to reassure them that they had not been forgotten. I found the last group the hardest to understand. They did nothing. After a thousand years of fighting, they became passive. It was as if defeat by God knocked all of the fire out of them. Once they were in Hell, they simply waited. They accepted God's punishment and waited for a time when He would set us free to work in His name again. They said that the chance would come to make right what we had done and regain His grace. They called themselves Reconcilers, but they were mocked as fools, even traitors, and their beliefs and commitment did little to protect them in the eternity that followed. As centuries upon centuries built up like the sand on a beach, they too succumbed to the pain and became as monstrous as the rest of us.

I can't remember the detail of what happened anymore. I can't recall all of the deeds I did in Lucifer's name. I cannot forget, though, that the war waged in Hell never ended. The Princes of Hell struggled with one another from the moment the lie of Lucifer's treachery was voiced. I'm sure that they struggle to win the upper hand even now.

Remembering

I have just read what I have written, and part of me — the part that is Anila, I think — wants to laugh. I look around at the living room of the small house in East London I call home, and wonder if any of this can be true. I lived through it. It is more a part of me than this place, than these chairs or the desk I lean on to write. Yet, somehow this desk seems more real, more comprehensible and more important than the struggles of the Princes of Hell.

I cannot afford to think this way. I am still their servant, and though I do not truly understand this world anymore, I have duties to perform. I just don't know to whom I owe my loyalty. Should I continue to serve my master and win his freedom, as he commanded? Should I risk his displeasure and seek Lucifer instead? Should I seek out God and beg forgiveness?

I will keep this book to remind me of what I was before I took Anila's body for my own. I will fill it with my memories of Hell and the thoughts that I can truly say come from the part of me that is demon or angel, but certainly not human. That way, I can remember what is me and what is Anila. I need her body. Do I need her lingering feelings and memories? I do. If I dispense with Anila entirely, I become what I was before. I become a being of anger and despair. I don't want to be that way anymore. I was an angel: God's servant and a bringer of death. Surely some of that is left within me? Can I be what I once was?

Descent

I argued with my husband — with Anila's husband, Tony — this morning. He accuses me of being surly and withdrawn. He says that I just watch him, and do not talk and love him like I used to. He's right, of course, but how can I do what he wants? I am not Anila. I cannot be the person he needs me to be. I am in her body and I share her memories, but she is dead, and even I, an Angel of Death, cannot say what that means.

And yet, I want to reach out to him, to draw him to me, to feel the warmth of his body against my own. I want to rest his head on my breast and take the worry from him. These feelings must be Anila's, for I have never comforted anyone in my existence before. Yet, they feel as much a part of me as my power over this world, and perhaps more so than the memories of the time in Hell.

I do not like to think about that time. My desires then were less comforting. During the war, we created a refuge for the souls of the dead, a place of hope, but it soon became the anteroom to our terrible prison. God taunted us with the spirits of the dead, letting us touch them while living humanity remained barred to us. For when we reached out to human spirits while we were imprisoned, it was not to reassure them, but to silence them or to take pleasure in their torment if we could not. We were so lost in hate that we just didn't care. Our pain and guilt twisted us, and eventually we sought to attack the very things that we once loved: the souls of mankind.

We made them suffer. Now, I'm making Tony suffer, and I'm not sure I can make amends for either crime. How can I make amends for those souls we ravaged over the centuries, when I can't even say the right things to make this one man stop hurting?

I can see why I'm hurting him. It's harder to recall why I ended up hurting all those souls through history. Looking back, it seems strange that we made the journey from desperately wishing to ease the pain of the humans to creatures that desired nothing more that humanity's pain, suffering and ultimately their utter destruction. And yet, the steps on that road are still clear to me, even if the scenery is a little vague. Guilt became pain. Pain became anger. Anger became hate. Hate created suffering. Those were the four small steps from angel to demon. How inadequate these words are to convey the changes those steps forced on us.

Perhaps I was wrong. I wanted to ease the pain of humans before, and it was the first step on the journey that has brought me here. Desire led to rebellion. Rebellion led to punishment. Punishment led to guilt.

Guilt. That's what I'm feeling now. Every move and gesture on Tony's part, the sadness I can see in him is filling me with guilt. I hate the fact that I am hurting him, and I hate myself for not being able to put it right with a word.

I cannot think about this anymore. The more I hate myself, the more I feel the echoes of Hell in me, and it is clouding my brain. I must be Anila for a little while and bring this man the comfort I wished to bring all humanity so very long ago. I cannot bear his pain any longer. I will find a way to end it.

Pain

My husband is asleep. I should sleep with him and be Anila for a while longer, but I cannot. I must focus my mind again and remember how I came to hate humanity, and how God's "gift" to us became the sharpest torment we endured. I think the cruelest thing He did when He cast us down was to all but bar us from the world we created for Him. If we had been utterly isolated from it, unable to sense or touch it in any way, it would have been easier. Memory would have faded over time, we would have created a new existence for ourselves within the place we had been given. It may have been a place of anger, hate and frustration, but how long would those emotions have lasted with nothing to fuel them? We would have found release and contentment in our prison over time, or so I like to believe.

He did not allow us that, though. No, He trapped us in a place where we could still sense humanity about us. Their living souls called to us through the cloudy glass of our prison, and we reached out to them, unable to touch them. At first they remembered us, and their pain at our disappearance from the world was great. God's loyal servants remained aloof from humanity, so it seemed to the surviving humans that the touch of divine had left the world. Death, the great mystery, now came to all of them, without any spirits to guide them and with no direct word of what it meant. Fear and loss are the parents of pain, and their child grew strong in the hearts of mankind. We wept in Hell to feel the pain of those we had championed and raged at Heaven for leaving us impotent to deal with it.

As time passed and we felt humanity slowly lose knowledge of us, the feeling of revenge turned into all-out anger. Humanity, for whom we had given up more than they could possibly imagine, had given up on us. Those we had sought to save abandoned us.

That was when angel became demon. That was when I, Magdiel, became a monster.

Power Plays

Something changed in Hell through this time. There was always a hierarchy amongst us, even before the rebellion. No one ever thought to question it. Our place and ranks were as God ordained them to be, and it never crossed our minds that they should be anything but that. We were made to be in that position, so why would we doubt our place? Even when we rebelled, one of Lucifer's first acts was to forge a new order that would bind us all together.

Yet the longer we were imprisoned, the less the old rules seemed to matter. Perhaps our rebellion against Him paved the way for us to rebel against every other aspect of our existence: first against the absent Lucifer and then our own superiors in the ranks of Hell. This was the third rebellion. Even as the factions of Hell fought against one another, they turned upon themselves as well. Our guiding lords became petty tyrants, dictating our actions for their own ends.

Where the princes once guided us, they now ruled us, forcing us to obey by calling upon our True Names. They dragged us into their fights, whether we wanted to go or not. The power of our Names was such that soon we never even questioned our motivations — we just did what we were told. Where once we were comrades fighting for a cause, we were now masters and servants, seeking the benefit of the few, not the freedom of the many. We were now slaves.

Bitter Tastes of Freedom

None doubted that our prison was inviolate, proof against any power we could muster against it. The Creator decreed that we would lie in darkness until the end of time, and this we believed. Yet just as we had resigned ourselves to an eternity of slavery and spite, the five Archdukes of Hell, Lucifer's former lieutenants and masters of his legions, suddenly disappeared. The shock was so great it silenced every petty struggle between us and left us filled with a mix of wonder and apprehension. We could sense that the stars still burned, the worlds spun in their courses and mankind still passed its days in ignorance and fear, so the sands of time had not yet run out. For a time I dared hope that it was Lucifer's doing, that the Morningstar had escaped his shackles and was going to set us free. But the walls of our prison did not fall, and the archdukes never returned. Hope gave way to despair. The Raveners claimed that Heaven took Lucifer's lieutenants from us so that they could share in the Morningstar's punishment. The Cryptics disagreed, and the factional struggles began anew.

Then Zaphoriel vanished. He held no high station among the fallen, nor was he much renowned for his deeds against the Host. We were amazed at his disappearance, but even more so when he abruptly returned. He

claimed to have been summoned from our prison not by God or His angels, but by a *man*. Zaphoriel said he had appeared in a circle of power, sustained by a potent ritual and bound by words of power crackling from the human's lips. Then the human demanded things of Zaphoriel, commanding him to relinquish secrets of his House's lore! We were awestruck. Bad enough that mankind had forgotten our sacrifices for their sake — now they thought themselves equal in authority to the Creator Himself? Zaphoriel raged impotently at the man, and ultimately was banished back into our midst.

Where had mankind gained such power? Had they freed the archdukes as well? If so, why had they not returned? Over time, more and more of our number were called from our prison and commanded to share what we knew or perform deeds at the summoner's behest. It was a humiliation that scarred our souls far more than the slavery we now suffered at the hands of our own, but at the same time, we found ourselves hoping to be the next one called. The more powerful amongst us commanded their vassals to share their Celestial Name with the human magi, that they might be drawn back to earth.

Some who were called did not return. Like the archdukes, their fate was unknown. The summonings continued, growing in frequency for several millennia, but as the world changed, it seemed that the number of magi dwindled, and the secrets to unlock our prison were lost. But we have not forgotten, least of all the Cryptics, who wonder how mankind could have discovered such knowledge and realized the power to make their desires reality in the first place.

Maelstrom

There were times when it seemed as though the walls of our prison might fall. Five times since our imprisonment a storm of terrible power raged across the spirit realm and battered against the seals of the Abyss. The most strident among us declared each time that the time of our release was at hand, that Creation was at an end, and that soon all our suffering would cease. Each time, they were wrong. We bathed in the hatred, fear and pain of the dead for a short time as they suffered in the throes of the Maelstrom. Afterwards we raged at the calm that settled in its wake, furious that nothing had changed. The gates of the Abyss remained as strong as ever, our freedom nothing more than a fading dream in a hate-filled mind.

And then, in an instant, everything changed. We felt the surge in pain that marked another upheaval, sharp and fiery, filling us with pain and ecstasy. We flocked to the barrier between Hell and the realm of the dead, eager to increase the suffering of those souls we could reach and share in the pleasure we would reap. And even as we

concentrated on those souls, we realized we could feel them with a clarity that had been denied us since the day of our imprisonment. We rushed toward those points of clarity. We pushed at the very outer boundary of Hell itself and then we saw the one sight we never expected to see. We felt the cracks the storm had made.

It is impossible to describe how we felt. The cracks were wide enough that the smallest of us could escape. While we expected them to disappear, to close up at any moment before us, they stayed, resolutely open. God's word did not close them. Angels did not defend them. We stared at them and hoped, feared and hated at once. The doors of Hell were open. We could go back to the world. Was our punishment at an end?

Exodus

In the end, the decision to leave was not ours. Our princes, seeing their chance, but knowing that the cracks were not wide enough to allow them to escape, invoked their servants' Names and sent them — sent *us* — flying into the raging storm beyond. We left Hell with fear and hope in our hearts and the commandment to free our masters coursing through our very beings. "*Free us. Free us, and vengeance will be ours.*"

From the moment the walls of our prison started to come apart, I could think of nothing but escape, but even as I left the Abyss, surging forward to serve my prince, I could not help but wonder. Would He be waiting for us? Had the time for further judgment come? Would our millennia of hatred be called to account?

Yet the angels did not come for me.

I hurled myself into the storm, heedless of its fury. All around me flew the ruined souls of those we tormented, and I tore through them, screaming my joy and my hate at the pathetic spirits that sought to bar my way. I rose through the storm, parting it before me, reaching upward from the Abyss to the world of the living. The dead clawed at me, the storm tried to grasp me, but neither could succeed for I was a demon, and I was free.

Still, the angels did not come for me.

I rose up through them, reaching for the world I had known, the world I was banished from longer ago than I could reckon. Then, hope and fear and anger and hatred burning within me, I saw the Earth, the world I had fought for, come into view. I was returning home, a refugee from a self-made Hell. At first the world was gray, a twisted reflection of itself seen through the eyes of hate, and then it was in front of me as I remembered it, vibrant, alive, the pinnacle of His Creation. For a moment I exulted, drinking in the long-forgotten glory of the world. For a moment I forgot everything but the beauty of Creation.

And even then, the angels did not come for me.

There were humans everywhere; more humans that I could ever have imagined existed. I had

tormented untold human souls through my imprisonment, but that was no longer enough for me. Instead, I sought out the angels, to let them feel the power of my hate. Yet I could not find them.

They were gone. I looked where creatures lingered on the brink of death, but no angel lingered to ease their pain. My fury growing, I looked for the watchful angels of the air or the muses haunting the indigo deeps or the angels of the wild tending their towering woods, but I found not a single one. Had they abandoned their posts? Were they in hiding? I could sense my fellow demons, but not a single member of Heaven's Host.

Confusion overtook me. It was an unfamiliar feeling in a being long given over to hate. How did the world operate without our kind? Did God no longer care for the world?

Exploration

I hovered over the world, braced against the wind, enjoying the freedom that I'd lost so long ago. Even as I fought against the storm that raged across the Veil, I could feel my senses coming alive with the siren call of duty. Living things all over the world called out for the end. It was refreshing at first, like returning home after a long and arduous journey, but then I opened myself to it and found it greater than I could ever have imagined. It was as if the whole world was crying out in pain, begging for its agony to end and the cycle to move on again.

The fury of the Maelstrom was incredible. I didn't know if it was the result of our escape from Hell, the cause of it or some sign of His anger with the world, but it was flaying the souls of the dead. Their agonies echoed through me as I hung there. Worse, though, was the constant moaning of the souls of the living. These were not the humans I remembered. They were haggard, weak things, the light of their souls dimmed to a feeble glow.

Unbelieving, I drew closer to a place where their cry sounded with particular anguish. It was as if the ground itself was crying out for its end to come. It had been pushed beyond its boundaries, beyond its God-given purpose and was crying for an end to its existence. I let that call draw me in, relishing the feeling of doing a duty I barely remembered. What I saw shocked me. The world was nothing like the one I knew. The beauty of Creation seemed to have been replaced by a monotony of shapes. Great rock slabs thrust their way into the sky, pale, soulless lights burning within. Where once stood gardens of beauty and great hills filled with all manner of life, were now gray blocks of stone and steel that seemed to have no purpose but to crush the spirit of those who lived in them.

People moved through those barren canyons, but they weren't humans as I understood them. These creatures we had given up the service of Heaven to console, protect and educate, had taken the divinity within them and squandered it. They seemed to see themselves and their works as something separate from the rest of the world.

Was this God's punishment on them? Were they paying their own price for our hubris?

The Pull of the Abyss

As I took in this vista, barely comprehending what I saw, the Abyss continued to pull at me, trying to drag me back into its horrible embrace. I felt it claw at my very being, telling me that this was not my place, that I belonged in Hell. Each second in the real world became a struggle against the impulse to let go and be sucked back into darkness. But my prince had commanded me with my Name, so I could not flee. I had to stay and find a way to free her.

More than that though, I would not go. There was too much to see, too much to understand, too much to do. The only sure way to survive as a being of spirit in a world of the flesh was to join with that flesh. I just had to find a body that would accept me.

I opened my mind and felt a thousand shattered souls, flickering like candles in the wind. One such broken spirit called out to me. It had been betrayed, and that betrayal had cost it everything that it had loved. I could sense my fellow demons reaching out to human spirits too weak or too starved to resist us and claiming the bodies in their place. Each of us found a wounded soul that resonated with our own nature, in the hope it would allow us to bond with the flesh more easily.

I moved toward one of the stone towers I saw before, drawn by a mix of anger, frustration, compassion and grief, and I found the small female body lying in a pool of blood on the floor. I felt the void within the corpse, the space where the soul linked with the thing of fleshy matter, and I poured myself into it. In that moment I, Magdiel the Slayer, become something at once more and less than I had been.

Rebirth

The moment I sank into that cooling flesh, the physical world reached out and pulled me. Even as I commanded the body to heal, the blood to flow and the muscles contract, I was assaulted by images still remaining in the mortal's brain. I let those memories rush into me as I concentrated on the body, on making it whole, on making myself part of it, anchoring myself against the pull of the Abyss.

I was overwhelmed. I had never imagined what the world felt like to a human. I had existed apart from the world of matter and flesh. I'd worked with it, but I'd never been part of it, never directly experienced it. Now I was part of it, and I had no idea how to deal with the feelings I was experiencing. All I knew was that I wanted more. I hungrily dived through these sensations; so

different from the ones I had been denied in the Abyss. The feel of the flesh, the air on my body, the blood on my chest, the movement of my hair, the lungs inflating inside me, my heart beating, my stomach complaining, the light on my irises and my eardrums vibrating. This was all new. The world looked utterly different from what I expected, the sounds that assaulted my ears almost incomprehensible to me.

I dove deeper into Anila's mind for explanation and guidance, for her memories and the lingering taste of her emotions, and I lost myself in a new rush of sensations. The memories that made up the person called Anila Kaul roared over me like a tidal wave of human experience.

The sharp pain of a paper cut gave way to the warmth of the sun on my face and the cool water around my body as I swam. I tasted the warm feeling of a curry cooked by my mother and the grief of her death. I felt the joy of dancing, and the rhythm of the music that guided the dance resonated in my bones.

I tasted Anila's first, tentative kiss with a boy who was jeering at her six months later for being a "paki." I felt the rain of a cold London morning lashing against my skin as Anila hurried to an appointment. I felt her joy as she rescued a child from an abusive parent.

I tasted the sting of her father's hand across my face as they argued over Anila's choice of husband. I experienced touch, the cuddle of a parent or the caresses of her lovers. A human sensation, so primitive compared to the meeting of angels, yet so utterly compelling, so completely consuming.

And then I lost myself completely as I found Anila's memories of her husband: the taste of his skin, the feel of his breath on me, the long, lazy night wrapped up in each other's arms. Nothing matched this but being in His presence. My memories of Him were of anger and punishment, not the love and passion of my husband.

Oh, Lord, why did you grant this to them and not to us?

Joined

I don't know how long I spent there, alternately living Anila's past and then just experiencing the sensations her body gave me. Eventually, I became aware of myself and sat crying on the floor. At first I cried with joy. I was free after so long, but more than that, I was alive, exulting in experiences that I had never dared imagine before or after I rebelled. Never once did I imagine what it would be like to be one of them. It was inconceivable to me that they might have lessons for us. Now I found that they did.

For the first time in longer than Anila could imagine, I cried out in joy and exultation to a Creator I have hated with a passion since I lay chained at His feet. I clambered unsteadily to my feet and spun around, joy filling my heart. I stumbled and fell, bruising my leg and loving the feeling of pain where I hit the floor.

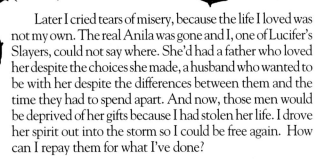

Later I cried tears of misery, because the life I loved was not my own. The real Anila was gone and I, one of Lucifer's Slayers, could not say where. She'd had a father who loved her despite the choices she made, a husband who wanted to be with her despite the differences between them and the time they had to spend apart. And now, those men would be deprived of her gifts because I had stolen her life. I drove her spirit out into the storm so I could be free again. How can I repay them for what I've done?

Reality

Neither joy nor pain lasted. However much I wanted to hold on to them both, I couldn't. They slipped away even as I tried to understand what I should do next. This world was nothing like I imagined. The box, no, the room I was in made no sense to me without Anila's memories. I used her memories for a while and experienced the things in that place as she would.

After an hour of this, I panicked. Was I losing my identity and everything I was to this human shell I taken shelter in? I tried to concentrate on Hell, on my hate, on my fall, my rebellion. Yet, I didn't want that. My mind was clear. The hate was buried deep in me, and I was thinking freely again, in a way I had not experienced since the early days of my imprisonment. I wanted this: this world and this life. And I wanted to be me *and* to be Anila. Memories of torment mixed with memories of a night in the pub. I was drinking with demons and torturing the souls of the departed with college friends. I bled into Anila, and Anila bled into me. The body was shaping me even as I tried to bend it to my will.

I don't have the words to describe what happened next. How can human language find a way to describe what a demon feels when it becomes, in a way, human? I could use words like confusion, madness, pain, anger, hate and love, but none of them really conveys what happened. The hate of the demon and the passions of the human met, and something of the angel I once was found new life in that fusion.

For a while, I was mad. The demon could not cope with the human experience, and the human body could not cope with the demon within. I lost my grip on what Anila called sanity and slid into a meaningless mass of sensations and memories. Eventually, I found clarity because I found something to focus on: Anila's attacker. I felt the knife plunge deep into my belly, again and again. He'd tried to kill me, and I didn't understand why. I needed to understand. There must be some reason behind it, some motivation that a mere human like Anila could never understand. I had to know *why*.

However, I knew that I had to protect Anila's existence first. I needed her life until I worked out what I wanted to do next. I picked up the phone and, using Anila's memories, I called the office. I told them I'd

been attacked and was shaken up, so I was going home. They asked me how the wife and child were that I had gone to visit. A memory flashed through my mind: Anila telling them to run. An enraged man coming at her with a knife, screaming abuse.

I told them that they'd gone, that they should be on their way to the battered wives' shelter. They seemed concerned, saying that I sounded odd. I nearly laughed at that, but kept my voice steady. My boss told me to take care. She said she'd take care of liaising with the refuge and reporting the attack, but that I'd need to file a complete report in the morning, if the police didn't come around to see me before that. I wasn't sure what she meant, and didn't have the time to probe Anila's memories to find out, so I just thanked her.

Then she asked me if I was okay and if there was anything she could do. I have existed since the dawn of time. I have fought battles with creatures whose very existence is just a myth to the people that clustered in the building around me. Yet I was brought close to tears by a simple act of human concern. It was like nothing I had ever experienced before.

I thanked her and told her I would be fine. Then I put the phone back on the hook and went in search of the man that had tried to kill me.

The Hand of Death

I found the would-be killer in an alley behind the refuge, hiding and watching. His name was David, and he'd been a crack addict for the last two years as well as a wife beater. He'd hospitalized his wife twice, and Anila had been assigned to help her get out of the situation.

Anila had arrived at the flat that morning, to tell the wife that a place was ready for her and her daughter in the shelter. As they'd been packing, the husband had arrived home, angry and coming down off a crack high. Anila tried to calm him down. She never saw the knife.

As I walked down the alley, calling his name, I could see the terror and incomprehension on his face. He thought I was a drug-induced hallucination, and he was afraid, which was good. I am an Angel of Death. He *should* be afraid.

He tried to run. I was faster. He tried to break my grip. I was stronger. I pinned him to the alley wall and stared deep into his eyes. "Why?"

"Why what?" he gasped.

"Why did you try to kill me?"

"You were taking my wife away. I couldn't let you. She's mine." He was angry again, the hate overriding his common sense. I saw a little of myself in him, a little of my own hate. I laughed in his face, and that just made him even more afraid.

"You're pathetic. You were damaging something you thought of as yours. You claimed rights that were not your

own and then abused them, just to protect your own twisted view of the world. You wanted to end my life for nothing more than a power trip. You don't deserve to live."

Then I showed him what I really am, which made me feel strong again, and I killed him. I don't know if I killed him for Anila or because he reminded me of the humans that rejected us after we were imprisoned or because he reminded me of what I was before or because he just deserved it. But I killed him nonetheless.

It was easier than I remembered. The man simply collapsed at my touch, his soul torn free and thrown to the storm that raged beyond the Veil. It made me feel empty somehow. I should be glad that Anila's attacker was dead. She had words for this — justice, revenge — but I just felt empty and sad. There was no trumpet from on high, no bolt from the blue to punish my transgression. After a while, I turned my collar up against the rain and went home.

Surviving Life

For a while I hid behind the memories of the woman I had been. I dealt with the police and went back to work. I rose each morning and packed lunches for my husband and I while he made the breakfast. We'd make the same small talk we made every morning before heading off to work. After all that time in pain, anger and madness, the sheer routine gave me an anchor to try to understand what I had become.

The one thing that I hated above everything else was the journey to the office. Each morning I would stand on the dismal gray railway platform and wait for the train to crawl into the station, late and overcrowded. Inside, the people were angry, frustrated and selfish, pushing each other for every little piece of space and comfort they could get. The needs of their neighbor meant nothing. Only their own journey to work was relevant. There was no sense of order, hierarchy or responsibility. The idea of community seemed to be utterly alien to them. All they cared about was themselves. Each jostled with the other for some little piece of power, and every single one of them was terrified of losing what little status they had.

It seems ludicrous, but in each and every such journey I saw a little of our imprisonment in the Abyss, as if our torment was reflected in them. Perhaps there is more truth in this than I realized: While I was in Hell, I remember lashing out in pain whenever I felt the presence of another soul. My brethren that remain there are somehow transmitting their pain and anger into the world. These people lash out whenever someone gets too close. Even in the closest confinement they seem isolated from one another.

CITIES

If the journey was bad, the destination was a thousand times worse. We once built a glorious world for humanity, yet they seem to have spurned the Creator's gifts — and our labor — utterly. Mankind has scavenged the ruins of ancient glory and built these gray shantytowns in their place. Their buildings never have and never will feel life. I cannot bring myself to call these cities "dead" because death implies that there once was life in the place, and I can't believe that that was ever the case. While there is a certain beauty and touch of the spirit in the occasional building, most seem designed to subvert the spiritual to the mundane physicality of the world. They grind the potential out of humanity by their sheer lack of aspiration.

The buildings loom large and close, cutting the light of the sun from the creatures that scurry beneath. The winds howl through these man-made canyons, chilling the body and the soul in a way that no canyon we built ever would. They fill the buildings with boxes, each worker separated from the nest by artificial walls. Then they go home to their larger boxes, not even seeking to greet or talk to their neighbors. Each soul seems to have found a way to isolate itself from others like it.

RELATIONSHIPS

I realize now that my marriage is something rare in this world. Anila chose to open herself up to another human, to trust and love him. I remember that love, in a way, from the comradeship we had in the days of the rebellion. Most of humanity seem to both desire and fear it, and so they are ever more isolated from the people around them. As I pore back through my memories, I can remember the community Anila grew up in, a tight group of immigrant Pakistanis in the East End. She never experienced a community like it again. Her father believed that society was coming apart, and she was inclined to agree. That's why she took the job she did: a social worker, doing her best to aid those in most need. Her marriage was a little symbol to her of the need to grow closer to others, not further apart.

In fact, there were small echoes of rebellion in the marriage. We chose to stand up for what we wanted in the face of much opposition. Anila's father opposed the

> I am sorry that I have to kill myself, but the other childrens at school make my life too sad to live.
> Every since we came to this country, they make names of me. I have no friends. School is hard because my English is no yet so good — but I try. I make you and Mama sad because I am sad. I cannot do that any more. I hope you will be more happy here now I am gone.
> Ravi

marriage and Tony's parents were less than happy with the idea of him marrying a "paki." For some reason, that shortening of the name makes it abusive. It seems that the color of my skin marks me as different in this city, and some people don't like things that are different. Yet humans of all colors walk these streets, and their souls seem little different from one another to me. It seems to be just another way they choose to isolate themselves from one another.

Love seems to be a commodity that is almost as rare on Earth as it is in the depths of Hell. The messages on the television constantly promote selfishness. Buy this for yourself to be happy. Buy this to be able to manipulate the people around you better. Buy this to have more sex.

Ah, yes, sex. Sex is one of the great benefits of having a body. I enjoy it thoroughly. While it lacks the immediacy of angelic unions, it certainly has a pleasure in it that I never expected. Yet, it is not the same thing as love, though society seems to have decided that it is an adequate substitute. People choose sex instead of love, selfishness instead of community. Is this really what He intended? Did our rebellion bring the world to this?

VIOLENCE

We fought because we had to. We defied Heaven because we felt we had no choice when He called us traitors. The Host descended on us, and we fought for a thousand years because we believed in the path we had chosen. Humans are different. I do not know if it is because that battle lives on in the culture of humans, the memory of those conflicts passed from generation to generation, or because they were just made that way. They chose violence as a first resort, not the last.

More than that, they kill. Often they kill randomly and unpredictably. They strike at those who are different, at those who threaten them in some way or even just those who prevent them having the power they feel is their right. I read in one of the newspapers that there has never been a time that there was not war in some part of the world. Children punch each other in the playgrounds. Men fight outside bars or at sports events. Husbands attack wives, children beat parents. People kill each other for no other reason than to take material things off their victims.

Violence has become part of these people, its motive inconsequential and its consequences rarely considered. I think that if every demon in the Abyss put aside his thirst for vengeance, humanity will ultimately destroy itself.

AUTHORITY

There is violence even in their authorities. Amongst the Host of Heaven, we knew our place. We were created to serve a particular function, and we never sought to do anything different. Yet, just as we fell to infighting in Hell, so the humans struggle with one another to gain power. Once they have power, they do their best to keep those beneath them in their place. I have seen little evidence in my time here of people genuinely desiring power to aid others. I find even less in Anila's memory. I remember her frustration with the petty local government officials and the uncaring police who did little to ease her job and less to help prevent the situations arising in the first place.

I have heard noble words about governing for the good of the people, and I see images of fat men and women, traveling in expensive cars and doing their best to ensure their own continued presence in positions of power. They pay lip service in their speeches to bettering the lives of the people they rule, and that seems to be enough for most people. They accept that these people will do the things they promise, and then distract themselves with food, drink, sex and other entertainment. Where has the bright, inquisitive humanity I watched with such longing gone? How did they become these downtrodden, submissive beings, an insult to those who created them?

Take the police. There is a phrase I have seen on television, from America, I think: to serve and protect. Yes, but to serve and protect whom? Certainly it's not the victims of crime, who seem to multiply in number each week. It's not the ordinary people who have yet to feel the attention of criminals, either. They are protected simply by not having attracted the attention of the wrong people yet. No, they merely serve as a sop to public opinion. The masses want to believe they are safe, so some thug in a uniform will convince them that this is the case.

Delusion and deceit became our stock in trade in our time in Hell. It appears humanity has learnt its lesson at least as well as we did.

The Human Condition

There is some hope, some goodness amongst the pain of this broken world. The human that occupied this body before me devoted her life to improving the lot of others. She was one of the few who realized just how much harm humanity is doing to itself. She worked to mitigate that suffering, despite the indifference of those in authority. The list of the problems she dealt with on a daily basis beggars my cruelest imaginations: rape, child abuse, poverty, spousal abuse, untreated mental illness and racial abuse. The list goes on and on.

Power seems to be all that matters to much of humanity, so much so that they are willing to take their fists to those they profess to love. I have spent months fighting to protect women whose husbands think it is their right to inflict whatever damage on their wives and children they see fit. Some allowed power to so

From: Sgt. Wilkins, Drugs Crime Prevention Officer
To: Social Work Unit
Subject: Possession of Drugs

I would like to remind you that possession of all classes of prohibited drugs is still a crime and should be treated as such when encountered. While custodial sentences are rare, the interrogation of users often provides useful leads. We can often cut a deal with users that allows us to bring in the dealers.

It is your duty as responsible citizens to report suspected and confirmed users to us as soon as you can. To be brutally honest, I think you would do everyone much more good by doing so. I do hope none of you are willfully concealing repeat users from us.

I am aware that you see users as people to be helped and not punished. However, once people become users, they become addicts and criminals quickly. I would much rather you directed your attentions to more deserving cases.

If we don't get to the users, we'll never get to the dealers. That would boost our clean-up rate considerably. So consider whether you are really doing any good by keeping this information from us.

Adrian Wilkins

twist their sexuality that they lust after children and force themselves upon them.

Others abuse their bodies with chemicals, seeking to escape the horror of their reality in altered consciousness. I have seen bodies at the point of collapse, destroyed by the drugs coursing through them and the neglect of basic needs that this causes. At times I could see nothing but the need to die within them, and at those times my true nature, the role I played in the early days of the world, becomes mine again. When it does, I give those souls release.

I cannot help but blame God for the condition of these poor creatures. If there was more evidence of His presence in the world, even some evidence of the work of the angels amongst humanity, maybe these people would not seek to touch the divine through chemicals. They could satisfy those needs in worship, the way they were designed to do. Perhaps there is a meaning for our new existences in this. We can finally achieve the respect and worship we sought so long ago by revealing ourselves to the humans at long last. We can bring focus and devotion into the empty lives that they pursue.

Yet, something within me rebels at this. I cannot tell if it's me, or some lingering taint from Anila that

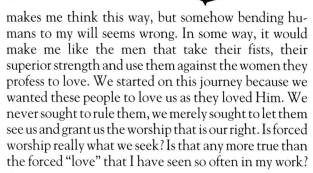

makes me think this way, but somehow bending humans to my will seems wrong. In some way, it would make me like the men that take their fists, their superior strength and use them against the women they profess to love. We started on this journey because we wanted these people to love us as they loved Him. We never sought to rule them, we merely sought to let them see us and grant us the worship that is our right. Is forced worship really what we seek? Is that any more true than the forced "love" that I have seen so often in my work?

The Unworthy

At times I feel like I have stepped off the train journey of my imprisonment and just started to see the world as it truly is. How easy it is to hate when you are isolated from the objects of your contempt by barriers not even the strongest of us could hope to breach. How much harder it is to do so when you see the suffering on the face of the one in front of you.

I find that some people behave in such a way as to make me angry, and then I can hate. So many people are petty, self-interested and so utterly lacking in any sense of the world beyond their own tiny lives that they do not deserve the gift of life any longer. Others, though, have been through so much and suffered at the hands of others that their misery touches that part of me that wanted to ease the suffering of humanity before we rebelled. I thought that part of me was long dead. I was wrong.

There are times when I wonder if we have truly returned to the same world we were banished from so long ago. Could God, even in His anger at our rebellion, really let the world come to this? Did we, a mere third of the Host of Heaven, have the power to bring the world so low? Or have there been forces at work here I don't comprehend? That really wouldn't surprise me. I no longer understand the thing that was once my calling: death.

Death

Death was the curse God laid on humanity for siding with us in our rebellion. Can He really have meant to cause them this much pain? Death stalks humans in so many ways. Take Anila's brush with death. It gets so hard to separate myself from her memories sometimes. Perhaps that's because the pains she suffered in life were offset by the joy she felt in her experiences. The feeling I get when my, sorry, her husband holds me is indescribable in terms of what we experienced in those long millennia isolated from Creation.

I am losing the thread again. I cannot lose myself in Anila's memories, however seductive they may be. Humans still fear death after experiencing it for millennia. A rare few I've met have enough faith to believe that there is life after death, but even they suffer a touch of doubt. I talked for a while to a priest who was working with one of my cases. He had been approached by a troubled child before he called us. This priest, one of those rare few who still truly believed, now found himself troubled with doubt. He looked at the suffering amongst his parishioners and wondered how God could allow it. Five years working in an inner city area had shaken his faith but had yet to break it. He saw death as a blessing sometimes, and he often found more peace in it than in the suffering of those who lived. I agree with him. Sometimes oblivion is better than suffering, and there were certainly times in the Abyss when I wished my existence would end. Yet, I do not entirely share his peace, for I know, without doubt, that life can continue after death. I just do not know what God does with the souls He takes. Are they granted oblivion, or does God have some other fate for them?

Even that seems less certain, though. The mechanism of death is broken. The Reapers are no longer at their posts, and the dead cling to life with a tenacity that amazes me. It is piteous to see a human soul desperately trying to hang on to some vestiges of the life it once had, unable to stray more than a handful of paces from a material thing that has become its link to the world. It was our job once to cleave the piece of the spiritual from the merely physical and allow it to go free, yet those Reapers that did not follow the Morningstar no longer seem to perform that function.

What is left? Restless dead, stoking the fear of death ever higher in the living. Some of these desperate shades have even found the strength of will to climb back into the bodies of the departed in stark defiance of His plan. How can He allow this? Does He no longer care?

Religion

The condition of this place, and the people both living and dead that inhabit it, make me wonder if He even watches over the world anymore. The humans were always His favorite creation, the ones whose concerns He put above our desires. Yet, He seems to have abandoned them, even as they abandoned us.

This land Anila grew up in deems itself Christian — a belief that God came to earth in a human body to understand the pain of the people He created. I find it hard to believe that He, whose anger I have seen, would be capable of making Himself as humble as the stories claim.

Yet, within my mind, this belief seems to battle with the beliefs of Anila's tribe, which dwell thousands of miles away in a place now called Pakistan. These Hindu beliefs her father adheres to seem to portray a multiplicity of gods, all of whom are, in some way, the same god. We demons are in both tales, but neither truly captures the essence of what we are or why we rebelled. When I think about it, the old anger, the hate that filled me in the Pit stirs deep in my heart. They forgot us! They forgot what we fought for and they

slander the names of those who died for humanity, calling us monsters and tempters. That's what we became, but it's not how we started. We did this out of love, yet the stories attribute nothing but hate to us. Truly, God's cruelty knows no bounds.

I find it in some way appropriate that the result of this lack of truth has been a decline in belief. Society seems to value cynicism and materialism more than any form of spiritual exploration. The result of this, and the confusion between the two faiths, was that Anila utterly abandoned faith. When faced with the choice of two religions, she chose neither. Few of her friends showed any real interest in any church or religion. Maybe this is another sign that He has left the world: With no god to worship, faith cannot be sustained.

Certainly the priest I mentioned earlier sometimes despaired of the Church. He would visit other churches when he got the chance and watch the respectable people troop up in their Sunday best, yet he could sense the lack of any belief in them. Church was something they did each Sunday because their neighbors did it and because it was the thing to be seen doing. It was an empty ritual without any meaning.

I watched one of those churches from afar one Sunday. There was enough faith in God within its walls that I could feel the pain of His anger coursing through me the closer I got to the church. I did not dare approach any closer then the other side of the street. The pain was too intense. If I needed any sign that our release is not His doing and that He has yet to forgive us, that was it. The faith in the building was strong, but that of the people that went in was negligible. Faith has gone. Ritual is all that is left.

Come, discover the truth of Christianity
"Boring, irrelevant and untrue?"
A talk by the Rev. James Andrews
Discover the meaning of life
St. Peter's Church
Wednesday, 8 PM

I saw that amongst my own people. They dressed like Hindus, followed the rituals and commemorated the holy days of the faith, but they failed to actually believe. It is as if the worship that God demanded is remembered, but no longer given. They follow the rituals of the past, with the same lack of understanding as children merely imitating their parents before they know the reasons for doing so.

Deluxe, Executive Living

Six modern, beautifully designed apartments for sale.

The ideal apartment for a young businessman, looking to make an impression. Each of the apartments in this former church has been designed by top interiors firm Cityscape. Located in the heart of town, the stained glass windows have been retained to give the apartments a truly unique feel. All finishes make use of the finest woods and luxury carpets. The apartments are sold fully furnished.

*24 hour security and concierge service. * One parking space per apartment.

Book for a viewing today.

Sole agents:

Hartnell, Kaye and McGuire

Viewing by Appointment Only

The Future

Yet I have only touched the surface of this world. It is a new place to me, and I need the memories of someone who understood it to function as part of society. I could exist outside it, but would I truly come to understand this world if I did that? No, there is no way I could survive in this world without using Anila, which means letting Anila be part of me. Or am I part of Anila?

It doesn't matter. I am free of Hell and experiencing Creation in a way I never conceived of before my escape. I understand reality with a depth I never comprehended when flesh was still a mystery to me. And perhaps I see a chance at redemption. I was an angel once. I gave that up to ease humanity's ignorance and fear. Now, I move among them as just another person, and I see that there is more misery than I could ever have conceived. Some of that may be the fault of me and my kind. Some of it may be the work of God. Much of it is, without doubt, the work of humans themselves. I don't understand much of this world yet, but with Anila's memories to guide me, I will learn. And once I've learned enough, then I will act.

The world has changed more in the time since our imprisonment than I would have considered possible. Humans are an inventive people. Technology continues to baffle and amaze me. Telephones are one thing that I'm still not accustomed to. We demons have never needed such toys to communicate, no matter how far apart we were. Computers are slowly becoming clearer, but this Internet is a strange concept. It is a place of thoughts that is accessed not with the mind, but with the eyes and fingers. People have taken ideas and given them layers in a way that I would never have expected. It is as if, in His absence, humanity has taken the mantle of Creation upon themselves.

I must understand this world before I can decide what to do next. I have been free for weeks, yet I am no closer to understanding how I was freed than I was when I first left the Pit. I'm worried that pursuing my mission to free the Princes of Hell would be the wrong thing to do. I remember how I was before I became Anila, how the hate, anger and pain were all that filled me. If creatures like that were unleashed on the world now, with none of Heaven's angels to face them, I shudder to think what would happen to the people of the world. The revenge of the demons would be terrible. I remember how we twisted and tormented the spirits of the dead. How much more would we do to the living?

No, for now I will stay as Anila and live Anila's life. I will bask in the love of her husband and seek to understand the mysteries of the modern world. Anila's job gives me access to so many people, and I can encounter death again and again. Perhaps I will come to understand how it works once more. I may have to kill more humans to study it, but I must make sure that those I kill deserve the death I grant them. Anila's memories demand that of me. I consider it a fair exchange for her life, her body and her love.

Earthbound

We are not alone. The demons that escaped Hell before us, those who disappeared so many ages past, are here among us. I'm setting this down now, as best as I remember it. Anila's mind has not the ability to store memories as well as I could before I took this form. Hopefully this will allow me to retain the details I might otherwise lose.

The visitation was not dramatic. A demon did not come to me wrapped in unearthly flame and bearing a sword of hate. It came to me in a café, just around the corner from work, wearing a bad suit and dirty shoes. Somehow, that was worse. It moved unnoticed through humanity, using its followers and puppets and doing whatever it felt like with them.

I'd felt a strange ache in my skull for hours. Anila would have called it a headache, but that didn't seem right. It felt like — well, it felt like Hell — and I did my best to ignore the feeling. Thinking too much on Hell brings the anger back and clouds my thoughts. I didn't want that to happen.

"Magdiel. How good to see you in person."

The shock ran through my body. It was my Celestial Name, spoken aloud for the first time since I had escaped. The man in front of me was nondescript. Young, with an ill-fitting suit hanging off his lanky frame. The earring and close-cropped hair were the only things that stood out as different about him. He asked me to walk with him a while.

Eventually I asked him if he were a demon like myself.

"Oh, no. I'm human, but I speak for one that was once like you. My body and mind are just something the Master uses to ease communication with you. From others of your kin, I've learned that you sometimes have trouble remembering where you end and where the mortal begins. My Master suffers no such restrictions.

"And he is the source of my power. Remember that," he said, stealing a sideways look at me. He was a puppet — I could see that — but the force behind him, the creature that was pulling his strings, was far more powerful than I, or indeed any of us newly arrived from Hell. I could sense the sheer malignancy of it even through this fragile mortal conduit. I asked what he gained by serving such a master. He had only one answer: power. I asked him what he meant by this, and he seemed to take that as an excuse to show me. He indicated a homeless man who was begging by the side of the street.

"He's going to die. In two minutes, he'll throw himself in front of a car."

"How do you know?" I asked, not sensing the imminence of death around him.

"Because I wish it so."

As the man walked past my visitor, he glanced briefly at the man and whispered something under his breath. I could feel the fabric of reality warp briefly as something *changed*. The man staggered toward the road, a strange expression on his face. I moved to stop him.

"No, Magdiel," the puppet whispered. I stopped. I had no choice. I could feel his master's will beating at me. "Watch and listen," he said

The man stood by the side of the busy road, and then, with an economy of movement that surprised me, threw himself to the ground in front of an oncoming car. Death. The destruction of the body did not bother me. It was just meat, spilling all over the road. I could sense the spirit coming loose, though, the moment it separated from the flesh as the brain was crushed under the tires of the car. And then… nothing. No angel. Just the departure of a soul, and I had no idea where it had gone. I felt the anger growing in me.

"Guilt. Amazing what it will make people do," chuckled my visitor.

"What did you do?" I asked.

"The merest touch of the Master's power. Other humans love it, you know. They yearn to have the cares of the world taken from them. It's so much easier for us to do it when the Master grants us the power.

He's been free for thousands of years and has gained more power than you can believe. This city was not always as it appears."

He gestured dismissively at the grimy streets.

"It takes *work* to make something as bleak as this. He's rather proud of it; sometimes he shows me, filling my eyes with visions. Once, all around us were trees and the river was clean and free-flowing. Invaders from overseas had made their way here, and their strength was more than the primitive people here could withstand.

"One of the defeated natives had a spark of the power in him. He tried to summon spirits of the river to aid him against the invader and to avenge his fallen brothers. In his anger and hate, he summoned the Master instead. His anger made him easy to manipulate. In the end, my Master freed himself from his bonds and the druid became his slave. So did the druid's family, generation after generation, until the present day. Through them, this city became my Master's, more or less. Oh, not in the petty mortal sense of telling people what to do, but in the sense that enough of the people who mattered were focused on him. Soon, my family came to serve him willingly. My father introduced me to his service, as his mother did him. It was the greatest thing he ever did for me. I worship my Master, and he gives me strength.

"Can you imagine it? God tried to imprison him, but he defied God. He escaped and won the worship that is his birthright. His time in Hell only made him a stronger ruler."

The man's laughter disturbed other people on the street, as if they could hear something, but not place where it was coming from. A couple of them looked visibly upset at the confusion. I shushed him, which only caused him to laugh more.

"So human of you, 'Anila.' You are a demon, not some petty mortal. Don't demean yourself by aping their ways."

We walked in silence for a while. Eventually he showed me into a house in a run-down street off the main road. Steps descended into a dark basement, which opened onto a wooden ladder that descended deeper still. These, in their turn, led to a dank tunnel that must have been hundreds of years old, yet was lit with electric lights strung from the dank ceiling. The smell was appalling, leading me to suspect that we were somewhere near the old Victorian sewers. The pressure I felt was growing. It felt like one of us, only a thousand times more powerful and different somehow. Alien. I know what demons and angels feel like, and this was something else — and I was being taken to its lair.

"So, why do you and your kind not rule this city still, then?" I asked, eager to break the silence. "Why have I heard nothing of your master in the weeks since I escaped?"

"You're an astute one, Magdiel. He told us you were." He grunted in disgust. "God may have turned His face from the world, but the weight of His awful influence remains. We did not face a host of angels or a thousand years of war. Just a handful of humans too lost in their worship of Him, too eager to shed blood for His greater glory. They could not harm our Master, so they turned their attentions to us, his followers, instead. They burnt us, tortured us and killed us. They killed our children, they killed our wives, they wiped out entire families, so that they could think themselves holy."

"And what happened then?"

> God is DEAD! God was a LIE!
> Come and find the TRUTH in the old ways!
> Magic is ALIVE and the spirits of the land want YOU to share in it!
> All who are interested in realizing their mystical potential, meet in the park on Friday evenings. Bring a drink, and learn the truth in comfort!
> You are more POWERFUL!! than you imagine!!

TEMPTATION

He looked uncomfortable for a moment, then the mask of confidence dropped quickly back into place. "The few of the Master's followers that remained took his sacred reliquary and hid it from the murderous fires of the Church. And… he slept. He waited. Our ancestors went into hiding as well, passing down the rites of worship from generation to generation, and in return, the Master blessed us with power and prosperity. With no enemy to rally against, it was only a matter of time before the Church lost its vigilance, and ultimately, its faith in an uncaring Heaven. And he was right. You've seen it for yourself. The very fact that you're here, Magdiel, proves it. Now my Master has awakened once more and called his worshippers back to his side."

He led me into a vast chamber that looked as if it had been hewn by hand out of the rock. Like the tunnel, it was lit with electric lights. Many people were working in there. They worked with electrical devices I didn't understand, reading, writing, planning. There was a whole cult down there, all of them touched in some way by the thing that was once one of us.

The puppet indicated that I should sit down. The he sat opposite me and leant forward to look deep into my eyes. "Humanity has lost its way. They scorn the

trappings of religion, but deep in the emptiness of their souls, they yearn for someone to believe in. Someone like *you*, Magdiel. Together with my Master you can make the people of this city believe again, offering their faith and their souls to you, just as you always wanted. Think of it. Your final victory is at hand. You may have thought the rebellion was over when He cast you into the Abyss, but the war rages on. My Master wants you to know that, Magdiel. God has withdrawn from the field. Join us, and all the world will be ours in the end."

For a moment, I was his. I imagined sweeping away the filth of the city above and remaking it in our image, as it was before when the world was new. I imagined a return to justice, burning away the suffering that festered among the people here. I imagined centuries of punishment for the weak and the faithless who had forsaken me.

I imagined my father begging me for forgiveness, crying his misery at the thought that he had rejected me, after he had seen the glory of what I had become. I imagined my husband, bound at my feet, no longer able to leave me, to hurt me, trapped forever in worship.

And within me, some part of me that was both Anila and Magdiel before the fall, rebelled once more. Before their horror, the hate within me receded. I sat silent for a long time, the demon and the angel warring within me. The angel would have lost, but for Anila. She was gone, but I was the inheritor of her strength, her determination and her values. She would not let me lose.

"No."

"I don't think I heard you correctly. Are you refusing my Master's offer?"

"I am. We are not demons, no matter what humanity may believe. We are *angels*. We would not win by enslaving humanity. That was never what we wanted. We wanted to be loved, not worshipped. Your master, it appears, has forgotten this."

For a moment, I thought he was going to strike me. Then his anger gave way to panic. I didn't need to be able to read his mind to know what he was thinking — he'd failed his master. Then a grin split his face. It was not a pleasant thing.

"Poor, deluded creature," he said, but the voice had changed. It echoed with the emptiness of the void, and smoke seethed from the puppet's throat. "You'll learn. And when you do, I'll be waiting."

I ran. I hadn't known fear in a long time, but I felt it then. I found a way out of the tunnel that led into a railway goods yard. One of the railway employees tried to stop me, and I struck him down without a thought, heedless of anything except escaping the thing beneath the earth. It's only now that I realize that I was allowed to escape. He sounded confident that I would return.

What frightens me the most is how tempting the offer truly was.

PUNISHMENT

I saw that face again, the one the demon borrowed, a few days later. It was on the latest missing persons bulletin circulated around the office. I fear that the man in that picture will never be found, at least not in any way his friends would recognize.

DECISIONS

I hoped for time to understand this world before I decided what to do. I'm not sure I have that luxury anymore. There are battle lines being drawn. The demons who disappeared from the Abyss in ages past are here, lurking in the dark places of the earth, and they have become more terrible than any Prince of Hell. They seek to enslave us and shape the world in their image, even as my brethren seek to free the lords of the Abyss and further their own disparate agendas.

I cannot allow this. The world is on the edge of ruin already. Mankind has suffered enough for our sins.

My one hope is that there are others like me, other fallen who have remembered that they were once angels. If I have to take on those loyal to Hell alone, then I will fail. But, if there are others like me who can remember what we once were, then we may have a chance. The angels no longer walk the earth, but demons do. Can a demon be redeemed? Each night, as I return home and lose Magdiel in the mundane pleasures of Anila's warm home, a loving kiss and the small talk of the day, I hope that I may be.

But if redemption is to come, it will be with deeds instead of words. There is time yet to act, while the Princes of Hell are still in their prison and the Earthbound work to gather their strength. I know I'm not alone. There must be others like me, who remember the angels they once were instead of the demon they have become. Together we can make the world right again, whatever the cost.

Let the Earthbound stir in their secret places. Let the lords of the Abyss rise up with their chains of slavery. I will not fear them anymore, nor will any of those who stand with me. I am Magdiel the Slayer, the Taker of Souls. I will change this world.

LOCAL GIRL GOES MISSING.
CULT SUSPECTED.

By staff reporter

Local girl Sandra Donaldson was reported missing by her parents a week ago. She has not been seen since.

Sandra, 17, has become involved in a local religious group claiming to be resurrecting the "old ways" according to flyers found in the girl's bedroom and released to the press by police. Sandra is the third local teenager to vanish in similar circumstances in the last month.

"We have reports of several groups of this nature in operation in and around London," said Detective Inspector Gordon Lawrence at yesterday's press conference. "They appear to be targeting affluent areas and disaffected teenagers, who are still in their rebellious stage."

Several of Sandra's garments have been found torn and bloodied in a local park. Police confirmed that they are treating the disappearance as suspicious.

"Sandra is a quiet girl," said her mother, Elaine Donaldson, 42. "She spent most of her time at home reading, or going to the cinema with friends. It wouldn't be like her to get involved in something like this."

Mrs. Donaldson broke down in tears and had to pause before continuing. "I'd just like to say to whoever's got Sandra that I miss my little girl and I want her back."

Detective Gerhard Liebner hated Berlin's suburbanites, especially the affluent kind. Their neighborhood — their world — was a special place where crime was just a big city problem and everybody knew each other from the coffeehouses or school meetings. When something did shatter suburbia's idyllic myth, people convened in the streets, whispering to their neighbors from their apartment stoops with that falsetto, "Did you hear...?"

Liebner wanted to drift through each and every suburb like a harbinger, shattering their placid reality with glimpses of the great, ancient clockworks moving the cosmos around them. He wanted to show them the vast gulf of the Abyss where time moves like a snail in molasses and screams are as sharp as razors. Tonight, though, he didn't need to. The typically white-collar crimes and bored teenage antics of the suburbs had given way to something of spectacular violence.

Liebner almost relished the horrified looks on the neighborhood's residents gathered across the street or staring out their half-drawn windows. Nobody knew what was happening, they could only imagine what sent uniformed officers scurrying into the front yard to vomit.

A forensics photographer filled the house with bright pops of light, leaving brief, but garish afterimages of blood-splattered walls and black stains on the dark mahogany floor. The two corpses, Mr. and Mrs. List, were exposed to the world in all their brutalized glory. Mr. List was in the living room. The skin had been torn from the poor man's face. His torso was caved in and the vital organs crushed. Something drove its fist through him when he was on the ground... Liebner, noted the impact fractures in the wood paneling that radiated out from under the corpse. He suspected the spine was broken as well.

Mrs. List was in the kitchen. Something had shredded her flesh and ripped large pieces from her arms, throat and thighs. Ruta Seiben, the Criminal Pathologist, was making her observations while Detective Liebner bagged and tagged a kitchen knife covered in blood.

"Well?" Liebner asked, showing her the knife.

Seiben shrugged. "I'll let you know when I hit the lab, but these wounds look awfully... carnivorous."

Liebner grunted... definitely something unnatural. That's when he noticed a uniformed cop trying to get his attention from the head of the stairs leading into the basement. The rookie looked distinctly green, Liebner noticed on approach.

"What is it?" Liebner asked.

"Downstairs," he said.

Liebner followed the uniform down the stairs. The basement rec room had been converted into a bedroom for the List's only son. Posters for bands Liebner had never heard of covered the walls, while old laundry, books on magic and fast-food boxes littered the floor and sofa. The cluttered coffee table was laden with cigarette butts, magazines and discarded tubes of model glue. Carved into the table were words and designs.

"Go upstairs," Liebner said, "and tell Detective Weiner to search the rest of the house. Go!"

The uniformed cop shot upstairs. Alone, Liebner walked up to the table and ran his fingers across a fresh carving dug deep in the wood and filled like a tiny moat with clotted blood. It was an ancient script, older than human memory. The sigils spelled out a name Liebner had hoped never to hear again. *Golgohasht.*

CHAPTER FOUR: LEGIONS OF THE DAMNED

Lo, a shadow of horror is risen
In eternity! Unknown, unprolific,
Self-clos'd, all-repelling: what demon
Hath formed this abominable void,
This soul-shudd'ring vacuum?
—William Blake, *The Book of Urizen*

PYRAMID SCHEMES

"I don't understand… why me?"

I glare at Hannah Klein, hoping to shock her into silence, but I can't help but wonder if I'm making a terrible mistake. I saw the bodies. Golgohasht feasted on them. Can I endanger her like this? "I need your help. You're the only one who knows what I am. Besides," I say, "you're a witch."

"Wiccan… yeah."

"Fine. The point is, you're curious. You've got questions."

"Sure, but I doubt you're going to tell me everything I want to know."

"No," I say, "not everything."

"Then what?"

"I'm going to tell you enough… enough to know what you're getting into. We'll start with what you want to know, then go into what you might not want to hear."

"Great." she says. "Let's start with what has you so worried."

"I've just come from a murder scene in Templehofer Dam. A teenage boy named Jeremy List savagely killed his parents and is currently at large. Except that I don't believe Jeremy committed the crime. I think he's been possessed by a demon known as Golgohasht. If so, every soul in this city, demon or mortal, is in terrible danger."

Hannah frowns. "What makes this Golgohasht any worse than, say…"

"Me, for example? Because he was a monster long before he was hurled into the Abyss. He not only exults in bloodshed and pain, he feasts on the souls of those he destroys. He cannibalizes them for their power and their memories. If I don't find him and destroy his host body soon, he will hunt and feed until there is no force on earth powerful enough to stop him."

THE POSSESSION

"All right. Next question: What's a host body?" Hannah asks.

"We assume mortal form by possessing people, borrowing their memories and mannerisms. It helps us acclimate to this world and restores us to our senses. Generally we seek out the bodies of the weak-willed or those whose spirits have been broken."

"You're in the body of a weak-willed cop?"

"Better to say Liebner's will was crushed from too many years of witnessing violence and corruption. It left a hole in his mind and soul that I could slip into. I'll get to that more in a moment."

"Fine," she says. "You said their memories restore you to your senses. How?"

"An unexpected side-effect to possession is becoming too deeply rooted in someone else's memories. Particularly strong memories exist as emotional imperatives, reminding us of events in terms of how they felt. If the person endured a life-altering emotion, like lost love, extreme disappointment or bitter anger, it strikes a sympathetic chord in us. If that someone also bears an untouchable spark of nobility, one that can't be suppressed, it affects us. We recognize the emotion and nobility because we first felt it aeons ago when God turned His back on us. For the first time in ages, we associate with something outside our own misery, and it reminds us of the beings we once were."

"Okay," she says, "then what's the problem with, er…"

"Golgohasht. The problem is, this… restoration is more an exception than the rule. The emotions and strength of character must be strong enough to stir us from our millennia of torment."

"Is that what happened to you?" she asks.

"I…" I stop. The question catches me off guard and I'm overwhelmed. My salvation came at someone else's expense. How do you express that in easy terms? I shift the focus back to Jeremy. "The boy's memories only provide Golgohasht with instructions on how this new world works, but nothing about Jeremy says he's anything more than a self-indulgent brat."

"Why?"

I smile. "Gerhard had a lot of experience with people like Jeremy. The boy was a drug user who sniffed glue and paint-thinners. His parents tried helping him, but they broke before he did. They eventually washed their hands of him and left him to his own self-destruction. That's how Golgohasht found his way in."

FRESH MEAT

"So you possess living people who've lost their souls?"

"Metaphorically speaking, yes. We are drawn to people whose spirits have been eroded by despair,

anger, addiction — mortals who have lost the essential spark of humanity that sets them apart from every other living thing. When we find such a person, we force our way into their bodies, driving them out to face oblivion or burying them deep in the dark recesses of their own minds, helpless to interfere."

"Is that what happened with Jeremy?"

"It's possible Jeremy's addiction withered his soul, but it's only conjecture at this point," I say. "If Jeremy did OD, then it's likely his last act was pure self-indulgence; wanton hedonism with no concerns except for his high. He probably had virtually no regrets about feeding his addiction regardless of the physical and mental cost, leaving no traces of humanity to check Golgohasht's madness and hate."

"That's quite an assumption," Hannah says.

"Well, the second option is that Jeremy's OD was suicide."

"In which case his life was nothing but regrets," Hannah says, "and Golgohasht might have been brought to his senses."

I shake my head. "You didn't see the crime scene. If Golgohasht was feeling any regret, it was because there weren't enough victims to sate his appetite."

"Are there any other possibilities?" she asks.

THE SOULLESS

"Well," I say, "there's always brain death. Jeremy, for instance, slowly eroded his faculty of reason and destroyed his brain. In essence, he deprived himself of free will and conscious effort. Other people might be victims of happenstance who become vegetables thanks to a blow to the head or spinal cord—"

"—or disease that shuts their brain down, like bacterial meningitis?" Hannah says. "You can't tell me these people don't have souls anymore."

"Sorry. The cruel truth is that by this point, the soul is still tethered to the body, but only by a spider's thread. When the brain is so far gone that it needs someone else to survive, we simply move in, snapping the soul's last anchor with no conscious effort."

"You're kidding," she says aghast.

"Think about it," I say. "You're trapped in a prison of flesh that won't die for weeks… even years. The soul wants to vacate and for all intents and purposes, it's already gone. Possession, in this case, is only a formality. It's a changing of the guard."

I watch Hannah's face darken as she roots about the pile of books on her desk in search of a cigarette. It makes me wonder if she might have lost someone she loved to a coma or disease.

"Another possibility is the simple erosion of human identity," I say, trying to move the subject along.

"Call it the ego, or the will to live — people can lose their grip on life from years of terrible stress, emotional problems, or in Jeremy's case, drug use." I tap my chest. "Look at me. Gerhard was only twenty-nine when he succumbed, his idealism crushed by corruption and double-dealing in the *Polizei* and the pointlessness of police work. He became a hard drinker and fell into a deep depression. Ultimately it all ground him down until there was little of his soul left. In a sense, he was little better than a walking corpse, and there are all too many others like him out there on the streets."

The Insane

"What about the mentally ill?" Hannah says.

I nod. "Mental instabilities like severe autism render the host incapable of truly exerting their free will, making them vulnerable."

"But what about their souls? Are they also… weakly tethered?"

"Not so much weakly tethered as simply unable to assert their will in opposition to ours. As to what happens to them… honestly it depends. Some are forced out of their body, to whatever fate awaits them, while others, I suspect, are driven deep into the recesses of their brains, helpless to interfere with the demon's wishes. So, yes, we possess the insane. We find them in *Gropiusstadt* alleyways, with so many track-lines that their veins have collapsed and left long clefts up their arm. We find them in the deepest, darkest rooms of *Invalidenhaus* or in the rest homes for the elderly, which are some times far worse than any asylum. When it comes down to it," I admit, "we are demons, most times even after we find a host."

"You keep mentioning free will." Hannah asks, a flash of insight illuminating her face. "What if Jeremy *let* Golgohasht in?"

Free Will

"Damn it!" I say. She hit on something I hadn't seriously considered before. "We found some occult books in Jeremy's library, but I put it all down to teenage fantasies."

"What books did he have?"

I riffle through my pocket notepad. "Let's see… he had the *Necronomicon*…"

"Crap," she says dismissively.

"…*The Goetia*…"

"Some useful stuff, but not enough," she says.

"…*The Book of the Golden Dawn*…"

"Maybe."

"…*Summoning Spirits*…"

"That's it," she says.

"You're kidding?" I say. "I flipped through it, but it's nothing but a traffic jam of Enochian, Kabalistic and Goetian principles. Sure, it had some gems, but there were too many damn holes."

"There are with most books, but many pagans use the Internet these days to fill in those gaps."

"Someone's posting summoning rituals on the Internet?"

"It's the Internet. What do you think?" Hannah says.

"But I didn't find any occult paraphernalia. No candles, no altar…"

"When I conduct a ritual, I rely on a circle for support. The altar could be at someone else's house."

I grab Hannah by the wrist and drag her out the door behind me.

"I assumed Jeremy wasn't bright enough to invite Golgohasht in," I say, "but if someone spoon-fed him the information deliberately, then it's possible Jeremy could have made himself a willing vessel, and Golgohasht would be much stronger in the bargain. That's the advantage to voluntary possession. It allows a demon to acclimate quicker and grow into its abilities faster. The drawback to voluntary possessions, from a demon's standpoint, is that most mortals do so in exchange for considerations or a pact. If Jeremy drew a pact with Golgohasht—"

"Then you'll need to know what those terms were," Hannah says.

"Exactly," I say in a mad scramble down the stairs to the car.

"So?" Hannah asks. "Where to?"

The Trail of Faith

"First I've got to talk to Jeremy's friends."

"Why?" Hannah asks.

"Golgohasht sees the world through Jeremy's eyes. The bonds Jeremy had with his friends are ones that the demon can now exploit to gain the faith he needs to survive." I look sidelong at Hannah. "Just like I need you."

"There are plenty of people who believe in demons," Hannah says.

"I'm not talking about belief. I'm talking about *faith*. It's a tangible quality to us, invisible but ever present, like the air we now breathe. It's the fuel that feeds our souls. Without it, we're powerless."

"Faith is not knowing," Hannah says.

"Forget all that philosophical crap. Faith is about closing your eyes and leaping into the void because you *know* that someone will be there to catch you. It's about believing in the unseen, about surrendering a part of yourself to an idea or a dream, and in so doing making that dream real. In today's society, that kind of generosity of spirit is difficult to come by, and is better nurtured over time than ripped from a person's soul."

"So what does this have to do with Jeremy's friends?"

"Golgohasht will likely go after people Jeremy knows. Think about it. You're new to the world and your only anchor is what your host knows. Are you going to approach people who already know and trust you or try to build a bond with a total stranger?"

"Makes sense," Hannah says. "So who do we start with?"

I hand her my cell phone. "You dial. I'll give you the number."

REAPING FAITH

Hannah and I walk through the white halls of *Siedlung Neutempelhof* Children's Ward, past open doors and crying children. Michael Havis's father waits outside the door of his son's room. Jeremy had visited Michael shortly after the murders.

"How is he?" I ask, shaking his hand.

"Still weak. Doctors say it was a mild stroke."

"What happened?"

"Like I said over the phone, Jeremy slipped into my son's room, and they had a conversation."

"About what?"

"I don't know. It was muffled. My wife dialed 110, and I burst in the room to catch him. Only—"

"Only what?"

"Michael was having convulsions and Jeremy was halfway out the window with a fucking grin on his face and a bloody nose. I ran to Michael…"

"I understand, Mr. Havis. We'd like to speak to Michael alone, if that's all right."

"Why?"

"He'll be more likely to open up if he isn't worried about saying the wrong thing in front of his father."

"Michael's a good boy."

"Of course. He's not in any trouble. But you know how kids are." Mr. Havis finally nods. Hannah and I enter the dark room alone.

Michael is a heavyset, black-haired boy in his mid-teens. His eyes are dull, and his heart monitor beeps in sluggish tempo. Doctors say it was a stroke. I know better.

"Golgohasht manifested in front of Michael, and it was ugly," I whisper to Hannah. "Our torment does that. We may have been beautiful before the Fall, but the millennia of anguish have made our visage monstrous. If we wish, we can temporarily transform our host body into a reflection of what we once were."

"So what happened?" Hannah asks.

"Golgohasht dropped the façade that is Jeremy List and manifested his true, terrible glory. Imagine how Michael must have felt, facing a beast from the Pit, knowing in that one instant that God and demons are all too real. In one terrible moment, his life became a collection of past sins and transgressions. And he was afraid."

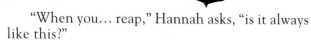

"When you… reap," Hannah asks, "is it always like this?"

"Reaping isn't all pain and suffering… though in Golgohasht's case it probably is. It can be kind, like manifesting to a crying child and letting her know her dead mother is in Heaven now and loves her very much. Reaping is all about what will make them believe in the glory of the unseen. Most demons rely on primitive emotions like terror or pain. Others, like myself, go for the hope and comfort, because everything we do leaves a mark on our souls as well. By doing some good in this world, we break the cycle of pain in ourselves. We slowly revert back to the angels we once were rather than turning back to the old ways of madness and hate.

"I feel sorry for Michael," I say. "Golgohasht put him through all this pain and suffering for the equivalent of spare change. Reaping faith from people only gives an immediate benefit. The faith doesn't come from conviction, but from fear or awe, which fades with time and is ultimately wasteful. You can only reap faith from a person so often before they become jaded. That's why nurturing faith through a pact is so much more effective. It's more of an investment, and the return isn't as quick, but it nets a steady flow of faith that we can count on from day to day."

Hannah considers this, but then she shakes her head. "There's a problem here."

"What?"

"If Golgohasht went to Michael to reap faith from him, why stop there? Why not go after his parents too?" She considers the sleeping boy. "Does a pact have to be voluntary?"

"Yes," I say slowly, looking at my thrall with a mixture of respect and wariness. "But like any agreement, it can be made under duress."

I step to the bedside. "Michael," I say, whispering gently to the boy. His eyes flutter slightly. I know I won't get much out of him, but I figure he's not the only one involved. Maybe he can direct me to someone else.

"Michael," I whisper, "who else has a pact with Jeremy?" I put my hand on his chest, easing the pain and rising panic. He doesn't need an actual stroke. Michael stares at me, and I smile.

"I can save you from the pact, Michael," I say, "but I've got to stop Jeremy before he does this to someone else. Who else had a pact with him?"

The boy's eyes widen in horror. He whispers, "Rickie Metzger," more to himself than me.

PACTS

I leave my cell phone number at Jeremy's school and a message for Richard Metzger to call me.

We sit in my car, waiting for Richard's call, and in the meantime, I explain a little about pacts. Hannah will need to know everything if she's going to help.

"At their simplest, pacts are contracts binding us for a service in exchange for someone's faith."

"I always thought it involved parchments drawn up in blood or sealed in wax?"

"Quaint, but no. Our pacts are a verbal agreement made voluntarily between us and a mortal. We offer a service, like limited wish fulfillment, and in exchange, you open a conduit through which we draw upon your spiritual strength. In fact, the conduit transcends space. It'll exist no matter the distance between us.

"That's why pacts are so important to us. It means a person's conviction in our power is strong enough that they're willing to surrender a portion of themselves to get what they want. Actually, offering someone your hope is easy enough. Damn psychic hotlines and quick-fad diets are popular because they give people what they want to hear — easy solutions without any hard work. The only difficult part is getting them to open up and admit they want something in the first place."

"Sounds like it should be easy, then," Hannah says.

"Pacts are complicated, because it means seducing people with partial truths. That's the real trick behind it. Most demons dupe mortals into believing in them without scaring them away or revealing too much about themselves. If the mortal has any hesitations, *any*, that'll break the pact if we haven't fulfilled their wish. Once you complete your end of the bargain, though, we're bound together."

"Is that what you did with me?"

"No. I never lied or hid any truths from you. Doesn't our pact stipulate that I can never hurt you?"

Hannah nods, but now there's a hint of suspicion in her eyes. A calculated risk, but one I'm willing to take.

"You're fortunate. Some demons manifest flagrantly so there's no doubt as to what they are. It's like putting all their cards on the table, only instead of terrifying their victim, they use their power to help the mortal in some small way. Maybe free them from debt, send their brother's cancer into deep remission or temporarily kill the cravings for drugs and booze. After that, they let you come back when you're ready. Drug dealers pull the same crap to get people hooked. Give them a taste of opportunity and hope, and they'll do the rest. That's free will working in their favor."

"What about our pact?" Hannah asks.

"Ours takes longer, but it builds an important level of trust. It's about discussing your intent with someone who needs your help. See, no matter how skilled we are at manipulating people, they'll eventually figure us out the same way I'm unraveling Golgohasht. Manifesting

your power and offering a free ride is manipulating someone. People know when they've been swindled, and the last thing you need is to enter a pact with someone who's now out to get you."

FRIENDS AND NEIGHBORS

My cell rings and we both jump.

"Detective Liebner speaking."

"Um, hi. It's Rickie," a nervous voice says.

"Hello, Richard. Can you talk freely?"

"Yeah, I'm on a friend's cell."

"Richard, you're not in trouble," I say. "I just want to help you."

"Okay."

"I need information about Golgohasht."

A long silence stretches across the line before Richard whispers, "How do you know about him?"

"Don't worry," I say. "I deal with this kind of stuff."

"You do?" he says, scared.

"Believe it or not, I help people like you all the time."

"How?"

"By stopping creatures like Golgohasht. I can't do that though unless I know more about what happened."

"Will it make the voices go away?" he asks, almost sobbing.

"I'm not sure, Richard, but it'll stop them from becoming stronger."

The next few minutes turns into a rambling confession, but it's pretty much what I expected. Still, hearing it from Richard gives me a stronger picture of Golgohasht and what I need to do. I take notes before finally hanging up the phone.

"Seems Jeremy and his friends were dabbling in magic. Richard said they found the material on something called a floating domain — a secret website with a constantly changing address. It supposedly contained rituals to summon and bind their own demonic slave. Certainly these kids didn't have the experience or knowledge to perform a true summoning, but the ritual was enough to catch Golgohasht's attention. I suppose he'd escaped like the rest of us and had only just found his way across the Veil. Richard said they could feel a presence enter the room, and on a whim Jeremy offered his body to the demon."

"What happened then?" Hannah asks.

"Richard and his friends ran, but Jeremy visited each of them, forcing them into pacts for foolish things like better looks or stronger bodies. He had to give them something in exchange for their faith to seal the bargain. Fulfilling a wish made sure Golgohasht and the children were linked together until the demon decided otherwise. Since then, he's been siphoning them, torturing them by breaking their morale and inflicting stigmata — what I call pact wounds."

"You can hurt us?" Hannah asks. I can see the fright in her eyes.

"I promised not to hurt you, remember? If I hadn't, I could take enough faith to break your will, then start robbing faith at the expense of your health and sanity."

"But I'm safe?"

"On my very Name," I say, gently putting my hand over hers. "But Golgohasht has no such scruples." I start the car and pull into *Gneisenau Strasse*. "He'll keep drawing enough faith from them forcefully to sap their will, and he's damaging their minds in the process. Richard is hearing voices because Golgohasht already sapped his will once."

"What? How's that possible?"

"Sapping a thrall's will is a good way to drive them nuts and dry their reservoir of conviction. If Golgohasht keeps doing this, he'll have virtual zombies who couldn't provide enough faith to light a candle. That's why most of us enter pacts and watch over our thralls with care. It's no small investment in time or energy, but it pays off in the long run."

"Can't these kids turn on Golgohasht?"

"Of course. A thrall can betray us at any point and reveal our secrets if they knew any. In fact, every little secret we let slip divulges a vital clue about our potential weaknesses. That's why most fallen are very careful with whom they confide in. It has to be someone they trust not to turn on them later. Forcing pacts on people and abusing them later only makes us vulnerable in the long run. We have to be subtle."

"Maybe Golgohasht has another plan in mind?" Hannah says.

"Nearly every demon first targets their host's circle of friends and family. They're the ones we know the best and who trust us the most. Besides, people tend to seek out others who share in their beliefs and interests. There's a fair chance that whatever our mortal host once desired is also shared by his friends. A body-builder looking to build the perfect physique will likely have gym friends he sees every day. A gambler hoping for the big score knows the local gambling halls. A pedophile stalking children will likely share stories with his Internet associates. We all have one acquaintance who we share stories with because we want friends who can relate to our interests. After that, it's easy enough to approach them and use evidence of personal success to draw them in. When you're suddenly pressing double your weights at the gym, people will ask how you did it. When you hit a winning streak with the local bookies, people want to know your secret."

"Are we that easy to ensnare?"

I shrug. "People are always looking for a free ride. Think about it. Somebody loses 50 kilos and everybody asks how they did it. They're not stupid — they know it was through dieting — but what they hope to hear is, 'It was the easiest thing I ever did! It's a new diet plan that burns calories while watching TV and eating cake.' That's what people want, and that's what we offer."

"I suppose the trick, then, is getting folks to believe in you."

"Exactly! That's when the game of subtlety comes in. Most demons fail their first attempts at forging a pact because they figure they can just reveal their true selves and remove any trace of doubt. What tends to happen, however, is that the mortal can't handle what he's seeing. He just runs away and rationalizes the event later."

"Then how do you do it?"

"In small steps," I say. "You figure out what the mortal needs, and the more you appear to hold the answer to their problems, the sooner they will come to you for help. Most demons reveal themselves at this point, when the mortal asks for help, but even then it's still risky. Just because someone asks a question doesn't mean they're ready for the answers. Some demons stage an event that reveals their power indirectly, supposedly with the demon none the wiser that an audience is watching. It gives the illusion that the mortal knows something the demon doesn't, which gives him a false sense of security when he approaches the fallen on his terms."

"And that's how you lured me in?"

"No. A few fallen, myself included, are not interested in head games. I figure actions speak louder than words, and I do my best to counsel those who approach me and help them think their way out of their situation if they can. If not, then we come to a mutually beneficial arrangement. It takes more effort on my part, but it's better than indulging in baser forms of manipulation. In the end, that nets me just as much of what I need."

FACES IN THE CROWD

"So am I an exception?" Hannah asks. "Do most demons only target acquaintances and families?"

"Again, our mortal hosts dictate who we encounter in life through old habits, hobbies and jobs. Most fallen stick to their host's former routines as much as possible because they're familiar and they reassure us. It also gives us contacts into the mortal world beyond friends and families. As a *Kripo* Detective, for example, I know cops in several stations, I have street contacts, and I question suspects and witnesses on a daily basis. Through this network, I hear gossip about who needs what and why. I can take my time investigating the person and determining everything I need to know about them before approaching them.

"See, everyone's job gives us some contact with people and a small degree of control, but the best roles in life are those where people in need come to us for help. It can be a banker with access to someone's financial records, a bartender who listens to people's problems or a factory worker whose only pastime on the assembly line is listening to daily gossip. It might be illegal work, like a drug dealer who knows the local junkies, a prostitute with a list of kinky clients, a bookie, a skinhead… anything. Life is all about contacts and getting to know people. We fallen capitalize on those contacts and figure out who needs something the most. After that, it's all a matter of convincing them we have something to offer.

"Some demons even do volunteer work, because it means dealing with people who are in need. Soup kitchens and the different hotlines — suicide, runaway, battered women, abuse, STDs — brings scores of needy people to us. And most often, these people are so desperate for help or companionship that they'll take it from whomever offers it. Giving these people hope is easy enough, especially since their needs are so obvious."

FAITH'S LITTLE TOYS

"So what do you get out of these offerings?" Hannah asks.

"Power," I say simply. "Faith does have the strength to move mountains, if you know what to do with it. I've got the knowledge, and you, Hannah dear, give me the fuel to work wonders."

"Such as?" Hannah asks with a wide, inquisitive grin.

"Well, healing for one," I say, counting off some of our abilities. "If I have a ready store of faith, I can repair nearly any wound I suffer. Further, while I still need to eat and rest like any other mortal, I don't suffer from illness or disease. This body still ages — that horrible curse is beyond even our power to overcome — but I can keep it strong and vital until the very end.

"Then there are physical enhancements," I say. "To kill Jeremy's parents, Golgohasht probably drove Jeremy's body to superhuman lengths. His physical enhancements are all reflections of his demonic self. He used faith to manifest his true form for a few minutes by 'overlaying' portions of himself on his mortal form. Actually, the human body can accomplish that easily because flesh is already a supple receptacle for faith. It's the reason why mortals can undergo psychic surgery, walk across burning coals or manifest stigmata. The body is a conduit of faith. It doesn't require as much effort, then, for demons to take that to the next level and alter themselves physically, like Golgohasht did.

There were deep claw marks on the bodies of Jeremy's parents, and the demon exhibited enormous strength to inflict some of the more terrible wounds. I also assume he fled the scene with supernatural speed."

"What else?" Hannah asks.

"Supernatural allure — allowing our celestial nature to slip past our skin. It's a reflection of our true form and our current state of grace. Golgohasht used it on Michael and Richard, but it wasn't necessary. Golgohasht didn't have to be there to take the faith — the pact's strong enough that he could have been anywhere in the world. I suspect he probably enjoys the rush of seeing people cower before his might. Now wait here."

"Why?" Hannah asks, then realizes we've pulled up in front of a strip club. "Never mind. I don't want to know."

States of Grace

Ingrid Deitz is a Lammasu, and she enjoys making it difficult to concentrate as we talk.

"Is this going to be business or pleasure?" she says, straddling my hips.

"Golgohasht is here. In the flesh."

"And why does this concern me?" she says, thrusting her milky-white breasts in my face.

"I need you to help me find him."

"You're the cop, Ahrimal," she purrs, running her hands across my chest. "That sort of thing's not in my line of work."

"Like hell," I say, batting away her hand as she tries undoing my tie. "I have information to trade."

She stops gyrating and looks me square in the eye. Her mortal side's telling her never to trust a cop offering a deal, and it's right.

"What information?" she asks.

"The *Polizei* are going to raid this place in the near future, looking for drugs. It could be tomorrow, or it could be next week. You want the details?"

Ingrid stands up with a huff and sits down next to me. "Shit. Make this quick," she says, suddenly all business. "What is it you're after?"

The Origins of Torment

"You served in the same legion as Golgohasht during the war. What made him snap?" I ask.

It's a simple enough question. When the war began, we were all idealistic and determined to convince God of the righteousness of our cause. But for a thousand long years we never once faced Him directly. We fought the Host of Heaven, our former brothers and sisters, and each blow we struck, each time the earth shook or the heavens were rent with fire, we felt that

pain in our own souls. I still can't look up at the scarred face of the moon without feeling hollow inside.

"Snap?" Ingrid says with a humorless laugh. "Who says he snapped?"

We couldn't understand why God and the angels still loyal to Him continued fighting us. Surely they could see we were right? Surely they weren't blind? Confusion and fear turned into frustration and anger. The more the others resisted, the more we were determined to show them the error of their ways. That was our first brush with emotions God never intended for us. This building rage and hostility affected us physically because we weren't meant to handle it. It was like a cancer deep in our breasts, a malignant tumor that only grew with time.

"But, the angels he consumed…?"

The growing hostility frightened us, but it also felt comfortable. The tides of war were turning against us. We'd become jaded, even bitter. After a while, we only had our anger to sustain us. So we allowed that tumor to grow.

"Golgohasht was always good at following orders, Ahrimal, no matter the cost."

"Someone *ordered* him to eat the souls of his fellow angels?"

"The war was turning against us," Ingrid says. "Our bitterness and anger were pushing the mortals away, costing us precious faith. So someone seized on the idea of stealing power from our foes by consuming their souls."

We were tainted before the Abyss, and our desperation only made things worse. When God threw us into that black gulf, we'd lost the war, and we'd lost the trust of the mortals we were trying to protect. Anger and fear ran rampant, as did the accusations. Without Lucifer, we were blaming everyone in sight for our downfall. That little seed of hate, our private anguish, blossomed like a bruised weed and fed our paranoia and suspicions. It lulled us into forgetting who we were and why we were there.

Schemes of the Soul

"Shit," I say. "That means Golgohasht's still taking orders. Who's he serving?"

"Oh, no," Ingrid says with a smile. "You've used up your credit, Ahrimal. You want more, it will cost you."

When we fled the Abyss and came here, our anger was a million times stronger then when God locked us away. Most of us thought we'd come here and wreak havoc on mankind for forgetting us and we'd piss on God's earth in the bargain. We didn't realize that our mortal hosts could act like a dam against our anger. For a fortunate few like Ingrid and myself, our hosts possessed qualities of compassion, courage and selflessness that gave us pause. We stopped and took stock of where we'd come from and what we'd done up to now.

"Look, Ingrid," I say, "I'll owe you for this."

"Owe me? Is that the best you can do? If so, let me show you the door."

In my case, Gerhard wanted to make a difference as a cop, but the world got the better of him. With other fallen, it's lost love, failed ambitions, forgotten hopes or simply a life undeservingly cut short that stirs them to pity. I'm not sure why, but these memories force us to think beyond ourselves for a moment, and it's enough to pull us from our fugue.

"All right," I say. "I can make your problems with the *Polizei* go away, if what you've got to say is worth the trouble."

"Oh, it is," she says. "Ever hear of a pyramid scheme?"

This sort of salvation doesn't work for everyone, but I'm grateful I'm one of them. Thanks to Gerhard's memories acting like a sieve, I managed to quash my anger. That's a good thing, because demonic anguish perpetuates itself by hurting others. In fact, the more torment you build up within yourself, the more you want to hurt and punish others. The less you have, the likelier you'll help others and play the positive influence. Unfortunately, it's far easier to inflict pain and suffering then it is to inspire and offer hope.

"What's that got to do with Golgohasht?"

"Well, I'll admit it's not the same thing as sending a chain letter," she says. "But there's a group of Raveners who've come up with a pyramid scheme of sorts, and Golgohasht is working for them."

Our torment affects us in many ways, from how we appear to how we act. Misery begets misery because the more torment we possess, the more our pacts and evocations reflect it. Our pacts appeal more to people's dark or negative side. They reward vice and purely material desires, turning our thralls into villainous caricatures. Corruption loves contributing to moral failure and degradation, and many pacts born from tormented demons reflect this philosophy. Our powers are also harmful, not through conscious effort, but because that's the energy we put out; strength to hurt people, knowledge to drive someone mad, inflicting pain instead of healing or pleasuring, and frightening victims over giving them hope. Even more obvious, our appearance is twisted and demonic because we look the way we feel. We are reflections of our bitterness and rejection. We are the manifested elements of searing heat and bone-shattering cold. More so, we are mirrors of everything we've seen and felt for the last millennia — thousands of years worth of misery and brutality rolled up into one terrifying form.

"What are they doing?" I ask, knowing it can't be good.

"It's simple when you think about it. A Ravener comes to earth and starts forcing victims into destructive pacts. He drains them without mercy until they're all so twisted and debased—"

"Oh, shit."

"—that they become prime candidates for the next wave of Raveners to possess, who then go on to form their own pacts."

"I've been looking at this all wrong. Lucifer preserve us. Ingrid, I've got to go."

"Wait." Ingrid pulls me close and whispers in my ear. She mutters two quick, ancient syllables that leave me breathless. "*Now* you owe me," she says, and I know I'll be a long time repaying her.

Hope turns everything around. If a demon can free himself from the cycle of anger and hatred and somehow help people, then that hope shines through in his actions and appearance. Naturally, it isn't that simple, but every bit of good builds momentum for the next action, making it that much easier to help more people. Soon, our powers reflect our state and do more good than harm. We can touch someone and heal them because we don't have to beget misery to make ourselves feel better. We can offer hope instead of pain because we know the difference between the two now. Even our anima regains some of its former glory. Slowly, the twisted imperfections fade away, and we see hints of someone we forgot about millennia ago. It's a strange feeling, like seeing pictures of yourself when you were a hundred kilos lighter and happier in life. Everything you do, and are, feeds off that sense of wellbeing. The anger is still there, waiting for you to slip through acts of cruelty or belligerence, but it's not your sole companion anymore.

Tricks of the Beast

"So he's trying to drive those kids insane, so his friends can posses their bodies?" Hannah asks.

I nod. "Unless I can stop him."

Exorcisms

"How? Find a priest and exorcise him?" she says.

I think she's kidding at first, until I get a good look at her face. "It's not like the movies, Hannah," I say. "Just saying some prayers and shaking a Bible in our face isn't nearly enough. To be honest, you don't really need holy offices to drive out a demon. If you can trap the demon in one place and best it with willpower and faith, you can drive him out. Which, by the way, is a great deal harder than it sounds."

"What about sanctified ground," Hannah asks, "or throwing holy water in his face?"

"Earth or water is only as powerful as the faith mortals place in it. How many people still go to church anymore and actually give of themselves to the worship of God? A thousand years ago, I would have agreed with you, but these days finding true holy ground or a source of blessed water is, sadly, very rare. No," I say, "no horror movie plot is going to nail Golgohasht. I have something in mind, and as you said before — you're my safety net."

I hand her paper covered with a diagram and lines of careful script.

"I know that's not how you'd normally do the summoning," I say, "but that's the one sure way of summoning me back from the Abyss in case Golgohasht kills me. I needed you to understand who, and what I was before giving you the ritual. That way, you'll have a better chance at calling me back."

Hannah smiles sadly. "I see. Okay, how does this work?"

SUMMONING

I'm taking a risk with Hannah, but I trust her to bring me back. The summoning ritual has just enough accuracy to rescue me. There's also enough wrong information to prevent a binding ritual from turning me into her slave. I'm pretty sure Hannah won't betray me, but I can't trust anyone enough to reveal our greatest weaknesses.

"The summoning ritual," I say, "is a typical spell among the thousands already out there. Everyone uses their own methods, from you Wiccans who invite the spirits in, to pagans who use *The Goetia*, to Kabala numerologists, to Loa horses… it's not a matter of truth. It doesn't mean shit. What matters in a ritual is the intent and the will of the summoner.

"Everything in the universe has a harmonic resonance, a vibrational key to which it responds. Ever see the pictures of the suspension bridge twisting in the wind? The bridge may be made of steel, but the wind hits the right resonance and the whole thing turns to taffy. Same principle with summoning rituals."

"How?" Hannah asks.

"The ritual itself is a focusing lens that targets a specific being or group of beings. Burning incense, making a circle, chanting out loud… all those help aim the user's will to reach out and snag the demon in question, and it provides us with a safe zone in which to manifest."

"Safe zone?"

"Very important. The fallen are bound to the Abyss, which means that once we're outside a vessel, like a mortal host or object, the Pit tries to pull us back in. The ritual circle, though, is a buffer zone, a safe area where the Abyss has no hold on us and we can interact with the summoner at her leisure.

"Real summoning rituals are rare because it takes time and effort to figure out who you want to find. It's like trying to find a random Hannah on the phone by dialing without the benefit of a phone book or operator. Rituals require intensive research to figure out the right protocol to establish contact. Some casters rely on light investigative work, targeting an entire infernal House in a kind of shotgun approach. Fire into a flock and I'm bound to hit something, right? This is also the best way to land in trouble. If you aren't picky about who shows up, you might receive the worst apple in the barrel… or the most poisonous."

"Okay," she says, "I get that."

"Most often, though, casters who target an entire House do so because they don't have enough information to pick a specific target. They lack a name.

"Real conjurers put the extra time to find a demon's Celestial Name. That way, they generally know what they're getting into. See, names are crucial to a ritual, which places rituals in two major categories and too many smaller ones to even think about. The first category is the broadest because it targets entire Houses. The second type of ritual uses a demon's title. This is the conjuring name, because it's also the one most summoners use when going after a specific demon."

Hannah nods. I feel guilty for not revealing the third type of ritual, but I can't. The third ritual is usually the domain of serious occultists who did enough research over the decades to uncover our True Names. True Names are the exact vibrational sequence of our entire being. It's our resonance, our frequency. Tapping it means the summoner has direct access into our psyche and can make us dance like puppets. The summoner can bind us into servitude.

The Last Great Secret

Hannah's back at home and I'm on the rooftop of the *Siedlung Neutempelhof* apartment buildings outside Michael's hospital. I figure he's in the greatest danger right now since he's closest to death. I could be wrong, but if Golgohasht needs allies fast, Michael's the pick of the litter. If Golgohasht shows up, I'm ready for him. You could say I've got his number, or at least part of it.

Everything he's done so far has left behind clues that only we fallen can register. Each clue is a vibrational fingerprint, one consonant out of numerous segments constituting Golgohasht's True Name. In simplest terms, every action betrays our nature and state of being. Most people see personality traits, but we are more sensitive to the frequencies comprising one another. In this regard, True Name is a misnomer because it implies a title. It isn't. It's literally who we are. Our True Name is a set of words that match the vibrations resonating through our

forms. Verbalizing the name sets off a series of psychic tumblers that opens us up like a vault. That means to learn someone's True Name, you must understand them first, and that means learning everything you can about them. Anything they handle, deal with, talk to or focus their powers on leaves behind some insight into their very being. Manifestations of power and violence leaves a vibrational echo in the air that sings with a part of their name. That's the main reason we demons must be careful. Our every action betrays our nature and potential weakness. Fortunately, Golgohasht wasn't expecting the attentions of one of the fallen, so he became careless. He left behind a veritable trail of useful clues. The way he killed the Lists left strong vibrations where he used his powers. Once I realized we were dealing with a demon, I knew to look for them. Also the manner in which Golgohasht forged pacts with Michael and Richard, as well as the way he reaped them of their faith, revealed still more insight into his identity. Best of all Ingrid gave me some real insight into Golgohasht by revealing his purpose here. More than that, though, she gave me two syllables from Golgohasht's True Name, gleaned over the years she fought beside him during the war.

Unfortunately, while I had an impressive collection of words, it wasn't enough to give to Hannah to summon or bind Golgohasht. Most summoning rituals are only half of the equation since few casters call forth a demon just to chat. Most want secrets or power, while others want to bind the demon into their service. In any case, they all incorporate a binding ritual into the process just in case the demon refuses to help or submit to enslavement.

Using only Golgohasht's Celestial Name, I could have risked Hannah's life in a ritual, but if the binding failed, he'd break free and go after her. Worse, I would have tipped my hand, and he would become that much harder to locate the next time. No, my best bet was to wait until I had the bastard's full name before using it against him.

And then I sense a ripple in the fabric of time and space, radiating in waves from within the hospital across the street. Golgohasht has arrived.

Power Play

Golgohasht is in Michael's hospital room, probably trying to scare the boy out of his mind. I can sense him — it's one more aspect of our natural abilities. All demons can sense one another when we use our lore or when we manifest our infernal form. In this case, Golgohasht registers like a ripple in water. I pick up some vibrations from his use of power, but not enough to add another syllable to his Name.

I quickly review my options, trying to figure out what to do. I'm improvising because I don't want to fight in the hospital. I need to drag Golgohasht out onto the rooftop where he's less likely to hurt anyone. Unfortunately, he has the same natural abilities I do, so I know my options are limited.

If I reveal my apocalyptic form, he'll sense it immediately. We're territorial creatures by nature, especially now because of the effort we have to invest in our mortal possessions, and I think Golgohasht is more territorial than most. He'll come after me first as the threat, then return to Michael at his leisure. Problem is, this means tipping my hand… not that I have a choice.

Instead, I reach within myself, a timeless moment where the shattered orbits of stars lie scattered across the heavens. I open my eyes to the myriad permutations of the Grand Design, peering into the shattered future. It unfolds in stutters, like glimpsing reflections in a broken mirror.

What I see isn't encouraging. Golgohasht is a Rabisu, fearsome even among a House of mighty warriors. In every case where he and I come to grips, he tears me to pieces with ease. So if I'm to defeat him, it will have to be a battle of wits. The Rabisu are courageous but impetuous to a fault. I have to provoke him, to force him to react without thinking.

I show myself, my *real* self, to this ruined world.

My indigo wings unfurl from my back and a nimbus of low light surrounds me. The moon's cratered reflection appears in my shadows and like an old sailing map, lines and meridians of yellow light cover my body. Golgohasht has to notice that. It won't take him long to get here.

I bend the light to my will, refashioning air into chimera. I must be subtle here. I can't fight him and set him off balance with pure nightmares. Part of our natural ability is an immunity to mind-altering effects. That's God's doing. He couldn't have us affected by the same card tricks He used to cow mortals, so He gave us the ability to see into the magic hat. We're immune to induced fear, but that's also because we've seen and lived through terrors that no illusion could ever match. Golgohasht will probably ignore my attempts to scare him and go straight for my throat. So be it. He'll see right through my illusions and think me defeated, and it will cause him to lower his guard.

I feel another flare of power from the hospital — Golgohasht is probably using his mastery of flesh and bone to move more quickly. I don't have much time left, but I can't let him plan his attack. I must spur him into recklessness. I fill my lungs and call out the first syllable of Golgohasht's True Name.

Somewhere in hospital, a panicked shriek rattles the halls. Golgohasht has no choice but to attack me quickly. He believes his very nature depends on it. I intone the second syllable.

The demon will hurl himself at me, which means that Golgohasht will use his apocalyptic form to alter Jeremy's body and transform it into a killing machine of muscle, teeth and claw. Each House has different visages that alter the shape of our mortal bodies. It's a shadow of our true form, before God stripped away much of our being. It's also what I meant when I told Hannah that the human body can manifest just about anything given enough faith. These physical enhancements are aspects of our essence that we can push through the flesh and bone, infusing sinew and muscle with enough power to shape it according to our will.

Golgohasht scales the building to the roof like a spider. He blazes in a nimbus of black light, with hammers of flesh and bladed fingers where his fists should be, saber-like teeth lining his distended, insect-like jaw. White-hot embers burn deep in his multi-faceted eyes. I'm not without my tricks, though. I've already grown bladed wings by the time Golgohasht sees me. He leaps, but I read the skein of fate and leap aside a moment before the killing blow lands.

Golgohasht scrabbles quickly to his feet. My wings swing at empty air as Golgohasht ducks under my blow. He spins and slams a meaty forearm across my chest. I fly back, fully aware he's ready to pounce on me wherever I land. Sure enough, I land hard, and Golgohasht is on my chest, screeching like a maddened beast and tearing into me with his claws. I bend the binding forces of the cosmos, fueling acceleration by force of will and hurling him a hundred feet away. He hangs momentarily in the air, manipulating the fundamental forces as well, before crashing to the rooftop. I have but a moment to put my plan into action.

Still, I hesitate. Studying the Grand Design gives me insight into the future, showing me the many possible outcomes of this event. The torrent of information is difficult to sort through in the best of times, with ample opportunity for reflection, but now… I have to make the right decision, choose the one course of action that will send Golgohasht back to the Pit. The only way I'm going to find that slim needle of hope in this mass of possibility is to draw on the darkness locked deep within my brain. It's amazing how ancient hate can focus the mind.

If I open myself to that darkness, knowing it will leave its mark on me, I'll lose some of the humanity I've fought so hard to keep. All for the sake of a handful of mortal children who will be nothing but dust in a hundred years anyway. Of course, if I let them be ravaged by Golgohasht, how much more of my soul will I lose?

It seems as though we are fated to sacrifice ourselves for mankind. I can only pray that they're worth it.

The darkness is sweet, welling up into my brain as my lips form words of power and the lines of causality spread before my eyes. I see Golgohasht spring to his feet, long black talons extended as he leaps for me. Hundreds of possibilities flash before me, but I plunge unerringly through them, driven by my rage, seeking the one chance that will bring ruin to my foe. When I find it, my lips pull back in a murderous snarl.

More words of power crackle in the air as I shape the light between us, and a perfect simulacrum of myself races across the rooftop at Golgohasht, brandishing a sword of elemental fire. At the same time I run for the edge of the rooftop, spreading my wings for flight.

Golgohasht laughs, a terrible sound like cracking bones. He sees through the illusion at once and leaps upon me like a lion, his long talons reaching for my throat.

I can see the scene unfolding in my mind. If I move a moment too soon or a moment too late, it will end with Golgohasht holding my severed head. I catch myself praying to the Morningstar as I turn, hurling myself backward off the roof.

Golgohasht crashes into me. His yellowed tusks are inches from my eyes, his carrion stench pushing its way into my nostrils. We fall, but the Rabisu is overcome with bloodlust, raking at my sides and arms with his serrated talons. The agony is indescribable, and I sense how close I am to death. So does Golgohasht, but the black joy he feels blinds himself to his peril.

I furl my wings and we twist in the air, placing Golgohasht between me and the approaching earth. Even as we switch positions, I call upon the forces of the fundament once more, and we plunge faster still, to terminal velocity and beyond. Golgohasht's leonine eyes widen as he begins to realize he's been tricked, but that's when I spread my wings once more and the heavier Rabisu falls free, his talons scoring my arms and chest to the bone.

The high wall outside the apartment building is lined with wrought iron spikes, more for decoration than anything else, but they serve my purpose well. Golgohasht strikes them hard enough to shatter the stone holding them in place, and he disappears in a cloud of pulverized masonry.

I do not land so much as fall to the earth. We demons can use faith to heal most wounds, but the damage inflicted by Golgohasht is beyond the pale. I watch a shower of bloody droplets scatter across the paving stones, and wonder if I will bleed to death before I can revert back to Liebner and stagger the few short yards into the hospital.

Golgohasht does not lie amid the rubble at the base of the wall. Only the torn and ruptured body of Jeremy List, pierced by a half-dozen iron spikes. Not even the fearsome Rabisu could repair the massive damage incurred by the fall. Part of me hoped he was falling still, shrieking in rage and pain as the Abyss waited below.

I let go of my apocalyptic form as the first hospital attendants emerge from the hospital and run toward me. The pain is immense, swelling to fill the entire world, and I welcome it, praying that its searing heat will scour away the blackness I've welcomed back into my heart. I know that I won't be so lucky, just as I know that the battle with Golgohasht is not truly over. He escaped the Pit once before and will do so again. It's only a matter of time before he can fight his way through the Maelstrom and return to this bruised and battered world. Maybe by that time I'll have been able to erase the stain on my soul, but if I have to give in to the darkness again to prevent a greater evil, then so be it. Heaven is forever lost to us, and Hell can't hold us back anymore.

All we have is this world, and what we choose to make of it. Me, I think it's worth any price.

The two men couldn't be more different.

The older man looked younger — a function of health, ease and confidence. He was handsome in a tough way, and he could make an off-the-rack suit look like tailored silk. When dressed in tailored silk (as today) he looked even better. His name was Jonathan Vuoto, but to his minions and colleagues, he was Johnny Bronco.

"So you need a big favor from me," Johnny Bronco said. "That ain't cheap."

His supplicant was pasty, pudgy and short. He looked slovenly even when he'd just shaved, and he could make any set of clothes look cheap and rumpled. He was wearing a plaid sport jacket that looked even worse on him than it had on the hanger. He had a nasty scar on his face and was wearing sunglasses, even inside. His name was Harvey Ciullo.

"I know," he said. "Thing is, I don' want to talk about it here. It's private, like."

Johnny smirked and looked around at his boys, who were rolling their eyes. Ciullo was a punk, a joke, a nobody. For a gag, Johnny said, "Sure. Come back to my office."

Inside, Harvey said, "The thing is, it's Sal."

"You have a problem with Sal."

"Sure. The thing is, this problem could get ugly, see?"

"And you want my help?" Johnny shook his head. "Harvey, you're on the way to becoming Jersey's most famous deadbeat. Why should I lend you money?"

"I don't want money. I just want you to stay out of things if they get ugly."

Johnny laughed. He laughed so hard he started to cough.

"Ugly? Ugly for who?"

"For Sal, of course."

This provoked more laughter. "You're gonna make things ugly for Sal? That's rich, Ciullo. You crack me up." Once again, his laughter turned to coughs — longer and more painful.

Gradually, Johnny Bronco became aware that something was wrong. Harvey wasn't nervous. Harvey wasn't laughing sycophantically. Harvey had pulled down his sunglasses, revealing an eye full of blood and pus. Harvey was looking serious and hard.

"Johnny, you been to the doctor lately?"

"Clean bill of health," the older man gasped out.

"You better get a new doctor then, 'cause your old one missed a couple tumors in your left lung. One's the size of a motherfucking golf ball."

"Crazy..." Johnny wheezed. Harvey leaned in.

"I see things now, Johnny. I see that shit in your lungs. I see your future, and unless you get on the stick it's a short one. I see Sal's future, too, and it's not much better."

Johnny looked up, puzzled and afraid.

"I'm *advising* you to get some serious treatment, fast. I'm also *advising* you to keep your nose out of it if things start to happen to Sal and his crew, you dig me? You don't want to end up as Johnny Bronchitis, now do you?"

Harvey reached out and patted Johnny on the cheek, then stood and jerked open the office door.

In a good semblance of panic, he shouted, "Hey... guys! Guys, get a doctor! Call an ambulance, I think somethin's wrong with Johnny!"

CHAPTER FIVE: HOUSES OF DARKNESS

In my beginning is my end. In succession
Houses rise and fall, crumble, are extended,
Are removed, destroyed, restored…
—T. S. Eliot, *East Coker*

THE SEBETTU

The seven Celestial Houses created by God defined the duties and the powers of each angel within them, refining their individual natures and shaping their identity within a rigidly structured hierarchy. Prior to the Fall, each House was governed by a central angel (referred to as the *autarch*), who directed the activities of his subordinates through a council of lieutenants. These lieutenants had their own circle of subordinates who reported on the activities of the angels under their authority, and so on, down to the lesser rank and file of holy servants. There was no allowance for promotion or demotion. The duties of each angel never varied, and the Elohim were content in their duties as the cosmos took shape, expecting nothing more than what the Creator gave them.

When the rebel angels broke from their brethren, their identity as members of a specific House remained as strong as ever, and in short order, the fallen re-established the hierarchy that had been lost, restoring the sense of focus and function that the angels craved. These rebel Houses, collectively referred to as the *Sebettu* (literally, "the Seven"), found themselves somewhat at odds with the feudal structure that Lucifer imposed on the infernal host at the beginning of the war. As time passed, the function of the rebel autarch and her lieutenants became focused on supporting the priorities and agendas of House members while simultaneously contributing individually to the war effort. Some among the fallen point to rivalries and intrigues that grew from intra- and inter-House competition that hindered the effectiveness of the legions during the war, but even as the tide inexorably turned against the rebels, neither Lucifer nor his lieutenants tried to disband the Sebettu or curb their influence. Forcing the fallen to reject any ties to their House, no matter how desperate the situation, was simply inconceivable.

DIVIDED LOYALTIES

During the war, the typical rebel found herself juggling her loyalty to her lord commander and the wishes of her House elders. Later, as internal factions split the host into competing philosophies, this balancing act became even more difficult. Each rebel had to decide, based on her own goals and desires, which master to heed and which to ignore when conflicts arose. These loyalties often shifted from day to day and moment to moment.

This issue of divided loyalty is even more acute now that the fallen have returned to Earth. Most (if not all) of the warlords, House elders and factional leaders remain trapped in the Abyss, leaving each demon with the freedom to choose where their allegiances now lie. They can choose to follow the orders of distant lords, seek to restore the primacy of their House or reject the old ways and shape a new order based upon the tenets of their faction.

Defiler

"I can show you things that will fill you with wonder. Just take my hand, and I'll change your life forever."

Before there was any land at all, the great oceans encompassed the world. The angels granted dominion over this vast and powerful realm were called the Nereids, and they were among the most beautiful of God's creations. They were the wellsprings and muses, and their powers resonated with the passions that led to art and quests for insight and truth.

The Nereids were meant to inspire humanity, to beguile them with mysteries and spur them to venture out into the world and discover its many hidden wonders. They were the spirit of longing personified, always alluring, yet ever out of reach. Their power gave them the keenest insight into human desires, but God's design ensured that the vast gulf of the sea would always stand between them. It was not long before they lamented their duty to Heaven and the love they bore for mankind. Looking back, many Defilers believe that had Lucifer not stepped forward to raise the banner of revolt, it would have only been a matter of time before a Nereid did the same.

The Fall galvanized the Defilers, who used their powers to inspire both mortal and rebel angel alike in the struggle against Heaven. They became living symbols of the struggle, reflecting the best qualities of the resistance and spurring others to do the same. More importantly, they sustained the morale of the rebels, even in the darkest days of the war, healing spiritual wounds that no Scourge or Devourer could touch. The devotion these fallen inspired led to some of the most heroic exploits of the war, becoming the foundation for romantic epics that still resonate in mankind's collective soul.

The loss of the war was a terrible blow for the Defilers, who never wavered in their conviction that the rebellion was just. Although they were more accustomed to isolation than most of the fallen, the Defilers were among the first to succumb to the agonies of the Abyss, excising the pain of their loss with hot knives of hate.

Now that the gates of the Abyss are broken and the Defilers are free once more, they are able to work their wiles in a civilization that prizes appearance above all. They can lead men and women to acts of obsession, jealousy and desire that ruin families, end careers or topple entire governments. Yet they can also encourage humanity's understanding of philosophy, fellowship and art, and provide a vision of beauty amid the bleak reality of the modern world. They were created as living mysteries, dangerous and beguiling, meant to inspire acts of courage and strength that fuel the growth of the human soul.

Factions: Defilers are most likely to be Faustians or Raveners. In the first case, they have become captivated by humanity — reacting with delight, or at least respect, to their renewed relationship with mankind. The Raveners act like spurned lovers, exacting an often subtle (but always unforgettable) revenge on those who have inflicted such a crushing betrayal. They break hearts and minds, and spread discord so as to watch groups crumble under bitter recriminations and violence.

Alternatively, some Defilers are disappointed by modern human civilization, and yet still become Faustians. They yearn for the beautiful vision they had before the war, and recognize that humans are an essential part of that.

Some Defilers may be well be fascinated by the quests of the Luciferans or Cryptics, depending upon their associations and experiences in the war. Very few of them become Reconcilers, though. Even if they wished it, most Defilers know that there is no going back to paradise, and now that the old barriers have been broken, they cannot be rebuilt.

Prelude: Defilers are drawn to the vain and the passionate. Their hosts are unlikely to have been spiritual or logical thinkers in life, but rather people with a deep joy in the physical and the immediate. They weren't necessarily promiscuous, but were just as likely to have spent all they had on the latest fashions or the fastest toys. Often they were obsessed with trivial things, constantly fine-tuning the present so as to ignore the grand sweep of changes around them.

Idealists who attract a Defiler are not interested in abstract theories and pragmatic realities, but in immediate action to change the world. The most farsighted candidates are artists who try to reflect vast slices of reality within their work, sure that they can capture the intricacies about them.

Other candidates might have been more profoundly affected by matters of the flesh. Those who have loved deeply or often and been denied, those who have supported a cause and been betrayed by it — these people might also be caught up in the present, where self-pity and thoughts of petty revenge replace true grief or anger.

Another category of likely hosts are those who have suffered for their art in a literal sense: starving artists, failed writers and skid row musicians who have had their spirits broken by rejection, debt and addiction.

Faith: Harvesting faith is a tricky act for many Defilers, because they are unused to close human contact. Getting people's attention is easy; focusing it is not. With indiscriminate use of her lore, a Defiler can gather a large group of followers very quickly (and possibly cause a few riots in the process), but such a crowd is of little use to her. Blind adulation and self-destructive longing is not faith, although with patience, it may provide a foundation on which to create it. In essence, a Defiler must convince her followers that they are worthy of such gifts as she gives them.

Many of those gifts involve expanding perception out beyond the demon and into the larger world. They allow thralls to develop their knowledge and, more importantly, their intuitive understanding of their surroundings. This could be a general feeling of enlightenment, or a more specific focus on a particular topic. It often manifests as works of art or expression in more direct forms, such as political or social activism. Such understanding often comes with renewed confidence as well, which might withstand even supernatural fear or coercion.

Character Creation: Social Attributes are paramount. All of them are important, and regardless of the condition of the host's body, an Appearance of 3 should be a bare minimum. Talents such as Empathy, Intuition and Subterfuge are instinctual, as is Survival. The Defilers' origin as water spirits gives them a litheness that usually translates to a high Dexterity and good ratings in Dodge and Stealth, and perhaps Brawl as well. Most are not concerned with detailed knowledge of modern academics and related subjects, and they see human politics as vulgar.

Starting Torment: 3

House Lore: Lore of Longing, Lore of Storms, Lore of Transfiguration

Weaknesses: Defilers can be frustrating, contrary creatures who can strike off on tangents and drag a whole party along into a spiraling morass of trivialities. They can overplay a deception well beyond the end of its usefulness, and can turn petulant and stormy with little provocation. To avoid this, they often just need a little room. The more ordered and claustrophobic a situation gets, the more likely they are to snap at their partners, do something unadvised or just wander off in a different direction. But such behavior is hard to predict, and it may even manifest itself days after the catalyst for it, if at all.

STEREOTYPES

Devils: Defilers often look on the Devils with distrust, because it seems the Devils are still trying to impose their vision on the world in spite of a thousand years of tragedy. Once they were the voice of God, now their only message is hateful demagoguery.

Scourges: There are many similarities between the two Houses, being concerned with the physical elements and the mysteries of life. This makes for easy friendships and an inclination to trust the Angels of the Wind, a tendency that occasionally leads to tragedy.

Malefactors: This House holds the most interest and attraction to the Defilers, because the Malefactors seem to truly grasp the intersection of beauty, mystery and function, even if only in the inanimate.

Fiends: Defilers don't really understand this House and the areas over which it holds dominion. The Fiends favor intuition over cold reason, which they see as anathema to a sense of true wonder and inspiration.

Devourers: There is a strange kinship between the Defilers and the Devourers, or so the Defilers believe. Both were given dominion over the wild and are, in a way, concerned with matters of flesh.

Slayers: To a large extent, the Defilers see the Slayers as kindred spirits who understand the pain of real loneliness and isolation, though the Slayers' moodiness and tendency toward introspection puts a strain on their relationship.

DEVIL

"Follow me, and I will give you your heart's desire. Worship me, and I will make you a god."

God's first and most perfect creations, the Heralds carried the Lord's standard, bringing His light to illuminate all of Creation. These greatest of all angels were the leaders and princes of the Celestials, shining examples of all that was glorious and right in the eyes of God.

First and foremost, the duty of the First House was to convey the will of heaven to the Houses of the Host, instructing them as to their evolving role in the creation of the cosmos. The Devils bore this enormous responsibility with pride, making their presence known among their peers only when absolutely necessary, but the freedom to alter the course of the cosmos at their discretion became a source of hubris that contributed to the Fall.

When the Grand Design finally culminated in the birth of humanity, the Celestials were surprised at the Creator's commandment to remain invisible and allow mankind to discover its potential without help. Their dissatisfaction found its voice in the greatest of their number, Lucifer the Morningstar. In the end, nearly half of the Heralds chose to side with the Morningstar, a greater percentage of defections than any other Celestial House.

Now cursed as Devils, these rebels became the generals, leaders and heroes of the rebellion. Armed with awesome powers of leadership and inspiration, the Devils set out to lead humanity to a new age, and to encourage mortals to renounce the Creator. But as the war raged on, the Devils grew distant from the humans they had once loved. From heroes and protectors, the Devils became demagogues and dictators, manipulating human pawns with honeyed words and poisoned lies.

Filled with pride and defiance, the Devils refused to believe in the possibility of failure — until Heaven prevailed, and the demons were imprisoned in the darkness of the Abyss. With Lucifer missing, the other demons turned upon their former leaders in anger. To defend themselves — and to mask their own doubt — the Devils used their powers of charisma and deception to turn the other demons upon each other.

But now the barriers around Hell are broken, and many Devils have crawled back into the world of mortals. For those Devils still dedicated to Hell, now is the time for humanity to be reminded of past glories and to bend knee in service to demonkind. Fallen Devils who seek redemption have a new opportunity — to save humanity from the evils that threaten to destroy it, to forge a new Utopia for mortal and celestial alike and perhaps to prove that Lucifer's crusade was ultimately just.

Factions: Devils are intensely political creatures, puppetmasters who live to control and manipulate others. They form the upper echelons of several of the major factions, leading other demons just as they once did in Heaven.

Unsurprisingly, most Devils are Luciferans, still loyal to the vision of the first and greatest rebel. They still follow the dream of casting the Creator down from His throne and leading humans to a glorious future.

After the Luciferans, many Devils find themselves drawn to the Faustians. While once the Heralds craved the love and respect of humanity, these Devils have decided that mortal worship and Faith is just as sweet a prize. With the power of humanity behind them, the Faustians strive to build an empire on Earth, with the Devils first among equals.

The mystery of Lucifer's disappearance wears heavier on Devils than on other demons — he was the greatest amongst them, and his disappearance threw the Devil into doubt and misery. For this reason, many Devils become Cryptics, desperate to learn the truth about the Fall, their mentor, and the true cause of their damnation.

The Heralds truly loved humanity, and some Devils still feel an echo of that love. These Devils are a minority in their House, and they are attracted to the Reconciler faction. If they can rebuild Eden, they reason, they may be able to earn God's forgiveness — and more importantly, the forgiveness and love of humanity.

Few Devils belong to the Ravener faction. To accept the failure of the war and embrace destruction would be to admit that Lucifer's rebellion was an error, and most Devils are too proud and arrogant to accept this. But some few Devils have succumbed to doubt and regret, and they want nothing more than to destroy the world that serves as a reminder of their foolishness and failure.

Prelude: Devils are social creatures, charmers and deceivers, and they are attracted on Earth to mortals who share that aptitude and have lost their souls in the pursuit of power and influence. A tendency to use other people as tools, control those around her and cultivate followers and hangers-on will also attract the attention of a Devil. Good examples of such people are politicians, executives, musicians, actors and charismatic preachers.

Whether they are the shining knights of Heaven or the black paladins of Hell, Devils have always been heroes — exemplars of courage fighting against overwhelming odds. Within the tainted soul of a Devil remains a core of heroism and nobility, no matter how twisted, and they respond to mortals who possess those qualities. A Devil might possess a decorated cop who has lost his soul to corruption or callous violence, a mother who shields her children from her abusive husband with body and soul or a once-idealistic politician crushed by the weight of scandal and double-dealings.

Faith: Devils are master manipulators, able to assess a mortal's desires and weaknesses in a glance, or direct a crowd of followers with just a twitch of a finger. One might think that Devils would find it easy to gather Faith from mortals — and it's true that Devils often have more success in gaining Faith than other demons. The process of gaining Faith from mortals is never effortless, though, and even the great deceivers of Hell must work for their precious spiritual energy.

The term "cult of personality" describes a Devil's entourage of thralls perfectly. The formation of a cult of worshippers is usually a high priority for Devils, and they make use of their most plentiful resource — mortal followers. A Devil's cult can resemble a pyramid selling scheme, in which each new worshipper seeks out and recruits new members who are easy marks for the Devil's charisma. Soon the Devil is surrounded by devotees, worshipping him as a god — the status he has lusted after since the Fall.

Character Creation: Unsurprisingly, Devils tend to emphasize their Social Attributes, especially Manipulation and Charisma. Many Devils also have strong Physical Attributes, due to their position as war leaders and paladins. Mental Attributes aren't as important to Devils, although many have high Wits ratings, as effective lying requires a talent for thinking on your feet.

No Ability is as useful to a Devil as Subterfuge, and almost all members of this House have high ratings in this Talent. Many Devils have strong combat and physical Abilities, reflecting their role as commanders and heroes in bygone times — Athletics, Brawl and Melee are all popular choices.

Starting Torment: 4

House Lore: Lore of the Celestials, Lore of Flame, Lore of Radiance

Weaknesses: The memory of their former nobility is something every Devil struggles to forget but never can. Devils know that they were once perfect princes of Heaven, but no matter how they try to pretend otherwise, their current existence is a hollow mockery of that perfection. The timeless imprisonment in Hell also filled most Devils with doubt, regret and shame — emotions they can never express. Wracked by these feelings, Devils are drawn to acts of foolish bravery and quixotic courage.

STEREOTYPES

Scourges: The demons of healing and disease are much respected by the Devils. Scourges can heal the worthy or infect the insolent — giving Devils extra tools for mortal manipulation.

Malefactors: Devils tend to look down on the artisans and inventors of Hell. Malefactors are also manipulators of mortals, working at a remove through their cursed artifacts, and Devils resent this incursion into their area of expertise.

Fiends: The first stars were Heralds, directed by the angels that became Fiends. Devils and Fiends have a long history of working together. Devils rely on Fiends to provide wisdom, detect flaws in battle plans and supply new insights into human weaknesses.

Defilers: While Devils resent Malefactors for manipulating humans, they have far fewer issues with the Defilers. Working together, a Devil and Defiler can target every human weakness. Occasionally rivals, the two Houses are usually allies.

Devourers: As onetime leaders in the War, Devils respected Devourers for their might in combat, but now most Devils see Devourers as violent and unpredictable relics.

Slayers: Devils have always looked down upon Slayers, the last and least of the angels created by God. Devils see themselves as princes, while Slayers are nothing more than undertakers and carrion crows.

DEVOURER

"It's been too long since I tasted blood on the wind. Tonight, we hunt once more."

The House of the Wild was granted dominion over every living thing that crawled, ran, flew or slithered across the earth. As the wilderness spread across the earth, the Angels of the Wild wove the countless strains of life into an intricate tapestry of beauty, majesty and power. The Angels of the Wild fulfilled their duties with solemn pride and a strong sense of personal honor, governing their realm with justice and compassion.

The birth of humanity was a source of both wonder and consternation for the Angels of the Wild. While God made it clear that mankind was meant to master the wilderness and every living thing within it, they were completely ignorant of its ways. This presented the angels with a paradox: Their duty was to protect and preserve the wild, but the greatest threat to the natural order was the ignorance of humankind, which they were forbidden to interfere with.

For all their reputation as impetuous, instinctual beasts, the Angels of the Wild were the most reluctant of the Host to consider defying the will of Heaven. In the end, though, those who joined the ranks of the fallen believed that there was no other way to be true to their mandate. Once committed, however, there were none braver or more devoted than the Devourers, who filled the ranks of the rebel legions and fought their former comrades without quarter across the length and breadth of Paradise. The Devourers were feared and respected by both sides, and they never lost their belief in final victory, even at the very end.

At first, the Devourers accepted their exile stoically, but separation from the living world eventually took its toll. Worse, the disappearance of Lucifer was a terrible blow to the spirit of the House as a whole, leading many to feel a deep sense of betrayal. As their anger and pain grew, they reverted more and more to their feral nature, trading reason and guilt for mindless instinct.

Upon their escape from the Abyss, the Devourers were shocked to discover how much the world had changed. The humans they fought and suffered for had forgotten all they had been taught after the Fall, raping the world of its dwindling resources and driving whole species into extinction. This realization was the last stroke for many Devourers, who surrendered completely to their monstrous urges in the desire to make mankind suffer for its crimes against nature. For the rest, the pain of the dying earth was enough to shake them from their fugue and spur them to restoring the earth and pulling mankind back from the brink of annihilation.

Factions: Devourers tend to fall into one of two factions, depending on how well their convictions weathered the agonies of the Abyss. Many Devourers still believe that their loyalty to Lucifer and the cause of the fallen must still be honored, and their newfound freedom comes with an obligation to reform the ranks of the infernal legions and resume the war against Heaven. Those who aren't Luciferans tend to become Raveners, as their sense of betrayal after the war and humanity's destruction of nature drives them to seek bloody vengeance on God's beloved children.

Outside these two factions, the next largest group of Devourers can be found among the Reconcilers. The Devourers in their ranks tend to be those who are weary of war and bloodshed, and feel that the only way they can atone for their past crimes is to rebuild the gardens that time has destroyed.

Less common are Devourer Cryptics, though a significant number seek answers to the manner of Lucifer's disappearance, both for the sake of their own honor and out of respect for their lost leader. These Devourers enjoy more success than might be expected, because other fallen frequently underestimate their intelligence and cunning.

Rarest of all are Devourers who follow the call of the Faustians, simply because deception is so foreign to their nature, and they chafe at the patience required for elaborate schemes. Those who are loyal to the faction do so because they believe that the only way to restore the earth is to subjugate mankind.

Prelude: On the surface, it would seem that Devourers would be drawn to people such as soldiers, drug dealers, gang members or police officers, individuals who have eroded their souls through lives of violence. Yet they are also drawn to stockbrokers, sales persons, fire fighters and political activists — individuals who pit themselves against enormous odds and are often emotionally scarred by the experience.

Unsurprisingly, Devourers are also drawn to hosts who share an obsession to protect — or exploit — animals and nature. An environmental activist whose zealous crusades have cost him his own humanity or a cold-hearted poacher are equally likely possibilities, depending on the demon's personality.

Faith: Devourers are masters at the art of reaped Faith. Indeed, their impulsive nature makes them more comfortable with such short-term gains than nearly any other demon.

Low-Torment Devourers are usually careful to restrict their reaping to criminals or individuals who by their actions are actively destructive to their environment. Even then, they avoid killing the individual if possible, preferring to gain Faith through acts of pain or terror in the hopes that the victim will take the experience as a warning and mend his ways.

High-Torment Devourers are less discriminate when choosing their victims. Anyone, even mortals who are sympathetic toward the demon's cause, can be a target. Faith is Faith, and such demons will take it wherever they find it, usually killing the victim in the process.

Devourers are drawn toward strong, aggressive individuals as thralls. They can be individuals who are no strangers to violence, such as gang members, soldiers or cops. Conversely they can be driven intellectuals, political activists, corporate raiders or entrepreneurs. When it comes to thralls, Devourers have no use for the weak or timid.

Character Creation: It's no surprise that the feral Devourers favor Physical Attributes above all, but Mental Attributes come in a close second. Many Devourers have at least two dots in Alertness, Animal Ken, Brawl, Dodge, Intimidation, Survival and Stealth. They may also inherit dots in Firearms and Melee from their hosts.

The less-common socially oriented Devourers tend to have high Intimidation and Leadership Abilities, as well as knowledge appropriate to their profession. These Abilities are often balanced out with some degree of Athletics, but combat-oriented Abilities are less common, at least initially.

Devourers draw upon a variety of backgrounds. Thralls are a favored choice, forming a pack that the demon calls upon when needed. Additionally they may also have allies and contacts to help them out, usually inherited from the host. More social Devourers may have careers in which they wield influence and have high Resources ratings.

Starting Torment: 4

House Lore: Lore of the Beast, Lore of the Flesh, Lore of the Wild

Weakness: Devourers have never been known for their tact, and most never know when to keep their big mouths shut. In situations where diplomacy is essential, Devourers can be brutally honest and quick to anger, prone to starting fights at the slightest provocation. It's fairly common for a Devourer to make a delicate situation worse simply by showing up.

Because of their lack of social skills, many Devourers can be easily manipulated. Some demons trick them into serving as bodyguards or assassins by playing off their sense of honor and obligation. Such manipulations are not without risk, however, for if the Devourer ever sees through the charade, he won't hesitate to seek immediate and bloody revenge.

STEREOTYPES

Devils: During the war, Devourers respected the Devils as noble leaders who sacrificed so much for the cause. Their mortal connections are respected, and they always seem to have opportunities for combat.

Scourges: On the field of battle, Devourers would rather fight with the Scourges than against them. The suffering that their power inflicts, however, alienates all but the most Tormented Devourer.

Malefactors: The Devourers enjoy a close kinship with the Malefactors, going back to the days when the two Houses worked hand-in-hand prior to the Fall. Devourers respect and admire the demons of the earth, and consider them friends until proven otherwise.

Fiends: The Devourers have little patience and less understanding for the Fiends and their arcane pursuits. The movement of the planets and the groupings of stars seem trivial compared to the visceral joy of the hunt.

Defilers: Devourers love the Defilers for their passion and inspiration, but their mercurial nature exasperates the steady, driven Devourer.

Slayers: The Devourers treat the Slayers with an equal amount of respect and pity, admiring their dedication to an onerous and painful calling.

FIEND

"You have questions, my friend, but are you prepared for the answers?"

In the beginning, God fashioned the great engines of Heaven to regulate the cosmos. Each orbit of a star and planet lay within the radius of a cog, a celestial flywheel linking other such gears in an enormous, interdependent mechanism. The heavens were laid out in an intricate tracery of orbits, ellipses, periods and constants, an impossibly vast design that defied total comprehension.

The seers captained these great orbits and circuits. They knew when and where everything would be, be it a day away or a millennia hence. They regulated the means by which the heavens affected the Earth, directing the swell of tides through the course of the moon and winding the Earth to cause the seasons to turn. Of all the angels, however, they were among the most distant from humanity. They loved their brothers and sisters of clay, but it was their lot to reside far above Eden and interact with mortals through mysteries woven in the vault of stars.

When the rebellion came, one central factor split the seers. It was one among their number, a seer named Ahrimal who first saw the dire portents that would reveal themselves as the Fall. At the time, Ahrimal and his companions believed that the impending disaster would occur if the angels *failed* to act, so they were among the most vocal proponents of rebellion. In fact, the Fall was the root of the catastrophe Ahrimal foresaw, and there is not a single Fiend to this day who is not haunted by that House's collective mistake.

Lucifer prized the Fiends as advisors and strategists, since their ability to divine the future earned him several quick victories. The war proved costly, however, for the Fiends did not anticipate its destructiveness. It was a sign of their hubris that they considered that the great design would not be upset by their actions.

Finally, God cast the condemned rebels into the Abyss, plunging the Fiends into a special hell of their own. Once, they were creatures of order and regimented existence, but the Abyss could not be codified, charted or piloted. Without the great engines of Heaven to provide a measured routine, they went mad.

When the walls to the Abyss were wracked by the Maelstrom, the Fiend sensed the great engines again and saw the cracks leading to freedom. Upon reemerging, however, they found the heavens derelict and undirected, while the great engine itself moved with rusted awkwardness. The Fiends had regained their touchstone, but it was cracked and worn, possibly beyond repair. But then the same could be said for them.

Factions: The Fiends prize the search for knowledge above all. Within their broken breasts lies a genuine need to recapture that absolute clarity when the universe hid few secrets from them. Some say their search for these shards of congruence is merely distraction from the inevitable inward examination that leads many Fiends to the Raveners. Almost no Fiend, however, believes that destroying the great engines of Creation will do anything more than condemn all the fallen to an even darker oblivion than the Abyss. For obvious reasons, many Fiends instead prefer the Cryptics and their search for truth.

Few Fiends are drawn to the Reconcilers, if only because the Fiends were always so distant from Eden prior to the war. Paradise was never truly their home, so why yearn for something never shared? Instead, the second-most popular faction among the Fiends are the Luciferans. Perhaps it's because Lucifer protected the Fiends from recrimination when the war was at its worst. The elders among the Fiends, however, say the fate of Lucifer has yet to run its course, though none will say why.

Finally, there are some Fiends who find themselves drawn to the Faustians. Some Fiends believe controlling humanity's destiny is just another course to be charted and directed. Others see modern humanity as an enormously complex organism equal to the cosmos itself, and a worthy successor to their skills.

Prelude: Fiends possess an affinity for patient seekers of knowledge, those, like themselves, who question the universe by boldly prodding it, by getting their hands dirty, and by stumbling about in the dark with little regard for body or soul. Be it a reporter who sacrifices ties to family and friends in the quest for the Big Story or an occultist willingly opening herself to spirits beyond her ken, Fiends are drawn individuals who barter their souls for enlightenment. The important truth to the Fiend isn't the question itself, but the quest for the answer and the struggle to obtain it. The harder someone vies to uncover lost or mysterious knowledge—and the more of themselves they lose in the process — the greater the lure to the Fiends.

Faith: Everyone has questions, but few people are willing to find the answers. The Fiends rely on this duality to fuel themselves. In fact, because the Fiends pose as avid listeners, people find it easier confiding in them, especially since they place themselves in positions of authority and knowledge.

Most Fiends of low Torment encourage the pursuit of knowledge rather than its acquisition. They target seekers of enlightenment, presenting themselves as sounding boards for ideas and asking just enough questions to nudge the mortal in the right direction. Once they grow into the mortal's confidence, they offer pacts to encourage the journey rather than simply fulfilling the goal.

By the same token, Fiends also despise mortals who seek only quick answers in life. They often reap Faith from this lot, showing them glimpses of the horrible fates awaiting them. They reap to fuel themselves as much as to punish, but they risk opening themselves to their Torment as they conjure their horrifying illusions.

Conversely, high-Torment Fiends rely on the selfsame quick-fix lot for their pacts. They use illusions to corrupt mortals and promise them material gains, separating those who prefer acquisition from those who seek esoteric pursuits. They reap from honest seekers as well, torturing them with half-truths and misinformation, and scarring their sanity with obscene secrets better left unsaid.

Character Creation: Fiends believe that knowledge is power, so they favor high Mental Attributes. Others rely on controlling others through their future sight, which makes Social Attributes their primary preference.

When it comes to Abilities, Fiend prize Knowledges above all else, with Investigation, Academics and Religion of principal interest. They are also adept in the mysteries of Linguistics, Occult and Research.

In dealing with Backgrounds, the two key choices are Allies and Contacts. The mortal's quest for knowledge means she established a network of mortal affiliates to facilitate her journey. It's also not uncommon for Fiend to have mortal mentors if the host was delving deeply into occult matters.

Starting Torment: 3

House Lore: Lore of Light, Lore of Patterns, Lore of Portals

Weaknesses: Curiosity is perhaps the Fiends' Achilles' heel. It was curiosity of the unknown that led to their downfall, and it's a need to investigate mysteries when confronted by conundrums that afflicts them now. This curiosity usually stems from an unforeseen chain of events that arises over the course of their actions. A subject may do or say something significant beyond the Fiend's carefully scripted chain of events. Most Fiends will want to know why this happened, focusing their analytical abilities to find the source of the anomaly, and in so doing losing sight of the task at hand.

STEREOTYPES

Devils: The Fiends know that while they possess vision, the Devils are the best-equipped to make such vision reality. The Fiends also feel a kinship with the Devils who understand the importance of planning and far-reaching goals.

Scourges: The Fiends reserve a quiet jealousy for the Scourges and their close ties to humanity. The Fiends envy the Scourge's facility with mortals, but their jealousy rarely manifests openly.

Malefactors: The Fiends blame the Malefactors for introducing poisoned knowledge to humanity that has since spread and ravaged the Earth. They are hard-pressed to forgive this House, save for the few Reconcilers seeking to right the mistakes of the past.

Defilers: The fluid and slippery Defilers confuse the Fiends as equally as the Fiends baffle them. They find the Defilers to be too transient and oriented in "the now" to hold their interest.

Devourers: Fiends respect the Devourers for their loyalty to Lucifer and proficiency as soldiers, but the Devourers are too short-sighted. They must be led, but the Fiends don't want that frustrating role.

Slayers: The Fiends appreciate the Slayers for their patience, and they frequently seek the Slayers out for counsel and assistance. A handful of Fiends believe that the Angels of Death will be crucial to the eventual redemption of the fallen, and they work to strengthen ties between the two Houses.

MALEFACTOR

"I know you've been hurt. I have something here that can make your life better again."

On the third day, God separated the seas from the land, and He gave stewardship of the land to a select group of angels. Named Artificers, these Celestials governed — and loved — the earth and all that lay within it. To them was given an affinity with soil, gems and stone; with the fires that smoldered below the earth's surface; and most especially, with metal.

To the Artificers was also given the responsibility of helping humanity use the earth — to till the fields, dig up the metals and to craft the tools they would need to shape their world. The angels took to their task willingly, eager to share their love for the earth with their charges.

But humanity was not equipped to deal with such responsibility. They tried to use the miraculous tools of the angels, but they were unable to make them work properly, if at all. Humanity became resentful of their hidden teachers and feared them for their perfection, while the Artificers grew confused and bewildered, unable to relate to humans in the same way they related to the predictable elements of earth and fire.

When war erupted between the rebel angels and the forces of Heaven, many of the Artificers gravitated toward Lucifer's side. They felt rejected by the humans they had tried to love, and angry with the Creator, who had tied their hands by forbidding angels to help humans directly. Moreover, they sided with the rebels because they felt that only their peers understood them, loved them, when the humans had simply refused to do.

When the rebels lost the war and were imprisoned in Hell, the Malefactors found it difficult to cope — separated from the earth and fire that was their reason for being. This terrible loneliness made most Malefactors cold and withdrawn, unable to interact well with even their fellow demons. They became cunning and thoughtful, preferring careful planning and patience to the emotional upheavals of anger and immediacy.

Now, released from Hell, Malefactors find themselves in a world transformed. Humanity has finally embraced the use of tools and become a race of makers, but in doing so, they have ravaged the earth and left it wounded and unloved. Those Malefactors still in the service of Hell swallow their pain and look for new opportunities to create havoc among humanity. For the fallen, the world is an open wound, and the urge to simply break down and cry is sometimes overwhelming. But if the world is to be healed, then the Malefactors must bear their pain and get to work, just as they did millennia ago.

Factions: Most Malefactors are Faustians, and have been since the final days of the war. With their penchant for manipulating humans with their poisoned chalices and cursed gifts and their desire to push humanity back into a subservient and respectful position, this Faction is a natural fit for the House.

Reconcilers form the next largest bloc within the Malefactors, especially among the fallen. For all their attempts to stop caring about the world, these demons can never truly sever their link to the land and nature. Loose in the world, many Malefactors are overwhelmed by a forgotten love, and they push aside old hurts to try to redeem themselves.

Malefactor Cryptics bend their natural cunning and intelligence toward unraveling the mysteries of the war and the Fall. For many Malefactors, this faction lends them a purpose they sorely need and is unlikely to push them into contact with humans.

Luciferan Malefactors are not very common. Most were too hurt and emotionally damaged by the Fall to retain faith in their lost leader. However, hope dies hard even in demons, and there are some Luciferans in this House. These demons tend to treat the Luciferan cause as a holy calling and throw themselves into it with great passion.

With their love of the earth and of tools — things that are crafted over time and with great care — an appetite for pure destruction is something rarely felt by these demons. Those few who do belong to the Ravener faction are terrifying indeed, often the most destructive and violent of the faction.

Prelude: Upon their escape from Hell, Malefactors usually gravitate toward souls that are as emotionally damaged as their own. Malefactors are in many ways lonely, insecure beings — separated from the earth that they once held closest. Their hosts tend to be similar individuals — lonely, needy people who have always felt that *something* was lacking in their lives, something that would have made them complete. Good examples of such individuals are drug addicts, the ugly or disfigured, people who cling to abusive spouses or teenagers trying to modify themselves with tattoos and piercings.

Another strong group of candidates are people who are alienated from other humans, and are more comfortable with machines or the earth — this matches the Malefactor psyche very closely. This is a broad category, which could include anything from a computer hacker who's only comfortable online to a sociopath who sees other people as merely things to an environmental activist who despises humans for despoiling the planet.

Faith: Malefactors often find it difficult to gather Faith from mortals, due to two factors. First, of course, is the fact that they have difficulty understanding and relating to humans, who aren't as predictable and dependable as stone. Being unable to truly *know* humans, Malefactors find it difficult to easily inspire them.

A greater impediment of sorts is the Malefactor's reliance on his tools and magical artifacts. A mortal will no doubt be dumbstruck and awed by the powers of a magic mirror, but that doesn't mean she'll *automatically* associate the mirror with the demon who made it or gave it to her. Unless the human makes a strong connection between the item and the Malefactor, the Faith simply vanishes into the ether.

When reaping Faith from mortals, a Malefactor must do so using an item he has created. This might be a mundane item — such as a silver knife used to flay a victim's skin away — or a miraculous creation, like a mirror that shows a mortal's inner beauty. The demon can use different tools whenever he attempts to reap Faith — the important thing is that the item is something he crafted himself, and that the mortal focuses on the item as her Faith is collected.

Malefactors are drawn to the same sort of people who attracted them as a host — the lost, the needy, the damaged. In particular, Malefactors tend to target people who are looking for something that will fix their life, end their problems — a concrete solution, not a metaphysical concept. The nerd who wants to be handsome, the writer stymied on his new book, the paraplegic wanting

her legs back — these are people who can be "helped" by a Malefactor, who can build a computer that inspires creativity or a mask that makes the wearer an Adonis.

Character Creation: Malefactors tend to emphasize Mental Attributes, particularly Wits, which governs creativity and cunning. As miners and workers, they also tend to have good Stamina and Strength ratings. Social Attributes are often low, due to the difficulty Malefactors have in relating to humans — although Manipulation is often emphasized, as the demons have some talents for using humans as tools.

To reflect their status as demonic inventors, almost all Malefactors have high Crafts ratings. Many also have excellent Research ratings. Subterfuge is popular — while Malefactors don't have the natural propensity for manipulation that Devils have, they work hard to transcend their shortcoming.

Starting Torment: 3

House Lore: Lore of the Earth, Lore of the Forge, Lore of Paths

Weaknesses: The primary weakness of this House is a problem with understanding human beings. Humans are unpredictable, messy creatures, and the demons find it very difficult to come to grips with them, even after pillaging the memories and personalities of their hosts. The demons are even slightly *frightened* by humanity. The Malefactors were confused and badly hurt by humanity's rejection, and fear of further rejection can subconsciously subvert and influence a demon's plans and actions.

STEREOTYPES

Devils: Malefactors often envy these smooth-tongued manipulators, who play upon human frailty so easily. For Malefactors, this takes effort and concentration, so they resent the Devils' skills.

Scourges: Air and earth do not mix, nor does plague touch stone. The Malefactors see the Scourges as inconsequential at best, nuisances at worst.

Fiends: Prophecy, portents and the movements of the stars — what do they matter in the grand scheme of things? Malefactors are practical demons, and they see the Fiends as useless.

Defilers: Like the Malefactors, the Defilers understand creation. They respect the Defilers, but they do not necessarily trust them.

Devourers: Malefactors do not understand the point of short-lived, messy animal life. Malefactors prefer to keep Devourers at arm's length, but they respect their strength.

Slayers: Human life and human death are both mysterious and fairly irrelevant to the Malefactors, who prefer the company of undying stone. They give the House respect, but little attention.

SCOURGE

"Nothing can protect you forever. So don't worry about forever. Worry about right now."

Before the Age of Wrath, the Guardian Angels had an enviable role in Paradise. Entrusted with carrying the sacred Breath of Life, their duties brought them in close contact with their beloved humanity. Even better, they were charged with the ongoing protection of every being they animated. Where another angel might have felt guilt for skirting the edges of the command against interference, the Angels of the Wind were wholly within their purview when they adoringly watched the humans that they secretly considered their own children, as well as God's.

But even as they keenly felt the pleasure of humanity's presence, they felt more keenly the pain of humanity's frustration. Their nearness was both torment and elation, and the tension between the two extremes eventually drove many to the snapping point. When the rebellion came, Lucifer found many eager followers in the Firmament. Indeed, other than his own House of the Morning Star, the House of the Rising Wind produced the most highly ranked angels to fall.

In the war, the Scourges were committed warriors. The condemnation of Heaven did not break their will: Far from it, the weight of the punishment that fell on humanity did much to steel the Scourges in opposition to God and the Holy Host. Poorly matched against the Fundamentals and Wild Angels in battle in the physical world, Scourges' speed of movement and powers of concealment made them excellent harriers, scouts and spies.

In this age of escape, the Scourges are widely respected. Their courageous exploits in the war have given them a deserved reputation for loyalty even *in extremis*. Every faction among the newly escaped fallen wants loyal defenders, especially those who can heal with the right hand and harm with the left.

Factions: The most hopeful Scourges tend toward the Reconciler camp. The concept of a world healed is more tempting to them than the notion of one ruled by the Faustians or ruined by the Raveners.

Other Scourges continue to pledge fealty to Lucifer, believing that he somehow escaped the rage of the punishing angels. If he could spare himself eons ago, maybe he's the key to sparing humankind now. Certainly, finding the only one of the fallen with a continuous experience in the world is usually considered a better way to find concrete answers than joining the Cryptics' debating society.

Faustians find few Scourges in their numbers. The Second House was, and in some way still is, intimately concerned with the safety of humanity. They may bless or curse, but coldly using people as tools doesn't come easily.

Prelude: Fearful souls cry out for defenders, and even in their fallen state, the onetime Angels Protector find that cry hard to resist. Scourges were once the parents to humanity — indeed, all life — and the needful call of one of their children still draws their attention.

But this world, the wreckage of Paradise, is full of fears, real and imagined. A Scourge may be drawn to genuine fear, only to find that it's selfish. Unlucky Scourges find themselves trapped in the bodies of those who dreaded the consequences of their own poor decisions, or those frightened of the final fruit of problems they've done nothing to solve or avoid.

Faith: On a practical level, gaining Faith from mortals is an easy job for Scourges. Health is a precious commodity for humanity. For some, no price is too high for a cure beyond the purview of medical science. Founding a church or cult based on "Spirits of Wholeness" is not challenging for beings who really *can* cure AIDS or repair a shattered spine or correct the deformities of a newborn with spina bifida. The primary challenge with these strategies is often an ethical one, as such structures promise, even implicitly, that the demon patron can protect the faithful forever. On the other hand, Scourges who have given up on humanity simply take an honest route and present themselves as spirits of health *and* harm.

Scourges who are cruel (or simply cavalier) tend to be wanton with the use of their thralls. God's particular curse on the Second House hit them hard, and the nagging knowledge that every human is doomed to die anyway can quickly lead to despair and callousness. From the perspective of an infinite being, what difference does it really make whether someone dies at 15 or 50?

Low-Torment Scourges are more likely to understand the temptation of resuming a protecting role. Accordingly, they are more likely to enthrall those they deem worthy of their protection. "Worthy" mortals who are willing to sell their souls are often hard to find, of course, but the bonus is that their moral qualities make it easier for the Scourge to resist wanton draining.

Character Creation: The people who draw Scourges tend to have low Social Attributes: A life lived in fear tends to limit one's chances to meet and greet. A nervous hypochondriac may have surprisingly high Physical traits, particularly Stamina, as a benefit of a life spent in the gym, running one more lap to try and keep the Grim Reaper at bay. Among Mental traits, Perception is often high, enhanced by a lifetime of jumping at every sound and nervously peering into the dark when home alone.

Habitual fear can also translate to an above average Dodge Ability. Often, the hosts possess a low-level Skill or Knowledge reflecting the nature of their personal bogeyman. For instance, low-level Medicine Ability is common for those who weren't medical professionals, but who were constantly concerned about their health. Someone who was less afraid of illness but who lived in terror of physical attack might have a dot or two in Firearms. Other, subtler fears — fears of intellectual of social inadequacy — could lead to studies of Etiquette or Academics.

Backgrounds vary widely, though many hosts who lived in selfish fear were misers with high Resources. For those whose fears are more justified — because they live in a dangerous area or situation — Contacts or Allies are common.

Starting Torment: 3

House Lore: Lore of the Winds, Lore of Awakening, Lore of the Firmament

Weaknesses: One problem other Houses have with Scourges — and which Scourges have with themselves — is their problems with mortals. Fallen Guardians tend to have extreme views about mankind. They're either seen as precious treasures who must be guarded and aided at every turn, or their brief and ultimately terminal lives are seen as pointless, worthless and finally absurd. Mortals are the central factor of a Scourge's existence, and one way or the other it's hard to keep their attitudes balanced.

An outgrowth of this problem is a tendency to judge things collectively. Scourges rarely make case-by-case decisions: They try to live their lives by absolute and inflexible principles. Therefore, some Scourges condemn Gandhi and Martin Luther King along with the rest of humanity, while others defend Hitler and Stalin as part and parcel of mankind. Seeing humankind as a harvest, it's hard for them to focus on individual seeds.

STEREOTYPES

Devils: Once the Angels of Light bore the animating will of God, but now God's will is sealed away, unknowable, and the Devils have no function. They may blather on with their own voices, but God's curse upon them is finally clear: They have been made pointless.

Malefactors: Humans love *things*, and the Malefactors supply them. That alone makes them worth something. Their pragmatism makes for a good leaven to a Scourge's abstraction — if one can convince them that they have as much to gain as you do.

Fiends: The world may be scrambled and broken, and the onetime Fates see as through a darkened glass, but they are not completely blind. Rather than despise them for what they have lost, the Scourges tend to respect the tattered remnants of insight that the Fiends still retain.

Defilers: They were once an ocean for humanity to explore. Now they've become a reef upon which men are wracked. On a practical level, their powers are worthwhile, but anyone can be *used*.

Devourers: Where others tend to dismiss the Devourers as mindless savages, the Scourges see deeper. Angry Scourges see the Devourers as a fit punishment for a human civilization sunk to their level. Scourges with more equilibrium wonder if Devourers might be the key to healing nature instead of harming it.

Slayers: While the Slayers tend to view their demesne of death as all-important and all-consuming, it must be said that the modern world offers a lot of good reasons for that belief. As the House with the best connection (however tenuous) to the fate of dead souls, they're important allies to cultivate.

SLAYER

"Love or hate me as you will, but live, now and until your final breath. In time, we shall meet again."

The last of the Celestial Houses, the Angels of Death were given the melancholy task of undoing all the wonders that that their peers created, ending lives and erasing great works so that others may follow in their place. It was a solemn role amid the many glories of the cosmos, but the reapers were as content in their labor as any angel — until the birth of mankind.

Like the other Celestials, the Reapers loved humanity and dedicated themselves to keeping Eden vibrant and dynamic, but mankind in its ignorance regarded the death of animals and plants with fear and sadness. Their reaction shocked and pained the Reapers, who longed to assuage mankind's fears but were forbidden by God's commandments. When Lucifer raised the banner of rebellion, many Reapers joined in the Fall for no other reason than the desperate desire to be loved instead of feared.

Then came Heaven's tragic counterstroke. The penalty for mankind's disobedience was the curse of mortality. Now the Slayers were forced to end the lives of the people they loved, and the pain they felt only alienated them further from mankind and the fallen alike. Though many served and earned terrible reputations as warriors and champions in the War of Wrath, the Slayers as a whole found themselves at the fringes of the conflict, focusing more of their energies to easing the deaths of humanity rather than contributing further to the slaughter.

Now in the wake of their mysterious release, the Slayers find themselves in a world that has suffered greatly in the absence of those meant to govern the ways of aging and death. The plight of the world and mankind convinces many Slayers that the only recourse left is to usher in the final night and grant the world a merciful death. A determined few, however, see the damage that has been done and believe that by restoring the balance, the Slayers might finally earn the peace and understanding from humanity they've craved all along.

Factions: Very few Slayers are Luciferans, because they were not fiercely loyal to Lucifer in the first place. He was the center of the rebellion, and they were at the fringes, concentrating more on saving humans and subverting the enemy's plans than winning battles.

There are more Faustian Slayers, but most of the House that are focused on humanity's potential actually become Reconcilers instead, turning their passion into a quest for God, and working toward re-creating the world as it was before the revocation of immortality. They do not see the encouragement of mankind's self-reliance to be useful, because they believe protection from death can only be granted by God Himself. Otherwise it's a closed system, and no amount of confidence, evolution or purification will suffice.

The Cryptics attract quite a number of Slayers, because the abstract and investigative nature of the faction suits many of their House. The Raveners attract their fair share as well. The members may say they have various reasons — that they are carrying out their God-given duty, or that they are strengthening the ranks of the spirits to lay siege upon Heaven, or that in the absence of God they have become the judges of mankind. But it's usually just a great envy of the living that leads them to delight in destruction, over and over again.

Prelude: Slayers are drawn to those who care little about their life — their hosts are far more likely to have destroyed their spirits by attempting suicide than any other House. People confronted by daily crime or violence are also particularly susceptible; cops, soldiers and addicts, for example. With every blow, directed at themselves or at others, they crumple inward a little more. Refugees, or victims of torture and abuse are other candidates. Then there are those whose souls have been worn down to nothingness by banality and neglect, who run blades across their skin simply to feel any sensation they can.

There are more reasons for soulessness than despair, however. Somebody who has spent a lifetime helping others, abandoning any thoughts of recompense, may attract a Slayer. People who are truly devoted to a religion or philosophy that focuses on the next life at the expense of their current one — or which holds that physical experience and desire is an illusion — are also suitable.

Faith: Philosophically, this House is in a difficult position when it comes to gaining followers and reaping Faith. Mankind was not meant to die, so Slayers trying to restore Paradise (mostly Reconcilers and Cryptics) must somehow lead humans to overlook their mortality — and the demon's place in their lives. For those preaching rebellion against God, death is the ultimate reminder of failure.

Some Slayers seek to bypass these questions altogether. They work to gather Faith, not as angels of death, but simply as angels. The easiest way to do so is to mimic a member of a different House — Devils (using pride) and Fiends (using secrets) are the most obvious. Another solution is to form a generic Church of All Angels, Church of One God or Humanity Ascendant. Others do make death the central tenet of the relationship with their thralls. Raveners have the easiest time — they can just create a murder cult and be done with it. High-Torment Slayers might not have a choice.

Because of their fascination with all facets of life, Slayers often seek out a diverse group of followers, even if setting up a death-centric sect. They are prone to somewhat arbitrary choices — selecting the first passably suitable option, or taking all that seek the demon out. Some even fix on a random face in the crowd and put all their effort into initiating *that* person, *that* soul, into the mysteries.

Character Creation: There is no group of Attributes that it is important to emphasize, although Mental is common (and Perception in particular). Strength and Charisma usually decrease below the host's original stats, but Stamina increases. Manipulation can be high, but the use of it might feel somewhat self-conscious.

Awareness, Intuition and Stealth are favored Abilities. Intimidation and Investigation are also good choices, and members of the House seem to quickly pick up a good scattering of knowledge from the world around them, so any would be appropriate. Such Abilities as Leadership and Empathy do not come naturally, but strange things could have happened during the war.

Starting Torment: 4

House Lore: Lore of Death, Lore of the Realms, Lore of the Spirit

Weaknesses: Before the war, Reapers were often shunned by other angels, lending them an air of detachment that often covers an intense scrutiny of the living world. Even the memories of their hosts seem more alien to them than for other demons. They may be adept at unraveling convoluted deceptions, but simpler things, particularly human motivation, can trip them up. And although they keep open and attentive minds, once they have come to a decision, they find it very difficult to admit they may have been wrong. As their Torment increases, their perceptions of the world become clearer even as, paradoxically, they feel further and further removed from it. Most of the damage caused by a high-Torment Slayer is an obsessive desire to make any mark they can upon a reality that is slipping away.

STEREOTYPES

Devils: When called upon to express an opinion, Slayers often seem to be strangely sorry for the devils. Their lies and ambitions might be met with a sad and patronizing smile.

Scourges: There was a lot of enmity between these two Houses during the war. Now the Slayers claim the Scourges as their closest brethren, and discount any previous ill will.

Malefactors: Slayers claim that artifacts — indeed all material objects — are just playthings, distractions from the real concerns of the world. Nonetheless, they seem to be able to work well with the Malefactors, and are happy to remain in their company.

Fiends: Some Slayers say that in the absence of God it is the dead that now ride dreams and shape the patterns of the stars. Therefore, the Fiends make up another House with whom they hold close kinship.

Defilers: The Defilers have bridged the gap between themselves and mankind, a gap that had been as profound as the Slayer's in its own way. Yet all they have done with their new opportunities is to act like spoiled brats and slatterns, or so a Slayer might say.

Devourers: Slayers advise the Devourers against hasty violence and the wasting of life. Nonetheless, they are happy to associate with the House, and they offer advice on numerous other topics as well. Some claim that this seems to manipulate the Devourers into roles as bodyguards, but of course the Slayers disagree.

THE FACTIONS

FAUSTIAN

The Faustians have observed the power of human faith and have concluded that, even trapped in an unfaceted singular world, the Children of Adam have power that is of the same nature as God's. Admittedly, their *degree* of power is miniscule, but every child born carries a spark of holy fire. Gather enough sparks together, and the fire could one day eclipse the sun.

Faustians find the general state of humankind greatly reduced since Edenic times — like grouchy grandparents, they are convinced that people today are weaker, stupider, sillier, less reasonable, less respectful… just generally devolved from the times they recall. But at the same time, humankind's aggregate ability to define the reality around them is, if anything, stronger than it was when they numbered in millions instead of billions. Yet humans are using most of their greatest strength to *repress themselves!* Their greatest faith is placed in proof — the one thing that doesn't *need* faith to be true. Consequently, even as their grasp on the world gets stronger, that very grasp constricts and constrains reality into ever tighter, ever narrower instances. It's possible that if they continue on this course, faith may define itself right out of existence, leaving behind a cold world of absolute, mechanical certainty.

While such a world has no place for God, it also lacks a niche for demons, and is therefore intolerable to the Faustians.

Humanity, as found in the fallen world, is a bonfire smoldering out of control, rapidly using up the obvious sources of fuel and in danger of guttering out. The Faustian philosophy is based on harnessing and husbanding this power — controlling the burn, renewing the fuel and building engines that can focus humanity's divine energies outward instead of inward. It will take careful guidance and leadership, of course, but in the end, human faith is, itself, the best hope of freeing the world from God.

Rivals: Faustians have a bemused tolerance for Reconcilers. True, Reconcilers cling to a foolish belief that they can make up with The Almighty, but once they get over that adolescent optimism, they might grow up to more mature (that is, Faustian) goals. Luciferans get much the same treatment. They may be taking the wrong road to victory against Heaven, but at least they've got the map out.

The Faustian ambition to perfect the human rebellion against God (or, depending on which Faustian you ask, to enslave humanity for a spiritual rebellion against God) runs directly counter to the Ravener policy of wrecking everything and killing everyone. Consequently,

Ravener demons are strongly encouraged to set aside their mindless wrath and regain hope. Failing that, the Faustians tend to sic their faithful humans on them.

A more subtle opposition exists with the Cryptics. The Faustians are quite confident that they've got it all figured out, and nagging questioners are more than just pests — they can imperil the resolve of the fallen doing the great work of building the future. Worse still, they can cast doubt into the hearts of mortal followers.

While Faustians despise Raveners as agents of chaos and destruction, their aggravation with Cryptics is deeper and more irksome because the Cryptics are so resistant to persuasion. To a zealous Faustian, an inconvenient question is worse than a Ravener's claw to the throat.

Houses: The grandeur and scope of the Faustian scheme appeals to many ambitious demons. Having humans do most of the heavy lifting that appeal, limiting it to those who are comfortable with getting others to do their dirty work. But for those who fit both categories, Faustianism is a perfect philosophy.

Devils, as the onetime order-givers for the Universe, are certainly used to seeing others do what they say, and as the First House they have the confidence to dare much. Defilers, too, have always had great hopes for the collective power of humanity: Inspiring them to apotheosis seems a captivating adventure. Finally, there are many Faustian Malefactors. For them, the appeal is not so much in the scope of the plan, but in its pragmatism. The Faustians have a plan, with concrete goals, that can be achieved *now*. The Malefactors' tremendous abilities to tempt and manipulate humans is just icing on the cake.

The only House that is notably absent from the Faustian edifice is the Second. Scourges are keenly — perhaps morbidly — aware of the frail, frightened and failing nature of humankind. Relying on such weak links looks (to them) like a recipe for failure.

Leadership: The Devil Belphigor is one of the strongest fallen who has yet returned to Earth, and he came back with the added bonus of a vessel that was both attractive and physically powerful. Belphigor quickly insinuated himself into the hierarchy of one of America's New Age religions and splintered off his own version of it. Working within its framework, Belphigor hopes to clear the world of divine interference before two generations pass.

The Defiler Senivel, her House's first ambassador to humankind, is also a Faustian, but one with a more humanistic bent. Where Belphigor sees the Faustian revolution as being demonkind's best hope, Senivel hopes it will prove to ultimately fulfill both mortals and Elohim. (Mortals by letting them replace God their Father at the helm of the universe, and spirits by giving them a new master to serve.)

Goals: Generally, Faustians are in favor of world peace and opposed to contraception — not for any benevolent reasons, but because they want more humans around, period.

Faustians have infested Rome and Jerusalem in hopes of finding (and harnessing) populations with high concentrations of faith. Their main outpost, however, is in the United States. (It seems clear to the Faustians that the US is currently the most powerful nation and, thus, best suited to be bent to their will.) Specifically, Belphigor's "Church of Scientific Spirituality" has purchased a large parcel of desert land outside of Flagstaff, Arizona. Miles from any other population center, they intend to start a city there from scratch, encouraging people "of the right sort" to settle there.

Observant fallen suspect that the site's proximity to a gigantic meteor crater is not accidental. One of the earliest fallen victories in the War of Wrath was when they felled great Vejovis, an angel of the Firmament. Many suspect that the "meteor" in the bottom of the crater is nothing less than Vejovis's ancient corpse.

CRYPTIC

Spending uncounted ages imprisoned in a lightless, soundless, *sensationless* void is a pretty harsh punishment, but it does provide one thing.

It provides a lot of time to think.

After the initial shock of defeat — after the horror and agony of Hell — even after the despair of untold eventless eons — some fallen have taken a step back and reconsidered their initial assumptions. Some have contemplated, taken stock and tried to puzzle out what went so disastrously wrong.

These inquisitive Elohim have reached some startling conclusions.

First and foremost, God's perspective is either omniscient or so removed and all-pervasive as to be *nearly* omniscient — especially when compared to such limited beings as humans and even angels. If a lowly light like Ahrimal could see trouble brewing, God surely foresaw it ages before that.

Secondly, God is either perfect or (again) close enough to make no odds. Therefore, the angels He created must have been either a perfect model of His desires, or as close to that model as reality could tolerate. While it's possible that the gross stuff of the material world was too weak to support perfect servants, it is unthinkable that God would allow that imperfection to take the form of disobedience… *unless rebellion was not an imperfection.*

Thirdly, Lucifer — as the first among angels and the closest to God in power — must, by virtue of his power and position, be closer to God's ideal than any other. The observed fact that he was the first and best of the

rebels is the clinching argument that the rebellion — with the consequent corruption of reality and ghastly punishment of men and Elohim — was actually the enactment of God's plan, rather than a deviation from it.

Now that they are freed from their durance, these Cryptics have taken their logical premises and used them as the foundation for new questions.

If God knew about the rebellion, surely He knew about the demons' eventual escape from the abyss. What, then, is His new plan for His unwitting servants?

Since Lucifer was not imprisoned and he answers no summons, what was the Morningstar's fate? Personal destruction for his role as leader? Some other torment, possibly even worse than Hell? Or — most likely — did he escape punishment because he was privy to God's plan all along?

Finally, and most importantly — if the fallen have been God's pawns all this time, is there any way to escape that fate in the future?

Or should they even try?

Rivals: The Cryptics aren't terribly fond of the Raveners — what's to like? — but they see the Raveners' mad, thoughtless flailing as ultimately meaningless. Like ants on a kicked-over hill, they mill about wildly but accomplish nothing.

The Reconcilers are too idealistic, but at least they're asking questions instead of trumpeting specious answers. No, the factions that really bother the Cryptics are the Luciferans and the Faustians.

Both groups have the same problems. They talk and they don't listen. They make proud declarations, which mostly reveal the gaps in their logic. They've got their eyes and minds shut, and they *pity* anyone who lacks their sense of blind, misled mission.

If the Raveners are milling chaotically and the Reconcilers are moping confusedly, the Luciferans and Faustians are building industriously — either the same anthill that got kicked last time, or an entirely new one. Neither is pausing to ask what their goals should *really* be.

Houses: Many Malefactors find their way to the questioner clique. It's a natural fit for their steady, methodical tendencies. Making up perhaps the most pragmatic House of all, angels of the House of the Fundament seem unusually able to examine their fundamental assumptions without castigating themselves for error. One can almost see them shrug and hear them mutter, "It didn't work. What will?"

A more fervently inquisitive House is that of the Slayers. While they may ask the same questions as the Malefactors, they have a wounding personal stake in the answers. In the war they were made to bring the atrocity of death upon their beloved humanity, and the guilt and sorrow they still feel demands answers.

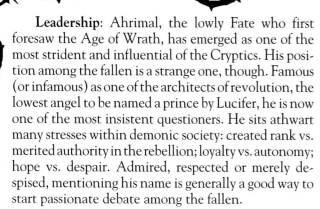

Leadership: Ahrimal, the lowly Fate who first foresaw the Age of Wrath, has emerged as one of the most strident and influential of the Cryptics. His position among the fallen is a strange one, though. Famous (or infamous) as one of the architects of revolution, the lowest angel to be named a prince by Lucifer, he is now one of the most insistent questioners. He sits athwart many stresses within demonic society: created rank vs. merited authority in the rebellion; loyalty vs. autonomy; hope vs. despair. Admired, respected or merely despised, mentioning his name is generally a good way to start passionate debate among the fallen.

Gipontel, a Fundamental and onetime Archangel, represents a more accessible faction of the Inquisition. A self-appointed coalition-builder, he encourages Cryptics to make truces with other factions and even ally with them in order to observe, understand and maybe even learn. If their contributions foster a more open and inquisitive attitude in others, is that such a bad thing?

Goals: Access to information — demonic, scientific, human historic, mythological or "other" — is an over-arching Cryptic urge. Any particular datum could hold a vital clue.

More immediately, the Cryptics have established their primary stronghold in Atlanta, Georgia, and they are rapidly beefing up ancillary safe houses in Dallas, Chicago and Washington, DC in the United States. Basically, they're aiming to get a tough cadre in place at every major airline hub. They're expanding similarly in Europe, starting from Heathrow in London. Smaller cadres have been assigned to Tokyo, Beijing and Rio de Janeiro.

The point of having strong defensive positions near large airports is that it preserves their mobility — and their ability to monitor the travels of other fallen. Their immediate goal is to create an inventory of every fallen who walks the Earth. Learning of the Earthbound has made finding those demons a priority as well.

These master lists — the *Scelestinomicon* (Book of the Rebels) for fallen, and the *Crucianomicon* (Book of the Tormented) for Earthbound — are meant initially to form the nucleus of an information network for all fallen. As the Cryptic faction grows, use of them may become more defined — or less open.

Luciferan

Angels are undying creatures, and when compassed by the span of an infinite lifetime, any setback short of destruction is a temporary thing.

Not every Hell-bound spirit lost faith. Not every fallen angel gave up hope. Even in defeat, some stayed true to the principles that led them to rebel. Love for mankind. Loyalty to Lucifer. A committed belief that their cause was right, and that Heaven and the obedient Host were wrong.

The Luciferans are as ready to do battle for their beliefs today as they were when they were hurled, spitting defiance, into their gloomy prison. While many are bowed, bitter and tormented, they are unbroken. Indeed, many find much encouragement in their new circumstances.

The world may be ruined, singular and mechanistic, but by the same token, there seem to be no angels left running the show. Even a vastly weakened army can triumph if it takes the field unopposed.

Add to that the heartening fact that they were able to escape imprisonment in the first place. If they are truly anathema to God, hated in His eyes and, by the words of His messenger, condemned to eternal torture… how has it come to pass that so many have re-entered the world of men? The Cryptics may mutter about divine subterfuge, but isn't it simpler to think that God's power is simply fading? That the demons of Hell find freedom because God's cages have lost their strength?

Most important, they point in triumph to Lucifer's absence from Hell. The Luciferans believe, not that he merited some unique punishment, but that he escaped punishment altogether. Perhaps their strongest stayed free, because their foes were unable to confine him! Perhaps the sundering of the Abyss is his doing! Perhaps the Adversary waits even now, watching to see who is still ready to fight… and who will prove too weak.

Rivals: The Luciferans are surprisingly tolerant toward the Raveners. Since the Raveners retain their military bent, Luciferans tend to regard them as soldiers with admirable zest. They just need some discipline, and they'll be useful once again.

The same sort of condescension and backhanded goodwill extends to the Faustians, only in reverse. To a Luciferan, a Faustian has sufficient discipline and the right *general* idea — they just need to remember who's boss.

No, the factions that earn Luciferan ire are the hesitant, the cowardly, the muddlepated and indecisive: the Cryptics and the Reconcilers.

Cryptics are like swimmers who question the dive in midair. They're so obsessed with sorting through myriad possibilities that they give little thought to the facts on the ground and the *here and now*. Neurasthenic navel-gazing is beneath the dignity of any Elohim, but that's nonetheless the Cryptics' main preoccupation. To the action-oriented Luciferans, the contemplative questioners are ultimately useless and weak.

The only thing worse than being weak is being treacherous. Therefore, the only thing worse than a quivering Cryptic is an ass-kissing Reconciler. These pathetic, deluded Elohim are like swimmers who turn in mid dive and try to climb back on the diving board! Apparently they weren't paying attention when the full implications of rebellion were discussed, nor when

the Heavenly Host damned them to the Abyss. You'd think a term in Hell would show them the truth about God's forgiveness, but instead they cling like lampreys to the idea of making peace with Him.

Houses: Lucifer ruled the First House, and Angelic loyalties die with difficulty. Many Devils still rally to the banner of their once (and future?) lord. Some may simply believe that, as Dawn Spirits themselves, their place in the Morningstar's new world will be a high one. Others — though they would never admit it — look to Lucifer to fill the void left by God's rejection. They crave orders to carry, and the Adversary was always good at giving them.

Some Devourers who fought well in the war remain loyal, buoyed up by memories of glory and hopes for revenge. By and large, these Devourers are less burdened by Torment than their fellows in the Ravener camp. Unlike the nihilists, Luciferan Devourers still have hope that something can be built from the world — once all the clutter is cleared away, of course.

Scourges are also attracted to the Luciferan cause for many of the same reasons as Devils. As the second rank of nobility among the Houses, there's a certain appeal to siding with the onetime Highest Angel. More than that, there's a profound appeal to believing that the Unholy Host is not just rising again, but that it never really fell. If that's true, then maybe the punishments meted out by God and declared by Michael can be foiled as well — particularly the devastating curse of human decay and death.

Despite this promise, few Slayers are Luciferan. As members of the Last House, there's no snob factor to appeal to them. More than that, though, the Slayers, whose punishment was arguably the most horrifying, seem the least able to believe that the first war was anything other than a decisive loss for the rebels.

Leadership: Grifiel, the highest rebel of Wild House, remains loyal to Lucifer despite all the misery and defeat he has endured on the Morningstar's behalf. Once a noble and honorable warrior, Grifiel has discarded his scruples and ethics one by one — along with his beauty, his sanity and his ability to love. He follows the Adversary less from conviction than from mad obsession. Denying Lucifer would be like admitting that everything he has lost and suffered is pointless. He'll be hurled back into Hell or reduced to nothing at all before giving up the rebellion.

While Grifiel retains the cunning and ruthlessness one looks for in a front-line leader, the Scourge Nazriel has emerged as the ultimate leader of the Luciferans — until the Morningstar returns, of course. Styling herself Nazathor, Princess of Majestic Liberation, she maneuvers her faction with care and caution — striking hard, but quickly sinking back into the safety of night. Reputed to be Lucifer's lover, few dare oppose her.

Goals: The primary goal of the Luciferan faction is, obviously, the location of their leader. Accomplishing this involves a threefold plan. First, Luciferan outriders are sent to scour the globe for any sign of demonic activity. Initially they were sent individually, but too many lone wolves got picked off by Earthbound, hostile demon factions or more mysterious beings. Now they're sent in packs.

Secondly, the Luciferans are keeping a close watch on the media. Specifically, they're trying to invest money in it and gain influential media thralls in order to get first dibs on incoming news that might involve demons. It also gives them an advantage covering up Luciferan activities, as well as a platform for sending out covert messages. But, as with the outriders, the Luciferans have found unusual opposition in the media as well.

Thirdly, the Luciferans are mounting an aggressive communications campaign among the fallen. Lucifer himself hasn't answered the call, but sooner or later, every Hell-damned Elohim whose name is remembered by a Luciferan can expect an invocation asking for information.

RAVENER

The Age of Wrath was long and hard. A lot of good people and valiant Elohim suffered and died. Illusions were lost. Honor gave way to pragmatism, which in turn sank beneath the weight of vengeance and anger and simple despair. Men discovered evil, and angels learned to embrace hatred. By the end of the war, many among the fallen had become little more than living engines of destruction, their joy in creation perverted into a love only of annihilation.

They were crazed, vicious and debased *before* the war was lost. *Before* they were stripped of the greater part of their power. *Before* they were condemned to a maddening Hell of isolation and loss for a term that felt like forever even to eternal beings.

Now, those bitter and wrathful Elohim have emerged from ages spent with no distraction save the pain of their own sanity eating itself… and they find a world as loathsome and corrupted as they themselves have been. Beholding a fouled planet, a debased and cruel humanity and a cosmos shrunk into a withered husk of its onetime glory, they see only one meaningful act.

Destroy.

Destroy everything.

Wipe away this cruel mockery of the Paradise they once designed. Give humanity the merciful silence of the grave. Destroy the works of God at any and all times, hoping perhaps to provoke Him into finally annihilating *them*.

Victory is impossible for the fallen, but they may yet be strong enough to wreck the prize — the world — even as it is wrested from their grasping claws.

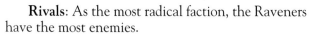

Rivals: As the most radical faction, the Raveners have the most enemies.

They hate the Luciferans for being willfully misled. If Lucifer engineered the Great Escape, just where is he? It's nauseating to watch beings who were once the *lords of Creation* scuttling around looking for a new bearded patriarch to lead them to glory, smite the wicked and tuck them into bed at night. They might as well wait for Godot as for their precious Morningstar.

Perhaps the only spectacle more repulsive than Elohim acting like children is Elohim acting like parents. The Faustians have gone from serving God, to opposing God, to being brutalized by God… to thinking they can *replace* God? The Raveners find this train of reasoning laughable, especially since the Faustians think *they're* the crazy ones.

While the Faustians and Luciferans are insane to think they can still make any kind of serious assault against God, they at least understand that there's a *war going on* and that it didn't stop just because one side was beaten into submission for a million years. The Reconcilers are, perhaps, the winners of the hotly contested "Most Despised by Ravener" label simply because they are the most optimistic.

About the only faction the Raveners even tolerate is the Cryptics, simply because they don't (yet) stand for much. Raveners figure they'll eventually get fed up with asking "Why?" and start smashing stuff. It's the only natural course for a realist.

Houses: The ravening Devourer is a stereotype for good reason. Devourers are perhaps the least inclined toward deliberate reflection, and Raveners are the faction of action. Unlike every other group, the Raveners hold out no hope for eventual victory, so why bother with plans for a hundred years from now or ten or even one? Living hard and dying harder are honorable goals to the virile Devourers.

The subtler Raveners are the Defilers who became soured on beauty by war and exile. Now dedicated to taking an ugly world and making it uglier, they are the oft-unseen velvet glove moving in the shadow of an Devourer's iron fist. A ravening Devourer who finds you will probably just kill you. A ravening Defiler is more likely to craft you into someone who destroys himself — after undermining or outright wrecking everything you once valued.

Arrayed against the Raveners are the majority of Malefactors. Perhaps their attunement to the Earth's depths makes the surface decay less offensive to them. Perhaps staid and careful natures used to working on geological time are uncomfortable with the faction's perceived spontaneity. Or perhaps they cannot repress their ultimately creative natures enough to pledge allegiance to destruction.

Leadership: Sauriel the Releaser commands the respect and obedience of his fellow Raveners. One of the few Slayers to pursue the Ravener philosophy, he is one of the few who can pursue vengeance and cruelty even beyond the grave. Once one of Lucifer's Archdukes, he leads by threat and intimidation more than persuasion.

His opposite number is Suphlatus. She used to be the Giver of Flowing Waters, but now is the Duchess of Dust. She believes (and loudly proclaims) that the fall of the rebellion was due to treachery from within — specifically, treachery by the one rebel who was conspicuously absent from the Abyss. "One who betrayed once would betray again," she declares, and she now sets herself the task of undermining the best efforts of men, angels and demons alike. The hatred between her and Nazathor is so potent that just to step between them is to be scalded by wrath.

Goals: While Raveners have a reputation for mindless carnage, they are actually fairly careful to choose targets that can be isolated and assaulted without reprisal. Raveners are particularly active in war-torn regions, where their viciousness can easily be blamed on either side (or, ideally, blamed on each by the other). To perform these missions, however, requires a safe base to which they can return. Ravener bases are currently under construction in northern Iraq, Macedonia, the mountains of Mexico and in Kashmir. More Raveners are being sent to western Africa, the Andes mountains in South America, and the areas between the Aral and Caspian seas. Raveners operate in North America, but in smaller numbers and with more subtlety than elsewhere.

RECONCILER

Angels are, by nature, creatures of virtue. Even the fallen remember their uncorrupted nature.

Some virtues come easily to beings of godlike wisdom and power. But the virtue of humility is not one of them.

Nonetheless, the silence of the Abyss gives much time for reflection. Like the Cryptics, the Reconcilers spent their time of imprisonment contemplating deep questions. But where the Cryptics looked outward and back, the Reconcilers looked inward… and forward.

Their most essential question was: *What if we were wrong?*

What if? What if the rebellion was as evil as Michael and the loyal Host said? What if God's punishing touch was somehow justified by the disobedience of His servants and children? What if Usiel and Lailah were right all along — that by trying to avoid the Age of Wrath, the Unholy Host only made it real?

If so — if the construction of Hell was necessary, if the sundering of the facets was merited, if the condemnation of the fallen was just — then what do the fallen do now?

Some believe that even in the eleventh hour, the mercy of God can be found. These Reconcilers listen with hope to the stories of Jesus, of Mohammed, of other human prophets and saviors. Maybe God *has* forgiven mankind. And if He can forgive them, might not His mercy extend to penitent servants as well?

Even if His punishment is eternal, and the Elohim are barred forever from His presence… well, might not the Earth be repaired? Perhaps not restored to the Paradise it was, but something great, and glorious, and maybe even *pure*, could be raised from the ashes. The fallen have lost much of their power, true, but the world is smaller as well. Surely a third of the Heavenly Host can still improve the universe, can still help and serve humanity?

This is the Reconciler's hope: to make peace with their Maker and jailer. Failing that, they hope to make peace with unending exile.

Rivals: The Reconcilers are modestly friendly toward the Faustians. After all, they share the goal of directly improving the world, even if they don't see eye-to-eye on how to do it or why. They are also open to Cryptics because they think the questions eventually lead to Reconciler answers.

No, the Reconcilers consider their main enemies to be the Luciferans and the Raveners. The Luciferans because their opposition to God is their primary, stated goal. (Granted, it's a goal for the Faustians too, but it seems ancillary to their self-aggrandizement.) That sort of concerted, organized resistance is the sort of thing that makes reconciliation much less likely.

If the Luciferans are despised for their orderly, stupid refusal to face facts, the Raveners are worse for their reckless, chaotic despair and nihilism. It's pathetic when a onetime minister of existence can't conceive a better goal than, "Shit on everything I made."

Houses: As the least destructive goal, reconciliation holds little appeal for antsy Devourers. While the idea of remaking the world might seem tempting to them, the Faustian program — which tends to be more active and less contemplative — gets those Devourers who still retain interest in improving things.

The abstract and long-term nature of the Reconcilers' goals tends to attract more thoughtful and conceptual demons, particularly those of the Second and Last Houses. Scourges and Slayers are both closely tied to human (and cosmic) decay and death, so the promise of renewal and reinvention is clearly attractive to them. Additionally, both Houses tend to feel guilt over the mortality and decline they inflicted on mankind. Of all fallen goals, Reconciliation holds out the most promise of making it up to them.

Leadership: The Devil Nuriel leads the Reconcilers, and her reputation is such to give even the most scornful Ravener pause. Before the Fall, she was the Throne of Inexorable Command. During the rebellion, she was Overlord of Daring Liberation, and many Elohim who oppose her cause still owe their existence to her superbly executed rescue raids during the Age of Wrath.

Nuriel is a warrior who has grown sick of fighting and seeks a better way. While she is the chief speaker (and planner) for the Reconcilers, its real philosophical soul is the Scourge Ouestucati, onetime Archangel of the Ocean Wind. One of the few fallen who is penitent without anger, she leads primarily by example. Her tranquility and hope give hope to others that they, too, may adapt to banishment.

Goals: The immediate goal of the Reconcilers is to take stock of the cosmos and learn as much as possible about its current condition. Doing so means exploring the human condition, so many Reconcilers are travelers, seeking a balanced view of mankind and man's world. They don't stop at the edges of human experience, though. They are seeking the truth about the supernatural as well. Have *all* the loyal angels really abandoned the world, or do any facets remain, even partially?

At the end of the narrow alley the junkie pleaded for a break. The pusher handed over the nickel bag with a sneer and headed for the busy street, failing to see the homeless man who sat in the shadow of a stinking Dumpster watching the familiar scene unfold.

Sam Ashbury saw the young detective shoot up in a dark corner of the alley, sobbing with shame and need, and he felt the familiar, unwelcome stirring of pity in his soul.

"Nice night for it," Ashbury said. The cop jerked, groggy from the smack but still half alert. He tossed the syringe into the piles of trash and dragged his pistol from its holster.

"Police officer!" The young cop staggered under the twin blows of drugs and adrenaline, his gaze darting between the alley's many pools of shadow. "Come out where I can see you!"

Ashbury could smell the desperation on the man — desperate enough to kill any witnesses to his shame. He considered the young man carefully, the words of power rising from memory. Ashbury slowly climbed to his feet and moved toward the man, his voice thrumming with energies meant to dissolve the mortal's anger and shame.

"Come on now, buddy. No need to go making things worse. You just look like you could use some real help, you know?"

For a moment, the detective could only stare at him, eyes wide and pistol wavering. Then tears began to spill down his cheeks and he slid down the wall to the alley floor. "God... oh Jesus, help me," he said again and again.

Sam hunkered down, started pulling his makings from the bulging pockets of his fatigue jacket. "How long has it been, buddy? How does a cop get caught up in something like this?"

"I've only... it's only been a year. I was in a car accident. They had me on morphine, and when I got out, I see the stuff every day down here, you know? Every day."

"Go on," Ashbury said quietly. In the dark, his fingers sorted through cogs, pieces of glass, lengths of bronze and other bits of junk.

"Half the damn force is on the take. Would you believe it? They throw me nickel bags and make me... I'm working for the goddamn *pushers* now, not the police." The detective closed his eyes and leaned his head back against the filthy wall. "Christ, why am I telling *you* this?"

"Because you don't want to be this way," Ashbury said. "You made a terrible mistake once, and now you'd do anything to make it right. I understand that. Believe me."

The cop lifted his head, looked at the unwashed bum sitting in the dark and fiddling with pieces of old junk. "I wish that were true. God knows I tried, but I can't... I've done so many terrible things. I don't *deserve* another chance."

Ashbury sighed. *Damn.* Now he *had* to help the guy.

"What would you say if I told you I could give you something that would free you from the smack? Give you your life back again, and maybe a chance to clean things up around here?" He picked up a small brass tube and raised it to the light, keeping his voice casual. "What would that be worth to you?"

The cop laughed bleakly and shook his head. "What the hell do you think? I'd sell my soul to get off this shit."

The fallen angel who called himself Sam Ashbury smiled slightly, feeling strangely sad. "You've got yourself a deal."

CHAPTER SIX: FEET OF CLAY

There is but one good; that is God. Everything else is good when it
looks to Him and bad when it turns from Him. And the higher and mightier
it is in the natural order, the more demoniac it will be if it rebels. It is not
out of bad mice or bad fleas you make demons, but out of bad archangels.
—C. S. Lewis, *The Great Divorce*

To play **Demon: The Fallen**, you create a character, a role that you play much like an actor playing a part in a movie, allowing you to take part in the story. The characters in **Demon** are the protagonists of the drama, facing different challenges to reach their goals. Rather than creating a new character each time you play, you can play the same character over and over. As the stories unfold, your character can grow and develop, like characters in a television show or a series of novels.

This chapter contains all the information you need to create a **Demon** character, from the basic concept to the various traits that describe the character's abilities. Read through the chapter carefully before creating your first character. Although you can easily create characters on their own, it's best to consult with your Storyteller, to ensure that the character fits into the overall story as much as possible.

TRAITS

Characters in **Demon** have different qualities. Some are strong, some are quick, and some are clever, while others are less capable. A character's various abilities are measured by traits — the numerical ratings that show what a character can do. When you create a **Demon** character, you assign point values to different traits as part of the process of describing your character.

Traits describe most of a character's quantifiable qualities such as strength, knowledge, skills and so forth. Most traits are on a scale from 1 to 5. A rating of 1 is poor, 2 is average, and 3 is good. A rating of 4 is unusually good, while a 5 is truly extraordinary, the peak of human achievement. Demons have the ability to enhance their traits beyond even this level, making them truly superhuman, though they generally fall into the same scale as mortals (at least while wearing mortal flesh).

A few traits (Faith, Torment and Willpower) are rated on a scale from 1 to 10 rather than 1 to 5. They're described in detail later in this chapter. Regardless, the rating of a trait is generally the number of dice you roll when you call upon that trait (see Chapter Eight for details).

COMMON TRAITS AND TERMS

Most **Demon** characters have the following traits, as shown on the character sheet.

Name: The character's name. Note that demons have True Names and Celestial Names, as well as the names of their mortal vessels, and they may have various other pseudonyms.

Player: That's you—the person playing the character in the game.

Chronicle: The chronicle is the linked series of stories your character takes part in, like chapters in a novel or books in a series. The name or title of the chronicle—usually provided by the Storyteller—goes here.

Attributes: The character's most basic traits, describing raw potential such as strength, intelligence, charisma and so forth.

Abilities: All of the things a character learns or practices (including certain natural aptitudes or talents) are considered Abilities.

Backgrounds: Background traits represent resources a character has picked up earlier in life, ranging from friends and contacts to wealth and possessions.

Apocalyptic Form: This space is provided to list the eight special abilities conferred by the character's apocalyptic form, for ease of reference.

Faith: This is a measure of the power a demon has reaped by acquiring mortal belief and worship, used to fuel the various powers of the fallen.

Torment: This trait reflects the lingering memories a demon has of millennia of exile in the Abyss. The greater a demon's Torment is, the more twisted and less human it becomes.

Health: Since they wear mortal flesh, demons are vulnerable to injury and even death much like mortals are, although the often have various means of avoiding injury and repairing their mortal vessels. This trait measures a character's current state of health and physical condition.

Nature: A term describing the character's true personality and motivations, deep drives and passions.

Demeanor: This is the attitude or personality the character presents to the world, not always the same as the character's Nature (since many people hide their true nature behind various demeanors).

Concept: A short description of the character's role or background goes here. Sum the character's concept up in a couple of words, such as "Cynical Detective" or "Idealistic Revolutionary."

House: The demonic House the character belongs to. A demon's House influences his attitude, outlook and abilities.

Faction: The faction that the character belongs to. A demon's choice of faction influences his outlook on humanity, the future of the fallen and his attitudes toward other demons.

Visage: This is the name of the character's apocalyptic form, determined by the character's primary lore.

Lore: The fallen have access to various kind of lore, knowledge of the inner workings of the universe and how to control them.

Virtues: The virtues of Conscience, Conviction and Courage represent the character's nascent human qualities of compassion and altruism, and they are used to resist the corruptive influence of Torment.

Willpower: Willpower measures a character's drive and dedication, the ability to overcome obstacles and succeed against all odds.

Experience: Even the fallen can learn from hard experience. Characters gain experience for completing stories and overcoming challenges. You can use experience to improve your character's traits.

DEMON the fallen

Name:
Player:
Chronicle:

Nature:
Demeanor:
Concept:

House:
Faction:
Visage:

ATTRIBUTES

PHYSICAL		SOCIAL		MENTAL	
Strength	●0000	Charisma	●0000	Perception	●0000
Dexterity	●0000	Manipulation	●0000	Intelligence	●0000
Stamina	●0000	Appearance	●0000	Wits	●0000

ABILITIES

TALENTS		SKILLS		KNOWLEDGES	
Alertness	00000	Animal Ken	00000	Academics	00000
Athletics	00000	Crafts	00000	Computer	00000
Awareness	00000	Demolitions	00000	Finance	00000
Brawl	00000	Drive	00000	Investigation	00000
Dodge	00000	Etiquette	00000	Law	00000
Empathy	00000	Firearms	00000	Linguistics	00000
Expression	00000	Melee	00000	Medicine	00000
Intimidation	00000	Performance	00000	Occult	00000
Intuition	00000	Security	00000	Politics	00000
Leadership	00000	Stealth	00000	Religion	00000
Streetwise	00000	Survival	00000	Research	00000
Subterfuge	00000	Technology	00000	Science	00000

ADVANTAGES

BACKGROUNDS		LORE		VIRTUES	
_____	00000	_____	00000	Conscience	●0000
_____	00000	_____	00000	Conviction	●0000
_____	00000	_____	00000	Courage	●0000
_____	00000	_____	00000		
_____	00000	_____	00000		

Apocalyptic Form
_____
_____
_____
_____
_____
_____
_____
_____

Faith
O O O O O O O O O O
□ □ □ □ □ □ □ □ □ □

Torment
Permanent
O O O O O O O O O O
Temporary
O O O O O O O O O O

Willpower
O O O O O O O O O O
□ □ □ □ □ □ □ □ □ □

Health
Bruised		□
Hurt	-1	□
Injured	-1	□
Wounded	-2	□
Mauled	-2	□
Crippled	-5	□
Incapacitated		□

Experience
☐

GETTING STARTED

Creating a **Demon** character follows five simple steps, described in the following pages and outlined on p. 123. Keep the following guidelines in mind when creating a character:

• The fallen were scattered widely by the opening of the Abyss and the Maelstrom, appearing in different places around the world. Distance as we know it has little meaning in the crossing between the Abyss and the mortal world. Therefore, demons may have taken nearly any mortal form, from anywhere in the world. Their mortal vessel may be young or old, male or female, and of nearly any ethnicity, nationality or background. The only requirement is that the mortal soul is too weak or too broken to resist possession (due to crushing despair, mental trauma, coma or similar circumstances), allowing the demon to enter. Certain mortal vessels may call for certain traits or Backgrounds. For example, an athletic body has decent Physical Attributes, while a wealthy vessel merits a look at the Resources Background (assuming the demon still has access to the mortal's wealth).

• The character-creation system is designed to create newly risen demons, those only recently returned to the mortal world and in possession of mortal vessels. Although the fallen once commanded earthshaking power, their abilities were greatly limited before their exile and weakened even more by their long imprisonment and terrible torment. It is assumed that demon characters are in possession of only a portion of their true power, but that it may grow over the course of the chronicle (through the use of experience).

• To reflect these limitations, you get a certain number of points to spend on various traits, as well as a number of "freebie points" you can use to improve different traits and fine-tune your character's design. This means that it's best to focus on characters who are capable in a few specific areas (or modestly capable in a number of areas) rather than trying to create characters who are good at everything. You may want to consult with your fellow players to see what their characters' specialties are, so you can ensure that your character complements them and has a unique niche in the group.

• Remember that a rating of 1 is poor, 2 is average, 3 is good, and greater than 3 is outstanding. That means that a rating of 2 isn't bad and a rating of 3 is above average. Don't worry if your character doesn't have dice pools of 5 or more for everything, that's not unusual. Also remember that your character is just starting out, so you'll be able to improve traits with experience as the chronicle progresses.

• Although the fallen are not the most sociable of creatures, they often gather together out of mutual need, particularly those dedicated to preventing the lords of the Abyss from returning. Hunted by the Earthbound as well as mortal and supernatural enemies, these demons have good reasons to band together, primarily protection and pooling their resources toward achieving their goals. Keep in mind that your character should be able to at least function as part of a group and have something to offer the other characters apart from frustration.

THE STORYTELLER AND CHARACTER CREATION

The Storyteller plays an important role in character creation, since he's the one who sets the tone of the chronicle and keeps an eye on "the big picture." That means the Storyteller can guide players, making sure their characters fit into the overall story of the chronicle, and adjusting the story as needed to accommodate the ideas and desires of the players. The character creation process can provide numerous story ideas based on the background and goals of the various characters.

If you are the Storyteller, start off by familiarizing your players with the character-creation process, step by step. Go over the character sheet with them and explain the various traits and what they mean. Then go over the outline of character creation, explaining how the players will build their characters.

Tell the players what sort of chronicle you want to run and get their initial ideas for characters, pointing out when you think a concept isn't suited to the chronicle and coming up with ways the player might want to modify it. For example, you might want to run a chronicle based in a specific city, so you'll want all the characters to live in the city, whether they've been there for some time or have only recently arrived. Be fair but firm when it comes to the character concepts your players propose. If a concept doesn't fit into your story framework, it's better to tell the player so in advance, allowing him the opportunity to come up with a new character.

You may want to set one whole game session aside for the players to create characters and for you to run the characters through their preludes (p. 128), giving everyone a firm idea of who the characters are and what they can do before the chronicle begins. Help the players individually create their characters, offering hints and suggestions and encouraging players to give their characters depth, personality and motivation (the list of questions on p. 129 may be helpful in that regard). Then run a prelude for each character (possibly including the other characters, if some of them have met before). Finally, you can run a short prelude or "prologue" about how the characters get together before the story opens and the chronicle begins.

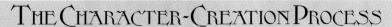

THE CHARACTER-CREATION PROCESS

- **Step One:** Character Concept

Choose concept, House, faction, Nature and Demeanor.

- **Step Two:** Select Attributes

Prioritize the three categories: Physical, Social and Mental (7/5/3). Your character automatically has one dot in each Attribute.

- **Step Three:** Select Abilities

Prioritize the three categories: Talents, Skills, Knowledges (13/9/5). Your character does not start with any dots in any Abilities.

Choose Talents, Skills, Knowledges.

No Ability rating can be higher than 3 at this stage.

- **Step Four:** Select Advantages

Choose Backgrounds (5) and Lore (3), and rate Virtues (3). Your character automatically has one dot in each Virtue.

- **Step Five:** Finishing Touches

Record starting Faith (3), Torment (based on demonic House) and Willpower (equal to sum of two highest Virtues).

Spend freebie points (15).

SAMPLE CONCEPTS

- **Criminal** — ex-con, gangster, Mafioso, Yakuza, drug dealer, pimp, thug, thief, fence
- **Drifter** — homeless, junkie, smuggler, biker, grifter
- **Entertainer** — actor, musician, comedian, artist, street performer
- **Intellectual** — professor, scholar, scientist, student, teacher, writer
- **Investigator** — detective, government agent, police officer, monster-hunter
- **Kid** — child, runaway, gangbanger, orphan, wealthy heir
- **Nightlifer** — club kid, barfly, raver, punk, junkie
- **Outsider** — immigrant, minority, conspiracy theorist, religious fanatic
- **Politician** — campaign manager, elected official, judge, political aide, speechwriter
- **Professional** — computer programmer, doctor, engineer, investment broker, lawyer
- **Reporter** — journalist, news anchor, photojournalist, tabloid reporter
- **Religious** — layman, New Ager, nun, priest, rabbi, shaman, zealot
- **Socialite** — dilettante, heir, playboy, prominent spouse

- **Soldier** — bodyguard, career officer, enforcer, mercenary, soldier
- **Worker** — farmer, laborer, retail worker, trucker

HOUSES

- **Devils** — Charismatic tempters and deceivers, able to twist souls with their honeyed words.
- **Scourges** — Bearers of plague and pestilence, these demons can harm (or heal) with a touch.
- **Malefactors** — Artisans of the fallen, able to create any wonder, for a price.
- **Fiends** — Masters of fate as written in the stars, dispensers of nightmares and curses.
- **Defilers** — Glamorous shape-changers, able to alter their form to become anyone's greatest desire.
- **Devourers** — Warriors of the fallen, given charge of the beasts and wild things.
- **Slayers** — Tormenters of the dead, able to raise ghosts and rip living souls from their bodies.

ARCHETYPES

- **Addict** — There's something you've just got to have, no matter what.
- **Architect** — You want to create something lasting.
- **Autocrat** — You get things done. Your way.
- **Bon Vivant** — Life is a banquet, and most poor bastards are starving.
- **Bravo** — Might makes right, and you're always right.
- **Caregiver** — Everyone needs someone to take care of them.
- **Child** — Won't someone take care of you?
- **Competitor** — Life is a contest you aim to win.
- **Conformist** — You know your place, and you stay in it.
- **Conniver** — Why work hard when you can get others to do it for you?
- **Curmudgeon** — Nothing is ever good enough.
- **Deviant** — What's normal?
- **Director** — There's an order to everything.
- **Fanatic** — You devote everything to your cause.
- **Gallant** — You love the spotlight and the adoration of the masses.
- **Gambler** — You're willing to risk everything on a chance for something better.
- **Judge** — You work to improve the system from within.
- **Loner** — You prefer to be on your own.
- **Martyr** — You were made to suffer for the benefit of others.

- **Masochist** — You test the limits of pain and endurance.
- **Monster** — A true demon, you delight in suffering and pain.
- **Pedagogue** — You know all the answers, and you're eager to share them.
- **Penitent** — You have sinned and must redeem yourself.
- **Perfectionist** — You expect and demand only the best from yourself and others.
- **Rebel** — Down with the system! Authority must be challenged.
- **Rogue** — You look out for yourself first.
- **Survivor** — You can handle anything life throws at you.
- **Thrill-Seeker** — What a rush! You're all about finding the next big thrill.
- **Traditionalist** — The way it's always been done is good enough for you.
- **Trickster** — Humor is your weapon and your shield in life.
- **Visionary** — You see the potential in things, the way they could be.

Celestial Powers

Lore of Awakening — The secrets of animating living and unliving matter.

Lore of the Beast — The secrets of animal summoning, control and possession.

Lore of the Celestials — The power to enhance the evocations of another demon.

Lore of Death — The secrets of death and decay.

Lore of the Earth — The secrets of controlling the forces of the earth.

Lore of Flame — The power to summon and control fire.

Lore of the Firmament — The power to view people and events across vast distances.

Lore of the Flesh — The secrets of restoring, enhancing and shaping living flesh.

Lore of the Forge — The power to shape raw matter into objects of wonder.

Lore of the Fundament — The secrets of the fundamental forces underlying the universe.

Lore of Humanity — The power to engage, influence and manipulate mortals.

Lore of Light — The secrets of manipulating light to create potent illusions.

Lore of Longing — The power to manipulate a mortal's deepest desires.

Lore of Paths — The power to find, create or seal pathways between two points.

Lore of Patterns — The secrets of reading the Grand Design and predicting what is to come.

Lore of Portals — The power to control doorways between spaces and dimensions.

Lore of Radiance — The power to inspire, awe and terrify mortals.

Lore of the Realms — The secrets of travel between the physical and spirit realms.

Lore of the Spirit — The power to summon, command and bind the spirits of the dead.

Lore of Storms — The secrets of commanding the power of sea and storm.

Lore of Transfiguration — The power to transform into the object of another's desire.

Lore of the Wild — The power to command the green things of forest and field.

Lore of the Winds — The power to call and command the winds.

Backgrounds

- **Allies** — Mortal allies you can call upon for aid.
- **Contacts** — Information resources at your disposal
- **Eminence** — Your status among your fellow demons.
- **Fame** — How well known your mortal host is among human society.
- **Followers** — Mortal helpers who are loyal to you.
- **Influence** — Power in the mortal world.
- **Legacy** — The degree to which your character recalls his divine existence prior to possessing his mortal body.
- **Mentor** — An experienced teacher or guide who gives you advice.
- **Pacts** — Mortal sources of Faith.
- **Paragon** — You're particularly strong in an aspect of your House's influence.
- **Resources** — Wealth and material possessions.

Freebie Points

Trait	Cost
Attribute	5 per dot
Ability	2 per dot
Lore	7 per dot
Background	1 per dot
Faith	6 per dot
Virtue	2 per dot
Willpower	1 per dot

STEP ONE: CHARACTER CONCEPT

Every **Demon** character starts out as an idea in the mind of a player. You slowly expand upon this basic idea, adding flesh to the bones and building up a character as complex and involved as you want. The process begins here and continues for as long as you play the character, adding layers of personality, history and experience to your basic idea. In this stage of character creation, you outline your basic concept, choose a House and faction and determine the character's Nature and Demeanor.

CONCEPT

The number of character concepts for **Demon: The Fallen** is virtually limitless, bound only by your imagination. Get an image or idea of the sort of character you want to play and try to describe it in just a few words — a stereotype or archetype such as "Slick Politician" or "Edgy Rebel." You can take a look at some of the sample concepts on p. 123 to get you started thinking of ideas. You may even want to jot down several different ideas as they come to mind, picking the one you like best. Once you've got your concept, expand upon it a little, maybe a couple of sentences or a paragraph, a quick sketch of the type of character you have in mind.

Characters in **Demon** are comprised of two distinct yet interrelated parts: the spirit of the fallen and the mind and body of its mortal host. The spirit of the fallen provides the character's personality, attitudes, goals, virtues and vices, while the mortal vessel supplies the character's memories, relationships and emotional attachments that allow the demon to relate to the modern world. When you begin developing your character concept, you are envisioning an ancient, infernal spirit, witness to the act of Creation and veteran of a war against Heaven, who is thrust into the life of a human being. As you go through the process of defining your character, keep this duality in mind and consider in what ways the demonic spirit views, accepts or rejects the experiences that his human host forces upon him.

These concepts will be your guide throughout the character-creation process. When you come to the other decisions you need to make, refer back to your concept to give you an idea of which way to go. For example, if you conceive of your character's mortal vessel as a real jock-type, Physical Attributes and Abilities such as Athletics are important. On the other hand, a social-climbing character is more likely to emphasize Social traits. That doesn't mean you can't occasionally cast against type, giving your socialite an interest in rock-climbing or shooting, for example, or your athlete some smarts as well, but a solid concept makes the rest of the process easier.

HOUSE

Each demon belongs to a particular House. Originally, each angel's House was synonymous with his duties, his purpose in the grand scheme of Creation. Now Houses are the basic divisions of different types of demons, describing their talents and predilections. Demons from the same House don't necessarily act exactly the same, but they tend to share some of the same views and interests, as well as some of the same abilities and insights into the nature of Creation.

Take a look at the descriptions of the various Houses in Chapter Five and see which ones suit your character concept best. Depending on the chronicle, the Storyteller may limit or disallow demons from certain Houses.

FACTION

At one time, the fallen were of a single mind with respect to humanity and the struggle against the tyranny of Heaven. Yet as the tide of the war inexorably turned against the rebel host, several influential leaders began to question Lucifer's ideals and the purpose of the struggle for mankind. Now that the gates of the Abyss lie broken, the fallen are drawn to choose sides among these competing factions as each struggles to further its agenda in the modern world.

Factions are playing and storytelling aids that help define a character's perspective and motivations. Look over the descriptions of the various factions in Chapter Five and see which group fits your character concept best. Note that you don't have to choose a faction if you don't want to, placing your character among the ranks of the unaligned. Characters can also change or join a faction during play, making for tense tales of political intrigue.

NATURE AND DEMEANOR (ARCHETYPES)

While House describes what type of demon your character is, Nature and Demeanor describe what kind of person your character is. These are personality traits, known as *Archetypes* because they sum up an individual's complex drives and desires in a few simple terms.

Demeanor is the personality and attitude of the demon's mortal host — the face it presents to the world at large. Many people play roles or wear "masks" in life, so Demeanor may not be the same as Nature. Sometimes it is, though, particularly for self-confident people or those who don't particularly care what others think of them. Demeanor can even change from time to time or situation to situation. Think of how many people act one way at work, another with their friends, and yet another with their family. You may want to pick a primary Demeanor for your character and others for when your character is in different situations.

Nature is your character's true self — in this case, it's the personality of the demon that inhabits the mind

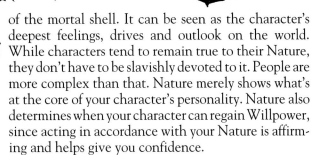

of the mortal shell. It can be seen as the character's deepest feelings, drives and outlook on the world. While characters tend to remain true to their Nature, they don't have to be slavishly devoted to it. People are more complex than that. Nature merely shows what's at the core of your character's personality. Nature also determines when your character can regain Willpower, since acting in accordance with your Nature is affirming and helps give you confidence.

As you consider a suitable Nature and Demeanor for your character, take into account how the personality of the fallen meshes with the life of his mortal host. If the two halves are completely different — a haughty Devil in possession of a mousy librarian, for example — it's entirely possible that the character's Nature depicts the true personality of the possessing spirit, while the Demeanor is the mortal face that the character shows the world. Conversely, its possible that the demon's personality and its mortal identity mesh seamlessly — a compassionate Slayer in the body of a mortician, or an impetuous but honorable Devourer in the body of a young policeman. In such a case, the Nature and Demeanor might well be the same.

For a complete description of the various Archetypes, see pp. 132-136.

STEP TWO: SELECT ATTRIBUTES

Now you begin assigning numbers to your character's traits. The first, and most basic, traits are Attributes, which define a character's raw potential. They say how strong, smart, clever, likeable and so forth your character is. Characters have nine Attributes, grouped into three groups of three. They are the Physical Attributes (Strength, Dexterity, Stamina), the Social Attributes (Charisma, Manipulation, Appearance) and the Mental Attributes (Perception, Intelligence, Wits).

Select one group of Attributes as the primary group for your character, based on your concept. This is the area at which the character is best. Then choose the secondary group, the one your character is average at. Finally, designate the tertiary group, the one your character is worst at. Of course, it's quite possible to be strictly average in your tertiary Attributes, it doesn't mean your character is terrible at them.

All characters begin with one dot in each Attribute, the absolute minimum capabilities of any character. You assign additional dots based on the priorities you assigned. You can assign seven additional dots to your primary Attribute group, five dots to your secondary group and three more dots to your tertiary group. You assign these additional dots any way you like within each group, as long as no Attribute is higher than five dots.

STEP THREE: SELECT ABILITIES

Like Attributes, Abilities are divided into three groups: Talents, Skills and Knowledges. *Talents* are intuitive abilities, either innate knacks or things your character has picked up from experience and practice. *Skills* are learned from training and regular practice, while *Knowledges* represent "book learning" and formalized knowledge, often acquired from study or schooling.

Select one group of Abilities as your character's primary group, one as secondary and one as tertiary, just like you do with Attributes. Your character concept will help determine how to prioritize Abilities. A scholar has Knowledges as primary, for example, while an athlete or street brawler is more likely to rely on Talents. It's a good idea to look over the Abilities in each category to see which ones suit your character concept. The category with the most suitable Abilities should be your primary one.

You get 13 dots to spend on primary Abilities, nine dots for secondary Abilities and five dots for tertiary Abilities. Note that characters do not start with any free dots in any Abilities, unlike Attributes. Also, you cannot increase any Abilities above three dots at this time, although you can do so using freebie points later on in the process (see p. 128).

STEP FOUR: SELECT ADVANTAGES

Now you further individualize your character by choosing traits that define your character's unique abilities and history. Advantages are not prioritized, instead you have a set number of dots to distribute among them. Plus you can buy additional dots with freebie points.

BACKGROUNDS

Your character acquires *Backgrounds* before entering the chronicle. They include various things such as allies, contacts and material resources. Like other traits, Backgrounds should suit your character concept. A homeless drifter isn't likely to have much in the way of Resources, for example. The Storyteller may require or disallow certain Backgrounds, or levels of Backgrounds, depending on the needs of the chronicle.

LORE

Once the fallen possessed tremendous powers that allowed them to shape Creation as their duties required. Their powers have weakened considerably since the Fall, but demons can still use the power of faith to work wonders. Each demon character knows certain *lore* that reflect control over a facet of Creation. You can allocate your character's starting Faith points to the lore your character

knows, and you can buy additional dots with freebie points. See Chapters Four and Seven for details on the various lore.

VIRTUES

Virtues define the mortal center of a **Demon** character, the qualities that the fallen cling to in the face of their Torment. Virtues combine the remnants of a demon's true divine nature and the awakened instincts and feelings of the mortal host. Together they give the fallen the ability to resist the draw of the Abyss, resist giving in to their terrible torment and seek redemption. Virtues define how easily the fallen can resist the darker impulses of their nature and avoid giving in to their Torment.

There are three Virtues. *Conscience* is a measure of the character's sense of morality, of right and wrong. *Conviction* is the strength of the character's beliefs, understanding and accepting the order of things. *Courage* is the character's ability to act on his beliefs, overcoming obstacles that may stand in his way.

Each character starts out with one dot in each Virtue, and the player may distribute three more dots among the Virtues. He may also use freebie points to increase them further. Virtues are important in helping determine the character's starting Willpower, so consider them carefully.

STEP FIVE: FINISHING TOUCHES

Finally, you can customize your character by spending 15 freebie points. You also need to determine a few other important traits.

FAITH

Faith is the source of a demon's power and very existence. Originally it reflected faith in God and His divine plan, but now a demon's faith is more a matter of self-confidence, faith in one's self and in humanity rather than any higher power. Faith measures how much influence a demon has over the fabric of Creation. It is also a reflection of the demon's confidence and assurance about his place in Creation and a measure of enlightenment and understanding of the universe. Characters start with a Faith score of 3, and players may increase it by spending freebie points.

TORMENT

The opposite of Faith is *Torment*. The fallen struggled with their decision to rebel and saw terrible things in their long war. They

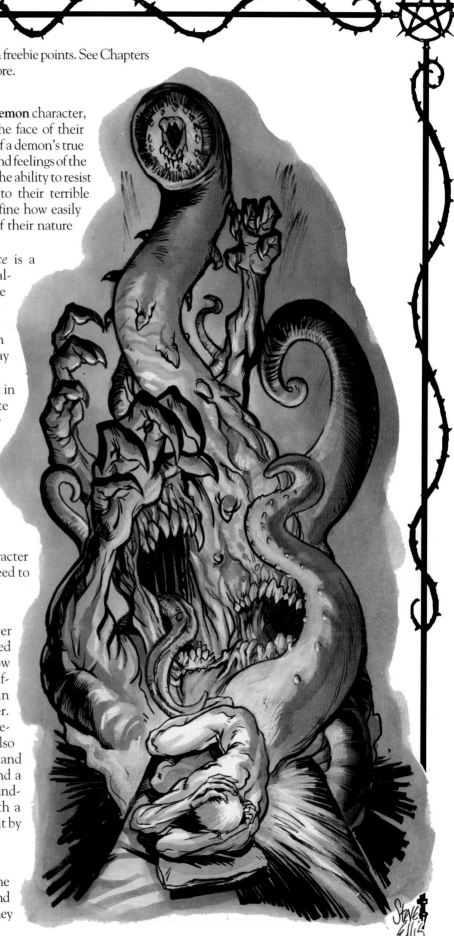

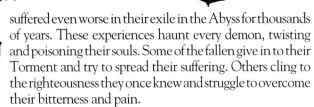

suffered even worse in their exile in the Abyss for thousands of years. These experiences haunt every demon, twisting and poisoning their souls. Some of the fallen give in to their Torment and try to spread their suffering. Others cling to the righteousness they once knew and struggle to overcome their bitterness and pain.

A character's beginning Torment score depends on which House he is from. Torment may increase or decrease depending on the character's actions during the game.

WILLPOWER

Willpower is closely related to Faith, since it reflects a character's self-control and determination. It's also the quality that helps demons keep from succumbing to their Torment. Your starting Willpower is equal to the sum of your two highest Virtues, although you may wish to raise your character's Willpower using freebie points, since it is so vital.

FREEBIE POINTS

You can now spend your 15 *freebie points* to customize your character's traits. These points can be spent on any trait you want. Each dot in a trait has a freebie point cost, consult the chart on p. 124 for the cost of various traits. You can use freebie points to increase an Ability above three dots, if you wish, or to improve areas where you feel your character needs it.

SPARK OF LIFE

Once you've got all of your character's traits worked out, give some thought to your character's other qualities. What do all those various traits *mean*? What sort of person is your character?

Take a look at your character's traits and give them some added depth. What is the character's Appearance score? What does the character look like? Someone with Appearance 3 is better than average looking, but in what way? Is it the character's body, face, expressions, hair, style or something else that adds up to that attractive Appearance? What does your character look like? How do other people perceive him? In what ways does the character's demonic soul reveal itself in its mortal mannerisms? Does the Devil inside the mousy librarian cause her to walk with a new sense of confidence and authority?

How do your characters' other Attributes manifest themselves? If your character is strong, is he heavily muscled or wiry? If he's got a high Intelligence, is he a know-it-all or the quiet type who thinks rather than acting? Do his Social traits indicate that he is comfortable dealing with others or somewhat awkward? How has that affected the way he thinks of people? How much of his charisma and social grace come from the demon's spirit and how much is ingrained habit from the human host?

Where did your character acquire her Abilities? Did they come from the demon's innate knowledge and experience,

are they recollections from the mortal vessel, or are they some combination of the two? What Abilities did the demon have before the Fall, and what did she learn during and after the rebellion? Are there any Abilities that belonged to the mortal vessel that the demon doesn't particularly care for but finds useful? What about Abilities that are completely new to the demon in some way (such as Computer)?

What about the character's Backgrounds? Are his allies and contacts aware of his true nature, or do they still believe he is an ordinary mortal? How did he acquire his followers and what do they believe about him? If the character has pacts with some mortals already, what are the details of those deals and what did the demon have to do to arrange them?

All these details flesh out your character and create a more complete picture in mind for when you play, helping you get inside your character's head. The more you know, the easier it will be to take on the role of your character in the game.

THE PRELUDE

Now that your character is ready to play, it's a good idea to test the waters a little with a prelude. A prelude is a short one-on-one session with the Storyteller, in which you get to play out some of your character's background and history leading up to the time when the chronicle begins. It helps give you a feel for your character and allows you to "fine tune" elements of background, personality, motivation and even game statistics by trying them out before the character enters the chronicle.

A prelude is more freeform than a regular game session, skipping around to cover the important points in the character's background, defining moments that help shape who the character is and will become. The player gets a chance to try the character on for size while the Storyteller gets to see how the player and character go together and how well the character suits the chronicle. Rolling dice and memorizing game stats isn't so important during the prelude, but if there are aspects of the game a player is unfamiliar with, it's a good time to learn them. The prelude can also serve as a chance to test out certain traits to see if the character is capable of what the player wants him or her to be able to do.

During the prelude, the concept of the character may change somewhat. This is perfectly fine, since the prelude is supposed to provide the opportunity for these kinds of changes. For example, players may discover that certain elements they had in mind work out differently when they play them out, putting a new spin on a character's background or personality. Players may want to tinker with their characters a bit after the prelude as well, fine-tuning them to reflect the events of the prelude or fixing problems they noticed the first

time out. Doing so helps ensure that players all start the chronicle with characters they're comfortable with.

For Storytellers, the prelude offers the opportunity to see characters in action before the chronicle begins and get an idea of what makes them tick. It's also a chance to lay the foundations for the chronicle in the characters' history. Storytellers can use the prelude to plant the seeds of relationships that may appear in the chronicle, such as romances, rivals, enemies and old friends. You can give the players a feel for the background of the World of Darkness and the history of the fallen by guiding them through some of its key moments, making them a part of the history rather than just passive observers. You can also use the prelude to foreshadow events in the chronicle, dropping hints about what is to come.

Generally, a prelude should cover major events in the character's life leading up to the beginning of the chronicle. For the fallen, this covers a long period of time, but it isn't necessary to detail every year, particularly the agonizing millennia of their imprisonment in the Abyss. Instead, hit the high points, the defining moments. You can begin with a look at how the world was when it was first made and the characters went about their duties as servants of God. Then you can play out scenes from the Fall and the rebellion, giving players a chance to experience them firsthand. Then comes the terrible judgment of Heaven and exile into the Abyss. You can play out the first moments of freedom when the fallen rise in their new, mortal bodies and have to face a world that is now alien to them.

It's quite possible that the characters may already know each other when the chronicle begins. In that case, the prelude is the perfect place to establish how they met, what their relationship was and what it has become. A prelude can follow two characters from their time as friends at the dawn of Creation to comrades during the rebellion to their separation and exile and their reunion in the modern world. It's also a great opportunity to build relationships with other characters in the story. Maybe a boon comrade from the rebellion is now an Earthbound adversary in the chronicle or a former rival is now a potential ally.

Don't worry too much about the game systems during the prelude. Use them more during recent events to give new players a grasp of how the game is played, but gloss over or ignore them entirely when dealing with the distant past, since the character's traits were vastly different (and more powerful) then, anyway. If you want, have a few suitable situations toward the end of the prelude where characters can take action and try out their traits. For example, a newly risen demon might have to deal with a gang of mortal criminals who think she's an easy mark, or perhaps with some police officers or soldiers. How players handle the situation (dice rolls and all) can tell you a lot about how they'll act in your chronicle.

Questions and Answers

There's a lot to take into account when creating the background of a **Demon** character. Take a look through the following questions when you're coming up with your character's background and consider the answers. They're the bare minimum things you'll want to know about your character before you begin playing him or her. Storytellers can also use these questions as part of the prelude to help players answer them in more detail and get a good handle on their characters.

• Who Were You Before the Fall?

The fallen all started out as something quite different from what they have become. Read through the history and House descriptions and consider what your character's role was in the time before the Fall. Each House had certain duties, but there is room for variation within that common theme. How did the character feel about his duties? What difficulties did the character face? What did she think of humanity — the most exalted of God's creations — back then?

• How Did You Fall?

The Fall is a defining moment for demons, when they decided to rebel against their Creator and follow the banner of Lucifer. What led your character to this momentous decision? Was it something that happened gradually, until the character was the first to rally to Lucifer's side when the call came, or was it something sudden, a single incident that showed the character the need to rebel? What motivated your character? Some of the fallen rebelled out of love and compassion for humanity and what they saw as God's injustice. Others rebelled because they longed for what they could not have, whether it was human company or human worship. Some joined the rebellion because they were swayed by others or uncertain in their faith.

• What Did You Do in the War?

The rebellion lasted for a thousand terrible years. What did you character do during this time? Was she repulsed by the need for war, horrified by its consequences, or did your character take to the role of the soldier all too well, glorifying in battle and bloodlust? Are there events from the war that haunt the character to this day? Did she accomplish great deeds (or commit great atrocities)? The zeal of many rebels faded as the rebellion went on and the things they were forced to see and do changed them forever. How did those events change your character?

• What Is Your Mortal Vessel Like?

The fallen walk the Earth clothed in stolen flesh. Give some thought to the life of your character's mortal vessel before it was possessed. What kind of person was he? What sort of life did he lead, and what finally brought him to the state where a demon could inhabit his body and take it for its own? The life and personality of the mortal vessel

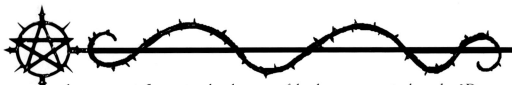

has a strong influence on the character of the demon, so consider them carefully. Generally, the fallen are drawn to vessels that resonate strongly with their own natures, so a Defiler is likely to be drawn to a mortal whose existence is defined by passion, especially passion denied or turned sour. Of course, on occasion, there is no apparent connection between the mortal vessel and the demon's nature, which can make for an interesting change of pace.

• What About Your Vessel Awakened You?

Something about your vessel's personality or memories shocked your character out of millennia of anguish and torment, restoring some semblance of sanity. What was it? For some vessels, it is a uniquely human suffering that reaffirms the demon's own twisted perceptions. With others, it is a uniquely human virtue, even in the smallest and most petty of souls. It can be the last spark of faith, hope, love or compassion in an otherwise hard and cynical soul, or it may be driving ambition, lust or hatred. The worst human beings can turn out to have some redeeming good in them, and the most apparently good people may hide some secret wickedness.

• What Are Your Goals?

Now that you have returned to the mortal world, what are your goals? Generally, characters in **Demon** seek to prevent the lords of the Abyss from returning to claim Creation as their own, but for what reason, and how does your character go about it? Does the character want to protect humanity or just keep more powerful demons from messing up the sweet deal he's got? What are the character's goals beyond keeping the fallen locked in the Abyss? Some demons see a spark of hope in humanity and try to fan it into a flame. Others want to avenge themselves on humans for abandoning them to their fate. Still others revel in the experience of material existence or the power of mortal faith.

• How Do You See Humanity?

What are humans to you? Are they children, followers, playthings, worshippers, sources of power, peers, threats, allies, enemies, food, tools, ideals, friends or perhaps some of each? The fallen each see humanity in their own way. Once, humans were the most exalted creatures in Creation, and the fallen fought and suffered for the love of them. For many, their love twisted and turned to hate in the thousands of years they suffered. A few clung to their love of humanity, or rediscovered it when they arose in human forms. Many demons are bitter and cynical toward humanity, although they may still find a hint of the love and admiration they once held for them. How does your character see and treat the human masses?

• How Do You Deal With the Mundane World?

Once masters of the forces of Creation, the fallen must deal with far more mundane concerns in the modern World of Darkness. Does your character maintain a semblance of her mortal vessel's life, or has she abandoned it altogether? Does your character maintain a semblance of a mortal life at all? Some demons find it useful to pretend to be the mortals they appear to be, while others disdain such an existence. They find it difficult, however, to deal with the requirements and the scrutiny of mortal agencies and governments. What about dealing with your vessel's family and friends? Have you cut all ties with them, or do you try to fool them into thinking you're who you seem to be? Do any of them suspect you?

Example of Character Creation

Jennifer is creating a character for Mike's upcoming **Demon: The Fallen** chronicle. Mike told the players that the chronicle will take place in Los Angeles, and that the characters should be at least somewhat neutral in the various conflicts going on between the different factions of the fallen. They'll be given the opportunity to choose sides fairly early on in the chronicle.

Step One: Concept

Jen looks over the outline of character creation and considers some possible character ideas. She wants to play a real "slick" character who's capable of manipulating people and situations to suit her needs, a real game-player. She also wants a character capable of learning some compassion and appreciation for other people's feelings. She also knows she wants a female character. She considers a Defiler, but rejects the idea as too stereotypical. Then the expression "devil's advocate" springs to mind, and she takes a closer look at the Devils. The concept of a heroic but arrogant and ruthless angel appeals to her, and the Devils' supernatural charisma and leadership abilities mesh well with her vision of a manipulative power broker. Having settled on the Devils as her choice of House, Jennifer turns her attention to the different factions that divide the infernal host. The Faustians, with their desire to subvert and enslave mankind seems like the obvious choice, but she decides that it would be more interesting to present the character's haughty manipulations in a context of zealous idealism. She does what she must, believing that her cause is righteous. Jennifer decides to make the character a Luciferan, one of the true believers of the rebellion.

Having established the character's House and faction, she devotes some thought to her history, first as an angel and then as one of the fallen. Jennifer envisions her character as a real idealist, proud and dedicated to the Host and its duties to the Creator. She creates the character's Celestial Name — Zaphriel — and to help envision her role, she gives her angel the title Messenger of the Dawn.

Zaphriel, Jennifer decides, devoted herself to the Grand Design as a way of showing her pride in her House and her status as one of the Heralds, as well as in hopes of earning esteem from the greatest of the angels, Lucifer himself. She rejoiced when mankind was born, but then like many among the Host, she grew increasingly troubled at humanity's innocence and suffering. Not only was her compassion sorely tested by their pain, she could not reconcile their imperfect existence with the perfection of the universe she helped create. When Lucifer put forward the idea of rebellion against God, Zaphriel didn't hesitate. She stood at the Morningstar's side as mankind's eyes were opened.

During the War of Wrath, Zaphriel was the image of the impassioned rebel, struggling against the tyranny of Heaven and winning fame as a fearsome warrior and knight of the Crimson Legion. However, as the war went on and both humanity and the fallen were changed in ways not even Lucifer had envisioned, Zaphriel became hardened to violence and slaughter. She commanded her fellow angels with ruthlessness and cold calculation, committing acts of destruction that once would have horrified the Messenger of the Dawn. Jennifer decides that Zaphriel fought to the last, still believing that Lucifer would find a way to triumph, and like many of the fallen, she accepted her imprisonment stoically, never believing for an instant that the war was truly over.

Having fleshed out her character's demonic aspect, Jennifer now decides that her character's mortal vessel is a corporate attorney. Originally somewhat mousy and put-upon, Laura Blake developed a serious drug habit to deal with her constant nervousness and anxiety. An accidental overdose and the disastrous effect it had on Blake's career opened the way for Zaphriel to possess her, and everyone noticed the change that came over Laura. She went from first-class doormat to queen bitch of the universe — from junior associate with two weeks to finish up her affairs to full partner of the firm in no time at all — making more than a few enemies along the way. She's now in a strong position in the firm of Hopkins & Mathers, but she's still aiming even higher.

Jen considers how Zaphriel's personality meshes with Laura's history and identity. She decides that Laura's Demeanor is that of a Director. She's a take-charge type who moves in and starts bossing people around, telling them exactly what to do. That attitude is just a mask for her true Nature, however, which Jen decides is Fanatic. Zaphriel is every bit the idealistic revolutionary, and every step she takes is only a means to an end — building her personal power, gathering as many of the fallen under her banner as she can, and starting a fire that one day will reach to the gates of Heaven itself.

STEP TWO: ATTRIBUTES

Prioritizing Zaphriel's Attributes, Jen chooses to make Social Attributes her primary category. Zaphriel is a manipulative, forceful, personality after all. For her secondary Attribute category, she chooses Mental, since she sees Zaphriel as pretty smart and sharp. Finally, she assigns Physical Attributes to the tertiary category, since those abilities aren't all that important to Jen's idea of her character.

Jen takes the seven dots for Zaphriel's Social Attributes. She assigns three to Manipulation, Zaphriel's prime quality. The Devil can wrap people around her little finger without them even knowing it. She splits the remaining four dots evenly between Charisma and Appearance, making Zaphriel/Laura both likeable and attractive, qualities that tend to distract people from just how manipulative she is.

For Zaphriel's five dots in Mental Attributes, Jen puts two dots each into Intelligence and Wits, knowing that Zaphriel is a skilled strategist with a mind as sharp as her tongue. She puts the remaining dot into Perception, giving Zaphriel an average rating of 2 in that Attribute.

The three dots in Physical Attributes are easy. Jen puts one into each for ratings of 2 across the board. Laura was average in physical pursuits, but then her chosen field didn't require a lot of physical ability.

STEP THREE: ABILITIES

Looking over the Ability lists, Jen decides that Laura's primary area has to be Talents. Although Law (an important Ability for a lawyer) is a Knowledge, it's one of the few that the character needs, while Jen sees

CREATING CELESTIAL NAMES

Characters in **Demon** have no less than three different names: the name of their mortal host, the Celestial Name by which the demon is known to his peers, and his True Name, which is a reflection of his complete identity. While the True Name is a collection of arcane symbols, sounds and concepts that don't actually need to be spelled out, the Celestial Name is one that you'll use often when interacting with other fallen characters, and it deserves as much thought as his mortal name.

There are any number of sources you can turn to for angelic names, from the Bible to less well-known religious texts such as the Apocrypha, to books like *Encyclopedia of Angels*, written by Rosemary Ellen Guiley. Additionally, names from Akkadian or Babylonian myth and history provide a wealth of ancient and exotic-sounding names to consider when naming your character. Take a look at *The Epic of Gilgamesh*, available at your local library or on the Internet, or the *Enuma Elish*. Both have a wealth of names that you can draw inspiration from or adopt as your own.

a number of Talents that fit her concept. She makes Knowledges secondary and Skills tertiary.

She takes Zaphriel's 13 dots in Talents and immediately assigns three (the maximum she can allocate at this stage) to Subterfuge. Zaphriel is an expert liar and has a great "poker face" for hiding her true feelings and motives. She puts two dots each into Alertness, Empathy, Expression, Intimidation and Leadership, all skills Zaphriel/Laura will find useful in her legal career as well as in demon society.

Zaphriel has nine dots available for Knowledges. Jen puts three into Law, making the character a capable attorney. She puts another two into Investigation, since Zaphriel/Laura will likely need to dig up the dirt on clients as well as her rivals, both mortal and demon. She puts two points into Politics, so the character knows how to handle things at City Hall. Jen puts a dot each into Academics and Computer, basic skills the demon can use in her day-to-day affairs.

For her five dots in Skills, Jen puts two each into Etiquette and Performance, which complement Zaphriel's other Abilities quite well. She decides to put the last dot into Firearms. The character owns a small pistol for "protection," and she knows how to use it.

Step Four: Advantages

Looking over the Virtues, Jen decides that Zaphriel's strongest Virtue is Conviction and her lowest is Conscience (she did possess a lawyer, after all). She puts two dots into Conviction, one into Courage and none into Conscience.

Zaphriel has a starting Faith of three, so Jen looks over the lore that suits her concept of Zaphriel as a "devil's advocate." The lore paths available to the Devils are Celestials, Flame and Radiance, plus the common paths of Humanity and the Fundament. Jen decides that Radiance suits Zaphriel's concept best and makes it her primary lore, putting two dots into it. She puts the remaining dot into Celestials. By selecting Radiance as the character's primary lore, Zaphriel's apocalyptic form is Qingu, the Visage of Radiance. Jen notes the form's special abilities on her sheet.

For her five dots in Backgrounds, Jen decides to give Zaphriel at least three dots in Resources, since Laura makes a fair amount of money at the law firm. She puts the other two dots into Contacts, knowing that the character has connections. She'd like to pick up another dot in Contacts and a couple of other Backgrounds, but she's out of points for the moment.

Step Five: Finishing Touches

Fortunately, Jen still has her freebie points to spend. She immediately spends some filling out Zaphriel's Backgrounds, giving her another dot in Contacts, a dot in Allies and one in Influence (for a total of three freebie points). She goes back over the character's Attributes and Abilities and decides to put an additional dot into Dexterity, raising it to a 3, for five

freebie points. That makes Zaphriel more graceful and better able to do things such as dodge and use her Firearms Skill. She also puts another dot into Subterfuge, raising it to a 4 for two freebie points (permissible at this stage of development). She gives Zaphriel the specialty "Convincing Lies" since she now has four dots in the Ability. She also gives Zaphriel's Manipulation the specialty "Deception." Laura is now a *very* capable liar and manipulator. She has five freebie points left over and decides to hold on to them at the moment.

She notes Zaphriel's starting Faith (3), Torment (4) and Willpower (5, equal to the sum of her two highest Virtues). She'd like to increase the character's Faith, but it costs more freebie points than she has. Instead, she uses the remaining five points to increase Zaphriel's Charisma another dot, giving her four dots in Charisma and the specialty "Speaker."

Archetypes: Nature and Demeanor

Everyone goes through life wearing masks, especially the fallen. They wear a mask of mortality, occasionally giving others a brief glimpse of the true nature that lies beneath. The rest of the world sees only what they are supposed to see and nothing more. We all have different ways of dealing with other people and situations, and the fallen are no exception.

Nature and Demeanor help define a character's personality. Nature is the character's true self, the demonic soul staring out through the eyes of its human shell. Demeanor is the attitude the character presents to the rest of the world, and in large part reflects the vestiges of the host's mortal personality. It may complement the Nature — in fact it may even be the same for characters who are particularly open about their true selves. But for most **Demon** characters, such openness is dangerous, so they conceal their true selves behind a façade.

The combination of Nature and Demeanor helps build a picture of the character's personality, goals and behavior. These definitions are not all-inclusive. After all, few people can be entirely described by just a couple of terms. Instead, they provide a basis for the character's personality, a foundation to start building from, adding depth as the chronicle unfolds and the character becomes more defined. The core of the character's Nature remains, giving the player a framework to hang it all from.

A character's Nature also has a particular game effect. Characters regain Willpower by performing actions that reaffirm their essential Nature, giving them a burst of self-confidence and a feeling of accomplishment. By satisfying the demands of their Nature (see the individual descriptions), characters

are eligible to regain a Willpower point if the Story-teller allows (see p. 163 for details).

Here are some sample Archetypes suitable for **Demon** characters. Players and Storytellers should feel free to create their own Archetypes if none of these suit the particular characters they have in mind.

Addict

There's something (or maybe someone) that you've just got to have. It's a driving passion — some might say obsession — in your life. It takes precedence over everything else. Your addiction might be drugs, or it could be any other sort of activity. Some fallen become addicted to the various pleasures of the flesh, from eating to drinking to sex. Others are addicted to collecting (everything from occult knowledge to "trophies" of their successes) or obsessed with a particular mortal. Addiction to mortal faith, in particular, is common among the fallen.

— Regain Willpower when you give in completely to your addiction and sate it.

Architect

Above all else, Architects want to create something lasting. As an Architect, you have a vision that you work toward making a reality. It might be a physical creation, or it might be more metaphorical, such as creating an institution or a lasting idea. There are some demons who have not fallen so far as to forget the glories of Creation and their former role in designing and sustaining it. They seek to recapture some of that lost glory through their efforts.

— Regain Willpower when you create something of lasting importance.

Autocrat

There are two ways to do things: the wrong way and your way. Some might say this attitude reeks of pride, even hubris, but let them. You see that things get done, and there's no denying that. Someone has to take charge, and you're the one to do it. It's not necessarily because you're the smartest or the most knowledgeable (although that may be true, too). You just know how to take responsibility for getting things done.

— Regain Willpower when you take control of a situation or group.

Bon Vivant

Once there was a time when the purpose of existence was pleasure. That time may be gone, but you still try to recapture it. Only those who have known the kind of pain and suffering you have can find pleasure in the simplest things. If you are dragged back down into anguish and torment, then everything you have fought for will be for nothing, so enjoy life! You may have serious matters to take care of, but there's nothing that says you can't have some fun along the way.

— Regain Willpower when you truly enjoy yourself and can share your joy with others.

Bravo

"The meek will inherit the Earth?" Not if you have anything to say about it! The meek don't get anything in this world except grief. The strong take what they want, when they want. Might makes right, which is good for you, since your know how to use your strength to get what you want. You respect strength in others when you see it, but weakness is just an opportunity for you to exploit. You do what it takes to get ahead.

— Regain Willpower when you achieve success through the application of force. This doesn't have to be physical force, it could just as easily be intimidation or social pressure.

Caregiver

The fallen fought and suffered because they cared too much, for humanity, for Creation and for their Creator. For some, nothing can extinguish their compassion for other creatures. They are always there when someone needs comfort or aid. For others, the *appearance* of caring is a useful tool. Empathy can earn you a way into a mortal's heart, and gratitude can be a heady reward, whether your succor was offered genuinely or not.

— Regain Willpower when you successfully comfort or aid someone else.

Child

All creatures are children of the Creator, but some are more childlike (or childish) than others. The true child is an innocent, inexperienced in the ways of the world and untouched by knowledge of good and evil. They are rare indeed in the modern age, but some seek a return to such a state of grace and find it in mortal flesh. The other side of the child is a constant need for attention. The child's demands must be satisfied and satisfied *now*. Children have no control over their passions, and they seek others to help care for them.

— Regain Willpower when you convince someone else to care for you or help satisfy your needs without any reward.

Competitor

All creatures are *not* created equal. Some are destined for greatness, while others are not. You have the ability to rise to the challenge and prove your greatness through competition. You see everything in life as a challenge to be overcome and an opportunity to show just what you can do. You may prefer a friendly competition or a cutthroat struggle where anything goes.

— Regain Willpower when you win a competition.

Conformist

You know your place in the grand scheme of things or, at least, you believed that you did once. You were

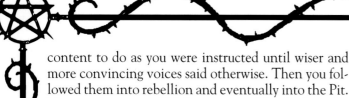

content to do as you were instructed until wiser and more convincing voices said otherwise. Then you followed them into rebellion and eventually into the Pit. Now you're in need of direction and leadership, the opportunity to be part of a group again and to offer your own abilities to that group.

— Regain Willpower when your group achieves its goal with your aid.

Conniver

Bargaining for souls… how trite. The way you play the game, your marks have no idea that you already own their souls and they're thanking you for the opportunity to do exactly what you want. After all, why struggle and risk your own hide when you can get others to do it for you? You understand the power that a carefully crafted lie gives you, especially when it's mixed with just the right amount of truth.

— Regain Willpower when you trick someone into giving you something you want.

Curmudgeon

The fallen rebelled for what they believed in, and they were punished. Humanity was given free will, and look what they've done with it. Is it any wonder that you're more than a little jaded and cynical about it all? You tend to see the worst in everything, picking out every flaw, pointing out every way things could go badly, and never missing an opportunity to say "I told you so" when they inevitably do.

— Regain Willpower when something bad happens just as you said it would.

Deviant

Some people just don't fit into the nice, neat categories society creates. That's you. You refuse to be pigeonholed or labeled, just as you refuse to conform to what everyone expects of you. You are who you are. If someone else can't deal with that, fuck 'em. You're no longer bound by the restrictions of any commandments, or by anything else, for that matter. There are more than a few, both fallen and mortal, drawn to your unique sense of self.

— Regain Willpower when you break with or ignore convention.

Director

Creation is an orderly thing. Once it ran with perfect precision and balance, everything in its place, the ultimate machine. Now, of course, parts of Creation are run-down, out of whack or simply not working right, and chaos is growing. You can't tolerate that. Nothing is more important to you than restoring and maintaining order and organization, within a group or in the world.

— Regain Willpower when you use organization to accomplish a difficult task.

Fanatic

You have a cause, and nothing or no one can sway you from it. You devote yourself entirely to your cause, surrendering all else to its higher purpose. The ends justify the means, and everything (and everyone) else can and will be sacrificed in the name of the cause, if needs be. Your cause may be in tune with the agendas of any of the factions of the fallen (see Chapter Five for more information), or it may be the cause of a mortal group or your own personal crusade. Whatever it is, you will see it through to the end.

— Regain Willpower when you do something that directly furthers your cause.

Gallant

Faith is the most intoxicating of elixirs, and you find yourself uplifted by the adoration and attention of others. You are a being of glory, and you cannot hide your light under a bushel. Instead, you would rather show mortals the wonders you are capable of and bask in their worship and admiration. Nothing excites you as much as a new potential convert to impress and win over. Each one makes you feel a little more alive and whole.

— Regain Willpower when you truly impress someone.

Gambler

Life is risk. It involves taking a chance; perhaps even a leap of faith, hoping things will turn out for the best. People who are afraid to take chances lead simple, dull lives, but you're not like that. You're willing to risk it all for the hope of something better. You're not foolhardy, but you're willing to take chances some people call foolish, if that's what it takes.

— Regain Willpower when you take a chance and come out ahead.

Judge

There is an order to Creation and understanding, and perhaps improving upon, that order is the key to success. You're a believer in systems for getting things done: legal systems, logical systems and bureaucratic systems. You believe in doing things "by the numbers" although there's nothing wrong with innovation, as long as it improves the system.

— Regain Willpower when you use careful and systematic reasoning to solve a problem.

Loner

You're on your own most of the time, and you're okay with that. The truth is, you prefer your own company. You may have habits or mannerisms that put other people off, you may not feel worthy of being around other people, or maybe you don't like company. You go your own way, working with others when it suits you before taking your leave.

— Regain Willpower when you accomplish something on your own that benefits someone else.

MARTYR

You were made to suffer, it seems. You accept your burden with dignity and determination, knowing that your suffering has meaning, either in the statement it makes or in the benefit it brings to others. All the suffering and torment of Hell could not break your spirit, so what is the pain of the mortal world by comparison? You may be truly sincere in your beliefs, or you may exaggerate your sacrifices for the attention and sympathy they bring you.

— Regain Willpower when you sacrifice yourself for your ideals or the good of someone else.

MASOCHIST

They think they can break you? They think you'll crack under the pressure? Bring it on! You're willing to pit your ability to endure against anything Creation can dish out. Not only are you proud of your ability to overcome pain, you actually *enjoy* it. You're driven to the extremes to test your limits and push them a little farther each time. Maybe you'll eventually run into something you can't handle, but you haven't yet.

— Regain Willpower when you suffer in a way you never have before.

MONSTER

Demon? You'll show them what a *real* demon is. They have no idea of the depths of what you've endured, but you're going to show them. All of humanity's myths and parables, even their mass-media horror shows, are only pale reflections of what you have become. You are evil incarnate, free to stalk the world. No atrocity is beyond your reach, as the world will soon discover.

— Regain Willpower when you commit a terrible act of evil.

PEDAGOGUE

Knowledge is the only thing of real worth in Creation, and the one thing you value, but knowledge is useless unless it is shared somehow. It is your responsibility to take what you know and teach others so they can understand and pass the knowledge on. The more everyone knows, the better things are. Some might call you a know-it-all, but that's usually only because you *do* know it all.

— Regain Willpower when someone benefits from the wisdom you've shared with him.

PENITENT

You are a sinner, among the most terrible of sinners. You committed crimes against God and Creation, and you have been rightly punished for them. Even the burden of guilt you feel is a part of your punishment. You have seen the error in your ways, and you only hope that you can be forgiven for what you have done. All

you can do now is try as best you can to make up for your past mistakes and make them right.

— Regain Willpower when you feel that you have made a step toward redemption.

PERFECTIONIST

You don't ask any more of anyone than you ask of yourself, but since you expect only perfection from yourself, most people don't see the distinction. You demand only the best, and you're not willing to settle for anything less. Others may not appreciate your exacting standards or attention to detail during the process, but they certainly appreciate the results. That's what drives you, the satisfaction of a job well done.

— Regain Willpower when you perform a task perfectly.

REBEL

You were one of the first rebels, and you still wear the title proudly. Authority *must* be challenged, or it becomes nothing more than mindless obedience. You take every opportunity to buck the system because that's how things change for the better, or just to prove how bogus it all is.

— Regain Willpower when you successfully weaken authority.

ROGUE

You look out for Numero Uno. Nobody else is going to do it, and everybody else would be better off taking care of themselves. You don't want to owe anyone anything. You take care of your own problems and let them take care of theirs. You have your own best interests at heart, although there's nothing wrong with a little enlightened self-interest that benefits everyone, as long as you don't get too entangled in someone else's business.

— Regain Willpower when your self-centered attitude brings you success.

SURVIVOR

What doesn't kill you only makes you stronger. Where others meekly accept their fate, you struggle against it. Nothing can bring you down, and you always find a way to win in the end. You're disappointed with everyone else's willingness to give up and take the easy way out, something you'd never do.

— Regain Willpower when you endure hardship or encourage others to do the same.

THRILL-SEEKER

You live for the thrill of danger, knowing that you're risking your life is what makes you feel the most alive. You're a daredevil, looking for the most dangerous thrills you can find to keep things interesting. There's almost no challenge you won't at least consider, and odds are that you'll try most of them. After

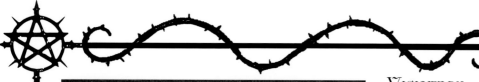

SPECIALITIES

Some characters may be especially good at certain areas or applications of their traits. For example, a scholar often specializes in a particular area of academia, a fighter may be known for a signature move, or an artist may specialize in a certain medium or style. Players may choose to apply specialties to a character's traits to represent this emphasis.

A specialty is a particular focus for an Attribute or Ability. A character might have the specialty "Tireless" on his Stamina, reflecting the fact that his energy is even greater than his level of Stamina would indicate. Another character might have the specialty "Acting" on her Expression, showing her focus on that particular mode of expression. Specialties help define and add depth to a character's various traits.

A character can apply a specialty to any Attribute or Ability rated 4 or more. When rolling dice for that trait in an area covered by the specialty, the player re-rolls any die that comes up "10" and adds any additional successes rolled to the total. Any re-rolled die that comes up "10" may be rolled again for additional successes, until no "10s" are rolled.

what you've endured, you want to feel your heart pounding, the blood rushing through your veins. Even death doesn't scare you anymore.

— Regain Willpower when you succeed at a dangerous task you've deliberately undertaken.

TRADITIONALIST

In a world that changes so quickly, the one thing you can rely on is tradition. You respect history and the traditional way of doing things is clearly the best. If it wasn't why would it have lasted so long? It's important to maintain traditional ways and values, and you're against changing them unless it's absolutely necessary. Tradition equals comfort, predictability and stability.

— Regain Willpower when time-honored ways of doing things turn out to be the best.

TRICKSTER

There are times when you just have to laugh at the absurdity of it all, the whole cosmic drama of existence. You often suspect that the whole thing is some sort of grand joke and you're the only one who gets the punchline. No matter how bad it gets, you manage to find the humor in every situation, and you do your best to lighten the mood. You'd much rather laugh than cry, and you share your insights with others through humor and satire.

— Regain Willpower when you managed to lift others' spirits or deny your own pain through humor.

VISIONARY

Some see the way the world is and ask, "Why?" You see the way the world might be and ask, "Why not?" You have a vision of something more, something greater than what already exists. You challenge the limits of Creation in hope of finding something better, rarely satisfied with the status quo. Naturally, those interested in keeping things the way they are find you threatening, but you don't care about the opinions of others. You follow your vision with the conviction that you can do more, that there's always hope.

— Regain Willpower when you inspire others to follow their dreams or ideals.

ATTRIBUTES

All **Demon** characters have certain basic Attributes, which define the capabilities of every person, as well as other creatures, such as the fallen. Attributes generally range between 1 (poor) and 3 (good), with exceptional individuals having ratings of 4 (excellent) or 5 (the peak of human ability). Some of the fallen and other supernatural creatures may have Attributes above 5, but they are fairly rare.

PHYSICAL

The Physical Attributes define the abilities of a character's body: strength, agility, endurance, health and so forth. In the case of the fallen, the Physical Attributes often define the abilities of the demon's mortal vessel, although some of the fallen do not inhabit mortal bodies. Physical Attributes should be the primary category for physical and action-oriented characters.

The fallen can use Faith to temporarily enhance their Physical Attributes even to superhuman levels. For details, see p. 159.

STRENGTH

The first punch connected with Harvey Ciullo's jaw, sending his sunglasses flying off and his head snapping around. Mickey followed it with a roundhouse left, but Harvey's hand came up, almost of its own volition, and caught Mickey's fist in a vice-like grip. He turned to look at the sometime bouncer as he tightened his grip, and Mickey dropped to his knees. Harvey, the demon Hasmed, stared down at him with one blue eye and one eye clouded reddish black with clotted blood.

"That first punch was free," he said. "Anything else you pay dearly for."

Strength is a measure of pure muscle power and the brute force a character can bring to bear. It affects how much the character can lift and carry, the damage done with melee weapons or unarmed attacks, and breaking things, from kicking down a door to snapping a mortal's arm. The character's Strength is added to the damage dice pool in hand-to-hand combat. It's also used for various feats involving pure physical strength.

Specialties: Furious Strength, Powerful Legs, Reserves of Strength, Unbreakable Grip

- • **Poor:** You can lift 40 lbs.
- •• **Average:** You can lift 100 lbs.
- ••• **Good:** You can lift 250 lbs.
- •••• **Exceptional:** You can lift 400 lbs.
- •••••**Outstanding:** You can lift 650 lbs.

DEXTERITY

Her breath came in quick gasps as Magdiel sprinted across the rooftops, her feet pounding on the tarpaper and gravel. They were close behind her and she was struck by the irony of her situation — an Angel of Death now become the prey rather than the hunter. She skidded to a stop at the end of the roof, arms pinwheeling to avoid a 10-story drop to the alley below. It was a wide gap, Magdiel wasn't sure she could jump it, but there was no other way off the roof, and her pursuers were closing in. She got a running start and flung herself into empty air.

Dexterity is a character's capacity for physical action. It covers such things as agility, speed, grace, hand-eye coordination and general athletic ability. Dexterity is used for most physical actions involving precision or control, ranging from shooting a gun to dancing to lock-picking.

Specialties: Coordinated, Graceful, Lightning Reflexes, Quick

- • **Poor:** You are clumsy and awkward. You drop things and trip a lot.
- •• **Average:** You're not a klutz, but you're not particularly graceful, either.
- ••• **Good:** You've got some grace or athletic ability.
- •••• **Exceptional:** You could become a professional athlete or dancer based largely on your natural talent.
- ••••• **Outstanding:** You have a grace and precision that's poetry in motion.

STAMINA

Alejandro stepped into the middle of the circle of hooting and howling gangbangers to face off against their leader, whose muscles gleamed with a thin sheen of sweat in the yellow light coming from the bare bulb hanging overhead. Alejandro deliberately stripped off his shirt so everyone could see the network of scars on his back and arms. Whatever they could dish out, he'd seen worse.

He smiled confidently at the big gang leader, who looked just the slightest bit shaken. "After you," he said.

The punch came without any warning, slamming into Alejandro's gut. He doubled over a bit as everyone yelled and cheered. Then he straightened up slowly. The noise died away.

"That the best you've got?" he asked the gangbanger. Behind Alejandro's face, Malakh the Hunter smiled.

"My turn."

Stamina is a measure of a character's overall physical condition, particularly health, endurance and toughness. Stamina governs how long you can exert yourself and how much physical punishment you can endure, from pain to hunger and thirst. It determines your resistance to illness and poison as well as your ability to overcome physical trauma. It also includes a measure of your determination and will to live.

Specialties: Determined, Healthy, Tireless, Tough

- • **Poor:** You get sick all the time and bruise easily.
- •• **Average:** You're pretty healthy most of the time, and you can take a couple of hits before you're out.
- ••• **Good:** You can climb stairs or run without getting out of breath quickly, and you rarely get sick.
- •••• **Exceptional:** You can run a marathon, and you're n excellent health.
- •••••**Outstanding:** You can survive week-long treks through the desert without food or water and similar trials.

SOCIAL

The Social Attributes govern personal interaction of all sorts. They describe such things as charm, persuasiveness, empathy, style and appearance. The fallen are dependent on human faith and goodwill in many ways, so they have learned how to play social games very well. Social Attributes should be primary for characters intended to be influential or good at dealing with people.

CHARISMA

When Gaviel entered the room, all conversation whispered to a halt and all eyes turned toward him. He wasn't much to look at, but his sheer presence charged the air like lightning. Everyone waited with bated breath to see what he would say. Gaviel milked the moment, drawing out the silence until it was almost painful before he turned to address his gathered followers.

"God is dead," he said, "and I've invited you all here to attend the funeral."

Some people have that certain something that makes you like them right off while others tend to put people off or simply creep them out. That quality is Charisma, the ability of attractiveness, charm and personal magnetism. Charismatic characters tend to get along well with others and make friends easily while those lacking in Charisma have an uphill battle getting people to like them. Charisma is used in conjunction with Abilities involving gaining someone's trust or cooperation. It's particularly useful to the fallen in gaining Faith from mortals (see p. 249 for details).

Specialties: Admirable, Born Leader, Eloquent, Silver Tongue, Sympathetic, Witty

- • **Poor:** There's just something about you that people don't like.
- •• **Average:** You're likeable enough and have a few friends.
- ••• **Good:** People tend to trust you and come to you with their concerns.
- •••• **Exceptional:** People flock to you and everyone wants to be your friend.
- ••••• **Outstanding:** You could easily be an influential political leader.

MANIPULATION

"Ladies and gentlemen, the kind of baseless allegations brought by Ms. Allemande against my client are all-too-common weapons used in divorce cases because accusations of spousal and child abuse carry so much emotional weight. You can't help but automatically feel sympathy for the victims in such a case. But the true victim here is Charlie Allemande, who tried only to be a good husband and father, and was repaid with cheating, lies and attempts to drag his name through the mud. If you consider the evidence in this case — particularly Ms. Allemande's testimony — then I'm sure you will see the truth. Thank you."

Laura Blake remained utterly dignified and composed as she returned to her seat, not allowing even a glimmer of the triumph she felt to show on her face. She had the jury eating out of her hand. Who cared that Allemande was as guilty as sin? He paid for the best, and she'd just given him an acquittal, and leverage to use in his divorce case.

Manipulation describes the character's ability for self-expression and using it to influence the feelings and opinions of others. Whereas Charisma is a more passive Attribute, relating to how people perceive you, Manipulation is active. Manipulation can be merely trying to get your point across, choosing the right words for a speech or creating just the right artistic composition, for example. It can also be outright attempts to change someone's opinion through oration, acting or other tricks.

Manipulation can be dangerous, since people don't generally like to feel manipulated. A failure on a Manipulation roll may earn a character the cold shoulder or a brush-off, while a botch may earn the subject's undying enmity. Of course, good manipulators rarely let people know they're being manipulated. It just seems like the character's ideas are always reasonable and sound. People with high Manipulation scores are either well trusted (if they're not known manipulators) or not trusted at all (if they are).

Specialties: Conniving, Convincing, Persuasive, Seductive

- • **Poor:** You rarely get your way, unless someone already agrees with you.
- •• **Average:** You can win arguments and get your friends to do you favors sometimes.

- ••• **Good:** You tend to get your way most of the time.
- •••• **Exceptional:** People do you tremendous favors, then thank you for the privilege.
- ••••• **Outstanding:** "So I just sign here in blood, right?"

APPEARANCE

Tulley watched the bouncers turn away even more pouting kids as they crowded around, looking to get in. The Inferno wasn't some mall, and they had to learn that. It was the hottest place in town, so they could afford to be choosy.

Then she stepped forward, the crowd parting in front of her. Tulley took one look at the red dress that fit her like a second skin, revealing in all the right places, the ruby lips and the midnight hair, the flawless skin, and his jaw dropped.

"You!" he gasped. The vision raised an eyebrow and gave Tulley a smile that made his heart skip a beat. She stepped forward and took his offered hand as he led her out of the crowd and into the club. It wasn't her first visit to the Inferno by any means, but she'd never worn this particular form before. So far, it was a success.

Appearance is a measure of a character's beauty, grace, style and overall attractiveness. It's more than just physical looks, although they're a part of it. It's also how the character carries herself and the kind of first impression she makes. Whereas Charisma is a measure of how likeable a character is, Appearance affects the kind of impression the character makes without having to say a word. It's the effect of a glance across a crowded room or the impact of a photograph (or other image of the character) on someone she's never even met.

Appearance is used for situations where the character must make an impression, either a first impression or a lasting impression, especially when actions and appearance matter more than words. In social situations where first impressions or appearances are important, a character's other Social Attributes are limited to a rating no higher than her Appearance score. It's hard to be likeable or convincing when people won't even give you the time of day.

Specialties: Attractive, Flawless, Graceful, Innocent, Seductive

- • **Poor:** You're nearly attraction-free. It may be your looks, your habits, your attitude or all of the above.
- •• **Average:** You don't particularly stand out in a crowd (which may be a good thing, sometimes).
- ••• **Good:** Strangers approach you fairly often, wanting to get to know you.
- •••• **Exceptional:** You could be a model, as people are often telling you.
- ••••• **Outstanding:** You're positively stunning. People react to you with either slack-jawed awe or intense jealousy.

MENTAL

Mental Attributes define qualities that involve thinking, memory, reasoning, awareness, learning and reaction time. They are the primary Attributes for characters who follow cerebral pursuits (like scholars) as well as those who prefer to outthink their opponents rather than overpowering or charming them.

PERCEPTION

"Hey, Detective, what do you make of this?"

Detective Gerhard Liebner crouched down next to the tarp-covered body where the uniform held something gingerly in a gloved hand, like he was afraid it would bite him. They were yellowed sheets of parchment, inscribed with characters and symbols written in what looked to be dried blood, probably the victim's. Liebner, or rather Ahrimal, saw they were Enochian. Someone was trying to send a message that was for sure.

"Bag and tag it," he said gruffly. At least now he had a good idea where to start looking.

Perception measures a character's ability to notice the world around him and to pick up on small details and nuances. It is often intuitive and unconscious, although characters can focus their perception when studying something intently or searching an area. Perception also influences how much the character pays attention to his surroundings. The absent-minded intellectual may be quite intelligent, but not very perceptive. Likewise the jaded wit may be very clever, but tends not to notice things.

Perception is used for most rolls involving a character's senses. This includes noticing details, detecting (and avoiding) traps and ambushes, picking up on subtle clues or hints, finding things and spotting other characters trying to hide.

Specialties: Aware, Discerning, Insightful, Intuitive, Sharp

- • **Poor:** Oblivious. You say "huh?" a lot. You might be self-absorbed, lost in thought or otherwise distracted all the time.
- •• **Average:** You pick up on all but the really subtle things.
- ••• **Good:** You tend to pick up on little details others miss.
- •••• **Exceptional:** Very little escapes your notice.
- ••••• **Outstanding:** Your observational skills could make you a brilliant detective (or spy).

INTELLIGENCE

"Can you fix it, Sam?"

Sam Ashbury glanced up from the spilled guts of the machine, scratching at several days' growth of graying beard.

"Sure thing. Nothing simpler. I can actually have it running better than before. I mean, I can fix anything, 'cept

the stuff that's really broken around here. Machines are easy, it's fixing people that's hard."

Intelligence measures reasoning ability and knowledge, the character's memory, problem solving and analytical faculties. It also includes elements of critical thinking, creativity and the ability to learn new information.

Intelligence is used for many scholarly or learned skills, particularly ones involving a large body of knowledge. It's also used for any intellectual challenge such as figuring out a riddle, piecing together clues of a mystery or doing complex math in your head. Intelligent characters aren't necessarily better at dealing with people (that's covered by the Social Attributes) or quicker on the uptake (which is handled by Wits).

Low Intelligence doesn't necessarily mean stupidity. It might just describe a character with a limited education or a simple thinker. Likewise, high Intelligence doesn't mean the same thing for all characters. It might be a tremendous memory for one, brilliant analytical thinking for another.

Specialties: Book Learning, Creative, Deduction, Memorization

- • **Poor:** You're a little slow, or maybe just not too "ed-ja-ma-cated."
- •• **Average:** You're no dummy, but you're not brilliant, either.
- ••• **Good:** You're pretty smart and probably well educated, too.
- •••• **Exceptional:** You're the brightest in your class, and most everyone knows it.
- ••••• **Outstanding:** Brilliant, a true genius.

Wits

Magdiel couldn't run forever. It was time to deal with her pursuers, now that she'd bought herself a few moments. The narrow stairwell and closet full of cleaning supplies didn't offer much but, as she quickly looked things over, a plan began to form. She glanced at the labels of a few bottles to confirm what she thought. There were certainly benefits to understanding all the many things that could kill, she thought as she pulled together the ingredients she needed.

Wits describes how quickly a character thinks, covering qualities such as cleverness, guile, reaction time, intuitive (as opposed to rational) thinking and so forth. Intelligence describes how well a character thinks, but Wits describes how fast. A character with a high Wits rating is rarely caught off guard or surprised for very long. He's able to react immediately to a changing situation while a character with low Wits plods along and works best with planning and contingencies.

Wits are used in situations when characters have to think and react quickly. They also influence things like keeping cool in a difficult situation and reacting with grace under pressure. High Wits characters are difficult to fool or manipulate, while those with low Wits are easy marks.

Specialties: Intuitive, Quick Thinker, Rapier Wit, Strategist

- • **Poor:** You hesitate and have difficulty making even simple decisions.
- •• **Average:** Pretty quick on the uptake, but surprises tend to overwhelm you.
- ••• **Good:** You can keep your head while everyone around you is losing theirs (perhaps literally).
- •••• **Exceptional:** You're never lacking for a clever comeback or a plan of action.
- ••••• **Outstanding:** You react at the speed of thought, before most people even realize what's happening.

Abilities

Whereas all characters have Attributes, Abilities are learned traits. Attributes reflect characters' potential, while Abilities are what they have learned to do with that potential. If you're strong, you can probably hit pretty hard, but you'll be that much more effective in a fight if you also know *how* to hit and where to hit to do the most damage. An Ability is usually paired with an Attribute (combining potential with training) to determine what dice pool a player rolls for a particular action.

Each of the Abilities covers a fairly broad range of activities or knowledge. Players may wish to have their characters acquire a specialty (p. 136) in an Ability, even if the character's rating in it is not yet 4 or higher. This reflects the fact that characters often learn specific aspects of Abilities rather than just the general knowledge.

Talents

Talents are Abilities that everyone has to one degree or another. They're known intuitively, and the only real way to improve them is through experience and practice. It's difficult at best to learn anything about a Talent from a book or a lecture. The best way to learn them is by doing them, over and over again. Characters with high ratings in Talents usually have a fair amount of experience in using them. If you attempt a Talent your character doesn't possess, roll the character's appropriate Attribute with no penalty in difficulty. Everyone has at least a little potential in Talents because they're so intuitive.

Alertness

"Who's there?" Ahrimal said to empty air and shadows. "You might as well come out. I know you're here."

A shadowy figure detached from the darkness in a corner of the room, and Ahrimal slowly closed his hand around the butt of the pistol in his coat pocket.

"I got your message," he said. "I'm here to deliver one of my own."

Alertness is the knack for noticing what's going on around you. It's typically paired with Perception and compliments it. Alertness allows you to take everything in, and Perception lets you pick up on the important details. Alertness is different from Awareness in that Alertness focuses on the physical world, while Awareness is for picking up on the supernatural world.

- • **Novice:** You pay a little more attention than most.
- •• **Practiced:** You don't miss much.
- ••• **Competent:** You've always got at least some idea of what's going on.
- •••• **Expert:** Very little catches you by surprise.
- ••••• **Master:** You're aware of everything around you, even things most people never notice.

Possessed by: Bodyguards, Hunters, Investigators, Journalists, Police Officers, Security Personnel

Specialties: Danger, Hidden Objects, People, Specific Sense (Sight, Hearing, etc.)

ATHLETICS

She almost didn't make it, her momentum giving out before she cleared the distance. Magdiel grabbed onto the ledge as her body slammed into it, then quickly pulled herself up onto the roof, rolling onto her back for a moment to catch her breath before getting to her feet. Let's see them match that, she thought.

Athletics encompasses all basic talent and training in athletic activities such as running, jumping, swimming, throwing, tumbling and so forth, as well as various sports. It doesn't cover weight-lifting (which is based solely on Strength) or athletic activities specifically covered by another skill (like Dodge or Melee).

- • **Novice:** Basic talent or training.
- •• **Practiced:** High-school athlete.
- ••• **Competent:** You could be a professional athlete.
- •••• **Expert:** Top-ranked in your sport.
- ••••• **Master:** You could compete in the Olympics.

Possessed by: Athletes, Health Enthusiasts, Jocks, Kids, Soldiers

Specialties: Acrobatics, Climbing, Dance, Jumping, Running, Specific Sport, Swimming, Throwing

AWARENESS

Gideon's eyes narrowed as he felt a presence and unnatural heat radiating off the woman in red. Her beauty was more than mortal, it was the sort that tempted martyrs and toppled kingdoms, the sort that Gideon knew all too well. As the woman turned toward him, he could see that she suspected what he was as well.

"Who are you?" he asked under his breath, "and what do you want here?"

As Alertness measures awareness of the natural world, Awareness measures a character's ability to sense the supernatural world. It's a kind of "sixth sense," the ability to look beyond the mundane façade of everyday life in the World of Darkness to see what's lurking beneath the surface. Generally, only supernatural beings such as the fallen, mages, spirits and such have Awareness, although there are a rare few mortals capable of it as well.

Characters with Awareness get hints, hunches and flashes of insight regarding the supernatural (how much insight depends on their Awareness rating and how many successes the player rolls). For example, they may be able to pick a supernatural creature such as a vampire or another demon out of a crowd or sense the use of supernatural powers. Awareness provides only raw information, a sense for the supernatural. Characters require more specific tutelage (in the form of the Occult Knowledge) to understand what it is they sense.

Characters can use Awareness to "scan" for anything supernatural in their vicinity. The Storyteller may also make secret Awareness rolls to see if characters sense the presence of an unknown supernatural force or being nearby.

- • **Novice:** You pick up strange vibes from certain places and people sometimes.
- •• **Practiced:** You know the supernatural when you see it or come in close contact with it.
- ••• **Competent:** You can sense the flow of hidden forces through the world, peering behind the veil of mundane life.
- •••• **Expert:** You pick up on subtle and hidden supernatural forces all around you.
- ••••• **Master:** You can sense a supernatural influence anywhere nearby, and you sometimes pick up on more distant forces, if they're strong enough.

Possessed by: The fallen, Mages, New Agers, Psychics, Spirits

Specialties: Demons, Magic, Places of Power, Spirits, Supernatural Effects, Vampires

BRAWL

Alejandro's smashing right hook spun the gangbanger around before sending him crashing to the floor. Still standing, Alejandro straightened up and wiped the blood from his split lip with his bruised knuckles.

"Anyone else?" he asked, grinning fiercely. There were no more takers.

Brawl covers a character's prowess in unarmed combat, ranging from brutal street fighting to the "sweet science" of boxing and everything in between. For the fallen, capable of changing their form, it also includes fighting with tooth and claw (and any other sort of appendage). It handles knowing how to hit and how to do the most damage, along with how to defend yourself. The character may have picked up the ability through training, hard experience, or a combination of the two,

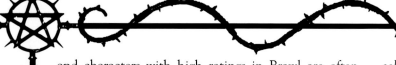
and characters with high ratings in Brawl are often familiar with multiple styles and techniques of combat.

- **Novice:** You know how to throw a punch without hurting yourself and the common places on the body that are the most vulnerable.
- •• **Practiced:** You can hold your own in a fight against most people.
- ••• **Competent:** You've fought regularly for some time (and you usually win).
- •••• **Expert:** You could be a professional fighter, even a title-winner.
- ••••• **Master:** Welcome to fight club. You're in charge.

Possessed by: Boxers, Gang Members, Martial Artists, Police, Soldiers

Specialties: Basic Self-Defense, Boxing, Dirty Fighting, Martial Arts Style, Wrestling

DODGE

It was only a glimmer of movement, the faintest of sounds, but Laura threw herself behind the body of a BMW in the parking garage an instant before the bullet hit one of the car's side panels. She kept low as she heard footsteps running away. Whoever it was had decided not to stay around to make sure she was finished. Their mistake.

Self-preservation is one of the most primal instincts, and Dodge represents that instinct taken and focused into the ability to get out of the way of danger. When you're attacked, you can use Dodge to get out of harm's way. It may involve diving for cover, sidestepping blows or fancy footwork.

- **Novice:** You operate mostly on reflex.
- •• **Practiced:** You've gotten some training (or taken enough hits) that you usually know when to duck.
- ••• **Competent:** You slip past many attacks with ease and grace.
- •••• **Expert:** When the attack arrives, you're usually not there.
- ••••• **Master:** You twist and turn to dodge bullets as they're coming at you.

Possessed by: Criminals, Martial Artists, Police, Soldiers, Survivors

Specialties: Cover, Fancy Footwork, Jumping, Sidestepping, Tumbling

EMPATHY

"It's just so hard to meet people these days," the guy said, polishing off his third drink. His expressions had become more expansive, and his desperation more obvious, with each one.

"I know what you mean," Sabriel replied. "I'm not usually into the bar scene myself." That was clearly the kind of woman he was looking for, a little uncertain, not part of this world, but closer to his own. "Why don't we get out of here?" she continued. "I'd love to see that comic book collection you were telling me about."

He smiled like she was a gift from God. If only he knew.

Empathy is the knack for reading other people's moods and emotions. For some it's a matter of body language and other non-verbal cues; for others it's an almost supernatural sense of what other people are feeling. Empathy also includes understanding how other people feel, whether you sympathize with them or not. It's useful for knowing when people are pretending to feel something they're not, covering up their true feelings or lying, although it's an inexact science, at best. The more time you spend interacting with someone and the better you know them, the easier it is to pick up on how they feel.

- **Novice:** You sometimes pick up on non-verbal cues or get "vibes" from people.
- •• **Practiced:** You're a good listener, adept at getting people to open up to you.
- ••• **Competent:** It's difficult to hide anything from you — you always find out sooner or later.
- •••• **Expert:** Nobody plays poker with you — you're just too good at reading people's expressions.
- ••••• **Master:** People are like open books to you — their true feelings written in every nuance and expression.

Possessed by: Caretakers, Counselors, Investigators, Parents, Social Workers

Specialties: Disorders, Emotions, Lies, Motives, Personalities

EXPRESSION

"The Commandments tell us what not to do. 'Thou shalt not' this and 'thou shalt not' that. I say do what thou wilt shall be the whole of the law, for nothing is true and everything is permissible." Gaviel thought the combo of Crowley and Hassan was a little trite, but it was exactly what this crowd wanted to hear, and it worked.

Words have a power all their own, and Expression covers the use of words to get a point across, evoke a particular feeling, or provide a convincing argument. It includes all forms of expression through language, from poetry to speech writing to creative writing. Characters can use it to compose written works or to put the right words together at the spur of the moment to deliver a rousing speech or a memorable toast. Used well, Expression can sway others' opinions, even hold an audience enthralled.

- **Novice:** You've got a basic grasp of sentence structure and proper word usage.
- •• **Practiced:** You have a broad vocabulary and use it well.
- ••• **Competent:** You always choose your words carefully for the best possible effect.
- •••• **Expert:** You could be a best-selling author or a high-placed speechwriter.

• • • • • **Master:** You can create works that touch millions of hearts and minds.

Possessed by: Actors, Business Leaders, Poets, Politicians, Writers

Specialties: Drama, Game Design, Improvisation, Poetry, Prose, Speeches, Technical Writing

INTIMIDATION

"I'm only going to tell you this once," Hasmed said, staring down at the man with his one good eye and his evil eye, swollen and cloudy red-black. "If you ever fuckin' mess with me again, I'm going to make sure you eat through a straw for the rest of your miserable life. Got it?"

Fear is a powerful weapon, and an excellent way of motivating people. Intimidation covers all the myriad ways to motivate someone through fear and overpowering force of personality. It may be as overt as a physical threat (backed up by a show of force) or as subtle as wearing a power-tie and sitting someone so they have to look up at you and acknowledge that you're in the superior position. It can be used to get other people to cooperate (even against their better judgment), back down from a confrontation or reveal information.

- • **Novice:** You know how to make people back down if you push hard enough.
- • • **Practiced:** You can stare most people down without too much trouble.
- • • • **Competent:** You can end fights with a look or a word before they even start.
- • • • • **Expert:** People defer to you without you even trying.
- • • • • • **Master:** You can cow someone with little more than a glance.

Possessed by: Bouncers, Bullies, Cult Leaders, Executives, Gangsters

Specialties: Bluffing, Frightening, Physical Threats, Stare-Downs, Veiled Threats

INTUITION

"Sephidor!" The Malefactor ignored the shrill cry, looking over the wiring of the crude bomb. It was an amateur job, obviously put together in a hurry, so the whole thing was a mess. He needed to disconnect the timer in the right way or they were going to be scraping Sam Ashbury's remains off the sidewalk. Unfortunately, he had only about 10 seconds to make up his mind. He took one of the wires and gripped it with his wire-cutters. Here goes nothing, he thought.

Some call it a "gut feeling" while others say it's subconscious logic, the ability to leap to the right conclusion without actually thinking it through — a matter of pure intuition. Intuition is the ability to choose between two (or more) options with a better chance of picking the right one. It represents that gut instinct for making the right decision at the right time. It's the ability to roll when a character makes a decision largely at random, like whether to cut the red, green or blue wire as the timer counts down to zero, or picking the right away out of a maze while running away from something. Players can call for an Intuition roll when they get stuck or need to make a decision quickly. Storytellers can roll Intuition for the characters in order to give them clues or help move the story along.

- • **Novice:** You've got a knack for making the right choice.
- • • **Practiced:** You've learned to listen to and trust your instincts.
- • • • **Competent:** When you have a "bad feeling" about something, everyone listens.
- • • • • **Expert:** You could make a killing in the stock market.
- • • • • • **Master:** You've always managed to make the right choice at the last minute… so far.

Possessed by: Daredevils, Entrepreneurs, Gamblers, Mothers

Specialties: Danger, Gambling, Insight, Inspiration, Luck

LEADERSHIP

"Are you bound by what some two-thousand-year-old book tells you? Are you slaves to what society expects of you, to the way your parents lived their lives?" Several people in the audience said, "No," but it wasn't forceful enough. "Are you?" he demanded. "No!" the response came again. "Are you willing to do what it takes to be free?"

"Yes!" they cried. Inwardly, Gaviel exulted. He had them. He would show them. He would lead them to freedom.

It takes a special quality to get a group of people organized and focused on a particular task, it takes Leadership. Leadership relates to both the ability to organize and direct people and the quality that makes people want to follow your lead, even look to you for guidance. Leadership doesn't necessarily make you good at solving problems, but it does make you good at organizing people to tackle them. It also doesn't mean that you'll make the right decisions, only that others will follow you. After all, Lucifer's leadership led the fallen to rebel, and look how that turned out.

- • **Novice:** You can get a group of friends or associates organized to handle a task.
- • • **Practiced:** People tend to look to you for guidance and direction.
- • • • **Competent:** You can take charge in most situations and even get strangers working together in a short period of time.
- • • • • **Expert:** Your followers like and admire you, and you know just how to motivate them.
- • • • • • **Master:** You could successfully lead a nation or multinational corporation.

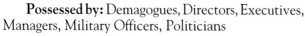

Possessed by: Demagogues, Directors, Executives, Managers, Military Officers, Politicians

Specialties: Delegating, Direction, Inspiration, Organization, Speeches

STREETWISE

Detective Liebner paid for his paper and sipped his coffee, already growing cold in its Styrofoam cup. He glanced over at the man who stood next to him, buying a couple of girlie magazines.

"It's going down tonight," the other man said, without a glance in Liebner's direction. "Around midnight, but you didn't hear it from me." The detective's only acknowledgement was a slight nod as the man walked off.

The streets have a culture all their own, a culture you're versed in. This Talent allows a character to fit into the street scene, gather information, make contacts, buy and sell on the black market and otherwise make use of the street's unique resources. It's also important for navigating the dangers of the streets, avoiding the law and staying on the right side of the wrong people.

- • **Novice:** You're known, and you can sometimes get what you're looking for.
- •• **Practiced:** You've got a reputation and some connections.
- ••• **Competent:** You command respect and know the right people.
- •••• **Expert:** You're a fixture of the street scene, truly on the inside.
- ••••• **Master:** You know everything happening on the streets, sometimes *before* it happens.

Possessed by: Beat Cops, Criminals, Detectives, Gangsters, Homeless

Specialties: Black Market, Connections, Gangs, Rumor Mill, Vice

SUBTERFUGE

"You know I respect your opinion, Roger," Laura said, leaning in a bit closer. "Everyone does. That's why I need your help to convince the partners to take this case. I know it can be a breakthrough opportunity for us."

"With you handling the case, of course," Roger said, sitting back in his leather office chair.

"Absolutely not," Laura replied. "We'd need more than a junior partner to handle this one. I was thinking we would be a team, but you would get the credit." And the blame, Laura thought to herself as she saw Roger rise to take the bait.

Subterfuge is the art of deception. Characters with this Talent know how to conceal their true feelings and act in a completely different manner. They're also good at noticing when others do the same thing. Subterfuge is used when telling a convincing lie, hiding one's emotions or reactions, or trying to pick up on the same from others. It's most often used to manipulate other

people, but characters also learn it in order to avoid being manipulated. Those with a talent for Subterfuge usually find themselves involved in intrigue and manipulation, one way or another.

- • **Novice:** You can get away with the occasional lie.
- •• **Practiced:** You've got decent poker face, and you know how to bluff.
- ••• **Competent:** You can keep track of complex lies and hide your feelings easily.
- •••• **Expert:** You can pull of complex con games with style and panache.
- ••••• **Master:** No one would ever suspect you; everyone trusts you implicitly.

Possessed by: Actors, Con Artists, Grifters, Lawyers, Politicians, Teenagers

Specialties: Con Games, Hiding Emotions, Lying, Misdirection, Seduction

SKILLS

Skills are learned Abilities acquired through study and practice. If you try to use a Skill your character doesn't have, roll the appropriate Attribute but increase your difficulty by one. Unskilled characters just aren't as effective as those who have studied and practiced.

ANIMAL KEN

The guard dogs bounded across the yard, barking fiercely, but Malakh stood his ground. He stared the dogs down with eyes that had once commanded all the beasts of the Earth, and a low growl started in his throat, a sound no human should make. The dogs stopped barking and whimpered, then scampered off with their tails between their legs, allowing Malakh to proceed unmolested.

This Skill deals with animals of all kinds, from understanding the behavior of wild animals to taming and training animals to perform tricks. It also allows characters to communicate with animals to a degree, or at least know what they want and get the animals to do as they're told. Some animals can sense the presence of the supernatural and react adversely to it. Others are attracted to it.

- • **Novice:** You know some basic animal lore and could train your dog yourself.
- •• **Practiced:** You can train other people's pets for them, and you've dealt with a number of different animals.
- ••• **Competent:** You can train animals for a living.
- •••• **Expert:** You can handle and train exotic and difficult animals such as lions and tigers.
- ••••• **Master:** You are one with the beasts.

Possessed by: Animal Breeders, Animal Trainers, Circus Performers, Farmers, Hunters, Zookeepers

Specialties: Attack Training, Calming, Communication, Guard Training, Specific Species (Dogs, Dolphins, etc.), Wild Animals

CRAFTS

"What is it?" the boy asked Sam, holding the box wrapped in grease-stained brown paper carefully, wanting to shake it, but afraid he might break whatever was inside.

"Something very special," Sephidor replied. "It's something you've always wanted. Open it and see."

From cooking to carpentry to sculpting, Crafts covers any sort of work with your hands. Characters can build, create and even make functional things or works of art using this Skill. The Storyteller sets the difficulty and time required for individual creative tasks; anywhere from a few minutes to days or more of work. Characters with Crafts must choose a specialty, although they don't gain a bonus for it until they have 4 or more ranks in the Skill. (Crafts is so broad that people usually focus on a particular area.)

- • **Novice:** You can do simple projects on your own.
- •• **Practiced:** You understand many of the subtleties of your craft.
- ••• **Competent:** You can earn a decent living at your craft.
- •••• **Expert:** People are consistently impressed with your work.
- ••••• **Master:** You're a true master of your craft, and probably recognized as such.

Possessed by: Artists, Carpenters, Chefs, Craftspeople, Inventors, Mechanics

Specialties: Any particular craft such as Carpentry, Cooking, Drawing, Painting, Pottery, Sculpting and so forth

DEMOLITIONS

The bomb had failed somehow, but it didn't matter. Soon he would be out of the city and then out of the country where there would be other opportunities. He used his key to open the locker at the bus station and was surprised to see a package crudely wrapped in paper and twine with a note taped to it. It read: "Thought you might want this back."

The blast leveled half the bus station, but there was only one fatality.

While almost anyone can make things explode, it takes skill to make them explode in the right way and at the right time. This is the Skill of making, setting and defusing various types of explosives. It also covers knowing where to place explosives for maximum effect, how to acquire explosive materials and even how to make them from scratch. Of course, getting explosives legally requires licenses and such, which may be an issue, considering what characters often use them for.

- • **Novice:** You can make effective Molotov cocktails and other simple homemade explosives.

STEVE ELLIS

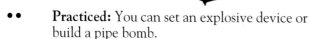

- **•• Practiced:** You can set an explosive device or build a pipe bomb.
- **••• Competent:** You can wire up a car bomb or similar explosive booby trap.
- **•••• Expert:** You can handle pretty much any type of explosive.
- **••••• Master:** You can set up a complex implosion of a massive building so it falls in just the right way.

Possessed by: Bomb Squads, Construction Workers, Soldiers, Terrorists

Specialties: Disarming, Homemade, Implosion, Placement, Remote Triggers, Timers

Drive

The bike roared along the rain-slick asphalt, streetlights strobing overhead. When he spotted the dark sedan pacing him, Aziuran grinned fiercely and opened up the throttle. The sedan sped up to follow as he led through the winding streets. He nearly skidded out making the tight turn into the alley that proved too narrow for the car. The motorcycle shot out of the alley, and Aziuran continued on alone.

While most characters can drive a car, the Drive Skill covers driving various types of motor vehicles under difficult conditions. More skilled drivers know how to drive a diverse range of vehicles and can perform stunts and dangerous maneuvers. They also know how to do things such as give chase or lose a tail, and they understand the limits of their vehicle (often by exceeding them more than once).

- **• Novice:** You can handle a vehicle under tricky conditions.
- **•• Practiced:** You can navigate through heavy traffic or multiple obstacles.
- **••• Competent:** You could be a professional chauffeur.
- **•••• Expert:** You could be a professional stunt or race driver.
- **••••• Master:** There's no vehicle or stunt you can't handle.

Possessed by: Bikers, Cabbies, Chauffeurs, Police, Race-Car Drivers, Truckers

Specialties: High-Speed Chases, Losing Tails, Motorcycles, Off-Roading, Sports-Cars, Stunts, Trucks

Etiquette

"It's a pleasure to meet you," Sabriel said with a dazzling smile. The senator returned it like she'd just given him a gift. He scooped up one of her hands and bent to kiss it.

"The pleasure is all mine, my dear," he replied.

Not yet, Sabriel thought, but it will be. For now, there was a party to work and so many more guests for her to meet.

Society has certain standards of behavior, although they vary from one situation to another. Etiquette provides guidance when it comes to proper behavior in various social situations. It allows characters to fit in gracefully, act properly, earn respect and deal with other people diplomatically.

Etiquette generally refers to the mores and manners of "proper" society, whereas Streetwise handles "street" or "lower class" environments. Characters are often specialized in the etiquette of a particular culture or setting.

- **• Novice:** You can fit in and avoid any serious social gaffes.
- **•• Practiced:** You know the language and rules well enough to look like you belong.
- **••• Competent:** You impress people with your grace and tact. You're an excellent host and guest.
- **•••• Expert:** The soul of tact, you could be a professional diplomat.
- **••••• Master:** You can handle nearly any social situation with aplomb while making it look easy.

Possessed by: Clergy, Diplomats, Politicians, Socialites

Specialties: Any specific sub-culture: Business, High Society, Japanese, Religious, and so forth.

Firearms

"That's it, just hold it firmly and squeeze the trigger. Don't let the recoil scare you. It's just a little kick."

Zormas watched with approval as the kid squeezed off a couple shots before turning to him, smiling in grim satisfaction. He wasn't a great marksman, but he'd hit the target at least. All it would take is a little more instruction. Zormas figured if the kid was going to bring a gun to school, he might as well know how to use it.

Sometimes the simplest way of handling a problem is by putting a bullet through it. That's when this Skill comes in handy. It covers recognizing, using and maintaining all types of firearms, from pistols to assault rifles and machine guns, although it doesn't cover heavy weapons such as bazookas or rocket launchers. Characters can roll Perception + Firearms to recognize a particular type of gun and Wits + Firearms to unjam a gun in combat. Usually the roll is Dexterity + Firearms to fire a gun and hit a target.

- **• Novice:** You've fired a gun a few times and know what to expect.
- **•• Practiced:** You visit the firing range on a semi-regular basis and practice with different types of weapons.
- **••• Competent:** You've used a gun in a firefight more than once. You can field strip and clean your weapon without consulting the manual.
- **•••• Expert:** You regularly get top scores in marksmanship, and you can handle almost any sort of firearm.
- **••••• Master:** You can field strip your gun in the dark or blindfolded, and you hit whatever you aim at.

Possessed by: Assassins, Gangsters, Gun Enthusiasts, Hunters, Police Officers, Soldiers, Survivalists

Specialties: Automatics, Fast-Draw, Handguns, Maintenance, Rifles, Shotguns

MELEE

As he came back up to his feet, Malakh's hand closed around a broken and discarded board. It was about the right length and solid. He gripped it like a weapon as he rose.

The gangbangers saw him defiantly clutching a scrap of wood and laughed. They had knives, chains, brass knuckles, real weapons. They weren't laughing a few minutes later, after Malakh gave them a lesson in the art of combat.

"Anything is a weapon, if you use it right," he said, dropping the board across one gangbanger's chest.

Fighting with a weapon in hand is almost a lost art, but characters with this Skill are acquainted with a variety of melee weapons, from simple clubs to knives, swords, and even exotic weapons like axes or maces. Any weapon that is wielded in close combat falls under this Skill. Thrown weapons are covered by Athletics. A character trained in Melee also knows about various kinds of weapons and combat techniques.

- • **Novice:** You've learned the right way to hold a weapon, maybe taken some lessons or been in a medieval recreation society.
- •• **Practiced:** You've wielded weapons in a few fights.
- ••• **Competent:** Not only have you been in armed fights, you've generally won them.
- •••• **Expert:** You could compete in bouts or teach most fighters a few tricks.
- ••••• **Master:** You have a skill usually seen only in movie action scenes.

Possessed by: Assassins, Fencers, Gangsters, Martial Artists, Police

Specialties: Any type of weapon, such as Axes, Clubs, Knives, Swords or any particular maneuver, such as Disarming, Parrying, Thrusting and so forth.

PERFORMANCE

"You're an amazing dancer," he said.
"So are you," Sabriel lied expertly.
"How'd you get to be so good?"
The Defiler smiled. "Years and years of practice."

This Skill includes all the performing arts, such as acting, dancing, singing and playing a musical instrument. Most characters will have a specialty, a particular area where they excel, although many performers are skilled in multiple areas. Characters use this Skill to give a successful and convincing performance. Combined with Expression, characters can create their own works and evoke particular feelings in their audience. Combined with Subterfuge, they can express a particular emotion and make it believable (important for actors). Fallen characters can also use Performance to enhance a role, either a disguise or part they've assumed to cover their true nature.

- • **Novice:** You're a talented amateur.
- •• **Practiced:** You're comfortable and capable in front of an audience.
- ••• **Competent:** You impress audiences with your performance.
- •••• **Expert:** You dazzle audiences with your performance.
- ••••• **Master:** You play to packed houses and regularly get standing ovations.

Possessed by: Actors, Amateur Performers, Dancers, Musicians, Singers

Specialties: Acting, Choreography, Dancing, Musical Instrument, Singing, Stand-Up Comedy

SECURITY

It was just sad, Sephidor thought, looking over the system. Somebody was getting sloppy if they thought this was enough to keep people out. Well, maybe people, but then that wasn't what the Earthbound should have been worrying about. He set the open panel aside and reached into a pocket for his wire cutters. He'd have this thing disabled in less than a minute.

Characters with this Skill understand how to secure people, places and things, and they know how to overcome the security measures others create. Security covers everything from making a location safe from intruders to setting up alarms and other security systems as well as circumventing them. Characters can recognize different security measures with a Perception + Security roll and figure out their design (and weak points) with an Intelligence + Security roll. Bypassing a security system may be Dexterity or Intelligence + Security, depending on the nature of the system.

- • **Novice:** You're familiar with the major types of home security and know a few tricks for dealing with locks and such.
- •• **Practiced:** You can hot-wire a car or pick a simple lock.
- ••• **Competent:** You're familiar with most security systems and burglary techniques.
- •••• **Expert:** You can set up a state-of-the-art security system, or get past one.
- ••••• **Master:** There's no system you can't improve or beat.

Possessed by: Bodyguards, Criminals, Security Consultants, Stalkers

Specialties: Alarms, Electronics, Escape, Lockpicking, On-Site Security

STEALTH

Magdiel approached like a shadow, gliding soundlessly across the darkened alley. The man standing beneath the bare bulb near the door hadn't seen her as he lit up a cigarette. Nasty habit, she thought, though she supposed it would be the least of his problems in a few seconds.

Stealth allows characters to sneak and hide, whether moving or standing still. Generally players roll Dexterity + Stealth against an opponent's Perception to escape notice. Storytellers might wish to make Stealth rolls secretly, since characters usually have no way of knowing they've been noticed until it's too late.

- • **Novice:** You can hide behind large enough objects or in dark enough areas.
- •• **Practiced:** You can disappear into a crowd and follow someone without being spotted right off.
- ••• **Competent:** People tell you to stop sneaking up on them.
- •••• **Expert:** You can sneak across an open courtyard or along a gravel path without being noticed.
- ••••• **Master:** You're like a ninja, practically invisible when you want to be.

Possessed by: Assassins, Commandos, Reporters, Spies, Thieves

Specialties: Crowds, Darkness, Hiding, Shadowing, Sneaking

SURVIVAL

"What do we do now?" the woman said in a plaintive voice. Alejandro looked back at the wreckage of the small plane, squared his shoulders and quickly started digging through the remains for anything of use. It would be dark soon, and they needed to get moving.

"We survive," he replied.

The world can be a harsh place. It takes skill to survive without the comforts of modern life. Survival covers making it in the wilderness (even the wilderness of the urban jungle) with only simple tools and resources. The more skilled characters are, the fewer resources they need in order to survive. They can live off the land, avoid the dangers of the environment, find shelter and so forth. Characters must choose a specialty for the environment they know best.

- • **Novice:** You've been camping a few times.
- •• **Practiced:** You've been camping a lot of times and taken a survival course or two.
- ••• **Competent:** You can care for a small group of people and keep them alive.
- •••• **Expert:** You can live off the land pretty much indefinitely.
- ••••• **Master:** You are one with your environment.

Possessed by: Boy Scouts, Campers, Commandos, Hunters, Survivalists

Specialties: Any particular environment such as Arctic, Desert, Forest, Jungle or Urban, or any particular aspect of survival like Hazards, Hunting, Shelter and so forth

TECHNOLOGY

"Did this all by yourself did you?" Ashbury said laconically as he looked things over.

"Spare me the sarcasm, Sephidor, can you fix the damn thing?"

"Oh, I can fix it. The question is, what's it worth to you?"

The fallen are not always familiar with the wonders of the modern world, but they acquaint themselves

with the works of humanity quickly. This Skill covers understanding, operating, repairing, and even building or upgrading electronic devices. Purely mechanical devices fall under the Crafts Skill (p. 145), while computer hardware and software falls under the Computers Knowledge (p. 149). Characters without this Skill may know how to operate various common devices, but they don't necessarily know how they work or how to fix them.

- • **Novice:** You can re-wire a lamp and do some common household repairs.
- •• **Practiced:** You can do some basic electrical work or build a crystal radio set.
- ••• **Competent:** You're a skilled electrical engineer (with or without the college degree), able to design and build various devices.
- •••• **Expert:** You can alter and upgrade existing electronic equipment.
- ••••• **Master:** You're ahead of your time when it comes to designing and building new technology.

Possessed by: Engineers, Repair Personnel, Technicians

Specialties: Appliances, Communications, Customization, Invention, Security, Vehicles

KNOWLEDGES

Knowledges are Abilities acquired through study, usually involving application of the mind, so Knowledges are most often paired with the Mental Attributes (particularly Intelligence). The rankings are described in collegiate terms, but formal education is by no means the only way of improving Knowledge. You may want to differentiate between Knowledges your character learned formally and those he learned informally (and without the prestige of a degree).

If your character doesn't have a ranking in a Knowledge, you can't attempt rolls involving it unless you have the Storyteller's permission. If you don't know anything about medicine, you're not going to be able to perform helpful first-aid, much less surgery. If you don't speak Japanese, you're probably not going to be able to understand it, and so forth.

ACADEMICS

"Fling away ambition," he said. "By that sin fell the angels."

"Don't start spouting that Biblical crap at me," Hasmed said to the other man. Devils just loved to hear themselves talk.

"That's not the Bible," the Devil said with a smile. "That's Shakespeare, which has far more truth in it, if you ask me."

This Knowledge is education in the "liberal arts," including history, literature, philosophy, sociology and psychology. It also tends to cover the character's general level of formal education and experience with the academic world. You must choose a specialty for this

Knowledge, though you still have a broad understanding of areas outside your specialty. Most Academics rolls are Intelligence + Academics to recall some particular fact, although you may use Charisma + Academics to favorably impress someone in academia or Manipulation + Academics to deal with the ins and outs of university bureaucracy. The difficulty of the roll is usually based on the obscurity of the knowledge you're trying to recall, from 4 (for fairly routine things) to 8 (for obscure information).

- • **Student:** You've got a high-school level understanding of the arts.
- •• **College:** You can keep up in most conversations about the humanities.
- ••• **Masters:** You have all sorts of trivia at your fingertips.
- •••• **Doctorate:** Your academic knowledge leaves most people in the dust, wondering what you're talking about.
- ••••• **Scholar:** You're a renowned expert in your chosen field of study.

Possessed by: Academics, Historians, Literary Critics, Professors, Trivia Buffs, Writers

Specialties: Architecture, Art, History, Literature, Music, Psychology, Sociology

COMPUTER

"So I guess that makes you a real search 'daemon,' huh?" Oh yes, Alazan never tired of that particular pun. He ignored the comment, and his fingers kept flying over the keys, the images on the screen of his laptop flashing past faster than most people could keep track of them. His body knew the rhythms well, so Alazan knew them. The screen blanked out, and a prompt appeared. He was in.

Operating and programming computers falls under this Knowledge. It ranges from the ability to use computers for routine operations to in-depth knowledge of hardware and software sufficient to be a computer programmer or engineer. A great many people have at least a dot of Computer, but many other people don't, and the fallen sometimes overlook how useful these artifacts of the modern world can be.

- • **Student:** You can operate a computer and use basic software for email and word-processing.
- •• **College:** You can do complex data-entry and analysis and write simple programs.
- ••• **Masters:** You can design your own programs that are as good as commercial ones. Sometimes better.
- •••• **Doctorate:** You can design your own hardware and software, even create some innovations. You also know how to crack most secure systems and get information from them.
- ••••• **Scholar:** You're truly elite. You know everything worth knowing about computers, and few systems are safe from you.

Possessed by: Engineers, Geeks, Office Workers, Programmers, Students

Specialties: Hacking, Hardware, Internet, Research, Software, Viruses

FINANCE

Piers pored over the stacks of printouts, which he far preferred to trying to read off a computer screen. The patterns just seemed to jump off a written page far more easily. Ah, there it was. They were cleverly and carefully buried, but there were definite signs of money being siphoned off. Piers had done his share of embezzling, too, so he knew the signs. There were plenty who would pay handsomely for this information, but Piers wanted someone who would act upon it, and he knew just the one.

Finance covers handling and making money, from accounting and keeping books to evaluating an item's worth and playing the stock market. It can be used to make money legitimately or for things like insider trading and other scams. In addition to providing a comfortable level of wealth (see the Resources Background, p. 157), Finance is useful in navigating money trails and similar affairs.

- • **Student:** Some basic experience in bookkeeping and finance.
- •• **College:** A degree in accounting or finance backed by some experience.
- ••• **Masters:** An MBA degree or the equivalent.
- •••• **Doctorate:** You could run a major corporation and make it more profitable.
- ••••• **Scholar:** You can make a fortune on the stock market.

Possessed by: Accountants, Fences, Businesspeople, Smugglers, Stock Brokers

Specialties: Accounting, Appraisal, Currency Exchange, Fencing, Laundering, Stock Market

INVESTIGATION

Detective Liebner crouched beside the body. She had been beautiful once, that much was for sure. Her face was untouched and surprisingly peaceful considering the violence done to the rest of her. Unnaturally peaceful, in fact. He doubted that the uniforms he'd brought with him noticed. The younger one looked like he was too busy trying to keep down his breakfast.

"It's not as bad as it could be," he said idly to no one in particular.

"What do you mean?" the younger officer said, as if he couldn't possibly imagine something worse.

"The blood," Liebner replied. "She's obviously been moved. Otherwise there would be blood all over the walls and floor after what our perpetrator did to her."

You're trained to look for clues and piece together evidence to solve mysteries, from investigating a crime to discovering secret or hidden goings-on. Investigation

is used for finding clues, putting them together, doing research and tracking down leads.

- • **Student:** Amateur armchair detective.
- •• **College:** Police officer.
- ••• **Masters:** Detective.
- •••• **Doctorate:** Federal agent, professional profiler.
- ••••• **Scholar:** Sherlock Holmes. There's no mystery you can't solve.

Possessed by: Coroners, Detectives, FBI Agents, Police, Profilers

Specialties: Crime Scenes, Forensics, Interviews, Leads, Research

LAW

"Can you help me, Ms. Blake?"

"Well normally in a case like yours, Mr. Allemande, I would say there isn't much hope." The man's face fell. "However…" she let the hope dangle in front of him for a moment. "The legal definitions of 'consent' have been challenged in the past, and much of this rides on your wife and son's testimony. I'm sure that there's something we can work with there. If there's a way to win this, you can be sure I'll find it."

Characters trained in the law know legal codes and procedures. More skilled characters can offer legal advice and figure out ways of dealing with legal matters. They may even be licensed to practice law. Jokes about lawyers and demons aside, the fallen have a natural knack for dealing with the law. They were the keepers of the laws of Creation, and they make passionate advocates and prosecutors. This Ability includes an understanding of religious and cultural laws, but divine law is a matter for the Religion Knowledge.

- • **Student:** Your favorite network is Court TV
- •• **College:** You're a pre-law graduate or have done a lot of reading up on the subject
- ••• **Masters:** The equivalent of a law degree. You could be licensed to practice law.
- •••• **Doctorate:** You've got a reputation for winning your cases and giving sound advice.
- ••••• **Scholar:** Devil's Advocate.

Possessed by: Criminals, Judges, Lawyers, Police, Politicians

Specialties: Civil, Contracts, Corporate, Criminal, Cultural, Religious

LINGUISTICS

"It is Enochian, isn't it?" Liebner asked.

"Yes, and no," Felding replied. "It's based on Enochian, but it's a crude and inaccurate transliteration, more likely based on some of the occult works of the 18th and 19th centuries than the true language."

The fallen understand well the power of words. Their understanding of the True Language is part of their power. All characters are assumed to speak,

read and write in their native language. The fallen gain this ability as part and parcel of the memories they absorb when inhabiting a mortal body. Dots in Linguistics allow a character to speak additional languages. The player chooses which languages the character understands with the approval of the Storyteller. In the case of the fallen, this often includes ancient or even long-dead languages, although Linguistics should not be required for these unless they are useful for something other than background flavor. A high level of this Knowledge also includes some understanding of the science of languages — their construction, design and internal logic. Characters may choose the study of linguistics as one of their "language" choices to get a more scholarly understanding of the topic.

- • **Student:** One extra language.
- •• **College:** Two extra languages.
- ••• **Masters:** Four extra languages.
- •••• **Doctorate:** Eight extra languages.
- ••••• **Scholar:** 16 extra languages.

Possessed by: Diplomats, Linguists, Spies, Translators, World Travelers

Specialties: Codes and Ciphers, Slang, any modern or ancient language, any written language

MEDICINE

"No, no," Anila said as the boy struggled to rise. "Lie still. I'm here to help." Her expert fingers probed gently at the back of his head, then down his neck to his arm and he winced, the breath hissing between his teeth.

"You've dislocated it," she said, sliding her arm around his. "Hold on, this is going to hurt a bit."

This trait represents an understanding of the workings of mortal clay, specifically the human body and how to treat it. It represents knowledge of anatomy, physiology and basic medical techniques and treatment at low levels. At higher ranks it includes diagnosis, treatment of disease and surgery, all the skills of a physician (whether or not the character has the license to be an actual doctor). Characters with this trait can treat the injuries and maladies or others. If they wish, they can also use their knowledge of the human body to cause damage.

- • **Student:** Basic first-aid and CPR training and understanding of anatomy.
- •• **College:** Pre-med student or trained paramedic.
- ••• **Masters:** You could be a licensed general practitioner.
- •••• **Doctorate:** Surgeon or skilled medical specialist.
- ••••• **Scholar:** Renowned for your skill and knowledge in the field.

Possessed by: Doctors, Lifeguards, Nurses, Paramedics

Specialties: Anesthesiology, Emergency Care, Pathology, Pediatrics, Pharmaceuticals, Poisons, Surgery

OCCULT

"So… what is it?" Alejandro asked, bending over the body. Felding cleaned his glasses before putting them back on.

"A vampire," he said. "From one of their less prestigious clans, I'd say, from the look of him."

"No shit," Alejandro replied, tapping the stake to make sure it was still firmly in place. "I always knew Caine was going to cause trouble."

There is a great deal of lore in the world about the occult, the mysterious, the mythic and the legendary. In the World of Darkness, some of it is true, but most of it is not. A character with knowledge of the occult not only knows the theories, myths and legends but also has the ability to discern fact from falsehood. Once, the fallen knew all there was to know about the hidden powers of Creation, but a great deal has changed since their imprisonment and there's much to learn. Knowledge of the occult is also useful in mortal circles for attracting followers.

- • **Student:** You've read some books and picked up the basics.
- •• **College:** You've read a *lot* of books and started to pick out the obvious falsehoods.
- ••• **Masters:** You know all the major occult lore and a number of obscure facts, although not all of it is true.
- •••• **Doctorate:** You can separate truth from falsehood, and you know most of what there is to know.
- ••••• **Scholar:** You're privy to secrets that few others are aware of.

Possessed by: Cultists, Exorcists, Mages, Neo-Pagans, Occultists, Parapsychologists

Specialties: Cultural Beliefs, Demons, Faerie Folk, Ghosts, Magic, Vampires, Werewolves

POLITICS

Milton leaned back in his chair, toying with the phone cord and glancing out the window as he spoke. "Really, Senator, there's no need for such language. You wanted the votes to get your little initiative passed, so you got them. Do you really care how? What matters is that I upheld my end of the bargain, and I expect you to uphold yours. Otherwise, well, I'm sure you can imagine all sorts of reasons why you don't want to piss me off. I'll be in touch, Senator."

You know the ins and outs of the political game, what the rules are, and who the major players are. You know who's in power and how they got there, along with their major rivals. You've also got a grasp of the issues and how they affect the political process. This is primarily an understanding of mortal politics, but politics is a fairly universal concept, so it carries over into the affairs of the fallen and is good for dealing with any political creature. To truly play the political game, of course, takes traits

like Expression, Performance and Subterfuge, but Politics gives you the knowledge to use them to good effect.

- • **Student:** Part-time political activist.
- •• **College:** Political science major, small-town politician
- ••• **Masters:** Campaign manager or political commentator.
- •••• **Doctorate:** You could hold a national political office.
- ••••• **Scholar:** You could move through the highest political circles in the world.

Possessed by: Activists, Lawyers, Politicians, Plotters, Vampires

Specialties: Bribery, City, Federal, International, State, Radical

RELIGION

"Oh, Hell is real," Gaviel said. "Very real, but it's not a place for mortal souls. Only the fallen are imprisoned there. So consider the possibility that you can't end up in Hell, no matter what you do in this life. Sheds a whole new light on the Commandments and the rest of your dogma, doesn't it?"

Recollections of Creation, the war and the Fall linger in humanity's collective consciousness as myths and legends. Around those beliefs, humans have built religions, some of which unite more people than any nation or force in the world. At the same time, religions divide people and serve as excuses for atrocities. As focuses for human faith, religions are a subject of keen interest to the fallen, and many study them, both for means of influencing and garnering worshippers and to find clues to the secrets of the past they have lost. Religion covers theology and comparative religious studies along with knowledge of major religions and (with increasing rank) knowledge of lesser-known ones as well. Characters often take a specialty in a particular religion.

- • **Student:** You've taken a course or two in comparative religion.
- •• **College:** Divinity student.
- ••• **Masters:** You could be a member of the clergy (yeah, right).
- •••• **Doctorate:** You debate religious ideas and principles with experts, and impress them.
- ••••• **Scholar:** You could create your own religion.

Possessed by: Believers, Clergy, Scholars, Televangelists

Specialties: Any specific religion such as Christianity, Islam, Judaism, Buddhism, Satanism and so forth.

RESEARCH

So the building was constructed in 1927, but the site it occupies has occult associations going back almost as far as there were records for the time, *Senachib* mused. *The financier behind its construction committed*

suicide following the stock market crash, or at least his death was ruled a suicide. It was clear that someone had invested a lot of time and effort into having a building there, but why?

For most questions, the answer is out there, if only you know where to look. Research is the skill of knowing where to look for information, gathering it efficiently and organizing it so other people can absorb it without too much trouble. With this Ability, you know the best places to start looking for particular information and the best ways to go about it. Research differs from Academics in that it involves looking for information, while Academics involves knowing information, and Research tends to turn up more detailed information than someone can recall from memory.

- • **Student:** You know how to use the card catalog in the library and your favorite search engines on the Internet.
- •• **College:** You actually know what the Dewey Decimal numbers mean and how to find things without a card catalog or search engine.
- ••• **Masters:** You're familiar with the best resources of particular subjects of interest to you.
- •••• **Doctorate:** It's not a matter of if you will find the information, just a matter of how long it will take.
- ••••• **Scholar:** You have tremendous information at your fingertips, and more only a phone call or email away.

Possessed by: Librarians, Researchers, Scholars, Students, Writers

Specialties: Genealogy, Government Documents, History, Internet, Rare Books, Religious Archives

SCIENCE

Detective Liebner glanced around the neat and sterile lab before catching the eye of the technician working there. The tech put aside some slides she was looking at.

"You got the report on that parchment we found?" he asked. She nodded, picking up the bagged evidence from the counter.

"Interesting stuff," she said. The writing was done in a combination of India ink and human blood, with minute traces of powdered gold, but that's not the really interesting part. The parchment itself is made from some kind of tanned hide."

"What kind?" Liebner asked, afraid he already knew the answer.

"We have to do a few more tests… but we think it's human."

This Ability represents an understanding of the physical sciences: biology, chemistry, physics, and so forth. Many characters have a specialty they focus on, but they retain a broad general knowledge of other sciences. The Storyteller sets the difficulty for coming up with a particular scientific fact or solving a scientific mystery according to the complexity of the task. Science is largely theoretical knowledge, Crafts and Technology cover its practical applications.

- • **Student:** You did well in high school science class.
- •• **College:** You have a broad general view of the sciences and a little practical experience.
- ••• **Masters:** You've done your own research and ex periments, probably even had a paper or two published.
- •••• **Doctorate:** You're a skilled researcher with deep understanding of the sciences.
- ••••• **Scholar:** Your research and theories are re nowned and respected.

Possessed by: Academics, Engineers, Researchers, Scientists, Technicians

Specialties: Biology, Chemistry, Geology, Metallurgy, Physics, and many others

BACKGROUNDS

Some traits are inborn, some are learned and practiced, and others are matters of experience, hard work and good fortune. Over time, people accumulate things like friends, contacts and favors. They earn money and acquire resources and may also gain fame or status. These traits are called Backgrounds. The represent the resources your character has to draw on, rather than personal abilities. They're rated just like Attributes and Abilities are, but they're not rolled as often. A given level of a Background represents an advantage your character has.

Backgrounds are related to a character's history. Often, the Backgrounds of the fallen are not actually theirs, but belong to the mortal form they inhabit. Lucky demons end up in the bodies of wealthy, influential people while the unfortunate end up in the shells of criminals, the poor and the homeless. Of course, the fallen living the lives of the rich and famous have to deal with hiding their true nature from friends, family and often the watchful eyes of the media, whereas others have the benefit of anonymity.

ALLIES

Whoever was out to cause Laura trouble didn't know who he was messing with. She sat calmly at her desk and picked up the phone, ignoring the slight trembling as she recalled how close the shot had come and thought about what would happen if she was forced back into the Abyss, with no hope of escape.

The phone rang, and a voice at the other end answered.

"I need a favor," Laura said immediately.

Allies are people (human and otherwise) who are willing to help your character out from time to time. They may be friends, allies of convenience or people who owe you a favor or two. Each dot you have in the Allies Background gets you one ally of modest ability. You can also choose to apply multiple dots to get a single ally of greater ability, or some combination of the two, chosen before the character enters play. You and the Storyteller can work out your allies'

names, histories and abilities, and the Storyteller may play them as supporting characters in the chronicle.

Allies are usually mortals, although more capable allies may not be. Although they may know about your character's true nature, allies generally aren't as aware about the true nature of the World of Darkness, unless they happen to specialize in the occult or the strange. Although they are friendly toward your character, allies have their own personalities, goals and needs. They're not likely to risk themselves needlessly for you, and they may occasionally ask for a favor in return for their help.

X   No allies.
•   One ally of moderate ability.
••   Two allies or one more capable ally.
•••   Three allies or a combination of more capable allies.
••••   Four allies or a combination of more capable allies.
•••••   Five allies of a combination of more capable allies.

CONTACTS

"She's a runaway," Anila said. "Sixteen, about five-two with short hair, dyed purple last time I saw her. I figured she might show up down there or at one of the other shelters. If she does, could you ring me at this number? Right, I know that you normally keep things confidential, Don, but she's a client and it's important. Brilliant, thanks."

She had to find that girl. She didn't have any idea what she'd gotten herself into, but Anila knew people in social services all over London. If the girl showed up, Anila would hear about it.

You know people and can get information from them. Contacts differ from allies in that they are usually only willing to provide your character with information and not other kinds of assistance. The Contacts background also represents your character's information resources in general, a network of associates, friends of friends and so forth.

A contact can generally provide you information in a particular area of expertise. For each dot in this Background, you have one contact with a particular area of expertise. If you want, multiple areas can be concentrated in a single contact for multiple dots, or some combination thereof. Contacts are characters and should be named and described, along with their area of expertise, before the character enters the chronicle. The Storyteller runs contact characters and sets the difficulty for getting information from them.

Generally, you can get information by rolling the appropriate Social Attribute (chosen by the Storyteller) + Contacts against a difficulty. Information in your contact's area is easier to get than more obscure or unrelated information. The Storyteller may also modify the difficulty based on your treatment of the contact. Fair and decent treatment makes contacts more helpful. A failure on the roll means the contact doesn't have the information or isn't willing to

give it to you. A botch may mean that the contact sells you out or passes word on to the wrong people about what you're looking for. Success doesn't guarantee exactly the information you're looking for. Contacts aren't all-knowing, and the Storyteller is perfectly justified in saying that a particular contact simply doesn't know something.

X   No contacts — you have to do all your investigating on your own
•   One contact.
••   Two contacts.
•••   Three contacts.
••••   Four contacts.
•••••   Five contacts.

EMINENCE

Piers only paused when the big bruiser moved directly between him and the door.

"You can't go in there," the bruiser said flatly, crossing his arms over his massive chest in emphasis. Piers only narrowed his eyes, not taking them off the beady ones before him.

"Oh, I think I can, unless you would prefer a one-way trip back into the Pit. Or could it be that you don't know who I am?" He let his true self show in Piers' eyes and all around his mortal vessel, and the bruiser paled and shuddered.

"Forgive me, sir," he stammered, quickly stepping aside. "I didn't recognize you."

Even in the time before the Fall, there was a definite order among the servants of the One. Since then, the fallen have developed a definite pecking order, with the strongest and most capable (or most cunning) at the top. This trait gives you a measure of influence and prestige in demon society. Lesser demons will tend to stay out of your way, and peers will respect you as long as you don't give them any reason to do otherwise. You may even be able to throw your weight around a bit with low-ranking demons and get the attention of higher-ups. Of course, greater prestige also brings with it a higher profile. Other demons are more likely to have heard of you and to know more about you. They're also more likely to bear grudges against you, or at least what you stand for.

X   You're down at the bottom of the ladder with most of the fallen, just another of the rabble from the Pit.
•   You were somebody once, maybe before the Fall or during the rebellion, and that counts for a something with some demons.
••   You've got a measure of influence, either an up-and-comer or a significant talent.
•••   You've got significant influence, enough to get lesser demons to do what you tell them (if only to avoid angering you).
••••   You're one of the movers and shakers of the local scene. Everyone knows who you are.

••••• You command the local court and have influence on a worldwide scale. You may have been a famous figure from the rebellion or earned your reputation since then.

FAME

"I'm sorry, you probably get this all the time, but I just love your work. I mean, there's just such a passion, a real energy to it. I'm a writer, too, actually. Well, not published like you, of course, but I've been working really hard at it and… God, I'm sorry! You probably have to listen to wannabe writers all the time."

"It's okay," Dominic said soothingly. *"Actually, it's rare to run into someone with such an obvious passion for the craft. Would you care to join me? I'd like to hear more about your writing. Perhaps I can offer a few suggestions."*

You have a measure of fame in mortal society, possibly as a performer, athlete, politician or other sort of public personality. Your fame gives you various perks, but it can also make it difficult for you to hide your true nature from the world. Fame is also very close to worship, and you might be able to parlay your fame into some additional Faith, if you play your cards carefully.

On one hand, fame gives you power and influence in mortal society. You can get away with a lot when you're famous, and people tend to defer to you. You're frequently recognized, and you can often get star treatment from people. On the other hand, it is difficult for you to go places without being recognized, and the media watches you carefully. Anything unusual about you is more likely to be noticed (although not necessarily in a bad way — the famous are expected to be eccentric). The Storyteller may reduce the difficulty of some Social rolls when you're dealing with particularly star-struck fans or the like.

X   Who? You might get your 15 minutes like everyone else, but they haven't come yet.

•   You're well known to a small circle or subculture, like the elite or the occult crowd of a particular city.

••   You're a local celebrity like a TV or radio personality. Most people in your area recognize you.

•••   You're known statewide or in a large subculture, such as science-fiction fans or academics.

••••   You're nationally famous, most people have at least heard of you. Many recognize you.

••••• You're internationally famous, a mega-media star, known (and mobbed with fans) wherever you go.

FOLLOWERS

"Are you sure that you're ready for the freedom I offer you?" Gaviel asked the young man kneeling before.

"Yes," he said defiantly, proudly. *"I'm ready to cast off the chains that I've been forced to wear."*

"Are you ready for the truth?" Gaviel intoned.

"Yes, I am ready," he replied.

No, you're not, Gaviel thought, but you will be. Until then, you can be of some use to me.

Followers are servants, worshippers or even loyal hirelings working for you. They're people willing to devote a substantial amount of their time (perhaps even all of it) to taking care of various tasks for you. A demon's followers are often (but not always) sources of faith and worship.

Although followers are assumed to be loyal to you, you have to maintain their loyalty through money, a pact or some other form of influence. Followers that are ignored or mistreated will eventually leave in search of greener pastures. Followers that are treated well will tend to remain loyal, although they still have their own goals and personalities. You and the Storyteller should work together to describe any followers you have and why they follow you.

Followers are usually people of modest ability. They may have a few useful skills, but they don't have any special abilities unless you choose to invest Faith in them (see p. 252). The Storyteller should see to it that your followers are useful without being overpowering — no cadres of elite commandos or secret ninja cults.

X   No followers — you work on your own.

•   One follower.

••   Two followers.

•••   Three followers.

••••   Four followers.

••••• Five followers.

INFLUENCE

As they sped along the highway, Tom spotted the lights flashing behind them.

"Oh, shit, it's a cop," he said.

"Don't worry about it," Laura replied.

"Don't worry about it! If he pulls us over—"

"I said, don't worry about it," she repeated. By now the cop had called her plate number in it, and it would only take a few moments for them to tell him whom he was following. Shortly thereafter, the cop sped up and passed them and Laura slowly slightly to let him go, smiling slightly. It paid to know people.

You can pull strings in mortal society to get things done or to get people to look the other way. Your influence may come from wealth, fame, political power, social connections, blackmail, religious fervor, supernatural power or some combination thereof. The greater your Influence rating is, the stronger and more far-reaching your influence is.

Exercising your influence usually requires a Social Attribute + Influence roll, although the Storyteller may waive the roll for minor exercises such as getting a traffic ticket fixed. The Storyteller sets the difficulty for an Influence roll based on what you're trying to get done. Appropriate Abilities (such as Subterfuge) and Backgrounds (such as Allies, Contacts or Fame) may lower the difficulty. The fallen are generally cautious in exercising their influence, since obvious uses may attract the attention of the Earthbound and other demons.

X   You've got no more influence than the average person on the street.

•   You can influence city politics and agencies.

••   You can influence state politics and agencies.

•••   You can influence regional politics and agencies.

••••   You can influence national politics and agencies.

•••••   You can influence international politics and agencies.

LEGACY

"Wait! Stop the car!" Steven shouted.

Andrea slammed on the brakes on the steep mountain road and edged over onto a narrow shoulder set aside for sightseers. Steven was out of the car before it had completely stopped rolling.

Hundreds of feet below, the wooded valley spread its rich, blue-green mantle, rising to the rolling hills ten miles east. Even after the long miles and the sleepless nights, Andrea felt her heart stir at the sight. "It's beautiful," she said, "but now's not the time—"

"Give me a minute," Steven said, cutting her off with a raised hand. He stared intently at the rise and fall of the panorama below. "This looks so familiar. Of course, there weren't any trees back then. This was all seafloor. But…"

"But?" Andrea said.

Steven pointed a tentative finger and a section of the valley floor. "Lord Iriel made his last stand down there, in one of our legion's last bastions. It was the best hidden and best defended stronghold we had left." He looked at his companion. "It could still be there."

The mortal mind is ill-equipped for the vast memories of the fallen, and much of what demons remember from the Age of Wrath and before is driven deep into their host's subconscious, where it can only be felt dimly, if at all. This Background allows you to recall more of your past memories than other fallen, permitting you access to more detailed information about personalities, places and events that occurred in Earth's prehistory.

Calling upon your memories requires an Intelligence + Legacy roll. The difficulty of the roll depends on the relative obscurity of the information you're after, at the discretion of the Storyteller. Remembering details about a close compatriot during the War of Wrath would require a difficulty of 6, while recalling the location of a specific battlefield or the location of a former bastion might require a difficulty of 7 or higher. The number of successes determines the depth and breadth of your recollections.

X   You have only the barest recollection of your former existence.

•   You can remember some details of the war and those you fought with.

••   You can remember a fair amount of information about the Fall.

•••   You remember the war and your exploits with some detail.

••••   You remember a great deal about the war and the time before the Fall.

•••••   You have a wealth of detailed memories of your past existence.

MENTOR

Piers stepped into the office. It was dark and opulent without becoming decadent. He closed the door behind him and waited quietly to be acknowledged.

"I wasn't expecting to see you so soon," a voice said from the high-backed chair facing the window that looked out over the lights of the city.

"There's a problem," Piers began. "I need your advice."

A great deal has changed in the mortal world since the rebellion, and the fallen are not always aware of how things have changed. They're also new to mortal existence and the various limits placed on their power. This Background gives your character a mentor, a guide and teacher who gives you advice and guidance. Most likely your mentor is a fellow demon who has been around the block a few times and has reason to want to help you. It's also possible your mentor might be a mortal well-versed in the secrets of the fallen and willing to help you out with the nuances of the mortal world. A low rating in this Background indicates a mentor with limited resources and influence, while a high rating gives you a mentor who commands respect (and possibly fear).

Your mentor acts on your behalf, although the Storyteller determines exactly how. Usually, a mentor offers advice, allowing the Storyteller to use the mentor to help guide you. Mentors may also use their influence or abilities to help you out, although most mentors like to see their charges do things for themselves. A mentor is likely to give up in disgust on a pupil who constantly asks for help. Mentors may also ask for something in return for their aid, which can lead your character into some interesting situations.

X   You're on your own.

•   A mentor of little influence or power.

••   A mentor of modest influence or power.

•••   A mentor of considerable influence or power in an area.

••••   A mentor with influence or power over an area like a city.

•••••   A mentor with tremendous power.

PACTS

"You're safe," Magdiel said. "There's nothing to be afraid of. No one can hurt you as long as I'm here."

"Thank you," the girl said.

"No, thank you," Magdiel replied. *"You give me the strength to protect you. You help give me the strength to go on."*

You've already established one or more pacts with mortals, granting them their desires in exchange for some of their Faith (see p. 252 for more on pacts). Each dot in this Background represents one pre-existing pact you can draw upon for Faith. You should work with the Storyteller to describe the nature of your various pacts, who they are with, their conditions and so forth. The Storyteller may even want to include the establishment of one or more of your pacts in the prelude.

Once your character enters play, the pacts provided by this Background function like any other. You do not have to have any dots in Pacts to create pacts in play, only to start with established ones.

X   You have no established pacts.
•   One established pact (1 Faith per day).
••   Two established pacts (2 Faith per day).
•••   Three established pacts (3 Faith per day).
•••• Four established pacts (4 Faith per day).
••••• Five established pacts (5 Faith per day).

PARAGON

"Well, that could have gone better."

Sephidor ignored the sarcastic tone as he looked at the stubborn machine. It should be well within his power to deal with the problem.

"Do you have enough juice to try again?" his client asked. Sam just smiled.

"If at first you don't succeed..." he replied and surprised the smartass by trying again right then and there. As many times as it takes, Sam thought. I'm in no hurry.

Each House of the fallen resonates with a particular facet of Creation they were set over by the Lord Above that forms the lore of that House. Some of the fallen are particularly capable in their primary lore. It might be a certain deftness with which they tug the strings of Creation or an insight into its inner workings. Whatever the case, these paragons are the virtuosos of their lore — potential masters of the art.

A paragon can re-roll a number of evocation rolls per chapter in his *primary* lore equal to his rating in this Background. This means that a paragon can use his primary lore more often and with greater effect without risking a loss of Faith.

X   You're no more (or less) talented than any other demon.
•   You can re-roll one evocation roll when using your primary lore.
••   You can re-roll two evocation rolls when using your primary lore.
•••   You can re-roll three evocation rolls when using your primary lore.

•••• You can re-roll four evocation rolls when using your primary lore.
••••• You can re-roll five evocation rolls when using your primary lore.

RESOURCES

The elevator doors opened, and his eyes were just as wide as he took in the room. There was a sunken living area with deep, rich carpeting. Tasteful paintings and pieces of sculpture were placed all around. The lighting was soft and indirect, and the furniture looked comfortable enough to die in, but best of all was the view. Tall windows looked out over a glittering city skyline.

"Wow! Is this place really yours?" he asked. "How do you afford it?"

Christina smiled, taking him by the hand and leading him in as the elevator doors closed behind them.

"Let's just say I love my work," she said wickedly, drawing him closer.

Once, all creatures were beyond material needs as such, but in the modern World of Darkness, it's whatever you can get. This Background measures your character's material resources, both possessions and wealth. The fallen generally start out with whatever their mortal vessels had (if anything) and go from there. Some have little difficulty accumulating wealth, while others have a harder time (or simply don't care about material things).

Your dots in Resources represent a "standard of living" your character has attained. It can usually be maintained fairly easily (although the Storyteller may put obstacles in your path from time to time). You get a basic monthly income from your resources, over and above your basic needs, which you can spend as you see fit. You also have various basic possessions, like a home, vehicle, clothing and so forth. The Storyteller determines if you are likely to own something based on your resources level. If you need to, you can liquidate your possessions for additional cash, although it takes time to sell them (especially large possessions like houses and cars).

X   No resources: You've got nothing but the clothes on your back, the stuff you can carry and maybe a little cash in your pocket.
•   Small savings: You have a small apartment and maybe a motorcycle. If liquidated, you would have about $1000 in cash. Income of $500 a month.
••   Middle class: You have an apartment or condominium and a car. If liquidated you would have at least $8,000. Income of $1,200 a month.
•••   Upper class: You own a house or other property and have a fairly nice car. If liquidated, you would have at least $50,000. Income of $3000 a month.
•••• Wealthy: You own a large house and probably more than one car (or a boat, or other vehicles). If

liquidated you would have at least $500,000. Income of $9,000 a month.

- ••••• Filthy rich: You're a multimillionaire. You may own a mansion (or several) and collect cars for a hobby. If liquidated, you would have at least $5,000,000. Income of $30,000 a month.

Virtues

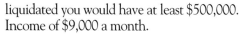

Once the fallen embodied certain virtues. In fact, their passionate devotion to their nations of right and wrong, their compassion for humanity, and their belief in the righteousness of their cause is what led them to rebel in the first place. The memories and mortality of their human hosts reawaken the fallen's virtuous selves, and they cling to those Virtues to hold off the memories of the aeons of torment they've suffered.

In **Demon**, a character's Virtues measure his dedication to those ideals. They influence how the character reacts in certain situations, and they affect when and how the character may be overcome by torment. The fallen need their Virtues to hold on to their sanity and resist becoming the insane creatures they once were.

Conscience

Conscience is the ability to distinguish between right and wrong, a moral compass and the ability to feel remorse for one's misdeeds. Conscience is what shocks the fallen out of their Torment when the first inhabit a mortal host. It is like holding up a mirror in which the fallen can see how twisted and hideous they have become, compared to the shining beings they once were. They see their deeds objectively for the first time and feel remorse at what they have done. Conscience is a measure of the character's dedication to a personal code of ethics and to doing the right thing.

- • Uncaring
- •• Normal
- ••• Ethical
- •••• Righteous
- ••••• Saintly

Conviction

All of Creation has a purpose, and everything happens for a reason. Once the fallen never questioned this. They understood that everything was a part of God's divine plan, and they took comfort in that certainty. The willingness to question God's will, to wonder *what* the purpose of certain things is, helped bring about the Fall and the rebellion. Now the fallen look for meaning in the seemingly random happenings of the world again.

Conviction is a measure of a character's innate understanding of the order of Creation. It is a combination of an almost Zen-like ability to accept circumstances with ease and grace and the ability to keep the faith in the face of any adversity. Characters with high Conviction *know*, on the deepest level, what must be, and they accept it.

- • Cynical
- •• Uncertain
- ••• Temperate
- •••• Faithful
- ••••• Unswerving

Courage

Courage is the strength of one's Conscience and Conviction, the ability to remain firm in the face of danger, fear or adversity. It includes bravery in the face of danger, but it's more than that. It's also the ability to withstand pain and hardship for the greater good or even to sacrifice oneself when necessary. Courageous characters can face nearly anything without flinching, and they have the ability to do what must be done, regardless of the consequences. While a high-Conscience character might know that an action is right, and a high-Conviction character

knows that it is necessary, it takes Courage to go out and *do* it, no matter how hard it may be.

- • Timid
- •• Normal
- ••• Brave
- •••• Resolute
- ••••• Lion-Hearted

FAITH

Faith is the core of the fallen's power, the ability that once let them literally move mountains. Although their power is no longer what it was, demons can still influence Creation in various ways through their Faith.

Faith is a combination of a demon's self-assurance, insight into the nature of Creation and closeness to the divine power they once wielded. Before the Fall, demons had faith in their Creator and drew their power from Him. Now the fallen place their faith only in themselves (and sometimes in humanity) and draw their power from their belief in themselves and mortals' faith in them.

Unlike most traits, Faith is rated on a scale from 1-10, since it can transcend the limits of mortality. The greater a demon's Faith is, more power it wields over the forces of Creation.

SPENDING FAITH

fallen characters have two Faith scores, permanent Faith and a pool of Faith dice. Permanent Faith is like any other trait. The Faith pool starts out equal to permanent Faith, but demons use Faith pool to fuel their various supernatural abilities, allowing them to perform amazing feats. Demonic powers come in three varieties, all fueled by the power of Faith: innate abilities, the apocalyptic form and lore. For details of these powers, see Chapter Seven.

Some powers merely require the demon to have Faith, meaning at least one die in their Faith pool. This allows the fallen to use their innate abilities at will, for example. Other powers, like activating the apocalyptic form or using lore, require a Faith roll (similar to a Willpower roll) or require the expenditure of Faith points to function.

For more details on how Faith is used, see Chapter Nine.

REVELATION

Although they possess amazing powers, demons do take a risk in using their abilities too often, the chance of Revelation. The more Faith a demon uses in a given scene, the more likely mortals are to see the fallen's true nature through the guise of mortal flesh. This may be awe-inspiring or terrifying, depending on the demon's Torment, but it is always a powerful experience for any mortal. The Revelation also announces a demon's presence to others able to sense the disturbances that happen when one tampers with Creation. This makes it more difficult for demons to conceal their activities from their enemies.

HIERARCHY OF SINS

Permanent Torment	Sins
10	There is no sin. You're already damned. Why not do whatever you want?
9	Casual violation of others: murder for no reason, thoughtless cruelty and torture, near-mindless savagery.
8	Premeditated violation of others: plotted murder or assassination, systematic destruction of another, long-sought revenge.
7	Sins of passion: murder in a fit of rage, giving in to feelings of hate, anger, jealousy or irrational prejudice, encouraging the same in others. Destroying particularly inspirational or meaningful objects. Doing personal harm through addiction or other self-destructive patterns of behavior.
6	Destruction of the works or Inflicting intentional emotional harm through cruelty or neglect.
5	Accidental violations: Doing harm to others through carelessness, negligence or t houghtlessness. Neglecting duties or responsibilities. Betraying another's trust.
4	Theft from or deception of others without just cause. Breaking your sworn word.
3	Doing harm (physical, emotional, or spiritual) to a mortal for any reason other than self-defense or the greater good.
2	Doing harm to any mortal creature for any reason other than self-defense or the greater good (a disrespect for the order of Creation). Permitting any lesser sin in your presence without at least trying to prevent it.
1	Any act of cruelty, selfishness or thoughtlessness. Allowing any such act in your presence without trying to prevent it. An unwillingness to sacrifice for the greater good.

The intensity of the Revelation is based on how much Faith a demon expends in a given scene. The more Faith used, the greater the effect.

For details on how Revelation affects mortals, see Chapter Nine.

REGAINING FAITH

Having lost faith in their Creator, the fallen can regain Faith only by taking it from mortals. They do so in one of two ways: reaping — taking Faith from mortal fear or awe — and pacts, deals made with mortals to acquire their Faith in exchange for something the demon provides. See Chapter Nine for detailed systems covering these two methods.

REAPING

Reaping is a quick, short-term means of acquiring Faith. All it requires is a mortal to believe in the demon's existence and power even for a moment. That moment is enough for the fallen to seize the mortal's faith, and take it for their own. Reaping can take any form that convinces a mortal, without a doubt, that the demon is a true supernatural being. A mortal being skinned alive by a creature from Hell has no doubt that it is real. Likewise a mortal who receives the aid of a shining guardian angel knows that a divine power has intervened. A Revelation is not enough in and of itself, though. The demon must *interact* with the mortal in some direct way. The Storyteller judges whether or not a particular action is enough to constitute a reaping. The fallen are cautious about reaping, simply because it forces them to reveal themselves to mortals and increases the chance of demon-hunters or other foes tracking them down.

PACTS

A more reliable way for the fallen to gain Faith is to establish *pacts*. A pact is a relationship between a demon and a mortal. The demon provides the mortal with a service of some sort and, in return, the mortal provides the demon with Faith. Pacts take time to set up and maintain, but they offer several advantages, including a continuing supply of Faith and the fact that the mortal does not need to be aware of the demon's true nature (at least at first).

Establishing a pact is relatively simple. The demon offers to fulfill a wish or desire for the mortal in exchange for the mortal's devotion and worship. If the mortal agrees, the demon spends a point of Faith and fulfills the mortal's wish to seal the pact. In order to be successful, the demon must fulfill the mortal's desire and the mortal must willingly accept the gift and the terms of the pact. The attempt fails if the demon doesn't live up to his end of the bargain or if the mortal refuses the pact. Once a pact is established, only the

demon can break it. As long as the demon upholds its end, there's nothing the mortal can do (short of destroying the demon, which is easier said than done).

The nature of the pact is entirely up to the demon. High-Torment demons tend toward corruptive pacts, offering mortals their secret desires, luring them with promises of power and luxury. Low-Torment demons may prefer pacts of genuine gratitude and devotion on the mortal's part, such as fulfilling someone's dream of becoming a great artist, or healing a critically injured or ill person. Demons often perform favors for mortals *before* establishing a pact with them. If the mortal refuses the deal, the demon can always revoke its favor to give the mortal something to think about. As they say, the first taste is free....

TORMENT

The fallen are all haunted by the past. The two greatest things they loved, God and humanity, both turned their backs on them and consigned them to millennia of torture and pain, but nothing Hell could offer was worse than the first terrible wounds inflicted by the betrayal of their Creator and their beloved charges. All demons carry a measure of that pain with them, and many are driven mad by it. A demon's *Torment* is a measure of the anguish and suffering it carries, and how it deals with those painful memories.

Like Faith, Torment is rated on a scale of 1-10, and it has a temporary and a permanent aspect. A demon with a permanent Torment of 1 is close to forgiving and letting go of the sins of the past, and deals with them extraordinarily well, for the most part. A demon with a permanent Torment of 10 is consumed by his own pain and torment, incapable of doing anything except inflicting the same on others. The greater a demon's Torment is, the less compassion and caring he is capable of feeling. A character's permanent Torment varies depending on his Celestial House, detailed in Chapter Five. All characters begin the game with a temporary Torment of 0.

THE WAGES OF SIN

Heartless acts of selfishness and cruelty only strengthen a demon's inner torment, hardening the soul and stoking the fires of resentment and hatred. The fallen who give in to the temptation to lash out at the world for their pain begin to wallow and drown in it. When a demon commits a sin against one of his Virtues, his temporary Torment may increase. The Storyteller should always warn players when their characters are about to perform actions that may cause them Torment, allowing them the opportunity to reconsider as the demon's Virtue tugs at the corners of his mind. In situations where a demon acts in a way that satisfies his immediate needs at the expense of his ethics, make a Conscience roll. In situations where a demon acts in a way that violates his personal beliefs, make a Conviction roll. When the demon chooses a course of action out of fear for his safety and at the expense of others, make a Courage roll.

When your character sins, make a roll using the appropriate Virtue, with a difficulty of 8. You cannot spend Willpower to get a success on the roll, nor can the roll botch.

• If the Virtue roll succeeds, the character feels remorse and a sense of horror at how far she has fallen. She refuses to give in to her demonic nature, and her temporary Torment does not increase.

• If the Virtue roll fails, your character exults in the rush of power, stoking the fires of her personal Hell. This must be what God felt like when He chose to exile your character to endless torment, the power to take lives into your hands and do with them as you please. Your character gains a point of temporary Torment.

When you have acquired 10 points of temporary Torment, these points are converted to a single point of *permanent* Torment. Once your permanent Torment increases to 10, your character is entirely consumed by it. Incapable of compassion or hope, the character passes into the hands of the Storyteller, no longer suitable for play.

ACTS OF KINDNESS

Where cruel and selfish actions increase Torment, kindness and selflessness are a balm to the torment of the fallen, those not too proud or lazy to seek it out, that is. Acts of kindness remind demons of the divine beings they once were, and they can help reduce one's Torment. Such acts must be truly kind and compassionate, done for no reason other than the act itself, without expectation of reward. Supposed acts of kindness aimed at creating a pact or winning over a mortal (or for any other selfish reason) need not apply. The Storyteller determines whether a particular act is sufficient to count toward a reduction in Torment. In some cases, a series of small good deeds (such as volunteer work) may count as a single act of kindness.

When your character performs a sufficiently selfless and kind act, make a resisted roll between Torment and the appropriate Virtue. Use your character's Conscience for situations in which he makes a sacrifice or puts the needs of another ahead of himself because he knows it's the right thing to do. Use Conviction in situations where the character performs an act at great personal cost to himself to remain true to his beliefs. Finally, use Courage for situations where the character displays gallantry and valor for the sake of someone else. You cannot spend Willpower on Virtue rolls.

• If Torment wins, your cynicism and emotional pain overwhelm the good deed. Why are you even bothering? It's not going to do any real good in the end. Look where all your good intentions got you before. They're not kidding when they say the road to Hell is paved with them. Your temporary Torment remains unchanged.

• If Virtue wins, your act of kindness affirms your divine nature and lifts you above your own suffering, if only for a moment. In that moment, you can see a shadow of what you once were. You lose a point of temporary Torment.

• On a tie, things remain unchanged, and you have to wonder if it really is all worth it.

THE BENEFITS OF EXPERIENCE

The fallen can also use experience (p. 164) to decrease their permanent Torment, representing lessons learned from existence in the material world, clothed in mortal flesh. Fallen characters can spend 10 experience points to decrease their permanent Torment by one point.

Whether through acts of kindness or experience, permanent Torment cannot decrease below 1. How can the fallen regain the innocence they have lost? How can they find it within themselves to entirely put aside the pain they have suffered?

EFFECTS OF TORMENT

A demon's Torment has a number of effects on the character's appearance and the way his powers work, depending on its rating and its relationship to the demon's other traits. In general, it reflects how much of the demon's inner anguish consumes its thoughts and feelings, as well as the demon's capacity for cruelty and compassion.

• If your Torment creates difficulty in using your lore (p. 169), your pain taints what you do. When you attempt to perform an evocation, compare the **successes** rolled to your character's Torment. If more of the successes rolled show numbers that are greater than the character's Torment score, then the evocation is performed normally. If a majority of the successes rolled show numbers equal to or less than the character's Torment, the demon's hatred and anguish perverts the process, causing the high-Torment effect instead. Conversely, you might decide that a situation calls for a more destructive use of your power. You can choose to use the high-Torment effect of your lore, but you automatically gain a point of temporary Torment as a result.

For example, Zaphriel is ambushed by a group of demon-hunters that rush her as she approaches her car. Knowing the character is outnumbered and possibly outgunned, Jen turns to Zaphriel's lore and sees that the high-Torment effect of Voice of Heaven inflicts bashing damage on every mortal for several yards around the character. Caught in a desperate situation, Jen decides to use the high-Torment effect. Zaphriel opens herself to her darker nature and utters a hissing shriek of blasphemies that send the mortals reeling. Though she escapes, the brief taste of ageless hatred still lingers. Zaphriel gains a temporary Torment point.

• The appearance of your apocalyptic form in a Revelation (p. 253) varies based on your Torment rating. If it is less than or equal to half your Willpower, your apocalyptic form is glorious and awe-inspiring. If your Torment is greater than half your Willpower, mortals may see you as awesome or terrifying, depending on their own point of view. If your Torment is greater than your Willpower rating, your apocalyptic form is nightmarish and horrifying.

For example, Zaphriel has a Willpower of 5 and a Torment of 4. When she reveals her apocalyptic form, mortals see her as a radiant figure of supernatural majesty, or a sinister, seductive spirit wreathed in a nimbus of hellish light. Later on, if Jen were to spend some hard-won experience points to lower Zaphriel's permanent Torment to 2, she would have purged her character of her malevolent desires to the degree that anyone looking upon her would see only the faded glory of an angel.

WILLPOWER

Willpower measures your character's drive, determination and self-confidence. Much like Faith, Willpower is rated on a scale of 1-10 and has both a permanent and a temporary rating. The permanent Willpower rating is used whenever a Willpower roll is called for. You use the full rating, regardless of how many temporary points you have. Temporary Willpower points can be "spent" for various effects, mostly representing sheer determination overcoming obstacles in the character's path.

Characters with no temporary Willpower left are exhausted, physically, mentally and emotionally. They've used up their reserves of determination and tend to be listless and unmotivated. They're also more likely to give in to circumstances rather than struggling against them. Characters can regain Willpower in various ways, but it isn't easy, so players should spend Willpower carefully.

•	Spineless
••	Weak
•••	Unassertive
••••	Diffident
•••••	Certain
••••• •	Confident
••••• ••	Determined
••••• •••	Controlled
••••• ••••	Iron-Willed
••••• •••••	Unshakable

SPENDING WILLPOWER

Willpower represents the ability to succeed through sheer determination. It's useful for a number of things.

• Players can spend a point of Willpower to gain an automatic success on a single action. Only one point of Willpower can be spent in a single turn in this manner, but the success is guaranteed and cannot be canceled, even by a botch. Therefore, characters can get at least a minimal success on an action through determination and effort. For extended rolls, extra successes from Willpower can speed things along.

You must declare that you are spending Willpower on a roll *before* you roll the dice. You can't spend it

HEALTH LEVELS

Health Level	Dice Pool Penalty	Movement Penalty
Bruised	0	Character is only bruised and suffers no dice pool penalties due to damage.
Hurt	-1	Character is superficially hurt and suffers no movement hindrance.
Injured	-1	Character suffers minor injuries and movement is mildly inhibited (halve maximum running speed).
Wounded	-2	Character suffers significant damage and may not run (although he may still walk). At this level, a character may not move then attack. He *always* loses dice when moving and attacking in the same turn.
Mauled	-2	Character is badly injured and may only hobble about (three yards/turn).
Crippled	-5	Character is catastrophically injured and may only crawl (one yard/turn).
Incapacitated	—	Character is incapable of movement and likely unconscious.
Dead	—	Character is no longer living (although this doesn't necessarily mean the end for demons).

retroactively to make a roll more successful or to cancel out the effects of a botch. The Storyteller may also declare that Willpower cannot be spent on certain rolls.

• You can spend a point of Willpower to ignore any penalties due to wounds or other distractions for one turn, focusing your concentration for a last-ditch effort.

• You can spend a point of Willpower to keep a Faith die from being removed from your Faith pool. This represents holding on to Faith through sheer dedication and force of will. You can spend as many Willpower points as there are failed Faith dice, up to your remaining temporary Willpower.

Regaining Willpower

Characters can recover Willpower in a few ways. Temporary Willpower can never exceed the character's permanent Willpower rating. The only way to increase the permanent Willpower rating is through experience (p. 164).

Recovering Willpower is usually a matter of reaffirming the character's sense of confidence and wellbeing, so certain actions and situations may allow a character to recover Willpower. Ultimately it's up to the Storyteller to decide when characters recover Willpower during the story. Storytellers should tailor the recovery of Willpower to suit the story, keeping in mind that it's a powerful and useful trait, so characters shouldn't be allowed to recover it too quickly, or else they won't face much of a challenge in the story.

• Characters regain all temporary Willpower at the end of a story (not necessarily game session, but story). The Storyteller may require the characters to achieve some particular goal or objective or otherwise feel like they succeeded (even just a little) in order to regain Willpower. In cases where the characters were frustrated or things came to a stalemate, a partial recovery of Willpower may be more appropriate.

• Storyteller's may allow characters to regain a point of Willpower after a full night's rest or equivalent opportunity to recharge their batteries and come at things refreshed. This assumes that the character is resting or relaxing, not otherwise engaged.

• If a character achieves a significant goal or performs a particularly impressive action that affirms his sense of confidence, the Storyteller may choose to award the character a Willpower point as a bonus.

• When a character behaves in accordance with his Nature, he affirms his sense of self and may be allowed to regain a point of Willpower (or more, for particularly appropriate actions). For example, a Director may regain Willpower after successfully using organization to get a group to accomplish a task.

Characters may be able to recover Willpower if they find themselves in dire straits and have to push on in order to succeed, for example, or if they refuse to give up despite the odds. Awarding extra Willpower makes things a little

DEMON: THE FALLEN

easier on the players, while withholding Willpower makes things more difficult. Fine-tune your game's Willpower recovery to suit the tone and style you want.

HEALTH

Although they have great supernatural power, most demons still wear stolen mortal flesh, so they are vulnerable to the various weaknesses of the flesh. The Health trait measures a character's physical wellbeing. Characters have seven "health levels," as shown on the character sheet and the Health Levels table. When characters take damage, they lose one or more health levels until they can recover them through rest or supernatural healing. Characters also accumulate penalties to movement, actions and dice pools due to the effects of their injuries. If a penalty reduces a character's dice pool to zero, the character cannot even attempt that action. A player can spend a point of Willpower for his character to ignore wound penalties for one action, though.

See Chapter Eight for more information on damage and how it affects characters.

FAITH HEALING

Demons can repair their mortal vessels with the power of their Faith, as long as they are conscious and capable of action. Spending a point of Faith heals either a single level of lethal damage or *all* levels of bashing damage. Faith cannot heal aggravated damage. Only time or more powerful abilities can do so. (See Chapter Seven for details.) Injured demons low on Faith may resort to reaping to replenish themselves.

DEMONS AND DEATH

Although they wear mortal flesh, the fallen are not mortal. Their bodies can die just like mortals' do when they exceed the Incapacitated health level, but the spirit — the immortal essence of the demon itself — lives on.

A demon who loses his mortal vessel has three options. If there is another suitable vessel nearby — a mortal body with a weak or absent soul — the demon can attempt to possess it. If there is no suitable vessel nearby, the demon may attempt to anchor himself to a particular place or object, becoming Earthbound and eliminating the need for a mortal vessel. Finally, if one of the demon's thralls is nearby, the fallen can use the pact of Faith to automatically possess the mortal's body.

If these options fail, the demon is hurled back into the Abyss and trapped there until

some outside force summons it back to the mortal world, such as a ritual of summoning. Some demons take care to ensure that at least one mortal follower or worshipper is capable of summoning them back to Earth and providing a new mortal vessel, although doing so means trusting a mortal with the secrets of summoning demons, a dangerous proposition itself.

For more information on possessing new bodies or physical objects, see Chapter Nine.

EXPERIENCE

Even the fallen are capable of learning from their experiences and mistakes. Characters grow and change over time, going through a process of self-discovery and development. Experience reflects the effects of this growth.

At the conclusion of each story (or chapter of a story, for long sessions), the Storyteller awards experience points to the characters. These points can be used to improve existing traits as well as acquire entirely new traits for the character. Players keep track of the experience points their characters have earned, and they spend them between stories (or during breaks in longer stories) to improve their characters.

The Storyteller has final approval on any use of experience to improve character traits or acquire new traits. Such improvement usually requires more than just spending experience points, it also requires the character to undergo training or practice enough to warrant the increase, and the Storyteller may place additional requirements on the character. For example, an increase in Faith requires something that truly affirms the demon's sense of self and understanding of the nature of Faith. The Storyteller can use efforts to improve traits as story hooks, sending characters off to find teachers or mentors, or providing them with opportunities to grow and develop in different ways.

EXPERIENCE COSTS

Trait	Cost
New Ability	3
New Lore	7 (10 if from a House other than the character's)
Attribute	current rating x 4
Ability	current rating x 2
Lore	current rating x 5
Background	current rating x 3
Virtue	current rating x 2*
Willpower	current rating
Faith	current rating x 7
Torment	10**

*Increasing a Virtue does not increase Willpower after character creation.

**This *decreases* the character's permanent Torment by one point.

164

Characters' traits generally should not improve by more than one dot per story, unless the story takes place over a long period of time. It takes time to make significant improvements.

NEW TRAITS

Improving existing traits is fairly simple. The character practices and studies to get better at the trait. Acquiring entirely new traits, however, is more difficult. Characters don't simply learn to speak a new language or pick up the basics of a new Ability overnight. Learning a new Ability generally requires a longer period of study and practice along with the necessary experience points. It may range from reading a few books or taking a night course to a months-long apprenticeship with a suitable teacher. The Storyteller has final say on how long it takes a character to learn a particular Ability, though most Abilities can be studied in the time between stories and other "downtime" of the chronicle.

New celestial powers are more involved, since one cannot learn them from anyone other than another demon. To learn a new celestial power, the demon must seek out a teacher and bargain for the knowledge, and demons are expert deal-makers. A potential teacher may ask for anything, ranging from a simple exchange of knowledge to favors to money, or anything else the Storyteller can think of. Knowledge of celestial powers is one of the most valuable things demons have, so they don't let it go cheaply.

AWARDING EXPERIENCE

Awarding experience is something of an art. Give characters too much experience and they both grow too rapidly for players to appreciate their growth and outstrip many of the challenges of the chronicle. Give them too little experience and the players may become frustrated with the fact that their characters hardly seem to change despite the momentous events they're acting out. It's necessary to strike a balance between generosity and stinginess, properly rewarding players for their efforts and encouraging them to keep coming back for more. The following guidelines should help you to give out the right amount of experience, but only you can determine what is right for your chronicle. Feel free to tinker with and adjust these guidelines as you see fit.

END OF EACH CHAPTER

At the end of each game session or chapter in a longer story, you should award characters between one and five experience points. One point is automatic. Every character should get at least one simply for experiencing the events of the story. Five points is truly extraordinary, reflecting a dramatic and nearly perfect performance on the part of the player.

One Point — Automatic: Every character receives one experience point for simply participating in the story.

One Point — Learning Curve: Ask the player what the character has learned from the story. If you agree that it has been a learning experience for the character, award an additional experience point.

One Point — Roleplaying: If a player has portrayed the character well, including remaining true to the character's Nature and Demeanor and providing some entertaining moments for the group, the character should get an additional experience point. Truly outstanding roleplaying may merit two extra experience points.

One Point — Heroism: Characters who truly manage to transcend their normal limits, performing acts of daring and heroism, are deserving of an extra experience point.

END OF THE STORY

At the end of a long story (covering several chapter or game sessions), you may choose to award a few extra experience points as a bonus if the players have done particularly well.

One Point — Success: If the characters achieved the goals they set out to accomplish, overcoming obstacles in order to do so, they can be awarded an extra experience point.

One Point — Danger: The characters get an extra experience point if they survived terrible danger or overcame great odds.

One Point — Wisdom: If a player came up with a brilliant idea or plan that helped the characters to succeed, award the character an extra experience point for the sudden insight and understanding.

You may award additional bonus points, if you feel they're warranted, but beware of handing out too much experience, unless you want the characters to advance more quickly.

post

The last notes stretched and fell away, and there was rapturous applause.

"He's very good," Tattenai said.

Sabriel shifted slightly so she could whisper to the new arrival. "Tolerable, perhaps." Despite her words, there was more than a little pride in her eyes. "You're late."

Down on the stage, Mike Halbedel spoke softly into the microphone. "This is *Christina's Song*. I wrote it for someone beyond words." He raised the bow and drew it across the violin slowly and sweetly, very differently from the dramatic beginnings of his previous pieces.

"Only a little. Hope I'm not interrupting."

Sabriel did not reply.

"Have you heard the story — an old one for these people — about the fiddler who swapped his fiddle for three prostitutes?" Tattenai said after a while, conversationally.

"So now I'm a whore, am I?" Sabriel's face was steady with concentration. "Maybe I should just have given him a bigger dick and done the world a favor."

"You underestimate yourself, my dear, and that kind of language does not suit your appearance."

A sly smile crept across her face, but she kept her focus. The music was building, the simplicity of the early movements dissolving into intricacies.

"I have it," she said. "Your Faustian friends accepted the conditions after all." Any sarcasm in the words was lost on Tattenai. He seemed to have stopped breathing as she reached beneath her jacket to retrieve a box, though there had been no room there for it. It was pretty but modern. Inside was something very, very old.

"I knew they would. If anyone could persuade them... And it is one of his own?"

"Of course. Can you not feel the Morningstar's breath about it still?"

Tattenai accepted the box and ran his fingers across it reverently. Then he hid it away.

"The Luciferans owe you a debt, Sabriel."

But she was not listening. She was lost in the music as it swelled to fill the auditorium. It was almost hymn-like — beautiful, sad and breathtakingly elaborate.

Tattenai looked toward the exit, but waited.

And then the pattern faltered. Notes dropped away almost imperceptibly. The music lost its momentum, tried to reassemble itself, then stopped in a single discordant screech."

"I can't," Halbedel sobbed. "I can't. Christina, where are you? I'm sorry, I'm—" He staggered and threw the bow away. People stepped in hesitantly from the sides of the stage, looking anxious.

The violinist reached into a pocket and drew a knife, long and brilliant in the lights.

"Christina," he said.

He drew the knife across throat, staggered and coughed up a wet scream.

Chaos erupted.

"He must have loved you very much," Tattenai said softly as he rose to leave.

"Our agreement, Tattenai," Sabriel said harshly.

"Yes, of course. The sculptor." He handed her a piece of paper with an address on it. He tried to smile. "Treat her well."

But Sabriel was looking down at the broken body on stage, with lust and triumph in her eyes.

Chapter Seven: Eyes of Fire

O for a voice like thunder, and a tongue
To drown the throat of war! — When the senses
Are shaken, and the soul is driven to madness,
Who can stand? When the souls of the oppressed
Fight in the troubled air that rages, who can stand?
—William Blake, "Enoch: The First City of Angels"

Powers and Principalities

In their time, they lit the void with starlight, shaped worlds from the primal aether and carried the breath of God to man and beast. Whatever else they have become after the darkness of the Abyss, the fallen remain avatars of creation, living manifestations of Heaven's Grand Design. Before they forswore their covenant with God, the fallen and their peers made up the boundary that separated the Creator from His creation, each Celestial House charged with interpreting a different facet of the design. In a sense, the angels were the lens through which the Creator's vision was subtly distorted, injecting a momentum of dynamic change that gave the cosmos a life of its own. It was this process of interpretation and conceptualization that was the source of the beings' power.

The angels took Heaven's Grand Design and defined its myriad potential, establishing each concept's existence by defining its relationship to the universe. Once these relationships were described, they could be manipulated by invoking their identity or *name*. As the universe evolved, each House accumulated a vast store of these conceptual relationships. They were the threads that comprised the fabric of the universe, the fundamental components of physical reality. The act of manipulating these names of power was called an *evocation*, and a House's store of evocations was referred to as its *lore*.

Performing an evocation, no matter how great or small, was a cooperative effort between angel and Creator. The Elohim provided the direction and the will to achieve the desired effect, but the power that fueled the act flowed from God alone. This arrangement, or covenant, between the Elohim and their Creator provided the necessary balance between angelic freedom and heavenly authority that made the creation of a universe apart from God possible.

BROKEN OATHS

When the fallen contemplated rebellion against Heaven, they knew that they would commit a terrible act, one that (by definition) would estrange them from God. None foresaw the full fury of the Creator's divine wrath, however. God declared the covenant with the fallen to be forever broken and denied them the power of His blessing, thus reducing the rebels to mere shadows of their former selves.

God's curse rendered the fallen impotent, unable to work their will upon the cosmos. Their struggle might have ended then and there were it not for the outpouring of faith from the newly awakened human race. While they were born in innocence, ignorant of the intricate workings of the cosmos, the souls of mankind resonated with the breath of God, and people gladly shared this divine spark with their would-be saviors. The fallen shone like angry stars once more, and the fates of man and demon became forever entwined.

FAITH

Characters in **Demon** use Faith to fuel their evocations, heal damage and transform their physical bodies into potent supernatural forms. Beginning characters start play with a Faith score of 3. This rating may be increased by spending freebie points during character creation and still further using experience points earned during play. If a character's Faith pool is exhausted, the only way she can continue to use her powers is by ravaging the mind and soul of her thralls (see page 249 of the Systems chapter for details).

FADED GLORY

The faith of mankind sustained the fallen throughout a thousand years of war, but the widespread belief that suffused humanity in ancient times is all but forgotten in the modern World of Darkness. The fire has faded to a few glowing embers, leaving newly freed demons to fight for what little heat remains. Where the fallen once roamed the earth as radiant spirits, they must now anchor themselves in human flesh, at best a difficult and desperate situation. Twenty-first-century mortals are so spiritually shallow that they make poor vessels for channeling infernal energies. Instead of overwhelming a host's identity or destroying it outright, a possessing demon's knowledge and identity is largely suppressed in favor of the memories and feelings resident in the mortal. The degree to which the fallen can store Celestial energy is therefore very limited. By the same token, however, the madness, hatred and pain inspired by a demon's long imprisonment can be equally diminished, providing a demon with a respite of sorts from its ages-long anguish and providing an opportunity to make the most of newfound freedom.

TORMENT

Within the scope of her accumulated lore, a demon can bend reality to her will, but achieving a desired effect requires intense focus and clarity of thought. Uncontrolled emotions, especially negative ones, exert a potent influence on a demon's evocations, with potentially horrific results.

Demon characters have a Torment score that reflects the degree to which they are consumed by the madness and hate engendered by ages of suffering in the Abyss. The higher the Torment score is the more monstrous a character becomes, and as the taint grows, it changes the effects of the demon's evocations. Each evocation has a normal effect and a *high-Torment* effect. When you attempt to perform an evocation, compare the **successes** rolled to your character's Torment. If more of the successes rolled show numbers that are greater than the character's Torment score, then the evocation is performed normally. If a majority of the successes rolled show numbers equal to or less than the character's Torment, the demon's hatred and anguish perverts the process, causing the high-Torment effect instead. Botches cancel out successes starting with the highest success rolled.

Demons may intentionally inflict the malicious aspect of their evocations if they wish, but not without a price. Each time a demon *chooses* the high-Torment effect of an evocation, she gains a temporary point of Torment.

INFERNAL MIGHT

Despite the limitations of demons' mortal hosts, the fallen are fearsome to behold, with a broad spectrum of powers and capabilities at their disposal. These powers can be divided into three distinct categories: *innate* powers, which all demons possess by virtue of their Celestial nature and that do not require a Faith roll to use; their *apocalyptic* (or revelatory) form; and their *lore*.

INNATE POWERS

All **Demon** characters begin the game with a common set of powers that reflect their nature and one-time role as agents of Creation. These are fundamental

qualities that are always considered to be active as long as the character has at least one Faith point available in his Faith pool. Innate powers include immunity to possession, immunity to mind control and resistance to illusion, among others. See the section on Innate Powers later in this chapter (p. 171) for details.

The Apocalyptic Form

During the Age of Wrath, the fallen could alter their physical form at will. When they battled the Host of Heaven, they could be titans of living iron or horrors wreathed in raging fire. Among humans, they often assumed the forms of men and women, luminous and terrible to behold, or wore the guise of animals that best suited their needs. The modern World of Darkness does not possess the atmosphere of Faith to allow such effortless transformation from spirit to flesh, but the fallen can use their stores of Faith to alter their host bodies temporarily and gain superhuman capabilities. This apocalyptic or revelatory form is a reflection of a demon's true nature, and its capacities vary depending on the character's primary lore (see the Lore section for details). When a character takes on her apocalyptic form, mortal witnesses suffer the effects of Revelation (see page 253 of the Systems chapter for details), with reactions ranging from terror to rapturous wonder.

A character's primary lore dictates which apocalyptic form she can manifest. In order for the transformation to occur, you either roll a number of dice equal to your character's current Faith pool against a difficulty of 6, or spend a point of Faith to gain an automatic success. If the roll is successful, your character's transformation occurs instantaneously.

When your character manifests her apocalyptic form, she gains access to a number of special capabilities ranging from trait increases to physical capabilities such as wings and claws. Each apocalyptic form provides eight special powers, but only four are available to characters with a Torment of 6 or less. The remaining four manifest when your character loses part of herself to her demonic nature. When your character's permanent Torment score reaches 7, you may select one of the form's four high-Torment powers and add it to her apocalyptic form. When her permanent Torment reaches 8, you may add another, and so on. If your character's permanent Torment is reduced later, her high-Torment powers are lost at the rate of one per point, in the reverse order in which they were gained. So, the power gained most recently is the first one lost when permanent Torment is reduced. Characters retain their low-Torment special abilities regardless of their Torment score.

In times of peril, a demon can tap into her dark nature and temporarily manifest a high-Torment power. The capability persists for the duration of a single scene, and your character gains a point of temporary Torment. Finally, your character doesn't have to manifest all of her special abilities when invoking her apocalyptic form. (A set of eagle's wings might be inconvenient in a crowded elevator, for example.) Declare which powers you want your character to invoke before making your Faith roll. If she wants to manifest different or additional abilities later she can, but another roll is required. There is no penalty for failing a Faith roll, but the character loses a point of Faith if the roll botches.

One's apocalyptic form persists for the remainder of the scene, or it can be "turned off" at any point before then that your character wishes.

Lore

A Celestial House's lore is nothing less than the collected secrets of the universe, evocations that encompass the foundations of reality and govern the forces that keep it in motion. Prior to the Fall, each House had its own specific sets of lore that reflected its duties within the angelic hierarchy. These evocations were considered the heart of each House, and they were guarded jealously as a matter of pride. Later, during the Age of Wrath, pride gave way to pragmatism, and many among the fallen exchanged bits of their lore with one another to gain whatever advantage they could against their more hidebound foes.

Characters in **Demon** are assumed to have mastered the lore of their parent House, but much of it lies buried deep in the subconscious of their hosts and must be recovered laboriously. As a host body becomes more and more conditioned to a demon's control and is capable of channeling increasing amounts of Celestial energy, one of the fallen is able to regain more of its former power.

During character creation, players choose their demons' starting lore from the three lore paths that are native to their characters' Celestial Houses, as well as from the two common lore paths with which all demons are familiar (see p. 172). You must choose one of the three House lore paths as your character's *primary* lore. These are the evocations the demon is most adept at and can recall most easily. After selecting your character's primary lore path, you have three dots to allocate among her available lore to determine her beginning evocations, with the restriction that no lore path can ever receive more dots than your character's primary lore. Additional lore dots can be purchased later with freebie points. Characters can gain new lore, including paths from other Houses, when you spend experience points during play

Example: *Jim's character, a Scourge, has five lore paths available to choose from at character creation: the House lore of Awakenings, Firmament and Winds, plus the common lore paths of Humanity and the Fundament. Jim has three dots to allocate among these five possible paths. First, he must choose the character's primary lore from one of the three House paths. After some thought, Jim chooses the Lore of Awakenings, allocating it one of his three dots. He then chooses to put his remaining two dots into the Lore of the Fundament and the Lore of Humanity. Later, in the finishing touches stage, he purchases*

another dot of lore, which he can add to the Lore of Awakenings or place in either the Lore of the Firmament or the Lore of the Winds. He could not allocate his extra dot to the Lore of the Fundament or the Lore of Humanity, as he only has one dot invested in his primary path, and he can't have more dots in a path than he has in his character's primary lore.

The number of dots allocated to a lore path determines the evocations a character is allowed to perform. In the previous example, Jim's Scourge can perform the first-level evocations for the lore of Awakenings, Fundament and Humanity. If he allocated his additional dot of lore to Awakenings, his character would be able to perform both the first- and second-level evocations, and so on. Each evocation calls for you to roll a relevant Attribute + Ability to determine what effects occur. The difficulty of the roll is usually 6, but it can be modified at the Storyteller's discretion based on the situation. You can add a number of bonus dice to this roll equal to your character's permanent Faith score if she ravages her thralls for additional power (see page 249 of the Systems chapter for details). Additionally, points of temporary Faith can be spent to gain automatic successes on an evocation roll, similar to the function of Willpower in the case of Attribute or Ability rolls. If the evocation roll fails, nothing happens; if the roll botches, however, the character also loses one point of Faith from her current pool. Depending on the evocation, your character's Faith pool also determines the power's range and duration. Only one evocation can be performed per turn, but a character can have multiple evocations functioning simultaneously equal to her permanent Faith score.

Later in this chapter, the lore available to demons are presented by the Houses to which they are assigned, and the Houses are addressed from highest to lowest in the demonic order.

Innate Powers

All demons possess the following innate powers, regardless of their House. These capabilities are unaffected by Torment, and they are always active as long as a character has at least one point remaining in her Faith pool. If a character has exhausted her Faith pool, she may still take advantage of these innate powers by drawing Faith from her mortal thralls (see page 249 of the Systems chapter for details).

Immunity to Mind-Control

Demons are immune to any form of mind-control and to supernaturally induced fear.

Immunity to Possession

For obvious reasons, the fallen cannot be possessed, but if an attempt at possession occurs while the character is devoid of Faith, it is possible to force the demon from its mortal host. In this case, the player is able to resist the attempt with a resisted Willpower roll. If the roll fails, the demon is forced out of its host body

and must find another anchor immediately or be drawn back into the Abyss. See page 258 of the Systems chapter for more details on dispossessed demons.

Resistance to Illusion

Demons are especially adept at discerning the real from the illusory, and they may attempt to penetrate illusions or supernatural forms of concealment regardless of the source. When confronted by an illusion or in the presence of a person or thing that is supernaturally concealed, the character can see past the artifice with a successful Perception + Alertness roll (difficulty 7). If the source of the illusion or concealment is another demon, the difficulty of the roll is equal to the opposing demon's Faith or Torment score, whichever is greater.

Resistance to Lethal Damage

When in their apocalyptic forms, demons can use their Stamina to soak lethal damage.

Healing Physical Damage

Demon characters may use Faith to heal bashing or lethal damage. You can spend one Faith point to heal *all* of your character's bashing damage, while lethal damage is healed at the rate of one health level per point spent. Separate Faith points must be used to recover from bashing and lethal damage. Aggravated damage cannot be healed in this fashion.

Invocations

The power of a demon's name is such that invoking it, even in conversation, is enough to draw that spirit's attention, no matter how far away he may be. What's more, the subject can attempt to ascertain who is speaking about him, where that being is and even what is said.

Demons take notice whenever their Celestial or True Names are spoken. The feeling manifests differently for each. Some experience a chill that races across their skin or down their spine, while others feel an invisible pull that tugs at their mind. If a character concentrates, she can attempt to determine who is using her name and why. Make a Faith roll (difficulty 7 if the Celestial Name is invoked, difficulty 6 if the True Name is used). The amount of detail gained depends on the number of successes rolled.

One success: The character receives a mental picture of the person who invokes her name.

Two successes: The character receives a mental picture of the speaker and his immediate surroundings, including the individual(s) he addresses.

Three or more successes: The character can hear what the speaker is saying for the duration of a single turn. If she wishes, the character may continue to eavesdrop on the conversation, though she hears only the voice of the individual who invokes her name. Eavesdropping on the conversation requires a successful Willpower roll (difficulty 8) in each successive turn. If the roll fails, contact is lost.

There is no distance limitation on this ability, not even between the physical and spirit realms.

The capacity to establish a connection between individuals by invoking names of power also allows demons to communicate with one another and their thralls no matter how far apart they are. To communicate with another demon, the character needs either the recipient's Celestial or True Name, and must have at least one point of temporary Faith available. Make a Faith roll (difficulty 7 if using a Celestial Name, 6 if using a True Name), and if successful, whatever the character says is heard by the recipient. Once this connection has been made, the recipient can reply if she has at least one point of Faith available in her Faith pool. Note that the recipient doesn't have to know the speaker's name to reply. Once the link has been established, it can be used by both parties. Contact lasts for the duration of a single turn. If the speaker (or the recipient of the invocation) wishes to continue the conversation, you must make a successful Willpower roll (difficulty 6) in each successive turn of communication. If the roll fails, contact is lost.

This ability is not limited to one-on-one communication. A demon can direct her message to multiple recipients in different locations up to a number equal to her Faith rating. The player need make only one Faith roll to send a message, and the difficulty is 7 regardless of the names used for the invocation. Otherwise, group communications use the same rules already described.

In the case of thralls, communication is automatic. The bond that already exists between mortal and demon provides the needed link, allowing a demon to contact her thralls without requiring a Faith roll. Additionally, a demon may address multiple thralls at once equal to her Faith score. Unless a thrall is specifically gifted with the ability to perform an invocation, though, she cannot initiate contact with the demon. In most cases, thralls speak only when spoken to.

Though there is no known way for an outside party to "tap into" this form of supernatural communication, nearby demons can detect its use as they would any other use of supernatural power. Likewise, since the participants must physically say what they want to convey, even as a whisper, it's possible for sharp ears to overhear at least a part of what is said.

Supernatural Awareness

The fallen are inherently attuned to the fabric of reality, and they are sensitive to energies and influences beyond the awareness of mortals. Players can make a Perception + Awareness rolls for demons to get a "feel" of the supernatural qualities of a given area. A hospital room might emanate a sense of pain and loss, imprinted by the emotions of the patients and doctors who've struggled and died within its walls. An otherwise unassuming basement might reek of the foul rituals performed there days before. Additionally, an alert demon can sense the use of supernatural energies within her general vicinity. The fabric of reality distorts momentarily when powers are used, and the fallen can feel the ripples caused by this brief disturbance. Highly perceptive demons can draw extensive information from these ripples, gaining a sense of where the supernatural event took place.

Demons can sense supernatural energies at work within an area equal to their Faith score in miles (so a fallen with a Faith of 5 can sense energies within five miles). If a character wishes to sense the energies at work in her area, make a successful Perception + Alertness roll (difficulty 7). If the roll succeeds, your character detects the momentary distortion caused by these energies. Additional successes provide further detail.

One success: The demon knows that something has occurred (or is occurring) in the vicinity and a general idea of how powerful the effect was or is.

Two successes: The demon gains a rough idea as to the direction from which the distortion emanates.

Three successes: The demon knows without a doubt the direction from which the distortion emanates, and he has a rough idea of the distance.

Four or more successes: The demon knows precisely how far away the disturbance is, and in what direction. If she knows the area well, she can work out exactly where the event took place or now occurs.

While demons can gain a sense of *where* an event occurs, it's impossible to tell from a distance exactly what kind of power or evocation is used. If they want more details they must investigate in person or send their agents to learn what they can.

While a demon's supernatural awareness usually functions only when the character actively searches for signs of distortion, the Storyteller can, at her discretion, make a reflexive roll on the character's behalf in the event of an exceptionally large flare of power in the vicinity.

Common Lore

While most lore is considered proprietary to the House that created it, two paths exist as tools that every angel (or demon) needed to further their work amid the wonders of Paradise. The Lore of the Fundament was the first, encompassing the basic building blocks of the physical universe, in effect creating a set of principles that provided the foundation upon which the work of all the Houses was based. The second set of common lore evolved among the fallen during the Age of Wrath as a means of facilitating contact between humanity and the rebel host.

Lore of the Fundament

• Manipulate Gravity

The demon can alter the way gravity affects her body, allowing her to leap enormous distances, hang suspended in the air or plunge at her foes like a meteorite.

System: Roll Strength + Athletics. The demon can leap (or climb) up to 20 yards per success, or fall a similar distance without suffering injury. Completely canceling the effect of gravity requires a number of successes equal to the character's Stamina. Characters who defy gravity aren't weightless, per se — they are still affected by outside forces as normal. The effects of this evocation last for a single turn.

Torment: Monstrous demons who perform this evocation leave a wash of turbulence in their wake, randomly increasing or decreasing the effects of gravity on surrounding objects or people who pass within a number of yards equal to the demon's Torment score. The Storyteller is free to use her discretion when describing the chaotic effects that occur in the monster's passing.

•• MANIPULATE ADHESION

The demon can affect her body's adhesion to physical objects. She can run up walls, hang from a ceiling or cling to the side of a moving car like a spider.

System: Roll Dexterity + Athletics. The difficulty is determined by the angle of the surface relative to the earth. Running up a steep slope is difficulty 6, while a vertical surface is 7. Moving along an inverted plane (like a ceiling) is difficulty 8. The character can move up to three yards along such a surface per success rolled. The effects of this evocation last for a single turn.

Torment: When a monstrous demon performs this evocation, the surfaces with which she interacts are warped by her passing, causing them to radiate waves of intense heat and leave patterns of the demon's hands and feet on the surface. Individuals coming into contact with these surfaces in the same turn as the demon touched them suffer one level of lethal damage.

••• MANIPULATE INERTIA

The demon can affect the inertia of anything she touches, stopping it dead or granting it irresistible force. She can snatch projectiles out of the air (providing she can see them), or throw an object farther than any human could imagine.

System: Roll Dexterity + Athletics. The demon can throw an object up to 30 yards per success rolled, regardless of her Strength. Snatching a projectile out of the air requires rolling a number of successes equal to or greater than the projectile's damage dice. For example, a thrown knife inflicts Strength + 1 damage. If the person throwing the knife has Strength 3, you must roll four or more successes for your character to catch the knife. Your demon has to be able to see the projectile to affect it. Rocks, knives, even arrows are possible candidates, but bullets aren't. If your demon throws a projectile at a target, each extra success achieved becomes an automatic level of damage. The effects of this evocation last for a single turn.

Torment: Items affected by a monstrous demon become inherently unstable for a period of time, creating potential for disaster for the next person who tries to use them. For a period of turns equal to the character's Torment, any item that was the focus of this evocation causes a botch on a rolled 1, 2 or 3 when used for any reason.

•••• MANIPULATE ACCELERATION

The demon can affect the acceleration of her own body, granting her supernatural speed and force.

System: Spend one Faith point and roll Dexterity + Athletics. Each success allows your demon to walk up to 10 yards per success per turn, jog 20 yards per success or run 40 yards per success per turn. If used in combat, treat these successes as automatic levels of damage for hand-to-hand, melee or ranged attacks using thrown weapons. These damage levels can be split among multiple targets if desired. The effects of this evocation last for a single turn.

Torment: The accelerations of a monstrous demon so disturbs the air around her that she is surrounded by an aura of blistering heat that radiates out a number of yards equal to the character's Torment score. Living beings caught within the area of effect suffer one level of bashing damage.

••••• MANIPULATE COHESION

The demon can manipulate the state of any inanimate matter she touches. She can walk on water or air or break down solid objects into their component particles.

System: The demon must be able to physically touch the matter she wishes to affect. Spend one Faith point and roll Stamina + Science. The difficulty depends on the matter involved and the degree to which it is affected. Changing water to ice or steam is difficulty 6. Increasing the cohesion of water or air to the degree that it briefly supports the demon's weight is difficulty 7. Vaporizing wood, cloth or other low-density material is difficulty 8, while doing he same to high-density material such as metal or stone is difficulty 9. Each success allows the demon to affect one cubic foot of matter. The effects of this evocation last for a single turn, after which the materials affected return to normal or remain in their current state if it's natural for the material in question. Living beings targeted with this effect suffer a level of lethal damage for each success gained on the roll.

Torment: Matter affected by a monstrous demon remains inherently unstable for a number of turns equal to the character's Torment, changing states at random. The Storyteller is free to use her discretion when describing the chaotic effects that occur in the wake of the demon's manipulation.

LORE OF HUMANITY

• TRANSLATE

The demon can understand (and be understood by) mortals, regardless of what language they speak.

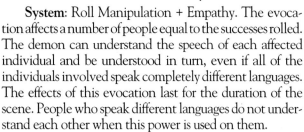

System: Roll Manipulation + Empathy. The evocation affects a number of people equal to the successes rolled. The demon can understand the speech of each affected individual and be understood in turn, even if all of the individuals involved speak completely different languages. The effects of this evocation last for the duration of the scene. People who speak different languages do not understand each other when this power is used on them.

Torment: Monstrous demons must overcome the obstacle of their own Torment, or the words they hear are filtered through their own anger and obsessions. After the evocation is used successfully, a Willpower roll is made with a difficulty equal to your character's Torment. If successful, your character understands the words of those around her as they are intended. If the roll fails, your demon's understanding of what is said is skewed by her own hatred and despair. A greeting is misunderstood as a threat, or an honest answer sounds evasive or outright deceptive. The Storyteller is encouraged to make this Willpower roll on behalf of the character and keep the results secret, tailoring the information the player hears accordingly.

•• INSINUATE

This evocation causes mortals to instinctively regard the demon as a potential friend, allaying any initial feelings of distrust or suspicion and engaging their interest in her. Unless gifted with a demon's resistance to mind-control, thralls can be affected by this evocation as well.

System: Roll Manipulation + Empathy. The evocation affects a number of individuals equal to the successes rolled. Each person resists the evocation with a Willpower roll. If the Willpower roll fails, affected individuals trust the demon within reason and talk freely and openly with her, lowering the difficulty of any of the demon's subsequent Manipulation rolls by one. The effects of this evocation last for the duration of the scene.

Torment: Monstrous demons who perform this evocation have the opposite effect on the mortals they encounter. Affected individuals use the demon's Torment as the difficulty for their Willpower rolls. If a roll fails, the person is overcome with feelings of revulsion and anger, and treats the demon with intense apprehension and fear. The difficulties of all Intimidation rolls directed at these individuals decrease by two.

••• FADE

Demons using this evocation literally fade into the background. Mortal eyes simply pass over them unless the demons choose to call attention to themselves. Demons (and thralls who have been gifted with the demon's resistance to illusion) are immune to the effects of this evocation.

System: Roll Presence + Manipulation. Mortals resist with a Willpower roll (difficulty 8). If successful, the demon goes unnoticed by mortals unless she does something to call attention to herself such as make physical contact or speak to them directly. These effects persist for the remainder of the scene or until the demon wills them to cease.

Torment: Monstrous demons who perform this evocation fade from the sight of ordinary mortals, but stand out like beacons for those consumed by anger or a lust for violence.

•••• CONFESS

Mortals engaged in conversation with the demon respond to his questions with complete candor. Unless made aware of it later with direct questions about events, the mortal affected by this evocation does not remember the details of the conversation. Unless gifted with a demon's resistance to mind-control, thralls can be affected by this evocation as well.

System: Spend one Faith point and roll Manipulation + Subterfuge. The target resists with a Willpower roll (difficulty 7). If your roll is successful, the demon can ask the mortal any questions she wishes, and the mortal answers with complete honesty. The effects of this evocation last for a number of turns equal to your character's Faith score.

Torment: Monstrous demons are able to draw out only a mortal's dark nature, learning her secret animosities, lusts and ambitions.

••••• ALTER MEMORY

The demon is able to manipulate a mortal's memory, changing or removing any recollection of his dealings, or planting memories where none were before. Unless gifted with a demon's resistance to mind-control, thralls can be affected by this evocation.

System: Spend one Faith point and roll Manipulation + Subterfuge. If your character attempts to alter or remove an existing memory, the difficulty is 7. Planting a completely false memory is difficulty 8. A resisted Willpower roll is made for the target (difficulty 7). You must achieve a number of excess successes determined by the Storyteller, depending on the intensity and breadth of the memory or memories that your character tries to manipulate. Editing or removing the memories of a brief encounter requires one success, while planting or altering a series of memories covering a period of days or weeks requires two or more successes. Altered or fabricated memories are permanent.

Torment: Monstrous demons who perform this evocation also cause bouts of sleeplessness, anxiety and despair that take days or weeks to subside. Nightmares persist for a number of nights equal to the character's Torment score. Each night, make a Willpower roll for the victim with a difficulty equal to the demon's Torment. If the roll fails, the victim loses a temporary Willpower point. If the victim runs out of Willpower points, she gains a temporary derangement.

DEVIL
(Namaru)

The mandate of the Heralds was to spread the light of Heaven to every corner of Creation and orchestrate the efforts of the entire Celestial Host in shaping God's Grand Design. Central to their duties was the Lore of the Celestials, comprising the knowledge of harnessing Heaven's will (and later, mortal Faith) to locate, inform and support the efforts of other celestials. No less important was the Lore of Flame, granting the Heralds mastery of the primal, purifying fire of creation, and a terrible weapon to wield against their foes. The Lore of Radiance, encompassing the secrets of inspiration and leadership, was not one originally bequeathed to the Heralds, but that evolved among the Devils during the Age of Wrath as these noble leaders and champions refined the power to inspire and command the mortal allies of the fallen.

LORE OF THE CELESTIALS

• LAMP OF FAITH

This evocation allows a Devil to detect the presence of mortals or other demons in her vicinity by causing their store of Faith to flare like a beacon that only she can see. Individuals glow with a pale blue light, varying in intensity depending on the strength of their Faith, while non-living objects lose color, fading into dark silhouettes.

System: Roll Perception + Alertness. This evocation affects all living beings within a radius in yards equal to the character's Faith. Demons targeted by this evocation (and aware of its use) can resist its effects with a successful Willpower roll (difficulty 8). Extra successes permit the character to detect these beacons of Faith through intervening obstacles, allowing the demon to detect hidden individuals as well. Seeing through an interior wall or door requires one extra success. Seeing through a brick wall requires two extra successes. Seeing past thick metal bulkheads or a vault door might require three or more extra successes. This special sight persists for a turn.

Torment: Monstrous Devils receive the opposite effect of this evocation; their eyes see only those individuals whose souls have become so hollowed out by their evil acts that they are literal voids of spiritual energy. These soulless individuals (including other demons with a Torment of 9 or more) appear to the demon as patches of blackness against the dark background of the physical world.

•• SEND VISION

In their former role as the Creator's divine Heralds, the Namaru were often called upon to convey God's messages across the length and breadth of the cosmos, delivering Heaven's commands as potent visions that filled a Celestial's mind with images of majesty and wonder. After the Fall, the Devils still made extensive use of this lore, communicating detailed orders to their subordinates in the rebel host or smiting their foes with frightening visions of infernal wrath.

System: Roll Manipulation + Expression. Devils may use this evocation to send complex instructions to fellow demons at the speed of thought. Unlike an invocation, this vision fills the recipient's mind like an illusion or a waking dream, playing out whatever scene the sender wishes to convey in the blink of an eye. The amount of information the sender can convey depends on the number of successes generated by your roll. Each success allows the sender to describe one turn's worth of action. For example, if a Devil wishes to instruct one of her fellow demons to go outside, get in a car and start the engine, the player would need three successes to fully convey her instructions. These instructions can be shared simultaneously to a number of individuals equal to your character's Faith. These visions can be sent only to recipients within the sender's line of sight. This power may be used on mortals and demons alike.

Torment: Monstrous demons use this evocation to shock or frighten their foes in battle. The sender can affect a number of targets equal to her Faith, as long as they are within her line of sight. Each success generated by your roll inflicts a level of bashing damage against the targets as they are struck with terrifying visions of the Devil's wrath. Unlike normal bashing damage, this mental assault cannot be soaked. If the evocation inflicts more levels of bashing damage than a target's Wits, the target must make a Willpower roll (difficulty 8) or suffer a temporary derangement.

••• PILLAR OF FAITH

Throughout the birth of the cosmos and the early days of Paradise, the Heralds were at the forefront of every major effort mandated by Heaven, bolstering the energies of other Celestials wherever necessary.

System: Roll Manipulation + Leadership. This evocation allows the Devil to add her Faith to the efforts of another, as long as the Devil knows the demon's Celestial or True Name and can draw a line of sight to him. Each success adds a bonus die to the target's next evocation roll. The Devil cannot provide more bonus dice than her permanent Faith score, and if the recipient's roll botches he still loses a point of Faith as normal.

The user of Pillar of Faith does not lose any Faith when "lending" it. Repeated use of this evocation on a single target does not cause bonus dice to accumulate.

Torment: Monstrous demons may use this evocation only to block or negate the efforts of another. This phenomenon works like any other resisted dice roll, with the Devil's successes negating any successes generated by her opponent. Again, the Devil must know the target's Celestial or True Name to perform this evocation.

•••• The Fire of Heaven

This evocation allows the Devil to channel her Faith as a withering blast of pure white fire, smiting her target with the wrath of a fallen angel.

System: Spend one Faith point and roll Dexterity + Athletics. The character may target any individual or object within a range in yards equal to her Faith score. Every success generated by the roll inflicts one level of aggravated damage (or lethal damage if the target does not deal in aggravated damage).

Torment: Monstrous demons are unable to focus the fiery power of their Faith in a concentrated bolt. It erupts from them in all directions as a storm of raging energy instead. When a high-Torment demon uses this evocation, the infernal fire strikes everything within a number of yards equal to the character's permanent Faith score. The blast inflicts one level of aggravated damage per success to everything in this radius.

••••• Hand of Faith

The mandate of the first Celestial House was to act as the voice of the Creator and to ensure that His Grand Design was fulfilled within the bounds of angelic free will. If one of the Celestials deviated too far from the Creator's design in the process of Creation, the Heralds were able to manipulate the evocation as it happened, modifying the outcome to within acceptable limits. Although this mandate was only rarely enforced, this evocation more than any other spawned the tendency of the other Houses to jealously guard their prerogatives and regard the Heralds with no small amount of resentment.

System: Spend one Faith point and roll Manipulation + Leadership. Hand of Faith allows a Devil to usurp another Celestial's evocation, directing its effects as she desires. You must generate more successes on your Faith roll than the player of the demon performing the evocation does with his, and your character must know the initiator's Celestial or True Name. If successful, the Devil can alter the evocation's target and its effects as if she were the one using the power. If the Devil does not roll enough successes to seize control of the evocation, the attempt fails and the evocation proceeds as originally intended. When used in combat, the Devil must have a higher initiative than the demon performing the evocation — Hand of Faith cannot be performed as a reflexive action.

Torment: Monstrous Devils are not able to manipulate other demons' evocations, but they can cause evocations targeted at them to rebound and affect their initiators. Again, you must generate more successes on your roll than the demon performing the evocation in order to succeed. If successful, apply the effects of the evocation against the initiator (if the evocation has an area effect, center it on the initiator). The Devil must know the initiator's Celestial or True Name to perform this evocation.

Bel, the Visage of the Celestials

The apocalyptic form of the Lore of the Celestials reveals the fallen as a luminous, lordly angel, radiating divine grandeur and authority. Her skin literally glows, wreathing her in an aura of golden light that shifts in intensity depending on her mood. Her eyes blaze with the cold light of the stars. Despite her actual physical appearance, the fallen seems to tower over everyone around her.

The Visage of the Celestials confers the following abilities.

• **Wings:** A pair of eagle's wings extends from the character's shoulders. At full extension, each wing is a third again as long as the character is tall. The character can glide up to three times her running speed per turn.

• **Lordly Mien:** The character's aura of divine authority lowers the difficulty of her Charisma and Manipulation rolls by two.

• **Enhanced Senses:** The character's five senses are heightened to superhuman levels, lowering the difficulty of her Perception rolls by two.

• **Increased Awareness:** The fallen is especially attuned to the fabric of reality, lowering the difficulty of all Awareness rolls by two.

Torment: As the character loses herself to her dark nature, her authority remains as strong as ever, but the glow that suffused her dims to a sullen red. Her wings turn leathery, and her eyes become as black as the void. Where she was once a vision of nobility, she now carries herself as a haughty tyrant.

The Visage of the Celestials confers the following high-Torment abilities.

• **Claws/Teeth:** The character manifests claws and fangs that inflict Strength +2 aggravated damage.

• **Scales:** The character's skin is covered with dark, lustrous scales that provide four dice of armor protection against physical attacks.

• **Increased Size:** The character's body grows to a third again its normal height, adding the following bonus Traits: +1 Strength, +2 Dexterity, +1 Stamina.

• **Dread Gaze:** Individuals (mortal or demon) who meet the demon's gaze and who fail a Willpower roll (difficulty 7) must forfeit their actions for the turn.

Lore of Flame

• Fuel

The Devil's command of flames allows her to fuel existing fires with the power of her Faith, turning a simple source of heat into a raging inferno with a thought.

System: Roll Stamina + Survival. If there is a source of fire or heat within a number of yards equal to her Faith score, the Devil can increase its size by one square foot per success.

Torment: Monstrous Devils fuel the strength of an existing blaze rather than its dimensions. Each success increases the fire's lethal damage rating by one. For more details on fire and its effects, see page 263 of the Systems chapter.

• • IGNITE

A Devil's mastery of fire as a fundamental force of Creation allows him to inspire its existence at will.

System: Roll Stamina + Survival. This evocation allows the Devil to cause flammable objects to burst into flame. The character may attempt to ignite any object within a number of yards equal to her Faith score, and you must obtain a number of successes in excess of the target's resistance to combustion. Gasoline, gunpowder or other explosive material might have a resistance of 1. Dry, flammable objects like wood or paper might have a resistance of 2. Inert metal might be rated 5. Water and strictly nonflammable materials cannot be ignited with this power. Fires ignited in this fashion are no more intense than natural flames, and they inflict damage accordingly.

Torment: Monstrous Devils are too fueled by hatred to perform this evocation with precision. All flammable objects within a radius in yards equal to the character's Faith score are affected. A single evocation roll is made with some materials igniting and others remaining unaffected, based on successes rolled.

• • • COMMAND THE FLAME

The Devil's mastery of flame allows her to direct a fire by the force of her will — the blaze swells, shrinks, moves and consumes all that she commands.

System: Roll Wits + Survival and total the number of successes achieved. The successes form a pool that you use in subsequent turns to control the progress of the fire. Rolls to control the fire are made against a difficulty of 8, although that may increase depending on circumstances such as active sprinklers and fire-retardant materials, at the Storyteller's discretion. Successes generated by the roll allow your character to cause the fire to grow by one square foot per success, shrink by the same amount or spread in a specific direction up to a yard per success. The player may add to this pool with subsequent Wits + Survival rolls on successive turns, if desired, but the pool can never exceed the character's permanent Faith rating. If at any time you fail to roll any successes, the fire burns out of control for that turn. If a roll botches, control is lost completely.

Torment: High-Torment Devils have less facility in controlling fire's movements, but their rage increases the flames' intensity. A monstrous demon's control pool is halved (rounded up) for all actions, with the remaining dice added as damage levels to the harm that the fire is capable of inflicting.

• • • • HOLOCAUST

This evocation is the ultimate expression of the power of fire. It consumes in order to make way for new life by transforming divine energy into cleansing flames.

System: Spend one Faith point and roll Stamina + Survival, although your dice pool for the roll cannot exceed the *target's* Faith pool. Your demon must physically touch her intended target to perform this evocation. Each success inflicts one level of aggravated damage (or lethal if the victim does not deal in aggravated damage) to the target *and* consumes one point of the target's temporary Faith. This form of attack can be used on inanimate objects as well. Most physical matter has no more than one point of Faith suffusing its physical being, though especially sacred objects may have considerably more. Physical objects burned this way are reduced to ashes when all their inherent Faith is consumed (objects therefore burn much quicker than normal).

Torment: Monstrous demons delight in feeding the cosmos to the flames. Roll your full dice pool, although damage levels inflicted in excess of the target's available Faith are taken from *your character's* Faith pool. Additionally, if the evocation causes more damage than the target is capable of sustaining, the remaining aggravated levels of damage are suffered by your Devil as she loses her focus in the ecstasy of destruction.

• • • • • RIDE THE FLAMES

By performing this potent evocation, a Devil does not merely command the fire, she *is* the fire, transforming her physical body into flame and directing it by the power of her will.

System: Spend one Faith point and roll Stamina + Survival. A Devil has two options when employing this power: She can either join her essence with an existing blaze or become a pillar of fire by converting her available Faith. In either case, your demon's body literally transforms into flame, consuming her clothes and any possessions she carried. While becoming a pillar of fire means the flame occupies the same dimensions as the character's physical body, your demon can increase this area by one square foot for each additional Faith point you spend.

Once transformed, your Devil is a formless mass that shifts size and shape according to her will. While in this state, you use the character's Willpower pool rather than her normal Attributes and Abilities to perform any actions, splitting this pool for multiple actions as normal. She may effectively travel anywhere air can go — under doors, through crevices. If she lashes out at an opponent in combat, roll dice equal to her Torment score to determine damage. The fire of your character's body is unaffected by water or other fire-suppression technology, as it is fueled by faith instead of a mere chemical reaction. The drawback to this condition is that the fire must be fed continually or it dies out. Each turn, your character must devote some of her Willpower pool to consuming flammable material. One success is sufficient. Failing that, her flame shrinks by one square foot at the end of the turn. The fire does not spread like a normal fire; it remains a self-contained entity, leaving only charred remains of the matter it consumes. If the fire shrinks to less than one square foot or you botch a Willpower roll at any point, your character transforms back into her physical form.

Torment: Monstrous demons are unable to fully realize the transformation into flame. These fallen become fiery, skeletal figures, instead, their blackened bones wreathed with flame, and howling their rage and pain with tongues of fire. High-Torment demons use their normal Attributes and Abilities to move, attack and otherwise act in a given turn, but they cannot move with the speed or ease of true, mutable flame. Furthermore, their bodies are wracked with agony. If they do not inflict at least one level of damage or combust one square foot of material per turn (with a successful Willpower roll), they suffer one level of lethal damage as the fire feeds upon their physical bodies.

Nusku, the Visage of the Flames

These demons reveal themselves in a blaze of yellow-orange light. Their skin glows with the seething brilliance of the sun, and their image shimmers like a mirage. Their eyes take on the color of burnished gold, and when angered, the Nusku radiate palpable waves of heat.

An angel's hair becomes a deep red or reddish-gold and thickens into a leonine mane. Open flames flare brightly in his presence, seeming to bow toward their master as the tongues of flame are drawn to the divinity in their midst.

The Visage of the Flames confers the following capabilities.

• **Shroud of Flames**: The angel is surrounded in a nimbus of supernatural flame that distracts and confuses her foes. The difficulty of all ranged or melee attacks directed at the character increases by one.

• **Immunity to Fire**: The character suffers no damage from heat or fire.

• **Extra Actions**: Faith points can be spent to gain extra actions in a turn at the rate of one point per action. These actions occur in order of descending initiative, so if a Devil with an initiative of 7 gains an extra action, she take her normal action at 7 and her extra action at 6. The player must decide to purchase extra actions at the beginning of a turn before any other actions have been taken.

• **Improved Initiative**: Add two to the character's initiative score.

Torment: As the fallen becomes consumed by her demonic nature, her skin turns black like smoke and seems to seethe with patterns of sullen red that pulse

with the demon's beating heart. Her eyes glow like coals, and her thick hair writhes in a spectral wind.

The Visage of the Flames confers the following high-Torment capabilities.

• **Claws/Teeth:** The character manifests claws and fangs that inflict Strength +2 aggravated damage.

• **Lashing Tail:** The character manifests a long, reptilian tail tipped with a curved, bony spike that inflicts Strength –1 aggravated damage.

• **Increased Size:** The character's body grows to a third again its normal height, adding the following bonus traits: +2 Strength, +1 Dexterity, +1 Stamina.

• **Fiery Blood:** The character's blood burns like magma. Flammable objects hit with more than a few drops burst into flame, and opponents in close combat suffer one level of lethal damage each time they successfully inflict damage on the character.

LORE OF RADIANCE

• VOICE OF HEAVEN

This evocation allows a demon to speak with a voice like thunder or with the clear, perfect tones of a crystal bell. The clarity and power of the demon's words command instant attention, forcing even the most frenzied mind to pause and consider what the ancient spirit has to say.

System: Roll Manipulation + Leadership. A Devil may use this evocation to affect everyone up to a distance of 10 yards times her Faith (difficulty 8), or focus on a single individual (difficulty 6). The player may issue a single command to the target, who may then attempt to resist the command with a Willpower roll. If the victim scores fewer successes than the Devil, he must obey the demon's command. When the Devil speaks, her voice can be heard clearly regardless of the level of ambient noise. She could speak into a raging typhoon and still sound as though she were speaking directly into the recipient's ear. This evocation has no effect on other demons or thralls with protection from mind-control effects.

Torment: Monstrous demons use this evocation to mouth a furious stream of blasphemy and hatred that is so charged with power that it strikes the minds of mortals and thralls like a physical blow. Each success inflicts one level of bashing damage to targets, though they can attempt to resist this damage by making a Willpower roll with a difficulty equal to the demon's Torment. Demons *can* be affected by this form of the evocation and can resist its effects using Willpower as well. If any damage is suffered, they must also make a Courage roll to avoid gaining a temporary point of Torment.

•• EXALT

The power of the demon's commanding voice is enough to instill hope in the weakest of hearts, spurring mortals to put aside their fears and steal triumph from the jaws of defeat.

System: Roll Manipulation + Leadership. Each success is a bonus die that the target may add to a single dice pool for that turn. The demon may affect a number of mortals (including thralls) up to her Faith rating. Each individual benefits from the full amount of bonus dice. Demons cannot be affected by this evocation.

Torment: The sneering tone of a monstrous Devil has the opposite effect on mortals. Each success is subtracted from the mortals' dice pools for actions taken in a single turn. If a target's dice pool is reduced to zero or below, the mortal may not act in that turn.

••• AURA OF LEGEND

This evocation awakens atavistic memories buried deep in the human subconscious, renewing the ancient bonds of fealty that once bound humanity and the fallen in the face of Heaven's tyranny. The ties run so deep that when they arise, it can sometimes drive all other thoughts from a mortal's mind, leaving only the urge to fulfill the ancient duty once more.

System: Roll Manipulation + Leadership. The Devil can affect a number of mortals equal to her Faith, as long as they are within line of sight and able to hear the demon's voice. If the number of successes rolled exceeds a target's Wits, she is immediately filled with a sense of devotion and loyalty toward the demon. She instinctively defends the demon from attackers, and follows reasonable orders without question. If your successes are less than the target's Wits, the target's player can resist the power's effects with a successful Willpower roll (difficulty 8). Thralls of other demons targeted with this evocation use their demonic masters' Willpower to resist its effects. Thralls with mind-control resistance can automatically resist the evocation's effects by spending one Willpower point. Mortals remain loyal to the demon for the duration of the scene. A person can be a target of this power only once per scene.

Torment: Monstrous demons do not inspire loyalty. They fill their victims with urges of hate and violence. Mortals affected in this way succumb to a murderous frenzy, attacking the nearest living beings within reach.

•••• THE MARK OF THE CELESTIALS

During the War of Wrath, both angels and demons found ways to signify their friends and enemies, subtly altering auras to make subjects easier to find or as marks of anger and shame so that anyone who encountered subjects would know their crimes and treat them accordingly.

System: Spend one Faith point and roll Manipulation + Expression. The Devil must know her target's name (in the case of a demon, the Celestial or True Name is necessary), and be able to touch him. She must then pronounce the nature of her mark so that the subject can

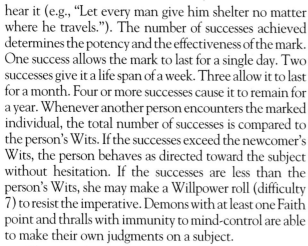

hear it (e.g., "Let every man give him shelter no matter where he travels."). The number of successes achieved determines the potency and the effectiveness of the mark. One success allows the mark to last for a single day. Two successes give it a life span of a week. Three allow it to last for a month. Four or more successes cause it to remain for a year. Whenever another person encounters the marked individual, the total number of successes is compared to the person's Wits. If the successes exceed the newcomer's Wits, the person behaves as directed toward the subject without hesitation. If the successes are less than the person's Wits, she may make a Willpower roll (difficulty 7) to resist the imperative. Demons with at least one Faith point and thralls with immunity to mind-control are able to make their own judgments on a subject.

Torment: Monstrous demons can create only marks that promise violence and misfortune for the bearer, and a Willpower roll is made for mortals who try to resist the mark's command (difficulty equals the Devil's Torment).

●●●●● Revelation

Although mortals and demons alike use artifice to conceal their true natures, this evocation allows a Devil to strip away a mortal's layers of deception and reveal them for who they really are. It's a moment of truth that many do not have the heart to endure.

System: Spend one Faith point and roll Perception + Intuition in a resisted roll against the target's Willpower. If you win the roll, your character sees the individual for who he really is — his Nature, attitudes and beliefs. If questioned, the individual cannot lie or be indirectly deceitful; his answers are direct and straightforward, sparing no detail. By the same token, the individual himself must face the harsh, unyielding truth about his strengths, weaknesses, virtues and faults. At the end of the scene, the target must make a second Willpower roll (difficulty 7). If successful, the target gains a permanent point of Willpower, having faced the worst aspects of her identity and accepted them. If the roll fails, the target loses one permanent Willpower. If the target botches the roll, the individual loses three permanent Willpower and acquires a temporary derangement.

This power has no effect on other demons, but it does affect thralls.

Torment: Monstrous Devils are not interested in revealing a mortal's personal virtue. They wish to only crush egos to render victims more malleable, or to stoke the fires of dark impulses. When a high-Torment demon performs this evocation, the effect exaggerates a subject's worst qualities, giving them greater emphasis than the rest of the individual's personality. If the mortal's player fails her initial Willpower roll to resist the evocation, the character's impulses override her identity for the duration of the scene.

Qingu, the Visage of Radiance

The apocalyptic form of the masters of Radiance is an incandescent figure wreathed in a corona of jewel-like color. Their physical features have more in common with the smooth perfection of marble than with human skin. Their voices are pure as crystal, and they cut through the petty din of the mortal world like a razor.

The Visage of Radiance confers the following capabilities.

• **Wings:** A pair of eagle's wings extends from the character's shoulders. At full extension, each wing is a third again as long as the character is tall. The character can glide up to three times her running speed per turn.

• **Inhuman Allure:** The character's voice and features are refined to inhuman perfection, adding the following bonus traits: +2 Charisma, +1 Manipulation, +1 Appearance.

• **Radiant Aura:** The character's body is wreathed in a corona of shifting, multicolored hues that distract and confuse her foes. The difficulties of all ranged attacks directed at the character increase by one.

• **Sense the Hidden:** The character is supernaturally adept at sensing mortals or demons who attempt to hide from her. The difficulties of all Perception rolls to detect hidden individuals within the character's line of sight decreases by two.

Torment: As the angel gives in to her demonic nature, the colors of her aura become muted, flaring up in angry reds and blues when she grows angry. Her features retain their alabaster perfection, but where they once inspired wonder, they now radiate an air of cold menace and cruelty.

The Visage of Radiance confers the following high-Torment capabilities.

• **Voice of the Damned:** The demon's voice seethes with inhuman hate and malice. The difficulties of all Intimidation rolls decrease by two.

• **Casts No Reflection:** The demon's image does not appear in a mirror. Nor can it be captured in a photograph or by a video camera.

• **Corrosive Spit:** The demon's spit sears like acid. A bite inflicts an additional health level of aggravated damage, or the character can spit at a target up to 10 feet away with a successful Dexterity roll. The spittle inflicts one die of aggravated damage, plus any extra successes rolled. Targets such as mortals that do not deal in aggravated damage suffer lethal damage instead.

• **Horns:** A pair of curved ram or bull's horns protrude from the character's forehead. If attacked in close combat, the character may make a free counter-attack at his foe. Roll Dexterity + Brawl. If successful, the character inflicts aggravated damage equal to Strength -1.

Scourge
(Asharu)

The Angels of the Firmament ruled the winds beneath the starry vault of Heaven and bore the living breath of God to man and beast. The Lore of Awakening was central to this sacred task, infusing the bodies of the newborn with the spark of life and keeping their charges free from sickness and injury. Before the Fall, each creature that received the blessing of life was bound thereafter to the angel who awakened it, allowing the guardian spirits to sense when their children were suffering or in danger and could rush to their side. This innate bond was lost to the Asharu after the Fall, but over time, the Scourges amassed a collection of lore that restored a fraction of their far-reaching awareness: the Lore of the Firmament. Secondary to their duties as investors of life, the task of directing the currents of air that sustained the life of Paradise was contained in the Lore of the Winds.

Lore of Awakening

• Find the Faithful

This evocation allows a Scourge to locate specific individuals, mortal or demon, by homing in on their store of Faith.

System: Roll Perception + Awareness. The difficulty depends on how much information your character has concerning the subject. If she has the subject's mundane name, the difficulty is 8. If the subject is a demon and the character knows the subject's Celestial Name, the difficulty is 7. If she knows the demon's True Name the difficulty is 6. The Scourge can detect and home in on an individual up to a number of miles away equal to her permanent Faith score. Demons being actively sought in this manner can use their supernatural awareness to detect the search as a reflexive action (see the section on inherent powers for details). If a demon detects the search, he may avoid detection with a Willpower roll (difficulty 8). If he gets more successes than the Scourge, he evades the search.

Torment: Monstrous demons can detect only sources of spiritual decay or corruption. They may use this evocation to seek out individuals whose Faith or Willpower has been reduced to zero.

•• Cleanse

Scourges use this evocation to purify a living being, be it plant, animal or human. By focusing their Faith on a target, any poisons, infections or diseased tissue are literally expelled from the body, emerging as a black, viscous fluid.

System: Roll Stamina + Medicine. The difficulty of the roll depends on the virulence and scope of the disease or poison. Cleansing a body of the effects of alcohol is

difficulty 6, while a virulent disease such as tuberculosis or cancer is difficulty 8 or higher. The process is all or nothing. The evocation overcomes the illness or it doesn't, and only one attempt may be made by a single demon on a single subject for a specific instance of an ailment or poison. A Scourge must be able to touch her target in order to perform this evocation.

Torment: Monstrous Scourges use this evocation to *spread* sickness and corruption. Each success generated by a Faith roll inflicts one level of bashing damage to a living victim. What's more, the victim suffers an additional level of bashing damage and loses one temporary Willpower point each day thereafter as the corruption spreads through the victim's system. The sickness cannot be cured with medical attention. It continues to affect the victim for a number of days equal to the Scourge's Faith score.

••• Heal

This evocation allows the Scourge to heal even the worst injuries of demon and mortal alike.

System: Roll Stamina + Medicine. The Scourge can heal all of a target's bashing damage or one health level of lethal or aggravated damage per success. The character must be able to touch her target to perform this evocation.

Torment: Monstrous Scourges use this evocation to poison a victim's body. Each success lowers a target's Stamina temporarily. If the target loses all of her Stamina, she falls into a coma and suffers one health level of aggravated damage (or lethal damage if a victim is not subject to aggravated damage) per hour per success remaining unless she receives medical attention immediately. Stamina is lost for a number of days equal to the demon's Faith score.

•••• Animate

This powerful evocation allows a Scourge to infuse non-living objects with the breath of God, giving them a form of rudimentary life.

System: Spend one Faith point and roll Intelligence + Crafts. The total number of successes achieved forms a dice pool that you roll for any actions that the animated object performs in a given turn. The object is not intelligent or self-aware, it is an extension of the demon's will. The demon may animate a number of objects equal to her permanent Faith score at one time. The effects of the evocation last for a single scene. A demon must first touch an object in order to animate it, but he can control it from a distance as long as he can see it.

Torment: A monstrous Scourge is capable of animating an object as easily as her low-Torment peers, but the objects she touches are filled with the taint of her anger and pain. Unless she controls them with an iron will, they lash out at the nearest living things they find, friend or foe.

Make a Willpower roll for each object per turn. The difficulty of the roll is equal to your demon's Torment. If a roll fails, your demon loses control of that object for the

duration of the turn and it goes berserk, attacking the nearest living being it can reach. If the demon is content to allow an object to run amok, no roll is needed.

●●●●● RESTORE LIFE

This potent evocation allows a Scourge to breathe life into the bodies of the dead, restoring their vitality if not their souls. Unless a soul is available to be connected to the body, the result is a mindless zombie under the demon's complete control.

System: Spend one Faith point and roll Stamina + Medicine. The difficulty depends on how long the body has been deceased. A freshly dead corpse is difficulty 6, while one dead for several days or as long as a week might be difficulty 7 or higher. Older bodies cannot be restored. If successful, the body is returned to life, but unless the Scourge is also able to furnish the body with a soul, the result is a mindless zombie that the demon can control. Disembodied fallen may possess these animated corpses with the Scourge's permission, or they can try to wrest control from the demon with a resisted Willpower roll. The effects of this evocation last for a single scene, unless you wish to spend a temporary Willpower point to make the restoration permanent. Your demon may restore a number of bodies at any given time equal to her Faith score. Subjects must be within your character's Faith score in yards to be affected.

Torment: A monstrous Scourge is capable of restoring life as easily as her low-Torment peers, but the bodies she raises are filled with the taint of her anger and pain. Unless she controls them with an iron will, they lash out at the nearest living things they find, friend or foe.

Make a Willpower roll for each raised body per turn. The difficulty is equal to your demon's Torment. If a roll fails, the demon loses control for the duration of the turn, and the body goes berserk, attacking the nearest living being it can reach. If your character is content to allow the body to run amok, no roll is needed.

DAGAN, THE VISAGE OF AWAKENINGS

The apocalyptic form of the masters of animation infuses the angel's mortal body with the blush of youth and vibrant health — even the oldest mortal vessel appears to be in the prime of life and moves with inhuman grace, speed and strength. This aura of life and vitality radiates as a palpable sense of warmth, like a beam of sunlight, and every living being touched is temporarily suffused with its power. Wilted flowers return to full bloom, the injured gain strength and the old forget their afflictions.

The Visage of Awakenings confers the following special capabilities.

- **Aura of Vitality:** Living beings (plant or animal) within a number of yards equal to your character's Faith are infused with restorative energy. Individuals within this area heal any bashing damage at the rate of one health level per turn.

- **Pass Without Trace:** The difficulty of the character's Stealth rolls decreases by two, and her passage does not disturb the surrounding environment in any way. She leaves no footprints and disturbs no foliage.

- **Improved Physical Capabilities.** The fallen gains the following bonus traits: +1 Strength, +1 Dexterity, +1 Stamina.

- **Wings:** A pair of owl's wings extends from the character's shoulders. At full extension, each wing is a third again as long as the character is tall. The character can glide up to three times her running speed per turn.

Torment: As the Dagan become consumed by their demonic nature, their command of life and vitality turns in upon itself, transforming their mortal bodies into a breeding ground for disease and cancerous tumors. They are covered with misshapen growths and weeping sores, and their flesh is damp and spongy to the touch.

The Visage of Awakenings confers the following high-Torment special capabilities.

- **Miasma:** The demon's breath reeks of gangrenous rot that can have a debilitating effect on her foes in close quarters. The demon can affect victims up to a distance in feet equal to her Faith score. Mortals and demons caught in the path of her exhalation forfeit their actions for the turn unless a successful Stamina roll is made (difficulty 7). If a roll botches, a victim is also infected by a virus or disease at the Storyteller's discretion.

- **Extra Health Levels:** The demon gains three extra Bruised health levels for the purposes of sustaining bashing, lethal and aggravated damage.

- **Viscous Flesh:** The diseased flesh of the Dagan sloughs away when pinned or trapped, leaving a would-be assailant covered in rotting flesh. The difficulty of grappling the demon increases by two, and the character can escape from bonds such as ropes or handcuffs with a successful Dexterity roll.

- **Extra Limbs:** The demon grows a second set of arms or a prehensile tail, at the player's discretion. Extra arms allow a character to parry or block hand-to-hand or melee attacks without sacrificing her own attack, or make up to two additional attacks of her own per turn (all which are considered multiple actions). A prehensile tail is half the character's height, uses only half the character's Strength (rounding down) to lift objects and allows the character to hang suspended.

LORE OF THE FIRMAMENT

● REMOTE VIEWING

This evocation allows a Scourge to see through the eyes of one of her thralls. This form of viewing is strictly passive; the demon is merely a spectator along for the ride.

System: Roll Perception + Empathy. The Scourge may see through her thrall's eyes for a number of turns

equal to the successes rolled. There is no range limitation for this evocation.

Torment: When a monstrous demon uses this evocation, it causes blood vessels to burst in the mortal's eyes. When the demon breaks contact, the mortal must make a Stamina roll with a difficulty equal to the Scourge's Torment. If the roll fails, the thrall is blinded for a number of days equal to the total number of turns the evocation was in effect. If the roll botches, the thrall is blinded permanently.

•• SCRY

The Scourge must know one of the names of her intended subject or be able to hold one of the subject's possessions: car keys, an article of clothing. The demon can observe the subject and her surroundings, no matter how far away.

System: Roll Perception + Empathy. The difficulty depends on the level of connection to the subject: Using a mortal's name or a physical possession is difficulty 8. A demon's Celestial Name is difficulty 7. A True Name is difficulty 6. The amount of detail gained depends on the number of successes rolled. One success provides only a visual image of the immediate area around the subject. Two successes expand the visual sphere out from the subject to a distance in yards equal to the Scourge's Faith score. Three successes adds audio; the demon can hear the subject's voice, but no one else. Four or more successes allow the Scourge to hear everything that occurs around the subject. This evocation lasts a number of turns equal to your character's permanent Faith score, or the connection can be broken voluntarily at any point.

Torment: The weight of a monstrous demon's attention causes a severe headache in the subject, as well as feelings of mounting paranoia and aggression. The Storyteller must make a Willpower roll (difficulty 6) for the subject in each turn that she is observed. If a roll fails, the subject suffers a level of bashing damage and reacts with increasing anger and aggression toward the people around her, increasing the difficulty of all Social rolls by two for the duration of the scene. If the roll botches, the subject gains a temporary derangement as well.

••• MOUTH OF THE DAMNED

This evocation allows the Scourge to speak and act through the body of one of her thralls. This is more like a form of remote control than outright possession, though. The demon remains firmly ensconced in her host body and simply directs her will through the bond between herself and her thrall, and he may do so at any distance.

System: Roll Manipulation + Leadership. The number of successes determines how many of the thrall's dice you can roll for any given action during a turn. This dice pool cannot be greater than the maximum number of dice the thrall would normally get for an action. When your demon speaks through her thrall, voice, expressions and mannerisms are the Scourge's.

The effects of this evocation last for a number of turns equal to your character's permanent Faith score.

Torment: Monstrous demons have few scruples about a thrall's faculties; an unfortunate mortal risks permanent brain damage when controlled. Each turn the demon performs an action with the mortal's body, the Storyteller makes a Stamina roll for the thrall. If the roll fails, the mortal loses one point from the relevant Attribute *permanently*. If the demon uses the thrall only to speak, the Storyteller makes a Willpower roll instead. If the roll fails, the thrall loses one point of Intelligence.

•••• TOUCH FROM AFAR

Scourges can use this evocation to direct their powers at a target outside their line of sight, as long as they know one of the target's names or possess an article of great personal attachment to the target, such as a treasured possession or a lock of hair.

System: Spend one Faith point and roll Manipulation + Awareness. Your demon can affect targets as far away as 10 miles times the character's *current* Faith pool. Then follow the system for performing whatever evocation your character uses, but the difficulty of the roll is determined by the amount of information she has on her target. If she only has the target's mundane name or a personal possession, the difficulty is 9. If the target is a demon and she has his Celestial Name, the difficulty is 8; if she has the target's True Name, the difficulty is 7. If the demon targets one of her own thralls, the difficulty is reduced to 6. Area-effect evocations are centered on the individual targeted.

Torment: The searing focus of a monstrous demon's attention fills a subject with visions of horror and madness. When a high-Torment demon uses this evocation, the Willpower roll is made for the target with a difficulty equal to the demon's Torment. If the roll fails, the target gains a temporary derangement. If the roll botches, the derangement is permanent. These effects are in addition to the results of whatever evocation the Scourge directs at the target.

••••• MANY PLACES AT ONCE

This evocation is similar to Mouth of the Damned, except that the Scourge is capable of speaking and acting through multiple thralls at the same time.

System: The demon can affect a number of thralls equal to her Wits score, though if she affects fewer targets than her total Wits, she can also control her own body at the same time. Otherwise, the demon's body falls into a deep coma until the evocation expires. Spend one Faith point and roll Manipulation + Leadership. Successes achieved form a dice pool to roll for each of the thralls under the character's control. In addition, the character may perform an evocation through *one* of the thralls under her control each turn, using her own dice pool. Multiple thralls can be controlled over a number of turns equal to your character's permanent Faith score.

Torment: Each turn the demon performs an action with a thrall's body, the Storyteller makes a Stamina roll for the mortal. If the roll fails, the subject loses one point from the relevant Attribute *permanently*. If the demon uses the thrall only to speak, the Storyteller makes a Willpower roll instead. If the roll fails, the thrall loses one point of Intelligence. Additionally, if a monstrous demon performs an evocation through the body of one of her thralls, the thrall gets a Stamina roll with a difficulty equal to the demon's Torment. If it fails, she suffers one level of lethal damage.

Anshar, the Visage of the Firmament

These Angels of the Firmament reveal themselves as lithe, ethereal figures with pale skin and large gray eyes. When they speak, their voice echoes faintly, as if from a great distance, and they alternate between bouts of quiet distraction and periods of intense, disquieting scrutiny.

The Visage of the Firmament confers the following special capabilities.

• **Enhanced Senses:** The character's five senses are heightened to superhuman levels, lowering the difficulty of Perception rolls by two.

• **Wings:** A pair of owl's wings extends from the character's shoulders. At full extension, each wing is a third again as long as the character is tall. The character can glide up to three times her running speed per turn.

• **Enhanced Intuition:** The character's uncanny insight lowers the difficulty of all Intuition rolls by two.

• **Enhanced Dodge:** The difficulty of all Dodge rolls decreases by two.

Torment: Monstrous Anshar seem to retreat even further from the physical realm, shrouded in a disturbing mantle of shadow and mist. Their skin turns an almost translucent gray, and their bodies become bony and emaciated, the skin stretched taught over their faces until they resemble leering skulls.

The Visage of the Firmament confers the following high-Torment capabilities.

• **Cloak of Shadows:** The demon is shrouded in a pall of darkness, making her features difficult to see in the best light and rendering her near-invisible at night. The difficulty of all Stealth rolls decreases by two whenever the demon stands in shadow or moves in darkness. If the character is attacked, the rules for Blind Fighting apply to the attacker. See page 240 of the Systems chapter for details.

• **Multiple Eyes:** The demon gains four to six extra eyes, sprouting from her head and/or neck. These extra organs give the demon 360-degree vision and lower the difficulty of all Perception rolls by two.

• **Improved Initiative:** The character adds two to her initiative.

• **Claws:** The character manifests claws that inflict Strength +2 aggravated damage.

Lore of the Winds

• Summon Wind

This evocation allows the demon to call up a wind seemingly from nowhere. The Scourge can control the wind's general direction and use it to gain increased distance on a leap or hamper the effectiveness of ranged weapons.

System: Roll Stamina + Survival. The total number of successes rolled determines the strength of the wind summoned. Depending on how the wind is used, this strength can be added as a number of automatic successes to an Athletics roll (to leap a long distance, for example), it can increase the difficulty of a ranged attack staged against your character, or it can be used as a dice pool to exert force against an object (such as pushing open a door, knocking a person over). The wind persists for only a single turn. Increased winds can be applied across any distance that your character can see.

Torment: When monstrous demons summon up a wind, it is tainted with the reek of a charnel house, stinking of death and decay. Anyone caught in this blast must make a successful Stamina roll (difficulty 7) or suffer one level of bashing damage that may not be soaked. If such a roll botches, the victim forfeits all actions that turn due to extreme nausea.

•• Fist of Air

This evocation allows a demon to manipulate air pressure, allowing her to crush objects, stun living beings or cause them to burst apart from within.

System: Roll Stamina + Survival. Each success inflicts one health level of bashing damage to living beings. If directed at non-living objects, successes rolled are considered Strength points on the Feats of Strength chart (see page 232 of the Systems chapter) to determine how much effect the blast of air has on a target. Your character must be able to see her target to use this evocation on it, and the effects persist for one turn.

Torment: Monstrous demons are capable of drawing on their hate to intensify the force of this evocation to the degree that it inflicts lethal damage on living targets.

••• Command the Wind

When a Scourge uses this evocation, he is surrounded by swirling winds that become extensions of his will. He can use these gusts of air to manipulate objects.

System: Roll Dexterity + Survival. The total number of successes achieved forms a dice pool that you can roll for your character to perform any action that involves moment or control of objects or targets. The difficulty of actions that require fine motor control (typing, putting a key in a lock) is 9. The Scourge can affect objects up to a distance in yards equal to her Faith score. The effect of this evocation lasts for the duration of the scene.

Torment: The winds stirred by a monstrous demon become a foul miasma that chokes the lungs of anyone touched by them. Every living being within the range of the demon's evocation suffers one level of bashing damage per turn that cannot be soaked using armor. Filtration or breathing apparatus such as gas masks provides the only source of protection from this poisonous air.

●●●● Wall of Air

While Scourges can stir air into an angry gale with but a word, they can also condense it into an impenetrable barrier, stopping solid objects as though they'd struck a stone wall. When this evocation is performed, the air visibly distorts, like old, wavy glass. The stronger the barrier is, the more opaque it becomes.

System: Spend one Faith point and roll Stamina + Survival. The total number of successes achieved is a dice pool that can be used to soak all ranged attacks (as if it were armor) or to make resisted rolls against all close-combat attacks. The wall covers 10 square feet times the character's Faith score, and your Scourge can make the wall any size or shape desired within that limit. A resisted Strength + Athletics roll (difficulty 7) must be made versus the wall's dice pool to push through it. The wall can be placed anywhere within the Scourge's line of sight up to a distance in yards equal to her Faith score. The wall remains in place for the duration of the scene unless removed sooner at your character's will. The wall fades immediately if your character is Incapacitated.

Torment: Monstrous demons create walls of air that resemble weaves of writhing gray mist and sear the flesh like acid. Individuals who attempt to force their way through the barrier suffer a number of lethal damage dice equal to the demon's Torment.

●●●●● Cyclone

This potent evocation allows the Scourge to infuse the air with the power of his Faith, stirring up a raging whirlwind in the time of a heartbeat. This furious storm affects everything it touches, but the demon can focus it against a specific target if desired.

System: Spend one Faith point and roll Stamina + Survival (difficulty 7). The total number of successes achieved determines the Strength of the wind that your character summons that turn. The storm affects everything out to a distance in yards equal to your character's *current* Faith pool: Light objects are tossed about, doors are blown open, windows are broken. Compare the Strength of the storm to the Feats of Strength chart (see page 232 of the System's chapter for details) to determine how much force the wind can exert. If your character wishes, he can focus the effect of the cyclone against a specific target with a successful Willpower roll (difficulty equal to the cyclone's Strength). A storm can be targeted within range of your character's line of sight.

Once per turn, roll a number of dice equal to the Strength of the storm. Each success inflicts one level of bashing damage to living beings caught within, or on whom the storm is targeted. Your character can make the

storm center upon himself, or he can center it elsewhere when targeting it, without personal harm in either case.

On each turn after the first, the storm loses one point of Strength and its radius shrinks by one yard, unless your character wishes to sustain it (make another Stamina + Survival roll and spend another Faith point).

Torment: The hungry heart of a monstrous demon's storm sucks the very air from the lungs of the living to add to its strength. Every living being (save your character) within the radius of the cyclone suffers one level of lethal damage each turn as they struggle for air. If the storm's Strength exceeds the demon's Willpower it spirals out of control, affecting everything it touches *including* the demon herself.

Ellil, the Visage of the Winds

The monarchs of the air reveal themselves as tall and lithe, with large eyes and swift, graceful movements. When in revelatory form, the Ellil are constantly surrounded by shifting winds that ebb and flow with the intensity of their emotions. Any smoke or steam in the area is often sucked by these winds into a swirling vortex that circles their heads and shoulders like an ominous halo.

The Visage of the Winds confers the following special capabilities.

• **Supernatural Vision:** The character can see five times as far as a normal human, allowing the Ellil to see objects at 50 yards as clearly as if they were 10 yards away as long as there is even a weak source of light (such as moonlight) present. This effect also lowers the difficulty of all visual-based Perception rolls by two.

• **Wings:** A pair of owl's wings extends from the character's shoulders. At full extension, each wing is a third again as long as the character is tall. The character can glide up to three times her running speed per turn.

• **Perfect Balance:** The difficulty for all Athletics rolls involving leaping and tumbling decrease by two.

• **Immune to Falling Damage:** The character does not suffer damage of any kind incurred as the result of a fall, regardless of the height.

Torment: Ellil who succumb to their demonic nature grow lean and hatchet-featured, their faces dominated by their large, unblinking eyes. Their once-magnificent wings grow ragged and mangy, and their tall figures become stooped; they prefer to crouch rather than stand. They are always restless, unable to sit in any one place for more than a few minutes at a time.

The Visage of the Winds confers the following high-Torment special capabilities.

• **Claws:** The demon's fingers and toes are tipped with thick, curved talons that inflict Strength +2 aggravated damage.

• **Extra Actions:** Faith points can be spent to gain extra actions in a turn at the rate of one point per action.

These actions occur in order of descending initiative, so if a demon with an initiative of 7 gains an extra action, she takes her normal action at 7 and her extra action at 6. The player must decide to purchase extra actions at the beginning of a turn before any other actions have been taken.

• **Quills:** The demon's shoulders and upper arms are covered with a ruff of sharp quills that pose a hazard to foes in close combat. An attacker who successfully hits a demon in close combat suffers one health level of lethal damage unless a successful Dexterity roll (difficulty 7) is made.

• **Caustic Bile:** The demon is capable of vomiting a stream of corrosive bile at her foes, able to strike targets up to a number of feet away equal to her Faith score. A successful Dexterity + Athletics roll is needed to hit a target. The bile inflicts Strength -1 aggravated damage.

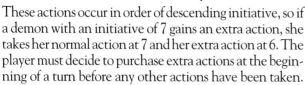

MALEFACTOR

(ANNUNAKI)

Though seldom seen, the Artificers were responsible for maintaining the ever-changing face of Paradise, carving valleys, raising mountains and extending plains in a slow, steady cycle of motion that stimulated all other cycles of physical life. This prime duty was represented by the Lore of the Earth, granting these angels the secrets of shaping rock and soil no matter how vast or small. Hand-in-hand with this enormous task went the responsibility of making the earth accessible to the living creatures that inhabited it by laying pathways from one location to another. The Lore of Paths is a subtle but potent collection of evocations that dictates how a physical object passes from one point to another. Humanity believes that the shortest distance between two points is a straight line, but that's only because the angels of the earth wished it so in times past. Though these potent arts were central to the existence of Paradise, their ways were slow and indirect by mortal standards. When the war began, the Annunaki sought a way to make their powers more immediately useful to their demon and mortal allies, which led to the synthesis of demonically enhanced weapons and tools. These methods, encompassed in the Lore of the Forge, are now considered to be the hallmarks of the Malefactors.

LORE OF THE EARTH

• EARTH MELD

This evocation allows the demon to bond her physical body with the earth beneath her feet. As long as the evocation is in effect, she cannot be moved or picked up or knocked down unless she wishes it.

System: Roll Strength + Survival. If successful, the Malefactor is bound to the earth and cannot be moved from that spot unless she wishes.

Torment: Monstrous demons can sink into the soil and move beneath the earth in any direction they wish. The number of successes rolled determines how many yards the demon can cover in linear travel. Each turn of movement requires a Strength + Athletics roll. If the roll fails, the demon is forced back to the surface.

•• ROIL THE EARTH

This evocation allows a Malefactor to cause the earth to give up its buried secrets. By concentrating on a particular kind of object (e.g., gold, iron, corpses), the demon causes the earth around her to roil and churn, forcing the objects of her desire to the surface.

System: Your character determines what she seeks within the earth, and you make a Strength + Survival roll. The number of successes rolled determines the radius in yards — including depth — from your character that is affected by the evocation. If the object or material is within that area, it is forced to the surface.

Torment: Monstrous demons can use this lore to create a kind of vortex that sucks objects below the surface. Demons or humans affected by the evocation may attempt to dodge its effects if they have an available action that turn. The target is buried a number of feet equal to the total number of successes that you roll. Digging out of the tomb of dirt requires an extended Strength + Athletics roll (difficulty 8), rolled per minute. Until the victim gains more successes than you rolled, she remains buried and suffers damage in the same manner as if she were drowning (see page 263 of the Systems chapter for details).

••• MOLD EARTH

This potent evocation allows the Malefactor to cause the earth to move and mold itself according to her whim. With a sweep of a hand, a wall of earth or stone can leap from the ground to shelter her, or a building's walls could flow like melted wax, creating a doorway that wasn't there before.

System: Roll Strength + Crafts. The difficulty is determined by the type of material affected (unpacked dirt is difficulty 5; granite, difficulty 6; processed materials like concrete is difficulty 7). The number of successes rolled determines how many square feet of the material the demon can manipulate. The affected material can be directed to assume any shape or form the demon desires within those parameters. The material affected must be within a number of yards equal to the character's Faith, and changes imposed are permanent.

Torment: Monstrous demons can affect the earth in the same fashion as less tormented demons, but the material manipulated is incredibly toxic. Living beings that make contact with this tainted earth suffer one level of lethal damage per turn of exposure.

•••• EARTH STORM

This evocation causes clods of earth and shards of stone or concrete to tear free of the ground and form a

whirling storm of deadly projectiles surrounding the Malefactor, providing protection from attacks and supplying the demon with missiles to hurl at foes.

System: Spend one Faith point and roll Strength + Survival. The number of successes achieved forms a dice pool that is rolled as armor to soak damage from any attacks directed at the Malefactor. The storm itself is centered on the fallen, and it moves as she moves. If the Malefactor wishes, she can sacrifice a die from her pool during any given turn to hurl a fist-sized projectile of earth or stone at a target. As with any ranged attack, roll Dexterity + Athletics to hit the target, with bashing damage dice pool equal to the character's Faith score. The evocation's radius extends for a number of yards equal to the character's Faith score. Individuals caught within this radius are whipped by gusts of stinging grit, increasing the difficulty of any actions taken by one. The effects of this evocation last for the duration of the scene.

Torment: The barrage invoked by a monstrous demon is more akin to a sandstorm, flaying living beings alive and wearing inanimate objects away in moments. The high-Torment version of this evocation does not provide extra soak dice or ranged attacks, but inflicts lethal damage dice equal to the character's Torment to everything caught within the storm's radius, except the demon herself.

Additionally, the swirling clouds of powdered dirt and stone serve to largely conceal the demon within, increasing the difficulty of ranged attacks directed at her by one.

••••• EARTHQUAKE

By focusing the power of her will, the Malefactor can stir the pent-up energies deep below the earth's surface and create a brief but powerful tremor that can reverberate across an entire city.

System: Spend one Faith point and roll Strength + Survival, and then allocate successes rolled between the *intensity* and *extent* of the tremor. The intensity of the tremor is added to the difficulty of any person's actions within the area and is used as a dice pool to determine damage to standing structures. A small wooden building like a shack has one or possibly two structure points, while a brick home might have as many as three or four. The difficulty for the damage roll is 6. If a building sustains more damage than it has structure points, it collapses.

The extent of the tremor determines its effective radius. One success causes the tremor to affect a number of square feet equal to the character's Faith score. Two successes affect a number of square yards. Three successes affect a number of square miles. Therefore, a demon can cause immense destruction on a small scale, significant destruction on a medium scale or minor damage across a large scale.

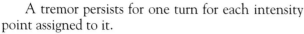

A tremor persists for one turn for each intensity point assigned to it.

Torment: A high-Torment demon causes the earth to heave and spew toxic clouds that are thick with ash and that reek of brimstone. In addition to the previously detailed effects, the stinging air increases the difficulty of all Perception rolls made within the affected area by two, and victims suffer one level of bashing damage each turn they are exposed to the fumes. These effects continue for a number of turns equal to the earthquake's intensity.

KISHAR, THE VISAGE OF THE EARTH

These angels manifest as towering figures with dark skin that ranges from a creamy brown to utter black, and their bodies appear as though hewn from stone, with muscle and bone etched in sharp relief on a frame devoid of soft flesh or fat. The Kishar are hairless, and the irises of their eyes have the clarity and color of gemstones: ruby, sapphire, emerald, garnet, topaz and diamond. The air about them smells of freshly turned earth, rich with the promise of life.

The Visage of the Earth confers the following special capabilities.

• **Increased Size:** The character's body grows to a third again its own height, adding the following bonus traits: +2 Strength, +1 Dexterity, +1 Stamina.

• **Immune to Bashing Damage:** The character is immune to attacks that inflict bashing damage alone.

• **Irresistible Force:** The difficulty of any Feats of Strength (see p. 232) performed by the character decrease by two.

• **Night Vision:** The character can see in total darkness as though it were daylight.

Torment: Monstrous Kishar are huge and misshapen, their stone-like skin covered in sharp-edged nodules and spikes, and fissured with deep cracks that ooze a black, oily ichor.

The Visage of the Earth confers the following high-Torment special capabilities.

• **Extra Limbs:** The demon grows a second set of arms. Extra arms allow a character to parry or block close-combat attacks without sacrificing her own attack, or make up to two additional attacks of her own per turn (which are considered multiple actions).

• **Gaping Maw:** The demon's metabolism is like a blast furnace, capable of consuming virtually any material without harm. Metal, stone or flesh is chewed up and digested with ease. The difficulty of bite attacks is lowered by two, and a bite inflicts Strength +4 aggravated damage.

• **Spikes:** The demon's body is covered in sharp, stony spikes, adding two dice of aggravated damage to the Kishar's unarmed attacks.

• **Ichor:** A foul black ichor covers the demon's body, making him difficult to grab or restrain. The difficulty of any grapple attempts directed at the demon increases by two.

LORE OF PATHS

• FIND PATH

This evocation permits the Malefactor to determine if a path exists between herself and a destination that fits the criteria she requires. The path is visible to only the demon and anyone she touches, revealing itself as a faint, silver-blue line, like a ray of moonlight.

System: Your character sets the criteria for the path she seeks, and you make a Perception + Survival roll. The number of successes required depends on the criteria set and the distance covered. For example, if your character wants to find a path through a stretch of impenetrable forest or swamp, you might need only one success. If she wants a path across an open field that allows her to move unobserved, you might need two or more successes. A path that leads her unharmed through a raging house fire might require three or more successes. If the roll fails, the path cannot be found.

Torment: Monstrous demons are able to seek paths just as their more human peers can, but the difficulty for such rolls is equal to the demon's Torment. The more murderous the demon is, the less she is prepared to perform a concentrated search.

•• LAY PATH

At this level, a Malefactor doesn't have to look for a useful path. She can lay one to suit her needs, though it's not something that can be done on the spur of the moment.

System: The demon determines the criteria of the path she wishes to lay, and the distance it is to cover. You make a Dexterity + Survival roll. The difficulty of the roll increases according to the complexity of the path. A shortcut that reduces travel time, allows the user to pass unobserved, and is wide enough to permit multiple people to walk it at once is very complex, and it could have a difficulty as high as 9 or 10. You must gain a number of successes equal to the length the path covers in hundreds of yards. These successes can be gained through an extended action, but they must be gathered over successive turns. Using the previous example, if your Malefactor wanted to lay such a path between two points that were 500 yards apart, you would need to gain five successes at a difficulty of 9 or 10. The path, once laid, is visible to only the Malefactor (though successful use of the Find Path evocation can detect it like any other path), and remains usable for a number of days equal to your character's permanent Faith score. The player can make the path permanent by expending a temporary Willpower point.

Torment: Monstrous demons can lay paths as well, but the taint that becomes worked into the fabric of a trail makes the course unpredictable and dangerous. Rolls to

traverse a path laid by a monstrous demon botch on a roll of 1 or 2. A botched roll causes the traveler to exit the path at a random point along its length, determined by the Storyteller — a potentially fatal mishap if the path in question leads under a lake or through a mountain.

••• CONCEAL PATH

Paths, once formed, can be found and followed by any demon who has the eyes to look for them — unless they are camouflaged by the demon that made them.

System: Roll Perception + Survival. Any demon who attempts to find the path later must gain more successes than the Malefactor when searching for the hidden route. This concealment lasts for a number of days equal to the character's permanent Faith score, or it can be made permanent with the expenditure of a temporary Willpower point.

Torment: Monstrous demons do not hide a path so much as they lay a trap for the unwary. When the evocation is performed, the successes rolled become automatic levels of bashing damage that are inflicted on any other being that steps onto the path. This trap can be detected with a supernatural awareness roll (see p. 172), but it cannot be avoided or disarmed. Unlike the more benign form of concealment, this trap cannot be made permanent. It disappears after a number of days equal to the demon's Torment score.

•••• CLOSE PATH

This evocation allows a Malefactor to seal both ends of a path, denying its use to both friend and foe until it is opened again. Paths closed in this way are often "locked" using special words that can then be used as a kind of key to allow specific individuals access to the path while restricting others.

System: Spend one Faith point and roll Dexterity + Survival. You must gain a number of successes equal to the length the path covers in hundreds of yards, and the effort can be accomplished in an extended roll over a period of successive turns. If successful, the path is closed. If travelers walk the path at the time, they are trapped within until the demon chooses to open it again. You can spend a temporary point of Willpower and for your character to create a keyword that other demons (and thralls) can use to unlock and travel the path.

Paths closed with this power can be forced open with a successful Willpower roll. The difficulty is equal to the Willpower that the Malefactor had when he closed the path, and the roll must net a number of successes equal to the closer's Faith score at the time. Forcing open a path in this way can be done as an extended action performed over a period of turns.

Torment: Monstrous demons do not close paths — they collapse them. Again, you must gain a number of successes equal to the length the path covers in hundreds

of yards, and your character can make the effort as an extended action over a period of turns. If successful, the path collapses and is destroyed. If travelers walk the path at the time, the consequences are dire. The Storyteller rolls Dexterity + Survival for each person (difficulty 8). If a roll is successful, that victim exits the path at a random point along its length. If the roll fails, she is lost between the physical and spirit realms and begins to suffocate (refer to the drowning rules on page 263 of the System's chapter for details). The Storyteller can continue to roll for a trapped victim each minute until she escapes or is killed. If the character dies, her body does not return to the physical realm.

••••• WARP PATH

This evocation allows a Malefactor to warp the nature of an existing pathway, altering one or many of its parameters. The path can be traveled in a shorter or longer period of time, it can lead travelers back to their point of origin, it can lead to a different destination entirely, or it can simply loop back upon itself without end.

System: Spend one Faith point and roll Dexterity + Survival. If your character wishes to increase or decrease the time to travel the path, travel time is altered by a factor equal to the successes rolled. If she wants to change the destination of the path or cause it to loop back on itself, you must roll a number of successes equal to the length of the path in hundreds of yards. The duration of the effect is a number of days equal to your character's Faith score, it or can be made permanent by expending a single Willpower point.

Torment: Monstrous demons create warped paths that prey upon the minds of travelers, as well. In addition to any alterations made to the path itself, travelers crossing it must make a Willpower roll upon reaching their destination. If the roll fails, they gain a temporary derangement. If the roll botches, the derangement is permanent.

ANTU, THE VISAGE OF THE PATHS

The angels of the pathways closely resemble mortals at first glance. Their skin is deeply tanned, as though they'd spent a lifetime in the sun, and the skin around their dark eyes are deeply lined, casting their orbits in permanent shadow. It is only on closer inspection that the worry lines are revealed as intricate patterns that radiate from the angel's eyes and continue to run across the planes of her face, disappearing into her scalp and circling her throat in intricate tattoos. At night these lines reflect the moonlight in ghostly traceries that seem to shift and realign themselves as the angel speaks.

The Visage of the Paths confers the following special capabilities.

• **Dead Reckoning:** Your character is always aware of where she is in relation to known landmarks, no matter how far away those landmarks may be. Unless

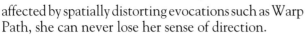

affected by spatially distorting evocations such as Warp Path, she can never lose her sense of direction.

• **Enhanced Perception**: The difficulties of all Perception rolls decrease by two.

• **Improved Initiative**: Add two to your character's initiative.

• **Flashing Fingers**: The character is capable of supernatural sleights of hand, seeming to conjure items out of thin air, only to make them vanish again with a flick of the wrist. She can draw an item from a pocket or conceal an item without detection on a successful Dexterity + Athletics roll.

Torment: Monstrous Antu cannot conceal the path lines crisscrossing their faces — they stand out as angry cuts of black and red against their tanned skin. The air shifts and trembles around them, waxing and waning depending on the intensity of their emotions.

The Visage of the Paths confers the following high-Torment special capabilities.

• **Pass Without Trace**: The difficulties of the character's Stealth rolls decrease by two, and her passage does not disturb the surrounding environment in any way. She leaves no footprints and disturbs no foliage.

• **Alter Size**: The demon can alter her physical size in order to slip through narrow gaps or crawl into impossibly small spaces. She can reduce her size to as little as a third of her original volume if desired. The difficulties of attacks directed against the miniature demon increase by two.

• **Mirage**: Air warps around the demon, creating an optical illusion that misleads an opponent as to how far away the being really is. The difficulties of all ranged attacks against the demon are increased by two, while those of close-combat attacks are increased by one. Other demons can resist these effects as they can any other illusion (see p. 171).

• **Relentless**: The demon can walk or run without need of rest, able to cover superhuman distances without pause. As long as she stays in motion she is unaffected by fatigue or hunger.

LORE OF THE FORGE

• ENHANCE OBJECT

This evocation allows a Malefactor to gain an innate understanding of an object and its intended function, simply by running her hands over it or working its moving parts. What's more, she can repair damaged objects or make adjustments that cause them to work better than before.

System: Roll Perception + Crafts. The difficulty is determined by the relative complexity of the object: A hammer is difficulty 5, while a car is difficulty 8. High-tech objects such as a computer are difficulty 10. A single success grants the demon an innate understanding of how the object is constructed and the way it works; she can operate it as though she possessed a basic familiarity with its capabilities. If the object is damaged, the demon can repair it with a single success. If she wants to improve the way it works, each success lowers the difficulty needed to use the device. This method of refinement can be done only once to any given item, and it normally lasts for the duration of the scene. The demon can make the effects permanent, if she wishes, by expending a temporary Willpower point.

Torment: Objects repaired or enhanced by a monstrous demon are tainted by the demon's hatred, infusing them with a tendency to inflict misfortune and death. On a roll of 1 or 2, such cursed items cause a botch when used. Weapons affected by this evocation strike the user or someone close to her when a botch occurs, at the Storyteller's discretion.

•• ACTIVATE OBJECT

With this evocation, the demon can cause mechanical objects to operate by simple force of will.

System: Roll Intelligence + Crafts. The difficulty is determined by the complexity of the object. Causing a door to open is difficulty 5, while making a pistol chamber a round and fire is 8. This evocation works only on objects that operate by simple, mechanical means. Hinges move, levers operate, but hammers don't pick themselves up and start banging away at nails. An elevator button could depress or a computer's power switch could turn on or off, but the inner workings of the computer's memory aren't affected. The character can affect a single object within a number of yards equal to her Faith score.

Torment: A machine affected by a monstrous demon's will often breaks or goes wildly out of control, damaging or destroying itself in the process. When making the Stamina + Crafts roll to activate the object, also apply the number of successes rolled as damage levels to the object.

••• SHAPE OBJECT

This evocation allows a Malefactor to take matter and work it with ease. A wooden board can be worked into a model ship, a plate glass window can be worked into a delicate glass crown or a steel pipe can be shaped by the Malefactor's hands into a razor-edged sword.

System: Roll Dexterity + Crafts. You must gain a number of successes depending on the complexity of the item your character wishes to create. A hammer requires one success, while a clock could require five or more. These successes can be gained through an extended action, allowing the character to work on an item, set it down and come back to it hours or even days later. The difficulty to create sophisticated machines, such as internal-combustion engines or electrical generators is 9 and could require 10 or more successes to complete. High-tech items such as computers pose a difficulty of 10 and

could require as many as 15 or more successes to complete. Items created exist permanently unless destroyed.

Torment: Objects created by monstrous demons are dangerous and unpredictable, equally capable of inflicting tragedy as they are of functioning as designed. Objects created in this fashion botch on a 1 or 2 when used, and the wielder or someone close to him suffers the consequences.

•••• ENCHANT OBJECT

This powerful evocation is the one most often associated with the angels of the earth: the ability to infuse objects with supernatural qualities that can make ordinary mortals into heroes — or monsters. Many such objects are specifically created for that purpose, but Malefactors are also adept at taking pre-existing items and infusing them with frightening new capabilities.

System: Creating an enchanted object is a laborious and expensive process, requiring substantial investments of time and energy. If the Malefactor creates the object intended for enchantment, the difficulty for performing the evocation is 6. If she works with an existing object, the difficulty is 8. To enchant an item, the demon must first possess a lore path that evokes the investiture in question. For example, if the demon wants to create a magic mirror that shows an illusion of perfect beauty to whomever looks into its depths, she needs to possess at least one dot in the Lore of Light, the path governing illusions. More complex effects could conceivably require a combination of pertinent lore. If the demon wanted the mirror to sense a mortal's deepest desire and present an illusion depicting it, he would need some measure of the Lore of Light and the Lore of Humanity. The Storyteller is the final arbiter on what lore is needed (and at what level) to create a particular object. Enchanted items draw upon the wielder's inherent belief to perform their supernatural functions. Mortals (including thralls) require a successful Willpower roll (difficulty 8) to access an object's abilities, while demons require a successful Faith roll (difficulty 6). This roll must be made each time the item is used. If either roll botches, the character loses one point of the relevant trait. Alternatively, characters can attune an object to them and create a permanent link that keeps the item energized at all times. Attuning an item thus costs one point of permanent Willpower (in the case of mortals and thralls) or 1 point of permanent Faith (in the case of demons). Once attuned, the character can use the device at will without requiring a dice roll to activate it.

If the demon possesses the required knowledge, make an extended Dexterity + Crafts roll and expend a Faith point. The number of successes required depends on the power and scope of the enchantment. A simple creation such as a knife that never loses its edge requires one success. A key that opens any lock requires five. A magic mirror that shows a mortal attaining her deepest desire requires 10. If a creation roll botches, the item is

destroyed. This evocation cannot be used on high-tech items such as computers or other electronic hardware.

Torment: Monstrous demons create cursed objects that consume the souls of their owners and wreak misery on those close to them. Cursed objects botch on a roll of 1 or 2, and the consequences of such a mishap are always directed at either the wielder or any friends or loved ones who happen to be nearby. Further, instead of making a dice roll to activate the object, mortals (including thralls) lose one point of Willpower with each use, while demons gain one point of temporary Torment.

••••• IMBUE OBJECT

While the ability to enchant objects made the Annunaki much sought after among the fallen, this evocation made them equally feared as well, allowing a Malefactor to bind a soul — mortal or demon — into a specially prepared reliquary or object.

System: Your character must prepare a suitable vessel to hold the spirit in question. This vessel must be made of natural materials and be shaped by hand. If the Malefactor made the vessel herself, the difficulty to perform the evocation is a 6. Otherwise, it's 8. With this vessel in hand, your character can use this evocation on any disinterred spirit (such as a demon stripped of its host body or a ghost) within a number of yards equal to her Faith score. Spend one Faith and roll Stamina + Crafts in a resisted roll versus the target's Willpower. If your effort is successful, the spirit is bound into the vessel. Mortal souls bound this way cannot interact with the physical world. Demons, on the other hand, can still use their inherent powers and their lore paths, provided they have available Faith. (Any existing pacts with mortal thralls remain in effect). The only way to free a soul thus bound is to destroy the vessel that contains it.

Torment: Monstrous demons who bind souls with this evocation are tainted by the Malefactor's Torment, twisting the spirits into maddened, malevolent entities. Mortal souls bound in this fashion suffer a permanent derangement, determined by the Storyteller. Fallen bound thus have their *permanent* Torment increased by the number of successes generated by the Stamina + Crafts roll used to anchor them.

MUMMU, THE VISAGE OF THE FORGE

The angels of the forge appear as giants hammered from the black iron of the earth, their powerfully muscled forms lit with veins of hot magma, and their eyes shining like disks of burnished brass. Their voices are deep and thunderous, like the roar of a furnace. When in their apocalyptic form, these fallen are immune to extremes of temperature and pressure. They can handle hot coals as mortals do ice cubes.

The Visage of the Forge confers the following special capabilities.

- **Master Artisan:** The difficulties of all Crafts rolls decrease by two.

- **Increased Size:** The character's body grows to a third again its own height, adding the following bonus traits: +2 Strength, +1 Dexterity, +1 Stamina.

- **Thunderous Voice:** The character's shout shatters glass and makes stone tremble. Individuals within a number of yards equal to the character's Faith suffer four dice of bashing damage. This ability may be used only once per scene, and it requires an action to perform.

- **Immune to Fire:** The character is immune to damage from fire.

Torment: High-Torment Mummu are nightmarish creatures of iron skin and serrated blades, surrounded by a haze of smoldering brimstone. Their eyes are twin globes of roiling fire, and wherever they go, electrical devices go berserk: lights flicker and televisions and radios are afflicted with static.

The Visage of the Forge confers the following high-Torment special capabilities.

- **Blades:** The fingers of the Mummu end in curved blades of razor-sharp iron, inflicting Strength +2 aggravated damage.

- **Extra Limbs:** The demon grows a second set of arms. Extra arms allow a character to parry or block hand-to-hand or melee attacks without sacrificing her own attack, or make up to two additional attacks of her own per turn (which are considered multiple actions).

- **Magnetic Field:** The demon is surrounded by a magnetic field intense enough to disrupt electronic devices within a radius in yards equal to the character's Faith.

- **Iron Skin:** The character's iron-like skin acts as armor, providing four additional dice to soak bashing, lethal *and* aggravated damage.

FIEND (NEBERU)

Humanity views the universe as an impossibly vast panorama of galaxies, stars and planets, each object adrift on a sea of emptiness, spreading like ripples in a pond. The Angels of the Heavens know differently — all elements of Creation, no matter how vast or insignificant, are dependent on one another in a delicate balance of power, motion and direction. It's a grand mechanism that only God could conceive, and one that the angels were ordered to monitor and maintain in perpetuity. Central to this task was the Lore of Patterns, allowing the angels of the Fourth House to study the motions of the Grand Design and predict possible problems before they occurred. Even then, the design was so large that even the Elohim could view only a small portion at any one time, leading to the creation of the Lore

of Portals — secrets that allowed the angels to travel the length and breadth of reality in the blink of an eye. Finally, like the Annunaki, whose duties would normally have kept them far from mortal eyes, the Neberu struggled to use their powers directly in the struggle against the Host of Heaven. The Lore of Light emerged during the war as the Fiends learned to use their knowledge of light — and perception — to weave potent illusions.

LORE OF PATTERNS

• SENSE CONGRUENCE

This evocation allows a Fiend to sense localities or people that are at the heart of a convergence of consequential forces. By reading the forces at work in the great design, the Fiend can use this power to always be in the right place at the right time.

System: Your character must specify what kind of event she tries to detect (e.g., the invocation of a summoning ritual, a car accident), and you roll Perception + Intuition. Your character can sense the pattern a number of days into the future equal to her Faith score. The number of successes determines how much information the Fiend receives. One shows the location where the event will occur, but not when or where. Two successes show the location and give an idea of when it will happen. Three successes show where and when the event will occur, as well as images of the people involved.

Torment: Monstrous demons are able to use this evocation to search only for impending events of violence and destruction.

•• TRACE PATTERN

This evocation allows the Fiend to view a particular event and analyze the various forces that caused it to occur. This insight comes in the form of vague impressions that sharpen into detailed images as the demon devotes her unblinking attention to them.

System: Your character must be at the location where the event in question occurred to work this evocation. Make a Perception + Intuition roll. The number of successes rolled determines how detailed the picture of a particular event is. One success depicts the immediate circumstances surrounding the event. Two reveal a few minutes preceding the event. Three successes might take the demon back a quarter of an hour to give a broader idea of the forces leading up to the event.

Torment: Monstrous Fiends can attempt to trace any pattern they wish, but they can focus on only sources of violence or injury that pertain to the event.

••• FORESEE

This potent evocation allows the Fiend to read the tides of fate in her immediate area and predict events and actions that are about to occur.

System: Rolls Wits + Intuition. The evocation takes effect for a number of turns equal to the successes rolled. This evocation protects the Fiend from being taken by surprise and takes the character out of the normal initiative system. As the other players and the Storyteller announce actions in Initiative order, you can interject your character's action at any point during the turn.

Torment: Monstrous demons are less interested in viewing the subtle shifts of patterns as they are in inflicting misery on their victims. The duration of the high-Torment version of this evocation is a single turn, but each success gives the demon a free dodge action that can be used against any attacks directed at the Fiend regardless of her own initiative.

•••• CAUSAL INFLUENCE

A Fiend can use this powerful evocation to gain insight into events up to several days into the future, and depending on her intentions, she can home in on which causal threads she must affect to achieve a desired result. It's worth noting that this power provides the demon with information only; it's up to her (or her pawns) to shift fate in her favor.

System: This evocation can be focused on a specific person (difficulty 6), place (difficulty 7) or upcoming event (difficulty 9). Spend one Faith point and roll Perception + Intuition. The number of successes rolled determines how many days into the future the Fiend can view regarding her subject. It also determines how many questions the player can ask the Storyteller about what the character sees.

The evocation fills the Fiend's mind with a torrent of images, showing the most likely fate of a specific person, place or event, barring any outside interference. The Storyteller describes the course of events as though the demon were an outside observer. She isn't privy to the thoughts of the individuals involved, and she must decide the context and meaning of relationships and actions herself. As the player listens to the Storyteller's description, however, she can ask specific questions about why a particular action happens the way it does. This can provide clues to the demon that she can then use to influence the situation.

For example, say a demon wants to observe the fate of one of her thralls. The player rolls Perception + Intuition and gets one success. She sees the events of the next day in the thrall's life and sees that he will be hit by a bus. Since the player rolled one success, she can ask one question of the Storyteller: Why does the bus hit the thrall? She then gets an image of the bus driver moments before the accident and sees that he is distracted by one of the passengers. Armed with this information, the demon can decide how she wants to try to affect the outcome according to her desires.

Torment: Monstrous demons use this evocation to gain insight into the dangers surrounding an individual, and how to manipulate these risks to *cause* injury or misfortune. The high-Torment version of this evocation shows the Fiend where the subject (be it a person, place or event) is at risk of suffering an accident or other misfortune, and it shows the best way to cause the tragic circumstances to occur.

In the example with the thrall and the bus, above, the high-Torment version of the evocation provides the same images, but the vision of the distracted driver indicates what must happen for the tragedy to occur. Because it's often difficult to tell the difference between a viewing that warns of a tragedy or that hints at causing one, the Storyteller has the option of making the Perception + Intuition roll on the player's behalf, presenting the information and letting the player decide what to do with it.

••••• TWIST TIME

This powerful evocation allows the Fiend to alter the flow of time within a small area, shifting it out of phase with the rest of the cosmos. The Fiend and anyone else within this bubble of distorted time may act faster or slower than the normal flow of the universe.

System: Spend one Faith point and roll Stamina + Intuition. The difficulty is determined by the effect the Fiend wishes to achieve. If she wants to speed time up (everything within the bubble moves faster than the world around it), the difficulty is 7. If she wants to slow time (everything within the bubble moves slower than the world around it), the difficulty is 8. If she wants to stop time (the outside world freezes in relation to the bubble) the difficulty is 9. The number of successes determines how many turns the evocation lasts. When the evocation is in effect, nothing and no one inside the bubble can interact with the world beyond, and vice versa. To the outside world, the demon and everyone within the bubble simply disappears. Within the bubble, actions may be taken as normal. Objects and individuals can exit the bubble (or be forced out), in which case they return to the normal time stream. If the Fiend herself exits the bubble, it collapses, returning the time stream to normal. Outsiders who enter the bubble's space do join its altered time unless your character wishes it.

The maximum amount of temporal distortion is determined by a multiple or factor of the character's Faith score. For example, if the Fiend performing the evocation has a Faith of 5, she could choose the distortion to be as great as five to one: five turns for every one turn spent in the bubble, or vice versa. The bubble is centered on the Fiend and has a diameter in yards equal to the character's Faith score. Once created, the bubble does not move.

Torment: Monstrous demons use this evocation to hurl unsuspecting victims out of phase with the time stream. To the victim, the experience is instantaneous and horrifying, a momentary brush with the void between realms that

System: Roll Intelligence + Intuition. The number of successes required depends on your character's familiarity with her destination. If it is somewhere with which she is intimately familiar, such as a doorway in her own home, only one success is required. If it is somewhere she has visited frequently, two successes are necessary. If the destination is somewhere that the Fiend has only recently visited for the first time, three successes are required. The demon must have visited her destination at least once before to be able to travel there with this evocation, and there must be a portal there identical to the type she enters. If she steps through a doorway, there must be a doorway at her destination. The Fiend can travel up to 100 miles for each point of Faith she has. Therefore, a Fiend with 10 Faith could travel up to a thousand miles away.

Torment: Monstrous demons performing this evocation are severely hampered by their lack of focus. If the evocation is successful, a Willpower roll must be made with a difficulty equal to the Fiend's Torment. If the roll fails, the Fiend is transported to a random (but familiar) location as determined by the Storyteller.

•••• CO-LOCATE

Akin to Teleport, this evocation allows a Fiend to use a doorway to tie two locations together for a short time, allowing others to pass through from one place to another.

System: Spend one Faith point and roll Stamina + Intuition. The difficulty is determined by your character's familiarity with the location she wishes to reach. If she is intimately familiar with the location, the difficulty is 6. If it's a location she has visited numerous times, the difficulty is 7. If she's been there only once, it's 8. If she's never been there before and goes merely by the guidance of another, the difficulty is 9. The doorway remains open for one turn per success achieved. Like Teleport, the demon must use an existing portal (doorway, window, manhole) to cross between the two locations. As many others can cross through (or back again) as may walk through the portal in the time that is available. The Fiend can travel up to 100 miles for each point of Faith she has.

Torment: Monstrous demons can create co-locations, but those passing through are momentarily exposed to the demon's Torment, and risk severe psychological trauma or madness as a result. A Willpower roll must be made for individuals passing through the portal, the difficulty of which equals the Fiend's Torment. If a roll fails, a victim gains a temporary derangement.

••••• DOORWAY INTO DARKNESS

This powerful evocation allows a demon to create a doorway into the shadowy space between the physical and spirit realms — a dark, lifeless reflection of the world. Demons can cross over into this bleak realm for

a short time or hide items from prying eyes and then retrieve them later.

System: Spend one Faith point and roll Stamina + Awareness. The evocation requires a portal — door or window — to form the threshold between realms, and the opening remains for only one turn. Individuals who pass bodily through find themselves in a bleak, desolate mirror image of the physical world, one wracked by howling winds that wear away at living minds. Mortals who cross over into this realm lose one Willpower point for each turn that they are there. Once their Willpower is gone, they gain a temporary derangement and suffer one level of bashing damage per turn that may not be soaked. Demons can remain in this shadow realm for a number of turns equal to their Faith score without ill effects. After that point, they begin to suffer bashing damage as well. This evocation must be performed again to open a doorway that allows a Fiend or another to return to the physical realm. Such a "return" opening can be created on either side.

Torment: When a monstrous demon opens a portal to the shadow lands, she risks losing focus and allowing some of the energies from beyond to slip into the physical realm. If the evocation succeeds, make a Willpower roll with the difficulty equal to the Fiend's Torment. If the roll fails, the winds of the cosmic storm seep through, causing all mortals in the immediate area to make a Willpower roll (difficulty 8). If their rolls fail, they flee in terror. If a botch results, the victims suffer a temporary derangement.

Nedu, the Visage of Portals

The angels of the threshold are tall, ethereal figures, their long limbs and lean bodies wreathed in a veil of shifting shadow. Their movements are as fluid as they are soundless, and their feet leave no impression to mark their passing. When they pass into deep shadow, their eyes shine with a cold, blue light.

The Visage of Portals confers the following special capabilities.

• **Pass Without Trace:** The difficulties of the character's Stealth rolls decrease by two, and her passage does not disturb the surrounding environment in any way. She leaves no footprints and disturbs no foliage.

• **Enhanced Perception:** The difficulties of all Perception rolls decrease by two.

• **Increased Awareness:** The fallen is especially attuned to the fabric of reality, lowering the difficulties of all Awareness rolls by two.

• **Wings:** A pair of swan's wings extends from the character's shoulders. At full extension, each wing is a third again as long as the character is tall. The character can glide up to three times her running speed per turn.

Torment: Monstrous Nedu are like living shadows, ebon and ephemeral. Their voices are like the keening of wind over jagged stones, and their touch is colder than ice.

The Visage of Portals confers the following high-Torment special capabilities.

• **Cloak of Shadows:** The demon is shrouded in a pall of darkness, making her features difficult to see in the best of light and rendering her near-invisible at night. The difficulties of all Stealth rolls decrease by two whenever the demon stands in a pool of shadow or moves in darkness. If the character is attacked, the rules for Blind Fighting apply to the attacker. See page 240 of the Systems chapter for details.

• **Improved Initiative:** Add two to the character's initiative.

• **Enhanced Dodge:** The difficulties of all Dodge rolls decrease by two.

• **Casts No Reflection:** The demon's image does not appear in a mirror, nor can it be captured in a photograph or by a video camera.

Lore of Light

• **Light**

This simple evocation allows a demon to fill an area with pale silvery light, akin to moonlight. The light seems to emanate from the area's surroundings, allowing individuals to move and act in the illuminated area without penalty. This evocation also has a more tactical application, permitting the demon to stun or disorient opponents with intense, blinding flashes.

System: Roll Stamina + Science. The evocation illuminates one cubic yard per success rolled, centered on the character. The light persists for a number of turns equal to the demon's Faith score. When used tactically, the intense flashes of light can be focused in a single direction. Any individuals, friend or foe, who look in that direction at the time of the flash suffer a number of levels of bashing damage equal to the successes rolled. Flashes of light appear for only a turn.

Torment: Monstrous demons fill their surroundings with inky, suffocating darkness, affecting an area as above. They can move unhindered though this darkness. Other individuals within the area of effect are effectively blind. Use the rules detailed on page 240 and 243 of the Systems chapter when necessary.

•• **Bend Light**

By exerting her will and manipulating the properties of light, the Fiend can bend waves around her body instead of reflecting them, giving her a powerful form of camouflage.

System: Roll Stamina + Science. The number of successes gained increases the difficulties of any Perception rolls or ranged attacks directed at the character

for the rest of the scene. Melee attacks are resolved as normal. Other demons and thralls with the capability are able to resist the effects of these illusions thanks to their inherent powers (p. 171).

Torment: Monstrous demons do not bend light so much as they distort it into crazed, eye-straining patterns. The number of successes rolled increases the difficulties of all attacks directed against the demon, ranged or otherwise, but do not affect others' Perception rolls.

••• PHANTASM

This evocation allows a Fiend to create ghostly images that perform a rote set of actions as directed by the creator.

System: Roll Intelligence + Performance — the difficulty is determined by the complexity of the illusory form created. A single, ghostly individual is difficulty 6, while a whole scene with various individuals is 8 or more. The number of successes generated determines how many actions the demon can program the image to perform. Once the image and actions are set, a loop is created that runs when the demon wishes, and that persists for a number of days equal to the character's Faith score. Other demons and thralls with the capability are able to resist the effects of these illusions thanks to their inherent powers (p. 171).

Torment: A monstrous demon's phantasms, no matter how simple or apparently benign they are, remain subtly disturbing, even on a subconscious level. A Willpower roll (difficulty 8) is made for individuals viewing one of these illusions. If a roll fails, the individual flees the area. If the roll botches, the individual flees and gains a temporary derangement.

•••• ILLUSION

This evocation is a refinement of Phantasm, allowing the demon to create images that seem completely real until touched. What's more, the demon is capable of directing her illusions and altering their appearance on the fly.

System: Spend one Faith point and roll Intelligence + Expression. The difficulty of the roll is determined by the complexity of the illusion the demon wishes to create. Creating the illusion of a static object such as a table is 6. A simple but more mobile object such as a thrown rock is difficulty 7. Living beings have a difficulty of 8 or higher depending on the level of detail. The successes rolled form a dice pool that is rolled thereafter to direct the actions of the illusion (e.g., to stage an "attack" on someone, to leap from one building to another) or alter its appearance. If a roll to direct or alter an illusion botches, the image disappears. Illusions created in this way cannot speak, and the Fiend must maintain a line of sight with a creation at all times or the

illusion disappears. A Fiend can maintain multiple illusions at the same time equal to her Faith score, but the dice pool to control each illusion is reduced by one for each extra image created after the first, to a minimum of one die per illusion. The effects of this evocation last for the duration of the scene. Other demons and thralls with the capability are able to resist the effects of these illusions thanks to their inherent powers (p. 171).

Torment: A monstrous demon's illusions are overtly unsettling, reflecting the demon's inner corruption in subtle but frightening ways. A Willpower roll (difficulty 9) must be made for individuals who witness these illusions. If a roll fails, a victim flees from the sight of the illusion. If the roll botches, he gains a temporary derangement.

••••• COHERENT LIGHT

The pinnacle of this lore path allows a Fiend to compress light to the degree that it assumes a degree of physical solidity, allowing her constructs to interact almost seamlessly with the physical world. Like Illusion, the images created by this evocation can be controlled directly by the demon, and its appearance can be altered from moment to moment.

System: Spend one Faith point and roll Intelligence + Expression. The difficulty of the roll is determined by the complexity of the illusion that your character wishes to create. A table is difficulty 6, a dog is 7, and a human is 8 or more. The successes rolled form a dice pool that is rolled thereafter to direct the actions of a construct or alter its appearance. Illusions created in this way cannot speak, and the Fiend must maintain a line of sight with the image at all times or the illusion disappears. If a construct is attacked or would otherwise suffer one health level of damage (bashing or lethal), the creation vanishes. A Fiend can maintain a number of illusions equal to her Faith score at the same time, but the dice pool to control each illusion is reduced by one for each extra image created after the first, to a minimum of one die per illusion. The effects of this evocation last for a number of turns equal to the character's Faith score. Other demons and thralls with the capability are able to resist the effects of these illusions thanks to their inherent powers (p. 171).

Torment: The constructs fashioned by a monstrous demon are shaped in part by her hatred and despair, and unless they are controlled carefully, the illusions act on their own, lashing out destructively at their surroundings. A Willpower roll must be made each turn for each construct, with the difficulty equal to the Fiend's Torment score. If a roll fails, an illusion attacks the nearest living being (save the Fiend herself) using its full dice pool. Note that the Fiend doesn't have to exert control over her constructs — she can simply

create them and turn them loose on her enemies if she wishes, leaving her mind free for other tasks.

Shamash, the Visage of Light

The apocalyptic form of the masters of this lore paints a demon in shifting patterns of shadow and pale, silvery starlight. These hypnotic images draw the eye and beguile the senses, at times hinting at subtle flashes that reflect the demon's inner thoughts. The Shamash are alluring, chimerical, deceptive, terrifying or achingly beautiful, often from moment to moment.

The Visage of Light confers the following special capabilities.

• **Enhanced Mental Acuity:** The character receives the following bonus traits: +2 Intelligence, +1 Wits, +1 Perception.

• **Night Sight:** The character can see clearly in utter darkness.

• **Chimerical Aura:** The difficulties of all Dodge rolls decrease by two. Other demons and thralls with the capability are able to resist the effects of this benefit thanks to their inherent powers (p. 171).

• **Unearthly Glamour:** The difficulties of all Manipulation rolls decrease by two. Other demons and thralls with the capability are able to resist the effects of this effect as well.

Torment: Shamash who lose themselves to their Torment are surrounded by chimerical forms that reflect the demons' hatred and despair, creating a horror show of monstrous apparitions that whirl and snap at one another in increasing ferocity depending on a being's mood.

The Visage of Light confers the following high-Torment special capabilities.

• **Hypnotic Visions:** The aura of light and shadow surrounding the demon distracts and disquiets the mind of her foe. Attackers must make a Wits roll against a difficulty of the demon's Torment score. If the roll fails, the attackers may not act until the end of the turn. Other demons and thralls with the capability are able to resist the effects of these illusions thanks to their inherent powers.

• **Dread Mien:** The difficulties of all Leadership and Intimidation rolls decrease by two.

• **Chimerical Attack:** The swirling illusions surrounding the demon attack others already engaged in close combat with the fallen. The chimerical figures have the same initiative as the demon, and they attack a single opponent in close-combat range. Use the demon's Torment score as the dice pool for the attack, inflicting a base damage of four aggravated damage dice.

• **Casts No Reflection:** The demon's image does not appear in a mirror, nor can it be captured in a photograph or by a video camera.

The mercurial angels of the deep were meant from the beginning to lead a lonely existence, close enough to inspire human hearts, yet eternally out of reach. The Lore of Longing, with its power to enflame human hearts, was the core of the House's collected wisdom, but mastery of wind and wave also led to the evolution of the Lore of Storms, allowing the angels of the deep to reach far over dry land as well. Ironically, once the Lammasu had forsaken their oath to Heaven and were able to show themselves openly to mankind, the rebels found themselves ill-equipped to relate directly with humanity. They were far more comfortable showing men and women the faces that they wanted to see rather than risk being viewed for what they truly were. Therefore, these mutable spirits refined the art of transforming their appearance at will to suit the expectations of those around them, and the Lore of Transfiguration emerged.

Lore of Longing

• **Read Emotion**

This evocation allows the Defiler to draw a person's deep-seated emotions to the surface, allowing the demon to gain greater insight into the subject's thoughts and desires by studying her body language and expressions. The victim is completely unaware that she is being "studied" in this way. To her, it is as if the Defiler is reading her mind.

System: This evocation works on only one mortal at a time. Roll Perception + Empathy. Each success is a bonus die added to all Social rolls directed at the mortal for the duration of the scene, or until the demon switches her attention to a new victim.

Torment: Monstrous demons are more adept at drawing out a victim's dark nature and fueling it in the process. The subject comes away from an exchange entertaining thoughts she hadn't dared contemplate before. A resisted Willpower roll is made for mortals targeted by the high-Torment effect of this evocation, with the difficulty equal to the Defiler's Torment score. If the roll fails, the mortal is driven to act on her darkest desires (making her boss pay for all the years of verbal abuse, for example, or entertaining the affair with a co-worker she's resisted for so long). The effects of this evocation last a number of days equal to the Defiler's Faith score.

• • **Empathetic Response**

This evocation permits the demon to read a subject's emotions and desires and react to them without thinking, molding her behavior to conform perfectly to the subject's expectations. The subject thinks the demon is

everything she expected or dreamed of, banishing any suspicion, hesitation or fear.

System: Roll Manipulation + Empathy. If your total successes equal or exceed a mortal's Wits score, the mortal reacts to your character with complete trust, obeying any reasonable request your character makes. This evocation can be directed at only a single individual at a time. The effects last for the duration of the scene or until your demon turns his attention to a new victim.

Torment: Monstrous demons use this evocation to inspire fear instead of affection. They mold their behavior to speak to a victim's worst fears, becoming the type of person that the mortal dreads most. If your successes equal or exceed the target's Wits, the mortal is completely intimidated by your Defiler. She takes no action against your character, and she leaves the area if at all possible. Any Intimidation rolls directed at the target are resolved with a difficulty of 4.

••• Manipulate Senses

With a touch, a Defiler can manipulate a person's nerves, enhancing perceptions and heightening sensation. The effect can be as broad or as subtle as the demon wishes, and the effects are often addictive unless the victim possesses a will of iron.

System: The Defiler must be able to touch her intended target to use this evocation. Roll Intelligence + Intuition. Each success adds one bonus die to the target's Perception rolls, but by the same token, all wound penalties the target suffers are similarly increased. Demons can resist the effects of this evocation if they wish by making a resisted Willpower roll (difficulty 7). The effects of this evocation last for a number of turns equal to the Defiler's Faith score. After the effects of the evocation wear off, a Willpower roll must be made for the target. If it fails, take the number of bonus dice the evocation generated and apply them as a *penalty* to all the mortal's Perception rolls for the remainder of the scene. If the roll botches, this penalty is permanent. In the case of a botch, the victim is addicted to the thrill of the evocation and can regain full use of her senses only by receiving the power's effects again.

Torment: Monstrous demons use this evocation to inflict searing agony or to warp the awareness of their victims. Subtract the total number of successes achieved from the victim's Perception dice pools for a number of turns equal to the Defiler's Faith score.

•••• Obsession

This evocation allows a demon to take one of a subject's interests or desires and heighten its allure to the point that the victim can think of nothing else. This obsession can be about a person, an idea or a project. During the War of Wrath, many Defilers used their wiles to become objects of desire to mortals, and then used this evocation to create legions of fanatically loyal followers.

System: To enact this evocation, the demon must first know one of her victim's long-held interests or desires and be within a number of yards of the subject equal to her Faith rating. Spend one Faith point and roll Manipulation + Empathy. The mortal can attempt to resist the evocation's effects with a Willpower roll (difficulty 8). If your roll succeeds, the mortal's desire becomes a source of obsession. He knows no peace unless he takes reasonable steps to make his desire a reality. A Willpower roll (difficulty 7) is made for him to undertake any action that strays from his obsession, and he is not able to eat or sleep until his desire is fulfilled. This evocation lasts for a number of days equal to the Defiler's Faith score, or until the mortal succeeds in sating his obsession, whichever comes first.

Torment: Monstrous demons use this evocation to make a victim psychotically obsessive, removing all inhibitions and exaggerating the victim's need to the point of physical pain. The victim does *anything* within his power to fulfill his desire, no matter how destructive or dangerous it is. Failing to do so reduces all dice pools by one until the subject can make a constructive effort toward his goal.

••••• Inspire

This potent evocation literally expands a subject's consciousness, permitting him to achieve heights of insight and awareness that border on the inhuman. The subject is able to draw upon the fullness of his mental potential, but when the power fades, the return to reality can be a blow for the person's sense of self-worth.

System: Spend one Faith point and roll Intelligence + Medicine. Each success allows you to add a point to a mortal's Mental or Social Traits, up to a five-point maximum. These bonus points persist for a number of days equal to the Defiler's Faith score. When the effects of the evocation wear off, however, the mortal loses one point of Willpower *permanently* unless a successful Willpower roll is made (difficulty 7).

Torment: Monstrous demons use this evocation in a similar fashion, but they push the victim over the edge from genius to madness, creating talented but dangerous lunatics. The high-Torment effect of this evocation provides bonus points to Mental or Social Traits *and* causes a temporary derangement. If the subsequent Willpower roll fails, the mortal loses a Willpower point permanently and the derangement becomes permanent.

Ishhara, the Visage of Longing

The angels of inspiration are visions of beauty, compared to whom even the radiant angels of the Namaru pale. Their golden hair and perfectly sculpted features are the romantic ideal spoken of in mortal poetry and prose, and their honeyed voices melt even the hardest hearts.

The Visage of Longing confers the following special capabilities.

• **Enhanced Social Traits**: The character's physical appearance, poise and grace leave humans in

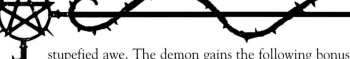

stupefied awe. The demon gains the following bonus traits: +2 Charisma, +1 Manipulation, +2 Appearance.

• **Lyrical Voice**: The difficulties of all Leadership or Subterfuge rolls decrease by two.

• **Enhanced Senses**: The character's five senses are heightened to superhuman levels, lowering the difficulties of Perception rolls by two.

• **Enhanced Intuition**: The character's uncanny insight lowers the difficulties of all Intuition rolls by two.

Torment: Monstrous Ishhara retain all of their dazzling beauty. If anything, their allure only deepens with the hint of shadowed malice that darkens their eyes and deepens their voices. What was once a source of inspiration is now a siren song that lures mortals to ruin.

The Visage of Longing confers the following high-Torment special capabilities.

• **Claws**: The character manifests claws that inflict Strength +2 aggravated damage.

• **Venom**: The claws and saliva of the Ishhara are poisonous. Targets exposed to the venom (either by a claw mark or a simple kiss) are subject to a dice pool of bashing damage equal to the demon's Torment. This damage can be soaked.

• **Extra Limbs**: The demon grows a second set of arms or a set of tentacles, at the player's discretion. Extra limbs allow a character to parry or block close-combat attacks without sacrificing her own attack, or make up to two additional attacks of her own per turn (which are considered multiple actions).

• **Casts No Reflection**: The demon's image does not appear in a mirror, nor can it be captured in a photograph or by a video camera.

LORE OF STORMS

• SUMMON WATER

The demon can summon water from any nearby source, causing anything from a sudden, concealing fog to a torrential flash flood.

System: Roll Stamina + Survival. The number of successes required depends on the amount of water the Defiler wishes to summon. If the demon wants to call up a thick fog (increasing the difficulty of all Perception rolls by two), one success is sufficient. If she wants to douse the area with a sudden shower, two successes are required. If she wants a torrent of water, three successes are necessary. A raging flood demands four successes or more. Individuals caught in such a torrent or flood suffer the effects of drowning (see page 263 of the Systems chapter for details) unless a successful Dexterity + Athletics (difficulty 8) roll is made. There has to be a water source of some kind within Faith in yards, no matter how small, for this evocation to work. The effects of this evocation continue for a number of turns equal to the character's Faith score.

Torment: The water that a monstrous demon summons is slimy and foul, spreading sickness and disease. Victims exposed to this polluted water risk developing deadly diseases that manifest within days or weeks. Mortals and demons exposed to this tainted water for more than one turn risk becoming infected unless a Stamina roll is made, with the difficulty equal to the Defiler's Torment. Also use the Defiler's Torment to gauge the relative virulence of any diseases. A Torment score of 7 inflicts a minor disease that might lower the character's dice pools, while a Torment of 10 imposes a lethal (and possibly highly contagious) disease that inflicts lethal damage. For more information on diseases and their effects, see page 262 of the Systems chapter.

•• WATER FORM

This evocation allows the Defiler to transform her physical body into water, either as a liquid or a mist.

System: Roll Stamina + Medicine. Once transformed, the character leaves her clothes and possessions behind. She can travel anywhere water or air can reach while in water or mist form, and she is immune to any damage. The Defiler can remain in this form for a number of turns equal to her Faith score.

Torment: The water form of a monstrous demon is polluted by its Torment, and contact with it causes chemical burns. For each turn that a victim is exposed to the Defiler's "body," she suffers one health level of lethal damage.

••• MANIPULATE WEATHER

This evocation allows the Defiler to nudge existing weather patterns, pushing away storm fronts or drawing them to her with surprising speed, and altering the local temperatures.

System: Roll Intelligence + Science. The number of successes achieved determines the severity of the weather pattern that the Defiler can manipulate. Affecting a minor rainstorm requires only one success, while affecting a thunderstorm requires two. Major storms require three successes to manipulate, and truly powerful phenomena such as tornadoes or hurricanes require four or more. Alternatively, the Defiler can raise or lower the temperature in her area by a degree per success rolled. This evocation affects an area with a radius in miles equal to the demon's Faith score. Note that all weather manipulated must be present. This power cannot spontaneously create new weather effects.

Torment: Monstrous demons increase the intensity of local weather patterns rather than alter their course, turning a spring shower into a raging tornado or a light snowfall into a blizzard.

•••• COMMAND THE STORM

A Defiler can use this evocation to create weather patterns at will, conjuring a storm out of thin air or banishing a hurricane with a wave of her hand.

System: Spend one Faith and roll Intelligence + Science. The difficulty is determined by the environment and the type of weather the Defiler wishes to create. Calling up a thunderstorm near the ocean is difficulty 6. Creating one in the middle of the Arizona desert is difficulty 9. Banishing existing weather patterns is resolved with a difficulty of 7. The number of successes rolled determines the intensity of the weather pattern that the Defiler can create or calm. A rain shower or a light snowfall requires only one success, while a tornado or a massive hurricane requires four or more. This evocation affects an area with a radius in miles equal to the demon's Faith score. Once summoned, the weather effect runs its natural course unless affected by additional evocations.

Torment: Monstrous demons can command the weather with equal ease, but their effects are always inimical. Storms bring damaging wind, hail and lighting. Even creating clear skies can invoke extreme temperature changes or suffocating humidity.

••••• INVOKE THE STORM

The Defiler can surround herself with a raging storm at will, creating wind, water and lighting in an area as small as a room or as large as a city block. The heart of the storm is centered on the demon, and it moves as she moves. It causes her no harm, though.

System: Spend one Faith point and roll Stamina + Survival. The difficulty is determined by the environment

the Defiler is in. Conjuring a storm outside, with rain clouds overhead, is difficulty 6. Conjuring a storm in the air-conditioned environment of an office is difficulty 9. The successes form a dice pool that you roll while your character directs the effect of the storm. If she wishes to use wind to knock someone down or blow open doors and windows, roll this dice pool in lieu of Strength. If she wants to fire lightning at a target, roll the pool against a difficulty of 9. Each success generates one lightning bolt that strikes the target automatically and imposes a number of lethal damage dice equal to the Defiler's Torment score. The storm affects an area with a radius in yards equal to the character's Faith score and lasts for an equal number of turns unless banished.

Torment: Monstrous Defilers raise storms that lash out indiscriminately at any living being caught in the area, punishing them with fierce winds and lightning. Each turn, roll a single die (difficulty 9) for each person within the storm's radius. If a roll is successful, someone is struck with a bolt of lightning. Furthermore, the buffeting winds increase the difficulties of all subjects' actions by two.

ADAD, THE VISAGE OF STORMS

The angels of the storm are tall, statuesque figures, their skins glistening like opal and their dark hair tinged with the deep green of the ocean depths. Blue flickers of ball lightning writhe and dance across their bodies, forming an angry nimbus surrounding their head and shoulders when their fury is aroused.

The Visage of Storms confers the following special capabilities.

• **Weather Sense:** The character can always intuitively sense changes in the weather up to a distance of 10 miles times her Faith score.

• **Immune to Electricity:** The character is immune to damage inflicted by electrocution.

• **Improved Initiative:** Add two to the character's initiative.

• **Shocking Touch:** The character's touch inflicts a number of bashing levels of damage equal to her Faith score. This special capability may be used only once per scene.

Torment: Angels of the storm who lose themselves to their demonic nature develop a rough, gray hide and triple rows of razor-edged teeth. Their eyes are featureless black orbs, devoid of warmth or compassion.

The Visage of Storms confers the following high-Torment special capabilities.

• **Teeth:** The demon manifests fangs that inflict Strength +2 aggravated damage.

• **Spines:** A long ruff of spines runs down the demon's back and along the backs of her arms. She inflicts an additional health level of aggravated damage with every successful attack in unarmed combat.

• **Shark Hide:** The demon's shark-like skin acts as armor, providing four additional dice to soak bashing, lethal *and* aggravated damage.

• **Ink Cloud:** The demon can expel a cloud of indigo ink that hangs in the air and blinds her foes. Individuals within a number of feet equal to the demon's Faith score are blinded for a number of turns equal to the demon's Torment, unless a successful Stamina roll is made. The cloud of ink lingers for a number of turns equal to the demon's Torment. Victims are subject to the Blind Fighting rules on p. 240.

LORE OF TRANSFIGURATION

• MIMIC

This evocation allows the Defiler to assume the exact mannerisms and vocal patterns of a subject, allowing her to disguise herself enough to fool a distant observer.

System: This evocation requires the Defiler to have spent at least an hour in close company with the individual she seeks to mimic. Roll Manipulation + Performance in a resisted roll against another person's Perception + Alertness. If you get more successes, the target believes that the Defiler is the person she attempts to mimic. Encountering someone who has never met the mimicked subject succeeds automatically. The effects of this evocation last for a number of turns equal to the character's Faith score. There

is no illusion at work here — your character's body actually changes — so other demons may be fooled with this power.

Torment: Monstrous demons can mimic the voice and mannerisms of others, but their Torment invariably bleeds through the disguise and unsettles any witnesses, inspiring feelings of discomfort and paranoia. Roll Willpower for someone who encounters the disguised demon, with a difficulty equal to the Defiler's Torment. If the roll fails, the mortal is so unsettled by the Defiler's presence that she flees the demon's presence.

•• ALTER APPEARANCE

The Defiler can use this evocation to alter cosmetic features of herself or others. She can change eye color, hair color, skin color and remove scars.

System: Roll Charisma + Subterfuge. The Defiler can alter one cosmetic feature per success rolled. The alterations remain for a number of turns equal to the Defiler's Faith score, or they can be made permanent by the expenditure of one Willpower point. Your character must touch a subject if another being is changed. There is no illusion at work here — your character's body or that of another actually changes — so other demons may be fooled with this power.

Torment: Monstrous demons can alter the features of themselves or others almost, but unless they maintain strict control, their Torment can cause disturbing deformities. When your character performs this evocation successfully, make a Willpower roll with a difficulty equal to his Torment. If the roll fails, he or his subject suffers a subtle but unsettling deformity. The difficulties of all Social rolls increase by two due to this deformity.

••• ALTER SHAPE

The Defiler can alter his own physical shape and dimensions, increasing or decreasing height, weight, shoulder width and girth.

System: Roll Charisma + Subterfuge. The Defiler can alter one physical feature per success rolled. Alterations persist for a number of turns equal to the Defiler's Faith score, can be dismissed prematurely or can be made permanent by the expenditure of one Willpower point. There is no illusion at work here — your character's body actually changes — so other demons may be fooled with this power.

Torment: Monstrous demons are capable of performing the same evocation, but the potential exists for deformities to warp their appearance. When your character performs this evocation successfully, roll Willpower against a difficulty equal to his Torment. If the roll fails, the Defiler suffers a crippling deformity and losing one point from a Physical Attribute for the duration of the evocation. You choose which Attribute is affected.

•••• DOPPELGANGER

This evocation allows the Defiler to alter her appearance completely, based on the expectations of her victim. She assumes the form of the person that the victim expects or wants to see.

System: Spend one Faith point and roll Manipulation + Empathy. The roll is resisted by the target's Willpower (difficulty 8). If your roll succeeds, your character assumes the physical form, voice and mannerisms of a person whom the victim expects to see within the context of the scene. If you wish, your demon can dig deeper into the victim's memories and assume the form of a specific individual for whom that the victim has strong feelings, but doing so increases the difficulty of your roll to 8. If your character attempts to use this evocation on a group of individuals, assuming a form that all of them might expect to see in a given situation, the difficulty increases to 9. The effects of this evocation last for a number of turns equal to your character's Faith score, unless terminated prematurely. There is no illusion at work here — your character's body actually changes — so other demons may be fooled with this power.

Torment: When monstrous Defilers perform this evocation, the result is a dark, sinister version of the victim's expectations. The difficulties of all Social rolls to manipulate the subject *decrease* by two as any inappropriate feelings or urges that the onlooker has toward the demon may be indulged.

● ● ● ● ● Shapechange

This evocation gives the Defiler complete mastery over the physical features of herself or others. She can transform herself or someone else into the apex of human beauty. She can also condemn those who displease her to a nightmare of twisted flesh.

System: Spend one Faith point and roll Intelligence + Medicine. Your character must touch a subject. A resisted Willpower roll (difficulty 8) is made for a target who refuses the change. If your roll succeeds, your character can alter her (or another's) physical appearance to anything she wishes. If she wants to alter another person's appearance to meet their own specific desires (as opposed to a willing subject's), the difficulty increases to 7. The Appearance Attribute is increased or decreased by one per success achieved in your roll, within the limits of 5 and zero for a mortal. Your character's or a subject's other Attributes and Abilities remain the same, no matter what shape is assumed. The effects of this evocation last for a number of turns equal to your Defiler's Faith score, or they can be made permanent by expending one temporary Willpower point. There is no illusion at work here — the body actually changes — so other demons may be fooled with this power.

Torment: Monstrous demons must exercise careful control when performing this evocation, or they risk creating a reflection of their Torment instead. If the evocation is performed successfully, make a Willpower roll with the difficulty equal to your character's Torment. If the roll fails, the subject assumes the form of a hideous monster. Mortals who witness this nightmarish figure flee in terror without a successful Willpower roll (difficulty 8). If a Willpower roll botches, the witness suffers a temporary derangement.

Mammetum, the Visage of Transfiguration

The angels of transfiguration reveal themselves as luminescent figures devoid of identifying feature or expression, haunting in their silence and deliberate grace. Their entire body is a mirror reflecting the moods and thoughts of those around them, shifting like quicksilver amid a riot of conflicting feelings and expressions.

The Visage of Transfiguration confers the following special capabilities.

• **Enhanced Empathy:** The difficulties of all Empathy rolls decrease by two.

• **Casts No Reflection:** The demon's image does not appear in a mirror, nor can it be captured in a photograph or by a video camera.

• **Pass Without Trace:** The difficulties of the character's Stealth rolls decrease by two, and her passage does not disturb the surrounding environment in any way. She leaves no footprints and disturbs no foliage.

• **Improved Dexterity:** Add two to the character's Dexterity.

Torment: Angels of transfiguration who are lost to their Torment lose their luminescence, reflecting their pain and hatred in a series of horrific visions of the Abyss. The creature is a walking panorama of tortured spirits clawing silently at the wall separating them from the physical world.

The Visage of Transfiguration confers the following high-Torment special capabilities.

• **Claws/Teeth:** The character manifests claws and fangs that inflict Strength +2 aggravated damage.

• **Improved Initiative:** Add two to the demon's initiative.

• **Venom:** The demon's claws and teeth are coated with venom. If the Defiler inflicts at least one health level of damage (bashing, lethal or aggravated) in an unarmed attack, a Stamina roll (difficulty 7) is made for the victim every turn thereafter for a number of turns equal to the Defiler's Torment score. If a roll fails, the victim suffers one additional health level of lethal damage.

• **Extra Actions:** Faith points can be spent to gain extra actions in a turn at the rate of one point per action. These actions occur in order of descending initiative, so if a Defiler with an initiative of 7 gains an extra action, she take her normal action at 7 and her extra action at 6. You must decide to purchase extra actions at the beginning of a turn before any other actions have been taken.

DEVOURER
(Rabisu)

The lords of wood and claw were made to rule the wild things of the world, shaping flora and fauna according to the Creator's plan and shaping each one's role in a complex and dynamic ecology. The Lore of the Beast defined their mastery of animal, fish and fowl, allowing them to summon, command and shape the bodies of their subjects, while the Lore of the Wild comprised the collected secrets of forest and field. The Lore of the Flesh came later, during the war, as the Rabisu turned their arts to shaping human flesh for the fury of the battlefield.

LORE OF THE BEAST

• SUMMON ANIMALS

This evocation allows the Devourer to detect the presence of animal life in the surrounding area and to summon those creatures to his side. These animals instinctively protect the demon.

System: Roll Perception + Animal Ken. If your roll succeeds, your character gets a detailed sense of the varied animal life in her area, from insects to mammals. The Devourer's awareness extends in a radius in miles equal to her Faith score. Armed with this knowledge, the Devourer can choose which animals of a single type she wishes to summon, up to the number of successes rolled. If the Devourer wishes to summon a swarm of vermin or insects, instead, the number of successes rolled determines the number of square yards that the swarm covers. These animals flock to the Devourer's side as quickly as possible and circle her protectively, attacking anyone who threatens. The effects of this evocation last for the duration of the scene or until the demon frees the animals.

Torment: Monstrous demons can summon only carnivorous animals, their Torment driving the creatures into a murderous frenzy. A Willpower roll must be made each turn with a difficulty equal to the Devourer's Torment. If the roll fails, the animals turn on the nearest human or demon, including the Devourer himself. The Devourer can attempt to regain control of frenzied animals with another Willpower roll in a subsequent turn.

•• COMMAND ANIMALS

This evocation extends the Devourer's influence over the beasts of the earth, allowing her to command one or more animals to do her bidding.

System: Roll Manipulation + Animal Ken. The Devourer can command a number of animals equal to the successes you roll. The animals must be in her presence already for this power to work. The evocation enhances the intelligence of these animals, as well. Assume that the creatures have an effective Intelligence of 1, though exceptional breeds may have ratings of 2 at the Storyteller's discretion. The Devourer does not have to speak to the animals to issue commands. Instead, she imparts her desires by placing them directly in the animals' minds. The effects of this evocation last for a single day.

Torment: Monstrous demons can command only carnivorous animals, and the weight of the demon's Torment makes them murderously aggressive. Unless they are in the Devourer's presence, they attack any mortal or demon they encounter if they fail an Intelligence roll (difficulty 7).

••• POSSESS ANIMALS

The demon is capable of possessing one or more animals and acting through them as an extension of her will. During the War of Wrath, many Devourers went to war possessing entire packs of terrible beasts that wrought havoc among the Host's human allies.

System: Roll Intelligence + Animal Ken. The Devourer can control a number of animals equal to the successes rolled. If this number is greater than the demon's Wits, her mortal body falls into a comatose state. Otherwise, she can still move and act with all her dice pools halved. Your character can control the animals up to a number of miles equal to her Faith score. This evocation lasts for a number of turns equal to your character's Faith score.

Torment: Monstrous demons can possess only carnivores, and Devourers must exercise iron will to avoid losing themselves to the feral nature of their hosts. Make a Willpower roll each turn, with a difficulty equal to the Devourer's Torment. If a roll fails, your demon succumbs to the animals' instincts. Her mind is subsumed completely into their will, and control of the character (and her animals) passes to the Storyteller until the evocation expires. If the roll botches, the evocation expires and the demon herself takes on the nature and instincts of the animals, becoming feral in her own behavior.

•••• ANIMAL FORM

The Devourer can take the form of any animal whose blood or flesh she has tasted. Conservation of mass does not apply, so a 95-pound woman can become an 800-pound tiger if the demon desires.

System: Spend one Faith point and roll Stamina + Animal Ken. If successful, the transformation takes a single turn. The effects of this evocation last for the duration of the scene, unless intentionally terminated prematurely.

Torment: Monstrous Devourers must exercise iron will to avoid losing themselves to the feral nature of the creatures they become. Make a Willpower roll each turn, with a difficulty equal to the Devourer's Torment. If the

roll fails, the demon succumbs to the feral instincts of the animal form she has assumed, and control of the character passes to the Storyteller until the evocation expires.

●●●●● CREATE CHIMERA

The Devourer is capable of manipulating an animal's physical body, enhancing its capabilities or mutating it into a hideous, fantastic creature that combines characteristics of numerous different animals.

System: Spend one Faith point and roll Intelligence + Animal Ken. Each success allows the Devourer to add one point to a specific trait, or to alter a specific feature of the animal's physical form. The laws of physics and the conservation of mass do not apply, so if the Devourer wants to make a winged tiger, she can. Too much change too fast can put a tremendous strain on the animal's psyche, though. Total up the number of trait points and alterations that have been added to the animal and make a Willpower roll for your character. If you get more successes than the total number of modifications applied, the animal comes through the process unharmed. If the roll fails, the animal becomes dangerously unstable. The Storyteller determines the specifics of the animal's altered behavior, and in the interests of creating tension can make the Willpower roll on your behalf, keeping the result secret until the animal's true nature manifests. The effects of this evocation last for a number of days equal to your character's Faith score, or can be made permanent with the expenditure of one Willpower point.

Torment: Monstrous demons invariably infuse their creations with the taint of their own Torment, creating pain-maddened, murderous beasts. No Willpower roll is necessary to determine the mental state of these creatures. They are invariably deranged, rabid beasts that exist only to kill and maim the living.

ZALTU, THE VISAGE OF THE BEAST

The angels of the hunt are fearsome in their strength and majesty, stalking invisibly through the darkness with panther-like strength and supple grace. The physical appearances of these fallen are many and varied, but most are powerfully muscled and covered in a pelt of fur, with large, golden eyes that glow like coals in the moonlight. They speak in a low, liquid rumble, and their howls chill the blood for miles when they hunt.

The Visage of the Beast confers the following special capabilities.

• **Increased Size:** The character's body grows to a third again its own height, adding the following bonus traits: +2 Strength, +2 Dexterity, +1 Stamina.

• **Enhanced Senses:** The character's five senses are heightened to superhuman levels, lowering the difficulties of her Perception rolls by two.

• **Claws/Teeth:** The character manifests claws and fangs that inflict Strength +2 aggravated damage.

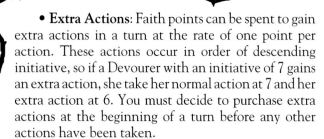

• **Extra Actions**: Faith points can be spent to gain extra actions in a turn at the rate of one point per action. These actions occur in order of descending initiative, so if a Devourer with an initiative of 7 gains an extra action, she take her normal action at 7 and her extra action at 6. You must decide to purchase extra actions at the beginning of a turn before any other actions have been taken.

Torment: Zaltu who are lost to their Torment look emaciated and diseased, their fur missing in patches or matted with filth or blood. Flecks of foam drip from their gaping jaws, and their skin thickens into a tough hide of gristle and nerveless flesh.

The Visage of the Beast confers the following high-Torment special capabilities.

• **Thick Hide**: The character's iron-like skin acts as armor, providing an additional four dice to soak bashing, lethal *and* aggravated damage.

• **Gaping Maw**: The demon can chew and digest anything it can get its teeth on. Metal, stone and flesh can all be ground up and digested with ease. The difficulties of bite attacks decrease by two, and a bite itself inflicts Strength +4 aggravated damage.

• **Extra Limbs**: The demon grows a second set of arms or a prehensile tail, at the player's discretion. Extra arms allow a character to parry or block close-combat attacks without sacrificing her own attack, or to make up to two additional attacks of her own per turn (which are considered multiple actions). A prehensile tail is half your character's height, uses only half his Strength (rounded down) to lift objects and allows your character to hang suspended.

• **Chameleon Skin**: The demon's skin allows it to blend with its surroundings. The difficulties of all Stealth rolls decrease by one if the demon is on the move; two if it's standing still.

LORE OF THE WILD

• WILDERNESS SENSE

The Devourer gains an immediate sense of the surrounding area, building a map in her mind of the region's natural features, the plants and animals that inhabit the place, as well as the location of any interlopers that the local fauna consider a threat.

System: Roll Perception + Survival. Demons in the area can attempt to avoid detection through a resisted Willpower roll (difficulty 7). If your roll succeeds, your character gets a detailed mental map of her surroundings to which she can refer as needed, along with the approximate locations of nearby animals and people. Although this evocation works best in wilderness areas, it can also be used in urban settings at a difficulty of 8. Your Devourer can gain insight into a given area within a radius of miles equal to her Faith score. The effects of the evocation last for the duration of the scene.

Torment: Monstrous demons who perform this evocation transmit their murderous nature to the surrounding area, causing the flora and fauna to react inimically to human trespassers. Any animals in the area react aggressively to trespassers, attacking them if they are able. Athletics or Survival rolls must be made for intruders to avoid harm or to escape attack, using the Devourer's Torment score as the difficulty.

•• QUICKEN GROWTH

The Devourer can fuel rapid and unchecked growth in the local plant life. Trees shoot skyward, vines swell, fissures spread through any object to which they are rooted and briars envelop their surroundings.

System: Roll Stamina + Survival. The Devourer focuses on a specific plant and causes it to increase in size by a number of cubic yards equal to the successes you rolled, all within the space of a single turn. Vines or roots inflict a like number of damage points to physical structures with which they are in contact (consider each success a Strength point and compare the results to the Feats of Strength chart on p. 232). Objects caught within the growth radius are swallowed up. The plant remains overgrown and causes damage for a number of turns equal to the successes you rolled.

Torment: Monstrous demons cause a plant to grow and entwine any living beings within reach, strangling or ripping them apart. For every living being within the plant's growth area, roll a number of dice equal to your Devourer's Willpower. Treat this as a grapple attempt, which victims can attempt to parry or dodge as normal. If the attack is successful, roll a number of damage dice equal to the Devourer's Torment. Each success inflicts a level of lethal damage.

••• COMMAND THE WILD

The Devourer can direct the rapid growth of local plants by force of will, affecting the environment in specific ways according to the demon's plan.

System: Roll Intelligence + Survival. Your character can affect a number of plants equal to her Faith score. Each plant grows a number of cubic yards equal to the successes you rolled, and expands in the direction and configuration specified by your character. If plant growth is directed at a specific structure, take the number of successes rolled and compare them to the Feats of Strength chart on page 232 of the Systems chapter to determine the damage inflicted on objects.

Torment: In addition to directing their growth, monstrous demons cause the affected plants to become inimical to flesh and blood, sprouting needle-like thorns and poisonous sap. The exact manifestation is determined by the Storyteller, but a successful Dexterity + Athletics (or Survival) roll must be made for anyone attempting to move through the area, lest they suffer a number of dice of lethal damage equal to the demon's Torment.

•••• POSSESS PLANT

The demon can take over the living essence of one or more plants, making them extensions of his will. The plants move with supernatural speed and strength, performing any action the Devourer desires.

System: Spend one Faith point and roll Stamina + Survival. The Devourer can control a number of plants equal to the successes rolled. Plants affected by this evocation must remain rooted in place, but they can perform any other action within the limits of their physical composition and size. A rose bush can entangle a victim, or ivy can pull apart the wall to which it's anchored. The effects of the evocation last for the duration of the scene. Consider the plants to have a Strength score equal to your demon's Willpower and refer to the Feats of Strength chart (p. 232) to determine the damage the plants can do to items. That same number of dice is used to make attack and damage rolls when the plants attack living targets, doing bashing damage.

Torment: Monstrous Devourers spread the taint of their Torment through any plants they control, destroying them from within and reducing them to lifeless husks within minutes. Each possessed plant suffers one health level of damage per turn that cannot be soaked. As a rule of thumb, assume that a given plant has one "health level" per cubic foot of volume. When all the plant's health levels have been consumed, the plant dies.

••••• MUTATE PLANT

The Devourer can manipulate a plant's composition and form at will, creating new, specialized breeds according to her desires.

System: Spend one Faith point and roll Intelligence + Survival. Your character can alter or add a new plant characteristic per success rolled. Alterations include increased metabolism (heightened speed of growth), thick bark or tough skin and thorns. These successes can be generated as part of an extended roll over a period of days (one roll per day), as the demon "tinkers" with her creation. The effects of the evocation persist for a number of days equal to your character's Faith score, or they can be made permanent by expending one temporary Willpower point.

Torment: Monstrous demons who use this evocation create plant life with a taste for blood. Make a Willpower roll with the difficulty equal to your character's Torment. If the roll fails, the plant's metabolism mutates spontaneously, developing natural weapons that allow it to kill and feed on living beings — including the demon herself. The plant's attack and damage dice pools equal your character's Torment, and damage is lethal.

NINURTU, THE VISAGE OF THE WILD

The angels of the wilderness manifest as an amalgam of the flora they command and the fauna that thrive beneath their aegis. Their skin is commonly covered by a fine pelt similar to a deer's, and they often possess hooves instead of feet. Their bodies are powerfully muscled, and their eyes change colors like the seasons, ranging from pale gray to deep summer green.

The Visage of the Wild confers the following special capabilities.

• **Enhanced Senses:** The character's five senses are heightened to superhuman levels, lowering the difficulties of Perception rolls by two.

• **Chameleon Skin:** The demon's skin allows it to blend with its surroundings. The difficulties of all Stealth rolls decrease by one if the demon is on the move; two if it's standing still.

• **Pass Without Trace:** The difficulties of the character's Stealth rolls decrease by two, and her passage does not disturb the surrounding environment in any way. She leaves no footprints and disturbs no foliage.

• **Extra Health Levels:** The character's vitality provides three extra Bruised health levels for the purposes of absorbing damage.

Torment: Monstrous Ninurtu are darker of hue, and their eyes take on the color of the silver moon. They swell in size, and their appearance exudes the kind of forbidding menace of the deep forests or the high mountains.

The Visage of the Wild confers the following high-Torment special capabilities.

• **Thorns:** The demon's shoulders, chest and arms are covered with needle-sharp, black thorns that inflict one level of aggravated damage to any attacker who successfully strikes or grapples the demon in unarmed combat.

• **Increased Size:** The character's body grows to a third again its own height, adding the following bonus traits: +1 Strength, +2 Dexterity, +1 Stamina.

• **Extra Limbs:** The demon grows a prehensile tail. A prehensile tail is half your character's height, uses only half his Strength (rounded down) to lift objects and allows him to hang suspended.

• **Venom:** The demon's saliva contains an intoxicating form of venom that affects a victim's will. If a victim is exposed to the demon's saliva (through an open wound, a kiss), she loses one Willpower point per point of the demon's Torment unless a successful Stamina roll is made (difficulty 7). If the victim loses all of her Willpower in this fashion, she falls into a death-like coma. The effects of the venom last for a number of days equal to the character's Torment.

LORE OF THE FLESH

• BODY CONTROL

This evocation allows the Devourer to alter the body chemistry of her host body and others. She can purge poisons (both natural and manmade) and increase or reduce metabolism.

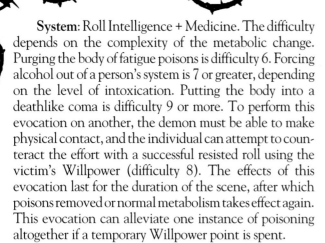

System: Roll Intelligence + Medicine. The difficulty depends on the complexity of the metabolic change. Purging the body of fatigue poisons is difficulty 6. Forcing alcohol out of a person's system is 7 or greater, depending on the level of intoxication. Putting the body into a deathlike coma is difficulty 9 or more. To perform this evocation on another, the demon must be able to make physical contact, and the individual can attempt to counteract the effort with a successful resisted roll using the victim's Willpower (difficulty 8). The effects of this evocation last for the duration of the scene, after which poisons removed or normal metabolism takes effect again. This evocation can alleviate one instance of poisoning altogether if a temporary Willpower point is spent.

Torment: Monstrous demons use a brute-force approach when performing this evocation, putting a terrible strain on a subject. After rolling, total successes are compared to the subject's Stamina. Successes that exceed the target's Stamina are suffered as bashing damage, which may not be soaked.

•• MANIPULATE NERVES

Like Body Control, this evocation allows the demon to manipulate a subject's nervous system. Strength and reflexes can be enhanced, senses can be dulled or sharpened, or the person can be subjected to waves of intense pleasure or pain.

System: Roll Intelligence + Medicine. The difficulty is determined by the complexity of the intended effect. Reducing the effects of pain is difficulty 6, while increasing the speed of a person's reflexes (increasing his Dexterity) is 7 or 8. Sharpening a person's senses (or dulling them) might require a difficulty of 9 or more. Each success increases or decreases a relevant physical trait or wound penalty by one, as appropriate for the effort. The effects of this evocation last for the duration of the scene. To perform this evocation on another individual, the demon must be able to make physical contact, and a resisted Willpower (difficulty 8) can be made to counteract your character's effort.

Torment: A monstrous demon risks inflicting severe physical damage to a subject by crudely manipulating the victim's nervous system. After rolling, the total successes are compared to the subject's Stamina. Successes that exceed the target's Stamina are suffered as lethal damage.

••• MANIPULATE FLESH

This evocation allows the demon to manipulate a subject's physical form (be it her own or another's), adding muscle mass, increasing bone density or expanding mental faculties.

System: Roll Intelligence + Medicine. Each success is a point that can be added to any of the subject's Physical or Mental Attributes. There is a risk, however.

Compare the total number of successes to the subject's Stamina. Any excess successes are suffered as bashing damage due to system shock. This damage cannot be soaked. To perform this evocation on another individual, the demon must be able to make physical contact, and the individual can attempt to counteract its effects — the Storyteller makes a Willpower roll (difficulty 8).

Torment: Monstrous demons alter flesh and bone without regard for their subjects' frailty. If performed on another, a Willpower roll is made for the subject, with a difficulty equal to the demon's Torment. If the roll fails, the subject suffers a temporary derangement that makes him uncontrollably paranoid and prone to violence. If the roll is botched, the derangement is permanent.

•••• RESTORE FLESH

The demon is capable of restoring an animal or person's body to its original form, no matter how torn or mutilated it has become.

System: Spend one Faith point and roll Perception + Medicine. Each success heals one level of lethal damage or all levels of bashing damage that the subject has suffered. Lost limbs or organs are restored completely, and any illness or poisons are purged from the body. Aggravated damage cannot be healed with this evocation, nor can the power resurrect someone who is already dead. The Devourer must be able to touch the subject to perform this evocation.

Torment: Monstrous demons are capable of performing this evocation as well, but their ministrations are invariably tainted by hatred and pain. The Storyteller makes a resisted Willpower roll (difficulty 7) for the subject. If successful, the subject gains a temporary derangement. If the roll fails, the derangement is permanent. If the roll botches, the subject becomes a mindless, psychotic killing machine.

••••• SHAPE FLESH

The demon is capable of transforming human flesh into any shape desired. Mortals or fallen can become monstrous creatures straight out of legend.

System: Spend one Faith point and roll Dexterity + Medicine in a resisted roll against the target's Willpower (difficulty 7). The player decides the form she wishes to create, along with its relevant physical capabilities, and the Storyteller determines the number of successes necessary to make the form a reality. These successes can be generated as part of an extended roll over a period of days (one roll per day) as the demon "tinkers" with her creation. As a rule of thumb, assume that each success confers or removes one Physical Attribute point or physical feature. The effects of this evocation last for a number of days equal to the character's Faith score, or they can be made permanent by expending one temporary Willpower

point. Devourers can use this evocation on themselves or others, as long as they can touch a subject.

Torment: Monstrous demons' alterations are invariably warped by their Torment, creating grotesque deformities that transform victims into walking nightmares. Such a hideous metamorphosis causes the victim to gain a temporary derangement and to suffer a level of lethal damage each day as a result of the intolerable strain placed on his body. Mortals who witness these creatures suffer the effects of Revelation (see page 253 of the Systems chapter for details).

Aruru, the Visage of Flesh

The angels of the flesh, who can alter their forms more completely than even the Defilers, manifest themselves as idealized versions of their own mortal forms. Their power exalts the mortal shells that they inhabit, removing any blemishes or deformities and refining their original features to perfection. In a way, this makes their appearance just as alien and wondrous as the shimmering apparitions of their Celestial kin.

The Visage of Flesh confers the following special capabilities.

• **Enhanced Social Traits**: The refinement of the character's features, mannerisms and voice provides the following bonus traits: +1 Charisma, +1 Manipulation, +2 Appearance.

• **Immune to Poisons**: The character is immune to damage or impairment from any toxins, including alcohol and nicotine.

• **Improved Initiative**: Add two to the character's initiative.

• **Casts No Reflection**: The demon's image does not appear in a mirror, nor can it be captured in a photograph or by a video camera.

Torment: High-Torment Aruru bear little resemblance to human beings, their original shape being lost in a swollen mountain of undulating flesh. Muscle, bone and organs roil and shift from moment to moment without the demon's conscious control.

The Visage of Flesh confers the following high-Torment special capabilities.

• **Extra Health Levels**: The demon gains three extra Bruised health levels for the purposes of absorbing damage.

• **Armor**: The demon's undulating mass of gristle and flesh provides four levels of armor for the purposes of soaking bashing, lethal *and* aggravated damage.

• **Gaping Maw**: The demon can chew and digest almost anything — metal, stone or flesh. The difficulties of bite attacks decrease by two, and a bite itself inflicts Strength +4 aggravated damage.

• **Regeneration**: The demon regenerates one health level of bashing or lethal damage per turn, automatically as a reflexive action.

Slayer (Halaku)

Although they are known today as the Angels of the Second World, the Slayers were originally mere agents of change, eliminating plants and animals that had outlived their purpose to make way for new, better generations. The Lore of Death granted them the power to end life quickly and painlessly, then render the bodies of the dead back into their constituent particles for the earth to absorb and begin anew. Of all the Houses, the Halaku were forced to evolve the most in the wake of the Fall. With the loss of mankind's immortality, the Slayers were thrust into a difficult and painful situation of ending human life, often well before its time, then surrendering the spirit to an unknown fate. The Lore of the Spirit grew from the Slayers' desire to prevent the loss of these souls, anchoring them to places on the earth in their former bodies, but this was not enough to protect the ghosts from the depredations of loyalist Reapers. Finally, the Halaku decided on a more desperate course: the construction of a haven outside the physical universe where God's Reapers could not find the souls of the dead. The first step in this plan was to learn the ways of stabilizing and traveling to pockets of reality that existed outside the physical cosmos, leading to the evolution of the Lore of the Realms and culminating in the creation of the spirit realm.

Lore of Death

• Read Fate

This evocation allows the demon to look into the eyes of a dead body and see the manner in which he or she died.

System: Roll Perception + Awareness. The number of successes achieved determines the amount of detail your character can determine about the mortal's fate. One success provides a picture of the moment of death. Each additional success goes further back in time, from minutes at two successes, hours at three and days at four. It also provides a broader context for the circumstances behind the person's passing.

Torment: Monstrous demons are able to discern a subject's fate only if that person died as a result of violence, whether accidental or intentional.

• • Decay

One of the Reaper's primary powers, this evocation accelerates the process of decay, reducing living and non-living matter to its component particles.

System: Your Slayer must be able to touch his intended target to perform this evocation. Roll Stamina + Medicine. Each success inflicts one health level of aggravated damage (lethal damage to a mortal). If performed on a dead body, each success removes a point from the body's Stamina.

When all the dots have been eliminated, the body is reduced to dust. The process works in a similar fashion on inanimate objects, but the difficulty varies depending on an object's composition. Decaying an article of wood or cloth, for example, is difficulty 7, while decaying a piece of plastic is difficulty 8. Decaying metal is difficulty 9, and stone is 10. Each success decays one cubic foot of material.

Torment: Monstrous demons affect people and objects in an area as opposed to single targets. Everything within a radius of yards equal to the character's Faith score is affected.

••• Vision of Mortality

This evocation saw frequent use in the War of Wrath, permitting Slayers to fill the minds of their foes with visions of impending death. Even battle-hardened angels found their mettle sorely tested by these bone-chilling sights, throwing down their arms and fleeing before the Halaku's remorseless advance.

System: Roll Manipulation + Intuition. The target resists the evocation with a Willpower roll, using the Slayer's Faith as the difficulty. If you succeed, the target abandons her action and flees from your demon's presence. If the target's Willpower roll botches, he flees and suffers a temporary derangement. This evocation can target individuals up to a number of yards away equal to your character's Faith rating. A target who wins the resisted roll cannot be subjected to this evocation again for the remainder of the scene.

Torment: Monstrous demons affect every living being around them as opposed to a specific target. The demon affects targets within a number of yards equal to their Faith score, and resisted Willpower rolls are made for each potential victim.

•••• Extinguish Life

The Reaper's touch means death. By placing a hand on a living body and exerting her will, a demon can sever a victim's soul from his body, killing him instantly. This capability can be used on the fallen as well, but rather than cause instant death, the evocation produces an icy chill that saps the vitality from a demon's body.

System: The Slayer must be able to physically touch her intended target to perform this evocation. Spend one Faith point and roll Strength + Awareness. Compare your successes to the target's Stamina. If your successes exceed the target's Stamina, he is killed instantly. If your successes are less than the target's Stamina, each one inflicts a level of bashing damage as the Slayer's icy touch saps the strength from the mortal's body. If this evocation is employed against another demon and the successes exceed the target's Stamina, each success inflicts a level of aggravated damage. If the successes are less than the demon's Stamina, apply them as levels of bashing damage.

Torment: Monstrous demons do not need to touch their victims to employ this evocation. Their icy hatred radiates from them in all directions, stilling the hearts of living beings. The high-Torment version of this evocation affects every living being within a number of yards equal to your character's Faith score.

••••• Unlife

This powerful evocation allows a living body to function without the presence of a soul or vital spirit, creating an unliving creature completely under the Slayer's control.

System: Spend one Faith point and roll Stamina + Medicine. A walking-dead creature has only one point in each of its Physical Attributes upon creation, though each extra success can be used to add additional points in any Physical Attributes, at your discretion. These creatures do not suffer wound penalties in combat, using their full dice pools at all times. They must suffer no less than 10 health levels of damage before being destroyed. Undead minions are mindless automatons, acting solely according to your demon's will. Each time your character wants one of her minions to perform an action, make a Willpower roll (difficulty 7). If your character controls more than one creature at a time, you must divide your Willpower pool among them per turn. A failed roll causes a zombie to continue the last action it was commanded to perform.

Alternatively, a Slayer can program a minion to perform a rote set of instructions; one action per point of Wits that your character has, all by spending a temporary Willpower point. Since these instructions are transmitted mentally, it's possible to create a detailed set of commands, including complicated travel routes and detailed physical descriptions. Once programmed, however, a minion cannot be given further commands. If the demon uses her Willpower to command the minion to perform an action outside the realm of its instructions, its programming is lost.

Slayers can raise and control a number of minions equal to their Faith at one time. The bodies must be within Faith in yards to be affected. The effects of the evocation last for the duration of the scene. If your character wishes, the effects can be made permanent by the expenditure of a temporary Willpower point per body. A permanent minion remains until destroyed, and it cannot be raised again thereafter.

Disembodied fallen may possess animated corpses with the Slayer's permission, or they can try to wrest control of programmed corpses from the demon with a resisted Willpower roll. Unless transformed by use of other lore, the demon's host remains a dead body with all due appearances, smell and physical limitations.

Torment: Monstrous demons cannot prevent their Torment from infusing creations with an unnatural craving for violence, raising flesh-eating monsters that must be held in check constantly or they attack any living thing they can reach, including the Slayer herself. If not programmed with a rote set of instructions, these creatures go into a violent frenzy unless their

creator makes a successful Willpower roll (difficulty 8) each turn. This Willpower roll is in addition to any to impose commandments from action to action.

NAMTAR, THE VISAGE OF DEATH

These angels manifest as shadowy figures wreathed in tendrils of ghostly mist that shift and writhe from moment to moment, occasionally reflecting the angels' thoughts in strange, symbolic forms. A pall of silence surrounds these figures, and their feet never seem to touch the ground. Their skin is as pale as alabaster, and their faces are constantly hidden in deep shadow.

The Visage of Death confers the following special capabilities.

• **Wings:** A pair of raven's wings extends from the character's shoulders. At full extension, each wing is a third again as long as the character is tall. The character can glide up to three times her running speed per turn.

• **Improved Initiative:** Add two to character's initiative.

• **Pass Without Trace:** The difficulties of the character's Stealth rolls decrease by two, and her passage does not disturb the surrounding environment in any way — she leaves no footprints and disturbs no foliage.

• **Casts No Reflection:** The demon's image does not appear in a mirror, nor can it be captured in a photograph or by a video camera.

Torment: Monstrous Namtar exude the cold aura of death, indiscriminately draining the life of every living thing around them. Flowers wilt in their passing, children grow glassy-eyed, and the old feel mortality grip their heart.

The Visage of Death confers the following high-Torment special capabilities.

• **Cloak of Shadows:** The demon is shrouded in a pall of darkness, making her features difficult to see in the best of light, and rendering her near-invisible at night. The difficulties of all Stealth rolls are lowered by two whenever the demon stands in a pool of shadow or moves in darkness. If the character is attacked, the rules for Blind Fighting apply to the attacker; see page 240 of the Systems chapter for details.

• **Deathgrip:** The demon's spirit can cling to life past the point of human endurance. If the demon's host body suffers eight levels of lethal or aggravated damage, she can still hold onto life with a successful Willpower roll. If successful, the character falls into a coma until the following dawn, at which point she rises with one health level and one less temporary Faith.

• **Aura of Entropy:** Plants wilt in the demon's presence, and living beings are suffused with an icy chill that saps their strength. Mortals and other demons within a number of yards equal to the demon's Faith lose one die from their dice pools unless a successful Stamina roll (difficulty 6) is made. The effects of this capability persist for the duration of the scene.

• **Damage Resistance:** The demon is capable of shrugging off damage that would cripple a normal human. She may ignore any wound penalties for the duration of the scene. Penalties for injuries incurred while in apocalyptic form apply again once human form is resumed.

LORE OF THE SPIRIT

• SPEAK WITH THE DEAD

This evocation allows the Slayer to communicate with spirits roaming the physical or spirit world. Spirits addressed in this way are compelled to respond, and they must answer the demon's questions to the best of their ability.

System: Roll Manipulation + Awareness. The spirit can attempt to avoid the evocation's compulsion with a resisted Willpower roll (difficulty 9). If the evocation is successful, the spirit must answer the Slayer's questions truthfully. The Slayer can affect any spirit within reach of her voice, and the effects of the evocation persist for a number of turns equal to the character's Faith score.

Torment: Monstrous demons can perform this evocation as well, but the spirits they contact become warped by the demon's Torment and grow inimical to living beings for days afterward. Spirits affected by this evocation become restless and hostile to the living for a number of days equal to the demon's Torment score if a Willpower roll (difficulty 9) fails.

•• SUMMON THE DEAD

Slayers can use this evocation to summon spirits to their presence, their influence reaching across entire city blocks. Spirits summoned in this fashion must come to the demon whether they wish to or not, and they remain until dismissed.

System: Roll Manipulation + Leadership. The Slayer can summon one spirit per success rolled, if any are present in the area. The evocation affects 10 square yards times the character's Faith score, and spirits within the affected area are drawn to the Slayer's presence immediately. They remain until the effects of the evocation expire or the demon dismisses them. The effects of this evocation last for the duration of the scene. At the Storyteller's discretion, a particularly potent or willful spirit could try to break the demon's control with a resisted Willpower roll (difficulty equal to the demon's Faith score) made against your Manipulation + Leadership successes.

Torment: Monstrous demons can summon spirits, but the effects of their Torment cause the beings to become inherently hostile to the living for a number of days equal to the character's Torment score if a Willpower roll (difficulty 9) is failed.

••• COMMAND THE DEAD

A Slayer may command a spirit of the dead to do her bidding, forcing the ghost to perform any actions that the demon desires if her will proves greater than its.

System: Roll Manipulation + Leadership. The Slayer may command any single spirit that can hear her voice. The spirit may attempt to counteract the effect with a resisted Willpower roll (difficulty 8). If the spirit's roll fails, it must obey the demon's commands to the best of its ability. The effects of this evocation last for a number of turns equal to the character's Faith score.

Torment: Monstrous demons can command spirits as well, but they warp any beings by the force of their Torment, causing ghosts to become maddened, violent entities that lash out at the living at the first opportunity. Once the evocation's effects expire, the Storyteller makes a Willpower roll (difficulty 8) for an affected spirit. The roll requires a number of successes equal to or greater than the number of turns that the ghost spent under the demon's control. If the roll fails, the spirit becomes malevolent and hostile toward the living for a number of days equal to the demon's Torment score. If the roll botches, the change is permanent.

•••• ANCHOR THE SOUL

This powerful evocation allows a Slayer to anchor a disinterred mortal soul (or a demon's spirit) to a physical object, creating a haunted artifact that traps the spirit in the physical world. In the darker days of the War of Wrath, Slayers used this evocation to bind the souls of mortals and angels to fuel powerful weapons and tools crafted by the Annunaki.

System: Spend one Faith point and roll Stamina + Awareness. The difficulty is determined by the nature of the object being used as an anchor. Binding a soul to something that was close to the person in life (difficulty 6) is the most effective kind of anchor, while foreign objects prove more challenging depending on their composition. Crystal, gems or precious metals are useful (difficulty 7), while natural objects such as wood, glass or bone are less so (difficulty 8). Synthetic objects such as plastic or high-tech items such as computers are challenging to use (difficulty 9). Your character must be within a number of yards of the spirit equal to his [your character's] Faith rating in order to affect it, and he must hold the intended anchor. The spirit can resist imprisonment with a resisted Willpower roll (difficulty 8). If you get more successes, the spirit is trapped within the anchor and cannot interact with the outside world unless the object has been properly attuned (see the Lore of the Forge, p. 190).

Demons bound to an attuned item can still access their inherent powers (including their lore paths), provided they have Faith available. (Any existing pacts with mortal thralls remain in effect). This evocation persists for a number of days equal to your character's Faith score, or it can be made permanent by expending a temporary Willpower point. If an anchor is ever destroyed, the spirit is freed immediately. Freed mortal souls disappear forever or become ghosts haunting a locale, at the Storyteller's discretion. Freed demons must resist the pull of the Abyss

and attempt to locate another host body or physical anchor (see page 259 of the Systems chapter for details).

Torment: Monstrous demons bind spirits with a shroud of suffocating darkness, imposing the slightest taste of the agony suffered in the Abyss. These trapped souls are so frenzied by their hardship that their despair leaks into the physical realm, surrounding their anchors with an aura of ill fortune. Individuals touching or carrying such a spirit anchor botch their actions on a roll of 1 or 2.

••••• RESTORE THE DEAD

This evocation allows a Slayer to anchor a spirit into any soulless physical body. This effort returns the ghost to the land of the living, at least for a short time.

System: Spend one Faith point and roll Stamina + Awareness. The Slayer must have the soul she wishes to restore in her immediate vicinity and be able to touch the body she wants it to possess. The body in question must have died only recently (i.e., within the last 48 hours). If successful, the soul is anchored to the body, healing any injuries the body may have had and returning the spirit to the land of the living. The new person has the same Physical Attributes that the body had in its former life, and the Mental and Social Attributes and Abilities of the new soul. The effects of this evocation last for a number of days equal to your character's Faith score, or it can be made permanent by expending one point of *permanent* Willpower.

Demon spirits without hosts can be placed into bodies through this evocation.

Torment: Monstrous demons who perform this evocation invariably taint the spirit with their own Torment, leaving the soul twisted by hate and pain. Once the soul has been restored, the Storyteller makes a Willpower roll for it with a difficulty equal to your character's Torment. If the roll is successful, the restored person suffers a temporary derangement. If the roll fails, the derangement is permanent. If the roll botches, the restored person becomes a frenzied monster, attacking the living until it is destroyed.

If a disembodied demon spirit is put into a body with the high-Torment version of this evocation, a Willpower roll is made for it, too. If the roll is successful, the possessing demon has a Torment score that's one point less than your character's. If the Willpower roll fails, the possessing demon's Torment score equals your character's. And, if the Willpower roll botches, the possessing demon's Torment score exceeds your character's by one point.

NERGAL, THE VISAGE OF THE SPIRIT

The angels of the spirit world appear as pale, serene figures reminiscent of the images of human saints, beautiful, silent and remote. Like others of their House, the Nergal move without noise or effort, seeming to glide along the ground as they move. Only their eyes, colored in shifting patterns of gray and black, hint at the bleak world beyond the mortal realm.

The Visage of the Spirit confers the following special capabilities.

• **Ghost Sight:** The angel can see the spirits of the dead that linger in the mortal realm, whether the ghosts wish to reveal themselves or not, with a successful Perception roll (difficulty 6).

• **Enhanced Social Traits:** The angel's beatific appearance provides the following bonus traits: +2 Charisma, +1 Manipulation, +1 Appearance.

• **Pass Without Trace:** The difficulties of the character's Stealth rolls decrease by two, and her passage does not disturb the surrounding environment in any way. She leaves no footprints and disturbs no foliage.

• **Wings:** A pair of raven's wings extends from the character's shoulders. At full extension, each wing is a third again as long as the character is tall. The character can glide up to three times her running speed per turn.

Torment: Monstrous Nergal are stained with the blood of the dead, their alabaster skin streaked with lines of crimson and black. Their eyes are orbs of clotted blood, and when they speak, their voices howl like the spirits of the damned.

The Visage of the Spirit confers the following high-Torment special capabilities.

• **Cloak of Shadows:** The demon is shrouded in a pall of darkness, making her features difficult to see in the best of light and rendering her near-invisible at night. The difficulties of all Stealth rolls decrease by two whenever the demon stands in a pool of shadow or moves in darkness. If the character is attacked, the rules for Blind Fighting apply to the attacker; see page 240 of the Systems chapter for details.

• **Howl of the Damned:** The difficulties of all Intimidation rolls decrease by two.

• **Aura of Dread:** The demon is surrounded by an aura of fear that saps the will of her foes. Targets within a number of yards equal to the character's Faith lose their normal initiative unless a successful Willpower roll is made against a difficulty equal to the demon's Torment. Affected individuals act last within a given turn. The Willpower roll is made every turn in which a person or another demon is in the Nergal's apocalyptic presence. Normal initiative resumes for a victim as soon as a successful Willpower roll is made.

• **Damage Resistance:** The demon is capable of shrugging off damage that would cripple a normal human. She may ignore any wound penalties for the duration of the scene, although penalties return and apply normally when human form is resumed.

LORE OF THE REALMS

• SENSE THE BARRIER

The Slayer is able to sense the relative strength of the barrier between the physical and the spirit realms in an area

as large as a city block, allowing the demon to home in on regions where the boundary is exceptionally thick or thin.

System: Roll Perception + Awareness. If your roll is successful, your Slayer can zero in on any regions of unusual strength or weakness in the barrier between the realms. As a rule of thumb, the barrier between realms tends to be strongest in areas where the influence of human faith is weakest. Therefore, a science lab that promotes cold intellect over intuition might have a strong barrier, while a graveyard or a church might have a weak barrier. Your demon can read an area that's 10 square yards multiplied by his Faith score.

Torment: Monstrous demons can sense only areas where the barrier is weak, drawn by the call of the spirit storm raging just beyond.

•• STEP BEYOND THE VEIL

This evocation allows the Slayer to physically cross the barrier into the shadow world, a lifeless mirror image of the mortal world. Doing so allows the demon to travel vast distances in the shadow realm at the speed of thought and return to the physical world at a corresponding location.

Crossing over also allows a demon to interact with the spirits of the dead that linger on the other side.

System: Roll Dexterity + Awareness. The difficulty is determined by the relative strength of the barrier in the area where your Slayer tries to cross. Doing so at a weak point (a church or graveyard) is difficulty 6. Crossing over in an old house or apartment building that has seen generations of occupants is difficulty 7. Crossing from a shopping mall is 8. Once in the shadow land, your character can fly across the bleak landscape with the speed of thought. Roll Dexterity + Athletics (difficulty 8), allowing the demon to cover a mile each turn per success rolled. The roads and buildings in the shadow realm are just as real to your demon as are their physical-world counterparts. She must traverse any physical obstacles and find her way to her destination just as she would in the mortal world. Upon reaching her destination, the demon can return automatically to the corresponding place in the physical realm, appearing as if from nowhere. All other actions are performed as normal in the spirit realm, but the furious storm raging there increases difficulties to 8, at the least. Furthermore, your Slayer loses a point of temporary Willpower each time a roll botches. If the demon loses all her Willpower, she is torn from her mortal host. The body is returned to the physical realm and the disembodied soul must fight the pull of the Abyss while searching for another anchor (see page 259 of the Systems chapter for details).

Your character cannot take passengers with her to or from the spirit or living realms.

Encountering and communicating with spirits in the dead lands is similar to meeting people in the living world. Spirits have their own identities and agendas and may be

willing or unwilling to interact with visitors. Demons can use Lore of the Spirit to encourage such interaction.

Torment: Monstrous demons that cross into the spirit world create a "seam" in the barrier that draws restless spirits into the physical world, resulting in temporary but intense hauntings. This seam remains in the area for a number of days equal to the demon's Torment score.

••• GHOSTWALK

This evocation allows the demon to exist simultaneously in both the physical and spirit realms. She can interact with both mortals and spirits, and pass through objects in both places.

System: Roll Stamina + Awareness. The difficulty is determined by the relative strength of the barrier in the area where the Slayer performs the evocation. Doing so at a weak point (a church or graveyard) is difficulty 6. Crossing over in an old house or apartment building that has seen generations of occupants is difficulty 7. Crossing from a shopping mall is 8.

If your roll is successful, your demon becomes a hazy, insubstantial form, able to see and be seen by individuals on both sides of the barrier. She passes through objects without harm, and vice versa, though she can interact with one realm or the other in a given turn with a Willpower roll (difficulty 8). If the roll succeeds, the Slayer can speak to individuals, handle objects, attack or be attacked in the realm to which she has attuned herself, just as if she were solid. The effects of this evocation last for a number of turns equal to the character's Faith rating. Your character cannot take any other beings with her to this "middle ground" between realms.

Torment: When monstrous demons perform this evocation, it causes the energies of the spirit storm to leak into the physical realm around her, causing wild and unpredictable spirit manifestations and hauntings.

•••• REACH ACROSS THE BARRIER

The Slayer can peer into and reach across into the spirit realm the same way a mortal retrieves something from a cupboard, placing or retrieving items between the realms at will. During the War of Wrath, this evocation was used extensively to place powerful weapons or other items beyond the reach of the Slayers' enemies. Many still remain there to this day, waiting to be found.

System: Spend one Faith point and roll Dexterity + Awareness. The difficulty is determined by the relative strength of the barrier in the area where the Slayer performs the evocation. Doing so at a weak point (a church or graveyard) is difficulty 6. Crossing over in an old house or apartment building that has seen generations of occupants is difficulty 7. Crossing from a shopping mall is 8.

If your roll is successful, your character can see into and "reach" across the barrier between realms—her hand and arm literally vanishes from mortal eyes until she

withdraws it again. She can place or remove any item that can be easily lifted with one or two hands. Mortals or demons cannot be forced across the barrier using this evocation. Items can be hidden away from the spirit world, however, placing them in the material world, out of reach from dead-land inhabitants. (But, of course, that might mean that real-world beings could find the items.)

Torment: Monstrous demons who perform this evocation risk allowing traces of the spirit storm to leak through into the physical world, causing surreal and terrifying side effects. If the evocation succeeds, the Storyteller makes a Willpower roll with the difficulty equal to your Slayer's Torment. If the roll fails, the winds of the storm seep through, subjecting all mortals in the immediate area to Willpower rolls (difficulty 8). If their rolls fail, they flee in terror. If their rolls botch, they also suffer a temporary derangement.

● ● ● ● ● PIERCE THE BARRIER

This evocation enables the Slayer to create a temporary doorway between the living and dead realms, allowing other demons to cross into the shadow lands if the portal's creator wishes.

System: Spend one Faith point and roll Stamina + Awareness. The difficulty is determined by the relative strength of the barrier in the area where the Slayer performs the evocation. Doing so at a weak point (a church or graveyard) is difficulty 6. Crossing over in an old house or apartment building that has seen generations of occupants is difficulty 7. Crossing from a shopping mall is 8.

If your roll succeeds, your Slayer creates a portal that other demons may bodily pass through into the shadow realm, allowing them to interact with the spirits of the dead and to travel through the dead lands. As many other demons may enter as you get successes on your roll. Living mortals and thralls cannot pass. Non-Slayers who make the transition are at a considerable disadvantage compared to the Halaku, being more susceptible to the ravages of the Maelstrom than those of the Seventh House. Furthermore, they cannot travel as quickly across the shadow realm as the Slayers can. They cover distances only as fast as they could in the physical realm. The dice pools for all actions taken by uninitiated demons are halved (rounded up), and these fallen lose one temporary Willpower point each day that they remain in the spirit realm. When their Willpower is exhausted, the demons become catatonic. Their bodies lose one point of Stamina each day thereafter. When a demon's Stamina is exhausted, her mortal body dies and her spirit is drawn back into the Abyss. The doorway created by this evocation lasts for only a single turn, and it is one-way. Spirits from beyond cannot normally use it to enter the living world.

Torment: Monstrous demons who perform this evocation cause the effects of the spirit storm to rage in the physical world in the immediate vicinity of the doorway, drawing spirits and causing horrifying manifestations to linger for a number of days equal to your character's Torment.

ERESHKIGAL, VISAGE OF THE REALMS

Angels of the Second World manifest as shadowy figures whose features are hidden in perpetual darkness. The air itself seems to wrap about them like a robe of night, conjuring the image of the cowled ferryman of human myth. Their hands are white and bony, like a skeleton's, and they move without effort or sound.

The Visage of the Realms confers the following special capabilities.

• **Dead Reckoning**: The character always knows where she is in relation to known landmarks, no matter how far away those landmarks may be. Unless affected by spatially distorting evocations such as Warp Path, she can never lose her sense of direction.

• **Pass Without Trace**: The difficulties of the character's Stealth rolls decrease by two, and her passage does not disturb the surrounding environment in any way. She leaves no footprints and disturbs no foliage.

• **Increased Awareness**: The fallen is especially attuned to the fabric of reality, lowering the difficulties of all Awareness rolls by two.

• **Conjure from Nothing**: The character is capable of supernatural sleight of hand, seeming to conjure items out of thin air only to make them vanish again with a flick of the wrist. She can draw an item from a pocket or conceal an item without detection on a successful Dexterity + Athletics roll (difficulty 6).

Torment: Angels of the Realms who surrender themselves to their Torment are walking portals to the land of the dead, exuding an aura of loss and despair that chills mortal hearts. Their voices are bleak and sepulchral, and their eyeless stare gives the boldest heart pause.

The Visage of the Realms confers the following high-Torment special capabilities.

• **Cloak of Shadows**: The demon is shrouded in a pall of darkness, making her features difficult to see in the best of light, and rendering her near-invisible at night. The difficulties of all Stealth rolls decrease by two whenever the demon stands in a pool of shadow or moves in darkness. If the character is attacked, the rules for Blind Fighting apply to the attacker; see page 240 of the Systems chapter for details.

• **Relentless**: The demon can walk or run without need of rest, able to cover superhuman distances without pause. As long as she stays in motion, she is unaffected by fatigue or hunger.

• **Voice of the Grave**: The difficulties of all Intimidation rolls decrease by two.

• **Dread Gaze**: Individuals (mortal or demon) who meet the demon's gaze and who fail a Willpower roll (difficulty 7) must forfeit their actions for that turn.

Naram-Sin slipped through the receptionist's office and into the executive suite. Arnold Horton, DynaCom's wunderkind and new CEO stood by the tall picture window across the lushly carpeted room, clearly enjoying the panoramic view of downtown Los Angeles. He did not stir as Naram-Sin joined him at the window, because the demon did not wish it so. Instead, the Devil took a moment to study the smug self-satisfaction glowing in Horton's eyes. Naram-Sin was not given to smiling, but the sight of the mortal's hubris amused him greatly.

"You've done well for yourself," the demon said at last. Watching Horton's lordly expression shatter into stark terror as Naram-Sin revealed himself was sweet indeed. Yet for all that, the demon's statement was perfectly true: Horton wore a tailored silk suit and a diamond ring on his little finger now, a far cry from the days of rumpled rayon he'd worn as a junior accountant for the company. Horton wasn't tall by mortal standards, but Naram-Sin still had to reach up to test the feel of the man's silk tie between thumb and finger. The demon wore the flesh of a middle-aged Chinese man, his small, dark eyes hidden behind round-rimmed spectacles. "I take it the terms of your new promotion were suitably generous."

"It's everything I dreamed of and more," Horton said, a little too eagerly. Unconsciously he smoothed his tie with one pale hand, effectively snatching it from the demon's grasp. "Of course, once I turned on the charm, they were putty in my hands." Horton straightened to his modest height, smoothing back an errant strand from his comb-over. "I've waited so long to be able to tell those fat bastards how things needed to be run around here. You have no idea how good it felt to make them squirm."

"I can guess," the demon said without a hint of irony.

"Not that there's much time for celebration just yet, though." Horton turned away from the window and cast a grim eye over the piles of papers arranged across the desk's marble face. "The problems with the company's business practices were much worse than I feared. Bankruptcy is the least of our problems. If we don't start cleaning things up, we could be looking at a congressional investigation." He smiled. "Of course, a quick trip to Washington will have the congressmen eating out of my hands."

"No doubt," Naram-Sin replied coolly. "But you will do nothing of the sort."

Horton paused, his reverie of self-congratulation swept aside. "Excuse me?"

"You will do your best to conceal this company's illicit partnerships and any other instances of criminal wrongdoing. You can even profit from them yourself if you want. Give yourself a hefty bonus for all your hard work." The demon's grin was devoid of warmth. "But the partnerships will continue."

Horton stared at Naram-Sin for a moment, his expression incredulous. "Did you hear what I said? If these partnerships continue, the company is finished, and quite possibly a number of people will go to jail. Including me."

The demon's eyes were inscrutable.

Horton shook his head. "Wait. This has to be a mistake. You wouldn't go to all the trouble to give me these gifts just so the company would fail."

"Trouble? Did you think I went to any trouble on your behalf, Mr. Horton?" The demon's voice was mild, his face expressionless. "Pulling the stars from the sky might cause me trouble. Crushing this obscene pile of stone you fools call a city might cause me trouble, if only momentarily. Granting you the power to overawe those fatuous little worms on the Board of Directors was no trouble at all, I assure you. I wanted to be certain that this company failed, and in a manner that will cause ruin and scandal not only here but in Washington as well. You will ensure that it happens."

The mortal's eyes widened. "You... you can't do this. I've given everything for this — my marriage, my family, my friends. I'll be ruined."

The demon smiled. Slit-pupiled eyes the color of sullen coals glowed from behind the wire-rimmed spectacles.

"Trust me, Mr. Horton. This is only the beginning."

CHAPTER EIGHT: RULES

Farewell happy Fields
Where Joy for ever dwells: Hail horrors, hail
Infernal world, and thou profoundest Hell
Receive thy new Possessor: One who brings
A mind not to be chang'd by Place or Time.
The mind is its own place, and in itself
Can make a Heav'n of Hell, a Hell of Heav'n.
—John Milton, *Paradise Lost*

All games have rules. Rules take a back seat to the story in a storytelling game such as this one, but they still have a very important role. Rules give structure to your game and provide your Storyteller an unbiased method of determining the outcome of character actions in those situations where fairness is a factor. Your Storyteller can also fall back on the rules and have you and your fellow players roll dice to add randomness to your story's events. The dice, in such cases, represent fate and the harsh reality that things don't always work out as planned.

The **Demon: The Fallen** rules presented in this chapter help you coordinate any number of situations that might occur in your game, from combat scenes to social interactions. Offered as guidelines only, they're as flexible as you want to make them. In the end, your Storyteller has the final say in all things. He uses the rules as tools, keeping the progression and benefit of the story in mind. Some Storytellers use the rules to the letter, with strict and regular application. Others forgo the rules entirely and guide the story intuitively. Both methods are valid, but most storytelling approaches fall somewhere between these two extremes. The game is yours to do with as you please.

THE BASICS

TIME

How you control the passage of time in the game affects the smoothness of play. You and your players imagine events as they transpire, talking them out and rolling results. Therefore, real time and your game's imaginary time differ. When your characters enter combat, it may take real-time minutes to roleplay mere seconds of game time. Alternatively, you may wish to

cover *weeks* of game time in just a few real-time minutes, assuming that nothing worthy of attention occurs during that period. You and your players can gloss over intervals between important events or slow the progression to a crawl when detailing critical moments.

The following six basic units describe the passage of game time in **Demon**:

• **Turn** — The smallest increment, and often the most important, a turn is the amount of time it takes a character to perform one action. This interval ranges anywhere from three seconds to three minutes, depending on the pace of events. When your Storyteller announces that play is measured in turns, he determines the length of time that passes during those turns, and it's crucial that he hold everyone to the same standard. The length of a turn can vary between events, but it must remain constant for all players at any one particular moment.

• **Scene** — A scene in a roleplaying game resembles a scene in a theatrical play. Your Storyteller sets the stage, and the players take their roles. The scene evolves in one location and usually encompasses a single, specific event. The flow of time within a scene can vary greatly. It might be played out in turns or run parallel to real time, or your Storyteller and fellow players may choose to fast-forward through parts of it, while keeping the location and the general events the same.

For example, a scene may begin in real-time, as your characters break into an office building. It then may move into turns as your characters become involved in a shoot-out with the thralls of an Earthbound. You might then fast-forward through disposing of the bodies and investigating the area, then move back into real-time as your characters argue over the meaning of the evidence they uncovered.

• **Chapter** — For the most part, a chapter represents one game session during which the Storyteller has set up specific challenges to overcome. From the moment you sit down and assume your role to the moment you pack up your dice, you're playing out a chapter in the story. The end of each chapter should leave you wanting more and asking questions, yet still feeling a sense of completion.

• **Story** — A story tells one entire tale, whether it comprises several chapters or is completed in a single session. It has an introduction, a plot arc that involves rising conflict and a climax that brings events to a conclusion.

• **Chronicle** — In the big picture, the term "chronicle" refers to a saga or a collection of stories. Your Storyteller has a goal in mind for the chronicle, a possible destination for your characters and a theme or overarching plot line that connects all

chapters into a coherent whole. As your game progresses, you and your fellow players write your chronicle, linking parts and pieces together and developing a full-blown epic.

• **Downtime** — When your Storyteller decides to fast-forward and skim over a period of time, he invokes "downtime." You may summarize events that transpire during downtime, but you do not actually have to play them out. Your Storyteller may say something like, "You watch the church all night, but no one comes out. In the morning, a police cruiser pulls up beside your car." Nothing happened while your characters watched, so there's no reason to play it out. Your Storyteller leaps ahead to the next interesting event.

SIMPLE ACTIONS

You play your character by describing the things he does as *actions* he performs. These actions may be as simple as looking at something or as complex as flying a helicopter. Depending on the challenge of the action, your Storyteller may request that you roll dice to determine whether your character succeeds. In **Demon**, a single action that occurs in one turn is called a *simple action*. (Other types of actions are described later.) In most instances, your character's actions succeed automatically by virtue of their ease. For example, speaking is not normally challenging. If another character intimidates yours into silence, however, a die roll may decide whether your character perseveres to speak his mind.

REFLEXIVES

Certain feats that your character attempts do not count as actions and thus do not take up an entire turn. These "free actions," called *reflexives*, occur instantly and require no thought or direction from your character. Examples include spending Willpower to ensure that an attempted action succeeds or soaking damage to ignore or avoid wounds. Reflexives do not interfere with your character's regular action in that turn. They're instantaneous "actions" that occur even though other activities occupy your character's attention.

ROLLING DICE

Your Storyteller has two options when deciding the outcome of your character's proposed action. First, he can simply make the call himself, announcing the outcome that he feels enriches the game. Otherwise, he can request that you roll dice to determine the course of events randomly.

Demon uses 10-sided dice that you can purchase in any game store. Each player needs about 10 of these dice, while the Storyteller needs more.

Ratings

As explained in Chapter Six, you begin to describe your character by distributing points to his traits. These point values represent your character's innate abilities, learned aptitudes and life experience. Your character has certain strengths and weaknesses, just like a real person. Your character may be a crack shot with a rifle or he may not know one end of a gun from the other. You assign a point value from 0 to 5 to each of your character's traits, based on the following scale:

X	Abysmal
•	Poor
••	Average
•••	Good
••••	Exceptional
•••••	Superb

Using Abilities as an example, having no points (dots) in a trait means that your character has never learned that particular Skill, Talent or Knowledge. One dot represents a basic understanding of it. Having two means that your character falls into the average human range in his grasp of the Ability. With three to five dots, your character surpasses the average human being and is said to have honed the Ability to good, exceptional or superb degrees.

Your character's trait ratings determine how many dice you roll when your character attempts actions related to those traits. The Storyteller decides which traits apply to a proposed action. He announces these traits and you roll one 10-sided die for each dot you have assigned to those traits. The number of dice you roll is called your *dice pool*. The number of dice in your pool varies based on the nature of the action and the applicable traits.

A dice pool typically consists of a number of dice equal to your character's relevant Attribute rating (a measure of strength, intelligence or charm), plus that of an appropriate Ability. That is, you use both your character's innate Attributes and learned Abilities to determine how well she succeeds at the attempted action. For simplicity and game balance, your Storyteller should never allow you to combine more than one Attribute or Ability in a dice pool.

If your character has no dots in an applicable Ability (Talents, Skills or Knowledges), your Storyteller may allow you a dice pool equal to your score in the Attribute relevant to the action attempted. Your character's innate Attribute still

offers you a chance to succeed, albeit a small one. The Storyteller determines which Attribute trait applies to a specific action, and he may increase the difficulty number (see Difficulties, p. 220) by one to represent the increased challenge. Your Storyteller is not obligated to let you roll an Attribute score alone, however, if doing so doesn't make sense in the situation.

Some traits, such as Willpower, have maximum ratings of 10, which is higher than Ability or Attribute traits can be. Your Storyteller should not usually combine these special traits with others to produce your dice pools. For the most part, these high-rated traits stand alone.

Other traits, such as certain Backgrounds (see Chapter Six) replace Abilities in a dice pool to add variety to trait use. Your Storyteller always decides when you roll and which traits form such a dice pool.

Difficulties

When you roll your dice pool, you need a target number, a *difficulty* that you have to meet or beat. This number ranges from 2 to 10, as determined by your Storyteller. Once you know your difficulty number, you roll your dice pool and each die that matches or exceeds the difficulty number gives you one success. The number of successes you roll tells you how well your character completes the attempted action. You need only one success to pull off a task minimally. The more successes you roll, the more easily and completely your character triumphs.

The default difficulty of any task is 6. Obviously, lesser difficulties make a task easier, and higher ones make a task harder. Any time this rulebook or your Storyteller fails to give you a difficulty number, assume that it is the average, 6.

Difficulties

3	Easy — running on flat pavement
4	Routine — finding a number in the phone book
5	Straightforward — telling a little white lie to a stranger
6	Standard — firing a gun, highway driving, tracking
7	Challenging — driving in city traffic
8	Difficult — driving in a car chase
9	Extremely difficult — maneuvering a U-turn at 60 mph

Degrees of Success

One Success	Marginal — good enough for now
Two Successes	Moderate — you did okay
Three Successes	Complete — task accomplished perfectly
Four Successes	Exceptional — you earn a bonus
Five+ Successes	Phenomenal — nobody does it better

Your Storyteller has the final say on difficulty numbers. He determines whether the attempted action is nearly impossible or impossibly easy, based on the situation. A difficulty number of 10 represents an almost insurmountable challenge — one you have an equal chance of botching as you do of succeeding. On the other hand, a difficulty of 2 represents a task so easy that your character barely has to think about it to accomplish it, and it isn't even worth rolling. These extremes should be rare, though. Difficulty numbers fall in the 3 to 9 range most of the time. Many modifiers and situational factors may play into this decision.

Ultimately, a roll of 10 is always a success, regardless of the difficulty number.

SUCCESSES, FAILURES AND BOTCHES

One catch to counting your successes in **Demon** is that you might not get to keep them all. Any 1s that you roll must be subtracted from your total number of successes. It doesn't matter how many successes you roll — if you roll enough 1s to cancel them out, your character fails the attempted action. Rolling more 1s than successes doesn't penalize you especially, but rolling 1s and *no* successes is a very bad thing.

FAILURES

It's a shame when it happens, but it does happen. You either roll no successes or you roll more 1s than successes. If either occurs, your character fails his attempted action. His shot misses, he can't figure out what is wrong with the car engine, or he turns onto a dead-end street and screws up his attempt to outrun the cops. Whatever the case, a failure may disappoint, but it doesn't hold the same catastrophic potential as a botch.

BOTCHES

Normally, dice that show 1s on a roll cancel out successes on a one-for-one basis. If you've rolled no successes for those 1s to cancel out, though, what you've got is called a *botch*. Where a failure hurts, a botch tortures, because a botch takes failure one step further. Not only does your character fail his attempted action, his life gets a lot more complicated.

Your Storyteller decides what results from a botch. The possibilities are endless, but in most situations, a catastrophe occurs. If you botch while your character attempts to shoot a gun, the weapon may jam. If you botch while your character jumps from one roof to another, he may fall. Simply failing these rolls might mean that your character misses the shot or barely latches onto the far roof by

his fingertips. Degree of danger differentiates between a failure and a botch. A failure usually results in a mild threat, whereas a botch lands your character in deep trouble.

Botches also allow the Storyteller to create odd but interesting consequences for your abysmal failure. Instead of making your gun jam, the Storyteller may decide that the bullet ricochets off a brick wall and hits an innocent bystander. Instead of leaving your character dangling precariously from the roof, the Storyteller might let him make it across — only to find himself in the middle of a Mafia execution!

Botches don't necessarily mean your character has to die, only that fate has thrown a gigantic monkey wrench into the works. A clever Storyteller uses a botch to raise tension a notch and introduce new opponents or provide impetus for character development. How would your character come to terms with shooting an innocent child accidentally? Botches make for good drama.

MULTIPLE ACTIONS

Your character has to act fast. Can he do two things at once? That remains to be seen, but he can certainly try. Let's say your character needs to dodge around a corner while shooting at an exorcist in pursuit — two actions, one turn. Both actions suffer from the attempt to perform them simultaneously.

In order to attempt multiple actions, announce all the things you want your character to do and the order in which you will roll them. Your character can attempt as many feats as you want him to try, but the more he divides his attention, the less chance he has of succeeding at any individual action. Calculate the dice pool for the first action, but remove a number of dice equal to the total number of actions you want your character to attempt in this turn. Then roll the reduced dice pool for the first attempted action.

Once you have determined the outcome of the first action, prepare to roll the second. Take the appropriate dice pool, remove a number of dice equal to the total number of actions attempted, as before, but also remove one more die. For each consecutive action after the second, continue to remove an additional die, cumulatively, from the pool. Therefore, the third action loses two extra dice, the fourth action loses three dice and so on. If your dice pool is reduced to zero, you cannot attempt that action.

AUTOMATIC SUCCESSES

Who wants to spend the entire game rolling dice? Doing so detracts from the game's flow and turns player attention from story to rules. **Demon**, therefore, offers a quick and easy method for determining success without rolling dice. In situations where your dice pool exceeds the difficulty number of the attempted action, the feat succeeds automatically. You succeed only marginally, though, the equivalent of rolling one success. You can roll if you want greater success, but you risk failing or even botching. You cannot get automatic successes during combat or stressful scenes; you have to roll. Automatic successes apply primarily to situations where the attempted action could be accomplished easily, without resistance.

There's also another way to get an automatic success on a roll: Simply spend a Willpower point (p. 162). You can do so only once per turn, and since you have a limited supply of Willpower you can't do it too often, but it can certainly help when you're under pressure to succeed.

TRYING IT AGAIN

Persistence often pays off, but prolonged failure can result in frustration, fatigue and diminished self-confidence. When your character fails an attempted action, the Storyteller may choose to let her try again.

In most situations, the task gets more difficult with each successive attempt after a failure. To represent these diminishing returns, the Storyteller increases the difficulty number for each subsequent attempt by one, cumulatively. The more your character fails and keeps trying, the more difficult the task becomes. Barring in-game time constraints, your character may keep trying for as long as the Storyteller allows.

Continued failure eventually renders the task impossible, however. The difficulty number gets so high that the chance of success is eliminated, and your character ends up beating his head against the proverbial wall. If you botch, the Storyteller might not allow your character to continue trying, and he may even rule that the character ruins his tools, loses the evidence or destroys the object completely.

The nature of the action determines whether this rule applies. It might if your character attempts to pick a lock, persuade someone of something, parallel park, research a topic at the library or wriggle free of ropes that bind her. It does not apply if your character fails an attempt to shoot someone, to detect an ambush, to catch a baseball, to notice a clue or to do anything else at which she has only one chance to succeed.

COMPLICATIONS

The basic rules described thus far are all you need to begin play. Everything hereafter clarifies and expands on those rules by offering more in-depth methods of dealing with specific situations. The following three sections describe general approaches to complex situations that might arise. For plenty of situation-specific complications, see Chapter Nine.

EXTENDED ACTIONS

At some point, your character will attempt an action that requires prolonged success, such as climbing a cliff or tracking a feral creature through the woods, and a single die roll won't do the task justice. Even though your character may succeed partially, that doesn't mean he's able to reach his ultimate goal in one turn. That's where the extended actions rules come in. Compared to a *simple action*, which requires only one success, an *extended action* requires multiple successes for even a marginal victory. It may require you to roll multiple times, as well.

When your character attempts an extended action, the Storyteller decides how many successes must be rolled for marginal success. You then roll once for each applicable period of time that passes, as determined by the Storyteller, until you have accumulated enough successes to accomplish the task. This method not only determines whether your character succeeds, it establishes how long it takes to complete the attempted action. Your Storyteller may call for a roll for each in-game turn, hour or even day that passes. The time factor depends upon the nature of the task. It is discretionary, based on how long the task might take under normal circumstances.

In most cases, your character keeps trying for as long as you like, though you may play a harried game of beat-the-clock. Time may be short; the sun may set in only a few hours. If your character takes a break from his task to accomplish something else, the Storyteller may decide that some of the successes gained are lost because your character has to reorient herself. You may even have to start counting from scratch again.

The more times you have to roll, the greater the chance is that you might botch and your character might bungle the attempt completely. On a botch, the Storyteller may decide that you cannot start again. Your character simply fails, he destroys his equipment, or catastrophe strikes.

RESISTED ACTIONS

Sometimes, your character's actions are resisted by someone who wants to keep him from accomplishing his goals. When two characters go head-to-head in this way, a simple dice-pool roll doesn't represent the situation adequately. Called a *resisted action*, this type of conflict pits the traits of two characters against each other, as each attempts to overpower the other. (As a simplified example, people in a tug-of-war are engaging in a resisted action.) You and your opponent roll your dice pools against a common difficulty number, or sometimes against a difficulty equal to an appropriate trait (or traits) belonging to the other. The opponent who garners the most successes wins.

When totaling the final result, each of your opponent's successes cancels out one of your own, just as 1s do. If, for example, you score four successes and your opponent scores three, then you've succeeded but with only one success, indicating a marginal accomplishment. Although your opponent can't stop you this way, he can still stifle your efforts and slow you down. Gaining an outstanding success on a resisted action rarely occurs.

At times, a combination of resisted and extended rolls may suit the situation. Certain resisted actions — car chases, debates, drinking contests or kick-boxing matches — extend over a period of time and require a series of rolls to determine success. In these cases, you and your opponent both roll several times according to the resisted action rule, but you add your successes over the course of a number of rolls. The first to reach the total set by the Storyteller prevails.

Sometimes, the Storyteller may forgo multiple rolls on what might seem like an extended action if rolling dice threatens to overshadow roleplaying. A single, resisted roll often suffices to determine the final outcome.

TEAMWORK

In certain situations, it makes sense for people to work together to improve their chances of success. Teamwork can apply when characters try to lift something heavy, research a particular subject, break down a door, intimidate someone or figure out a puzzle. All players roll their own dice pools and add their successes. You do not, however, add your dice pools together and make one big roll. Each player must roll separately, then you combine all the results. If anyone botches, the entire attempt may fail utterly.

THE GOLDEN RULE

The most important **Demon** rule to remember is that you control your own game. If a rule doesn't work for you, change it to suit your needs or don't use it. The Storyteller has final say on house rules. Just remember that rules consistency enhances players' enjoyment.

Consider the rules laid out in this book to be flexible guidelines. Every **Demon** game is different.

Types of Actions

Action	Example	Description
Simple	Throwing a punch, dodging a bullet	A one-shot chance of success or failure; success is determined by a single roll. The Storyteller determines the difficulty and the traits that form the dice pool. Automatic success is possible.
Extended	Mountain climbing, tracking in woods	Task stretches over a period of time and each stage renews the chance for failure or success. You make several rolls with the goal of collecting a stated number of successes. This procedure increases the chance that you might botch.
Resisted	Picking a pocket or disarming someone	Action pits two characters against each other. Each player rolls versus a common difficulty number, or one based on the opponent's traits. The two compare successes, and the difference between those determines the degree of success.
Extended & Resisted	Tailing someone evasive, wrestling	Using the resisted-action rule, the players roll repeatedly in order to acquire successes. The first to reach the total set by the Storyteller wins.

Some focus entirely on consent, in which all actions and their success or failure are determined by player decision, with the ultimate goal being the richness of the story. Others follow a strict regimen of randomness, with dice used extensively to introduce excitement and tension to the story. You decide which method to use, or whether you walk a path somewhere between.

Our Golden Rule is simple: "Above all else, play and have fun."

Examples of Rolls

As your game unfolds, characters will attempt all kinds of actions. The rules systems try to account for most things and are designed to be flexible for your needs. More than 270 combinations of Abilities and Attributes give you an incredible range of options when determining which of them applies to a given situation. You may even want to make up your own Talents, Skills and Knowledges to fit more specific character capabilities. The following examples illustrate the diversity of actions you may encounter in your game.

• You have to remove a fallen tree limb from the road before a pursuing car arrives. Roll Strength + Athletics (difficulty 8).

• The director of an art gallery invites you to a reception. You have to impress him with your style and grace to win his trust. Roll Manipulation + Etiquette (difficulty of the director's Perception + Etiquette).

• You've managed to break into an office building, but the guard will make his rounds any minute. Now where is that file? Roll Wits + Computer once per turn (difficulty 8). You have five turns before the guard shows up, and you have to gain a total of 12 successes.

• The Earthbound's thrall is patrolling the exit, but you might be able to slip past when her back is turned. Roll Dexterity + Stealth, resisted by the thrall's Perception + Alertness (difficulties equal opposing dice pools). If you succeed, you get out undetected.

• The cult members are confused after the death of their leader, and you have a chance to make them follow you instead. It all hinges on this one sermon. Roll Manipulation + Expression (difficulty 7).

• You know that crack house is around here somewhere, but it'll be tough to find. Make an extended Perception + Streetwise roll (difficulty 7) every five minutes with a target of 10 total successes.

• Twelve more hours to go on this cross-country drive, and you're the only one who can handle the eighteen-wheeler. Roll Stamina + Drive (difficulty 7) for every hour. You need 12 successes to arrive safely at your destination without having to make a lengthy stop.

• You have to distract the crowd while your allies sneak out the back. You get up on the club's stage and proceed to hurl profanities at the mob. Roll Appearance + Performance (difficulty 6).

• How did an idiot like this get hold of expensive government armaments? Time to work out which

senator is bankrolling these assassins. Roll Wits + Politics (difficulty 6).

• The time for talking has passed. It's time to shoot. Roll Dexterity + Firearms (difficulty 6).

• This deranged occultist has the information you need. Can you trick him into telling you what you want? Roll Manipulation + Occult (difficulty 8).

• You know the answer lies somewhere *inside* this mutilated body. Question is, do you have the will to perform a full autopsy before it's too late? Roll Stamina + Investigation once every hour (difficulty 7) until you gain a total of 15 successes.

• That cop just pulled you over, but you can't let him find the body in the trunk. Can you sweet-talk him into believing you're just a college student on her way back to school? Roll Appearance + Subterfuge (difficulty of the cop's Perception + Subterfuge).

• Someone has infected your computer with a virus. It's slowly eating away all the information you've stored. Can you track the virus before it destroys everything? Roll Intelligence or Wits + Computer once every five minutes (difficulty 6) until you gain a total of 10 successes. The longer it takes, the more information you lose.

• You dropped your cell phone and it fell apart. Can you fix it? Roll Dexterity + Technology (difficulty 8).

• Street people are disappearing, but none of the witnesses want to talk. Can you convince one of them that you want to help? Roll Charisma + Streetwise (difficulty 7).

• You've managed to get a pass into a high-security building. Can you determine what kinds of security systems are used in anticipation of returning uninvited? Roll Perception + Security (difficulty of the security company's Intelligence + Security).

Game Terms

Words, words, words. This list defines some of the terms used in this book, especially in the rules.

• **Ability:** A type of trait to which you assign point values when creating your character, and which determines how many dice you roll. Ability traits represent things for which your character has a natural Talent, as well as Skills and Knowledges he's acquired. Examples include Empathy, Firearms and Medicine.

• **action:** An action is any single activity or feat your character undertakes, including loading a gun,

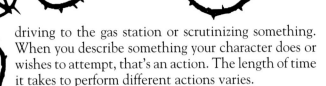

driving to the gas station or scrutinizing something. When you describe something your character does or wishes to attempt, that's an action. The length of time it takes to perform different actions varies.

- **Advantages:** This catch-all category includes Backgrounds as well as the more mystical capabilities that the fallen possess.

- **Attributes:** A type of trait to which you assign point values when creating your character, and which determines the dice you roll. Attribute traits represent your character's innate characteristics, such as how strong (Strength), personable (Charisma) or smart (Intelligence) she is.

- **Background:** A type of trait chosen at character creation that defines aspects of your character's life not directly related to his Attributes or Abilities. Examples of Backgrounds include who your character knows (Contacts, Allies), how much money he has (Resources) or how famous he is (Fame).

- **botch:** When you roll absolutely no successes and at least one 1 shows up in the roll, you botch and your character catastrophically fails the attempted action. If there are any successes — even those canceled by 1s in the roll — it is merely a failure, not a botch. A botch is much worse than a simple failure.

- **character:** In order to play **Demon**, you write up a character, a fictional person you then control in the game. Your character has statistics that represent his capabilities, history and personality. Storytellers likewise create fictional characters to populate the setting and interact with your character.

- **chronicle:** The grand scheme of your game, its overall picture, a chronicle is any story you build from start to finish with a central element of one city, one set of characters or one main, underlying plot.

- **dice pool:** The number of dice you roll to determine the success or failure of your character's action. Relevant traits dictate this number, plus or minus any modifiers. Your Storyteller tells you which traits apply.

- **difficulty number:** A value, assigned by the Storyteller, that a player must equal or beat on each die rolled to achieve successes toward an action. Certain modifiers may affect an action's difficulty number.

- **downtime:** An imaginary period during the course of the game when nothing of significance happens. Players can skim over the events that occur during downtime and fast-forward to the next important event.

- **experience points:** Through the course of the game, your character earns experience points, which you spend to increase his traits. Experience points

represent training, study and honing of capabilities. See p. 164 for more on experience points.

- **extended action:** This type of action requires that you accumulate a certain number of successes over a series of rolls and a period of time.

- **failure:** If you roll no successes and no 1s, or enough 1s to cancel out all your successes, your character fails his attempted action. A failure, unlike a botch, simply means your character has not succeeded and nothing extremely catastrophic occurs.

- **Faith:** This special trait, exclusive to demons, is a measure of the strength of their spiritual energy. Faith has both a permanent rating and temporary points. For more about Faith, see p. 159.

- **Health:** This indicator, which represents how wounded your character is, modifies your dice pools.

- **points:** Certain traits, such as Willpower, rise and fall temporarily throughout the course of play. In order to differentiate between your character's permanent score and his current level in a trait, we call the permanent value the trait *rating*, and the current value the *points* or *pool*. Mark permanent rating in the round dots on your character sheet and mark current level of points in the boxes.

- **rating:** Whereas *points* represent the temporary score of certain traits, the term "rating" refers to the permanent value of those traits. This designation applies to traits such as Willpower.

- **reflexive:** A situation in which dice might be rolled, but that does not count as an action for the purposes of calculating dice pools. Examples of reflexive rolls include soak rolls and Willpower rolls.

- **resisted action:** When another character opposes your character's attempted action, he creates a situation called a resisted action. Both players roll and compare the number of successes gained. The one with more successes wins.

- **scene:** A period of action usually set in one location and a particular time frame. A scene is often broken up into turns, though not always.

- **simple action:** An action that requires only one success to accomplish and that usually involves only one player. More successes indicate a higher level of achievement.

- **story:** The combination of several interconnected scenes. A story is usually characterized by an introduction, conflict, climax and resolution.

- **Storyteller:** One of the players in a roleplaying game takes the responsibility for creating the fictional environment and guiding the story. The Storyteller describes the setting, makes decisions regarding rules and assumes the roles of the main characters' friends

and enemies. He oversees the game and is the final judge on all rules calls.

• **success:** Any die roll that equals or exceeds the stated difficulty number.

• **system:** Any specific set of rules used in a certain situation for guiding the roll of dice to simulate dramatic actions.

• **Torment:** This trait describes how conflicted and anguished a demon's soul is — how far he has strayed from a state of grace. A character's Torment rating rises and falls over the course of the chronicle. See p. 160 for more information on Torment.

• **trait:** During character creation, you assign point values to varying descriptive elements. These

qualities, called traits, define your character's learned Abilities, innate Attributes and worldly Backgrounds.

• **troupe:** Your group of players, including your Storyteller.

• **turn:** An increment of time from three seconds to three minutes in duration used to resolve complex actions and events. A turn is roughly the time it takes your character to perform one action, and it should be kept consistent for all characters in the scene.

• **Willpower:** A measure of your character's self-confidence and internal control. Willpower works differently than most traits, as it is often spent rather than rolled.

He awoke in darkness, deep beneath the earth.

The temple of blue-veined marble dedicated to his name was no more, and his resting place lay beneath a thousand years of dirt and stone. His priests were long since returned to dust, his supplicants scattered by the vengeful hand of God, and the blood-soaked rituals that exalted his deeds were only footnotes in a handful of yellowed old books. Yet the pacts sealed in ancient times, promises of fealty in exchange for generations of wealth and power, were still unbroken. As his soul uncoiled itself in its casket of jeweled bone, he called out to the bloodlines of the faithful, summoning them to his side.

The land he rested in had had many names over the course of his slumber. Now it was known as Anatolia, in eastern Turkey. It was two days before the first of the faithful arrived. They were olive-growers from only a few miles away, and they busied themselves raising tents on the ill-omened hill beneath which he lay. Next came a pair of wealthy businessmen from Greece. A day after that, a family of four arrived from the south of France. Each new arrival greeted the rest as if in a dream, and the nights were soon filled with eerie refrains in a tongue not heard since the world was young.

It was a week before the man from England arrived, landing his company's helicopter in the field below the hill. The others welcomed him to their tents and prepared a feast in his name, for the blood of the high priest flowed in him, an unbroken line stretching back into the mists of ancient times. They danced in his honor beneath the fey moonlight, and when the sun rose on the following day, the first of his earthmoving machines arrived.

They worked through the day and into the night, tearing the hill asunder. By noon the following day, a bulldozer blade unearthed the first of the temple's foundation stones. By the time the sun set that evening, the faithful clustered before the door to the vault, chanting prayers they had heard in their dreams.

They brought his idol into the night air by the light of a blood-red moon, holding it aloft and shouting out his name to the sky. Ecstatic with triumph, they danced among the tumbled foundation stones and slashed their bodies with knives of jagged coral, pouring their salty blood over his graven head. Then at midnight, the man from England took the idol in his hands and spoke the words that writhed like worms in his head.

Within the reliquary, the demon stirred and stretched forth its essence. It flowed into the man like fiery oil, swelling his flesh and searing his veins. He reared above the crowd, twice as large as he'd been before, his skin blackening and splitting, blood vessels bursting and spilling a slurry of cooked blood and flesh.

Belial, the Great Beast, looked out on his blood-soaked supplicants and howled a challenge into the night.

CHAPTER NINE: SYSTEMS

*There are only two kinds of people in the end: those who say
to God, "Thy will be done," and those to whom God says, in the
end, "Thy will be done." All that are in Hell, choose it. Without
that self-choice there could be no Hell.*

—C. S. Lewis, *The Great Divorce*

Demon: The Fallen focuses on roleplaying and story development. Although dice take us out of the story and remind us it's just a game, they can also help develop the story. Rolling dice brings chance into the mix and represents the effects of character strengths and weaknesses. While many Storytellers choose to minimize dice-rolling as much as possible, certain situations may call for it. This chapter covers a number of specific dice mechanics, including general dramatic systems, combat, injury and recovery.

The systems here provide a foundation for covering some of the possible situations that might arise in your game. Written for ease of play, they allow you to return to the story as quickly as possible. If you have alternatives for these systems that work better, use them instead. Furthermore, if a player attempts a particularly clever or inspired approach to a problem, the Storyteller may award an automatic success rather than roll dice.

DRAMATIC SYSTEMS

Your story unfolds through the actions and interactions of the characters. Some of the Storyteller's jobs include keeping events organized, guiding the characters' actions so that they remain logical in both order and time, and describing the imaginary consequences of those actions. The Storyteller determines the difficulty of actions and oversees dice rolls to make sure that they represent events accurately.

Many factors modify dice rolls. Difficulty numbers can change based on the situation. Perhaps your action is opposed directly or your character's mental and physical condition is impaired or heightened. The Attributes and Abilities that form your dice pool may also change according to situational factors. The Storyteller makes a number of decisions when requesting rolls. These decisions might seem overwhelming at first, but the systems provided here help, and they can be mastered quickly. When all else fails, rely on common sense to resolve situations, and have fun. Even after the dice have tumbled, players whose characters have a specialty (p. 136) in a particular Ability may roll extra dice if any 10s turn up.

Attributes and Abilities are typically combined to determine dice pools in the following systems. A character

might not have an Ability he needs for the action, though. The player can either use another Ability that could also be applied to the situation, or he could decide to forge ahead using only the Attribute. Doing so makes the task harder (or even impossible), though, as shown on p. 220 of Chapter Eight.

Many of these systems involve more than just simple actions; some activities can demand a lot of time and effort. You may try a number of them again if the first attempt is unsuccessful, although subsequent attempts might impose a difficulty penalty at the Storyteller's discretion (see Trying it Again, p. 222).

Automatic Feats

Unlike reflexives, automatic feats use up your character's actions, but they don't require dice rolls. They take time and your character's attention, but because of their general ease, rolling dice would be superfluous. Your character has no trouble accomplishing the following actions under normal circumstances.

• **Getting to Feet:** Your character may rise to his feet from the ground or from a seated position without a roll as long as he's not hindered from doing so. In situations where it matters, rising takes one turn and is considered one full action. If your character attempts another action at the same time (such as firing a weapon), the multiple-action rule applies (see Multiple Actions, p. 222). Dexterity + Athletics (difficulty 4) is the roll to stand successfully in such a case.

• **Movement:** Your character may choose to walk, jog or run. Simply walking, she moves seven yards in one turn. When jogging, she moves (12 + Dexterity) yards per turn. When running at full speed, she moves (20 + [3 x Dexterity]) yards per turn.

Your character may move up to half his maximum (running) distance and *then* take another action that turn. Although doing so is not considered a multiple action, the Storyteller may impose a penalty to the action's difficulty number or to your dice pool. If your character moves *while* attempting a second action, though, such as crossing a room while shooting his shotgun, each yard covered subtracts one from the other action's dice pool.

Of course, injured characters cannot move at maximum speed, as per the limitations listed on p. 245.

• **Readying a Weapon:** Whether your character draws a knife or reloads his gun, he must spend a turn arming himself. Doing so usually requires no roll, although your Storyteller may request one under certain stressful circumstances. If your character readies his weapon in conjunction with another action, your Storyteller may ask you to reduce your dice pool for the other action (see Multiple Actions, p. 222) and roll Dexterity + Melee or Firearms (difficulty 4) for the readying attempt.

• **Starting a Car:** It takes a turn to start a car, and certain situations may make doing so more difficult, thus

requiring a dice roll. When people are stressed or hurrying, keys get dropped or won't go into the ignition. A Wits + Drive roll (difficulty 4) may come into play. Common sense determines whether a roll is called for.

• **Yielding:** The initiative rules determine who goes first in a situation (p. 237). You may, however, choose to yield your turn to a player or players following you in the order established. Basically, your character holds off to let another character go first. He may still act later, but you reserve your character's action until then. If everyone, including your Storyteller's characters, yields during a turn, no one does anything, and time moves forward to the next turn.

Physical Feats

The following systems present options related to the three Physical Attributes (Strength, Dexterity and Stamina). Actions involving these Attributes usually require dice rolls. Difficulty numbers vary based on the situation.

• **Climbing [Dexterity + Athletics]:** Your character may attempt to climb any number of things such as rocky cliffs, steel fences, building façades or trees. In most cases, climbing is best dealt with as an extended action. If the object has available handholds and presents few complications, your character moves 10 feet for every success. Therefore, your character could climb into or over a Dumpster with only a marginal success. It may, however, take several rolls to scale a cliff or climb a fence.

Your Storyteller may adjust this rate based on the difficulty of the climb. For example, she may decide that climbing a ladder allows your character to move 15 feet per success, whereas a more difficult climb (such as a coconut tree) might allow your character to move only one foot per success. Many factors can affect rate of travel, including the number of handholds, the smoothness of the surface or even the weather. Your Storyteller has final say in determining all these factors.

As with any extended action, you roll until you have accumulated enough successes. Botching on a climbing roll can prove disastrous, though your character need not necessarily fall to her death. She could get stuck halfway up or she may slip and lose altitude that she has to recover. Or she might indeed fall, causing serious injury or death.

• **Driving [Dexterity/Wits + Drive]:** A single dot in the Drive Skill gives your character the ability to drive a basic, manual-transmission car. (All characters are assumed to be able to drive an automatic.) Under normal circumstances, you don't have to roll to determine successful driving. Bad weather, the vehicle's speed, obstacles and complex maneuvers, however, can challenge even the most competent drivers.

The difficulty number of a driving roll increases as conditions become more hazardous. The Storyteller may, for example, increase the difficulty number by one if your

character attempts to drive in heavy rain or icy conditions. Speeding in an attempt to lose pursuers might increase the difficulty by two. Factors add up, as well. If your character maneuvers in heavy traffic she faces a +1 difficulty, but if your character's car also has a broken windshield, the Storyteller may make it +2, for a total of +3 difficulty.

If you fail a driving roll, your character is in trouble. You must make another roll to determine whether your character crashes or loses control. A botch usually indicates a major malfunction, a skid out of control or a disastrous collision. Your character may still attempt to drive if she has no Drive rating, but you have to roll based on Dexterity or Wits alone at an increased difficulty for every change in course, procedure or speed. Furthermore, if your character has only one dot in Drive, she may still attempt to drive a large truck or even a race car, but the Storyteller may ask you to make repeated rolls, as in an extended action, to determine whether she maintains control of the vehicle.

• **Encumbrance [Strength]:** Your character can realistically carry 25 pounds per point of Strength without penalty. If she attempts to carry more, every action involving physical exertion incurs an automatic +1 difficulty. Furthermore, every 25 pounds she piles on beyond what she can carry easily reduces her base movement by half. If your character tries to carry double her Strength allocation, she can't move at all. Your Storyteller makes the final call on what a character may realistically carry.

• **Intrusion [Dexterity/ Perception + Security]:** Intrusion covers both sides of security-related actions: preventing others from breaching established defenses or actually breaching others' defenses. Sample actions include evading or installing security cameras, lock-picking (or making a lock pick-proof) and avoiding or designing laser movement-detectors.

When breaching security set by another, your roll must succeed on the first attempt if an active security system is present. Failure to do so may activate alarms or set off internal defense systems. If no alarm is present, such as when your character simply attempts to pick a lock to an apartment, your character may continue trying. The difficulty number of an intrusion roll ranges from 5 to 9, depending on whether your character assaults a standard lock or Fort Knox. Certain tasks require that he have at least one dot in the Security Skill, and possibly more, to have any chance of succeeding. Furthermore, many intrusion attempts require special tools such as lock picks or electronic monitoring devices. On a botch, your character bungles the attempt and is in hot water.

When your character attempts to install a security system, roll only once as a simple action. The more successes you get, the better your character's security system is and the more trouble others have in overcoming it. The Storyteller may add your successes to the base difficulty of any future attempts to breach your system.

• **Jumping [Strength, or Strength + Athletics for a running jump]:** You make simple jump rolls versus a difficulty of 3. Your character manages to jump two feet vertically or four feet horizontally for every success you achieve. If your successes do not add up to at least the distance between your character and her destination, your character fails the attempt and lands short. This could be dangerous if, for example, she attempts to leap a chasm. On a failure, however, you may make a Dexterity + Athletics roll (typically difficulty 6) for your character to grab onto a ledge or other protuberance. A botch has far worse repercussions. Your character could be injured seriously, or she might even fall to her death.

You may attempt a Perception + Athletics roll (difficulty 6) prior to a jump to determine whether your character can gauge the distance. If successful, you learn how many successes you need for the leap. This way, you know in advance if the jump seems impossible, and you can change plans before it's too late.

• **Lifting/ Breaking [Strength]:** There's a limit to what your character can lift or break, as shown on the following chart. She may, however, manage to exceed her normal ability in extraordinary circumstances. To attempt to lift more than your character's normal capacity, roll a dice pool equal to your Willpower (difficulty 9). Each success temporarily adds one dot to your character's Strength and moves your character up the chart for the duration of that single action.

If your character fails the action, nothing happens. She simply cannot lift or break the object. If you botch the roll, though, your character might strain a muscle, break bones or drop the item on herself. A botched attempt to lift an object off someone else could end up inflicting further damage.

Feats of Strength		
Strength	Feat	Lift
1	Break a window	40 lbs.
2	Break a wooden chair	100 lbs.
3	Break open a wooden crate	250 lbs.
4	Break a 2" x 4" board	400 lbs.
5	Bend open steel chain links	650 lbs.
6	Break a steel fence	800 lbs.
7	Overturn a small car	900 lbs.
8	Bend steel bars	1000 lbs.
9	Break through a cement wall	1200 lbs.
10	Tear free steel rivets	1500 lbs.
11	Bend 1" sheet metal	2000 lbs.
12	Break a metal lamp post	3000 lbs.
13	Overturn a station wagon	4000 lbs.
14	Overturn a van	5000 lbs.
15	Overturn a truck	6000 lbs.

Several characters can team up to lift or break an object. Individual players roll separately, as per the Teamwork rules (p. 223), and they combine their successes. Their combined Strength scores determine the minimum of what they can do without rolling Willpower.

• **Opening/Closing [Strength]:** In order to have your character break down a door, you must make a Strength roll (difficulty 6 to 8, depending on the door). Standard wooden doors with basic lock mechanisms require only one success to ram open or slam shut. Breaking down a reinforced door might call for 10 successes, whereas a vault door might take 20 or more. Your Storyteller may deem this an extended action, with your character throwing herself at the door multiple times until it breaks. Any resistance makes this a resisted action, too, and it pits characters against each other. A botch might cause a health level of bashing damage to your character's shoulder or send her flying as the door suddenly opens — and she stumbles right out the window on the opposite side of the room.

As with most actions, teamwork makes it easier. Particularly solid doors might require a minimum Strength score even to dent. This system also applies to opening or closing other objects such as locked cabinets or boarded windows.

• **Pursuit [Dexterity + Athletics/ Drive]:** Chase scenes are a staple of both horror and action stories, and they're bound to occur often in your chronicle. In many cases, the formulas for calculating movement speed determine the outcome of the chase (see Movement, p. 231). If your character clearly moves faster, though, she eventually catches up with or escapes the other. Sometimes, situational factors tip the scales. For example, your character might reach safety before being caught, she might know the territory better or find a shortcut, or she might even lose a pursuer.

A basic pursuit is an extended action. Both players roll over the course of several turns to see who reaches a target total of successes first. That person either gets away or catches up. The pursued receives a number of free extra successes based on her distance from the pursuer when the action begins. On foot, your character receives one free success for every two yards head start she has on her pursuer. In a vehicle, she receives one free success for every 10 yards head start.

As you accumulate successes, your fleeing character outdistances her pursuer and increases her chances of losing him. Your opponent may have to make a Perception roll if your character extends her lead far enough to lose her pursuer. This Perception roll is modified based on

the pursuit rolls you've made. Add one to the Perception difficulty for each success you have gathered beyond your opponent's pursuit total. If your opponent fails this roll, he loses your character in a crowd, on a side street or in a maze of hallways and doors. On a Perception botch, the pursuer has no chance of finding your character again. If, you botch any of your rolls, though, your character may wind up in a dead end or trip and fall.

• **Shadowing [Dexterity + Stealth/Drive]:** When your character follows, stakes out or otherwise seeks to keep tabs on someone without being detected, she shadows that person.

Many factors play into how this system is handled. The Storyteller can call it a resisted action (see Resisted Actions, p. 223) and ask you to roll versus a difficulty number based on the target's Perception + Alertness (to avoid being seen) or based on his Dexterity + Stealth or Drive (if the target is actively evasive). You roll with those same traits, then you and your opponent compare successes to determine the outcome. A tie means that the stalker remains undetected.

The Storyteller may also call shadowing both a resisted and an extended action (see Extended Actions, p. 223). Or, to make the roll fast and easy, you could both roll the appropriate dice pool versus a difficulty of 6 (modified based on the environment). In this last case, your opponent must get at least one more success to spot your character. Shadowers who have trained together can combine their separate rolls into one success total through teamwork.

• **Sneaking [Dexterity + Stealth]:** When your character sneaks, attempts to pass unseen or hides, roll Dexterity + Stealth as a resisted action against Perception + Alertness rolls from anyone in the area who has a chance of detecting him. The difficulty on all rolls is usually 6, but certain situations may modify it in favor of either the sneak or anyone who might notice him. Unstable footing or lack of cover can modify Stealth difficulty, just as high-tech security devices or superior vantage points can add dice to the Perception + Alertness rolls of potential spotters. If your sneaking character fails, he isn't necessarily discovered, but he may make a noise that causes guards to become more alert for the next roll. On a botch, your sneaking character runs right into the people he is trying to avoid.

• **Swimming [Stamina + Athletics]:** Your character must have at least one dot in Athletics to know how to swim. Short swims require no roll, but long-duration or long-distance swims do. Your Storyteller may approach a long swim as an extended action with a difficulty based on your character's attempted speed, the weather conditions and the body of water itself. You may have to roll several times to achieve enough successes to meet the target. If you fail a roll, your character might lose some of her total successes, or you might have to make extra rolls. Your character runs into serious trouble on a

botch, such as a cramp or a boatload of enemies attempting to shoot her in mid-stroke.

• **Throwing [Dexterity + Athletics]:** When your character throws something (be it a knife, an ax or an ashtray), distance and accuracy determine whether it hits the target. Your character can throw anything that weighs three pounds or less up to a distance of (Strength x 5) yards. Each additional two pounds decreases the total possible distance by five yards. If your character can pick up an object, but its potential throwing distance drops to zero or below, the best she can do is hurl it to one side, approximately one yard. Obviously, if your character can't lift an object, she can't throw it.

The Storyteller may reduce throwing distances if the object is particularly awkward, or increase them if it is aerodynamic. To throw an object, roll Dexterity + Athletics versus difficulty 6 if target is closer than half the maximum range or difficulty 7 if the target is located between half and maximum range. The Storyteller may adjust the difficulty based on wind conditions, obstacles or whether the target is moving. On a botch, your character may release too late and hit herself or put her weapon in the hands of her enemy.

Social Feats

This section covers tasks involving the three Social Attributes (Charisma, Manipulation and Appearance). Many social situations progress best through roleplaying, so you're encouraged to avoid rolling dice if you can. Act them out instead.

• **Carousing [Charisma + Empathy]:** Some of the most secret information can come from the mouths of drinking buddies and loose-lipped friends. The ability to carouse and show others a good time comes in handy. If your character wishes to win someone over by carousing, roll Charisma + Empathy (difficulty 6). The Storyteller may modify this difficulty if your character faces a particularly surly crowd or resistant individual. The target's Nature (Bon Vivant or Curmudgeon, for example) may also affect the difficulty number. On a botched roll, your character says or does the completely wrong thing and manages to piss everyone off.

• **Credibility [Manipulation/ Perception + Subterfuge]:** The Subterfuge Talent covers attempts both to deceive and to see through a deception. When your character perpetrates a scam, roll Manipulation + Subterfuge— whether he tries to impersonate someone trustworthy, propagate a lie or groom a potential thrall. If your character attempts to detect a lie, roll Perception + Subterfuge. Both parties roll versus a difficulty of 7 and, as with any resisted roll, the one who achieves more successes prevails. On a tie, the lie remains undetected. Particularly expertly forged documents or other props may increase the difficulty for a character to perceive a scam, although teamwork increases the chance that someone sees through it.

The Storyteller may call for hacking or intrusion rolls during the preparation of the scam, depending on how it's set up. If you botch, the plan falls to pieces and, chances are, your scheming character is found out.

• **Interrogation [Manipulation + Empathy/ Intimidation]:** Asking questions is easy. Getting the right answers takes talent. When your character interrogates someone gently (Manipulation + Empathy), he asks strategic questions that lead the target to trust him and reveal information without realizing she's doing it. This requires a resisted action. Roll Manipulation + Empathy, whereas the target gets a dice pool equal to his Willpower, both versus a difficulty of 6. The one with more successes prevails. The Storyteller may also request multiple rolls throughout the course of an interrogation, or he may simply have opponents roll once at the beginning or end of it all.

Not all interrogation is gentle and manipulative, though. Sometimes, interrogators use violent methods to force information from their subjects. This approach involves a resisted roll as well. Whether his character uses torture of the body or the mind, the interrogator's player rolls Manipulation + Intimidation, and the subject rolls a dice pool equal to her Stamina + 3 or Willpower (whichever is higher). Difficulty is 6 for both. Torture may also be treated as a combination of resisted and extended actions. In-game time between rolls may vary, depending on the nature of the interrogation. The Storyteller determines how much time passes.

The victim suffers one health level, bashing or lethal, for every roll the interrogator's player makes during serious physical torture (whether the interrogator is successful in gaining information or not), or he loses one Willpower per roll of mental torture. Combining mental and physical torture has devastating effects on a victim. A botched roll can destroy her mind, cripple her for life or even kill her.

For every success, an interrogator (gentle or violent) gains above his subject's total, he drags out additional information. If the interrogator's extra successes exceed the victim's permanent Willpower at any point, the subject folds completely and divulges everything she knows. Your Storyteller determines the relevancy and extent of information gleaned through interrogation, as a victim often gives a skewed account based on her own perceptions and on what she thinks her interrogator wants to hear.

If two or more interrogators combine efforts, they add their successes. This rule applies even if they are playing "good cop/ bad cop," with one player rolling based on Empathy and the other on Intimidation.

• **Intimidation [Strength/ Manipulation + Intimidation]:** Intimidation has a passive and active side. Passive intimidation is used when your character's presence alone causes people to give him a wide berth or provide whatever he requests. The higher your character's Intimidation trait, the more people try to avoid annoying him. No roll is required.

Your character can also use Intimidation to actively coerce someone into doing something — or *not* doing something. This effort can be a glare, a snarled threat or a gesture, but the threat is evident. In this case, roll Manipulation + Intimidation as in a resisted action. Your opponent rolls her Willpower rating. Both roll against difficulty 6. The target player must achieve more successes than you do or her character bends to your character's will. If you botch, your character only embarrasses himself or seems full of hot air.

A character could forgo threats and physically manhandle the target to intimidate her. Roll for a physical attack according to the combat rules, then roll Strength + Intimidation.

• **Oration [Charisma + Leadership]:** Many situations call for a character to make a speech, from convincing a cult to accept you as its master to convincing the public that a politician is corrupt. Whatever the reason for your character's speech, roll Charisma + Leadership, usually versus a difficulty of 6. The Storyteller may increase or decrease the difficulty based on how receptive the audience is to the ideas expressed. If you fail your roll, the crowd rejects the character's ideas. If you botch, your character may damage her reputation severely, or the crowd may even decide to swarm her.

In the event that your character has time to prepare a speech in advance, the Storyteller may roll the character's Intelligence + Expression (difficulty 7) on your behalf. Success on this roll reduces the difficulty of the upcoming Charisma + Leadership roll by one. Failure changes nothing; a botch indicates the material is inappropriate or offensive to the listeners.

• **Performance [Charisma + Performance]:** A surprising number of the Fallen have strong performing or stage skills. Before the Fall, many Celestials devoted themselves to the arts, and those skills stayed with them even after their internment in Hell. When a character performs live before an audience, roll Charisma + Performance (difficulty 7). As with oration, the audience's mood can increase or decrease this difficulty, as can the show's complexity. One success indicates an enjoyable if uninspired effort, while additional successes make the performance a truly memorable event for even the surliest crowd. On a botch, your character forgets lines, hits the wrong chord or otherwise flubs.

MENTAL FEATS

The following systems cover tasks involving the three Mental Attributes (Perception, Intelligence and Wits). Occasionally, dice rolls related to the Attributes also involve Willpower. Difficulties may vary based on situational factors.

• **Hacking [Intelligence/ Wits + Computer]:** In order for your character to hack into a computer, roll

Intelligence or Wits (depending on the urgency of the job) + Computer versus a variable difficulty based on the complexity and security of the target system. Standard computer systems call for a difficulty of 6, whereas the difficulty could go as high as 10 for military or corporate mainframes. The number of successes you achieve is the number of dice (up to your normal dice pool) that you can roll thereafter to interact with the computer.

If someone (or the system) itself actively attempts to block your hack, a resisted action is called for. The contender who gets the most successes wins. On a botch, your character may be traced and may face repercussions.

• **Investigation [Perception + Investigation]:** Investigating a crime scene, rifling an occult library for clues or performing an autopsy all fall under the general system of Investigation. The Storyteller may call for an extended action when only one clue exists to be found. When multiple clues await the investigator, a simple action may be appropriate. In the latter case, the number of successes rolled determines how much the character finds. One success reveals small details, whereas multiple successes provide major clues or even allow your character to make deductions based on physical evidence. Teamwork certainly helps in investigations. On a botch, your character interprets clues erroneously or destroys them accidentally.

• **Repair [Dexterity/ Perception + Crafts/ Technology]:** Depending on your character's specialty, the Crafts and Technology Skills cover repairs as well as creations — everything from pottery to VCRs. Before your character can repair something, she may need to determine what's wrong with it. Obviously, a cracked vase is cracked, but it's much more difficult to determine why a car won't start. Use a standard research roll (see the following) to analyze the problem. Once your character knows what's wrong, the Storyteller sets the difficulty of the repair. This rating depends on the severity of the problem, the complexity of the broken item, the availability of tools, the quality of replacement parts and whether adverse conditions exist. An exceptional research roll may reduce the difficulty, if appropriate.

As a general rule, changing a tire has a difficulty of 4, whereas rebuilding a car's engine may have a difficulty of 9. The amount of time it takes to repair something also varies, and your Storyteller may treat the repair as an extended action. On a botch, your character may injure herself or irrevocably damage the object she's trying to repair.

• **Research [Intelligence + Occult/ Research/ Science]:** Your character may do research through computer databases, at a library, by studying a particular object or by talking to people. This effort takes time and a good deal of energy, though you typically make only one roll. The Storyteller determines how long research takes. The number of successes on the roll determines how much information your character manages to dig up. One success means that she finds basic information, whereas multiple successes provide more details. The Storyteller may vary the difficulty based on the obscurity of the information sought. If you botch a research attempt, your character discovers nothing at all — or worse, finds completely misleading information.

• **Tracking [Perception + Survival]:** Tracking is different from shadowing in that your character attempts to pick up the trail of someone or something, following physical evidence such as footprints, blood trails or tire marks. Tracking may be treated as an extended action with the possibility that the tracker could lose the trail at some point. The action might also be treated as a single roll with the number of successes determining the amount of information the tracker garners. In the latter case, multiple successes earn your character an understanding of the target's speed, shoe size, type of tire or even whether the target is alone.

The quarry may attempt to cover her trail with a Wits + Survival roll. Each success on this roll adds one to the difficulty of tracking her. Other factors may also affect tracking difficulty, such as weather, ground conditions or available light. If you botch, your character not only loses the trail but destroys it as well.

Combat Systems

Combat is an inescapable part of **Demon: The Fallen**. There is a war being fought — between the fallen and their former masters, between the horrors of the Earthbound and the protectors of humanity — and wars have battles and casualties. This is not a time for sitting on the sidelines — clashes and combats are inevitable.

Combat doesn't have to rule your game, however, nor should it. There are many methods of waging war. Some of the characters' enemies have bank accounts that can be disrupted, leaving them without resources. Some rely on the faith of their followers — cultists who can be deprogrammed or persuaded away, leaving their master powerless. Thinking is *always* an option that can be considered alongside opening up a can of whup-ass.

Combat ultimately plays an undeniable role in your stories, though. The following section details a combat system true to the dynamics, limitations and brutality of real battle, while still leaving enough room for high drama and creativity.

Feel free to ignore or change any of these systems, especially ones that create conflict among players or that interrupt the game's progress. The Storyteller can maintain realism in combat through event description without resorting to tedious rolls for every little move. Use the automatic-success rule (p. 222) where appropriate, and always strive for an outcome that's best for your story.

Despite their powers and abilities, demons still have many human frailties, and their host bodies can still be killed. When a character might die, the dice keep things

DESCRIBING THE SCENE

Part of your Storyteller's job is making sure players have an accurate mental picture of the environment and events surrounding your character. She describes the setting, weather, lighting and the actions of any Storyteller characters involved in the scene. This responsibility is crucial in combat situations, where you need to know the dangers your character perceives and the options from which she may choose.

During combat, the Storyteller describes the changing environment after each turn. Once all players have acted, the Storyteller explains what each character sees and feels. They may all have access to the same information, or each may have his own perspective on transpiring events. These descriptions should be as detailed and creative as possible. This is the Storyteller's chance to show off his narrative talents and turn a series of dice rolls into a dramatic, amusing and entertaining story for the benefit of all.

fair and prevent accusations of favoritism or bulldozing. Although no one wants her character to die, the dice ensure that events transpire without hard feelings.

TYPES OF COMBAT

Two basic types of combat occur, and both use the same fundamental system, with minor differences.

• **Close Combat:** Up close and personal, this includes unarmed combat (Dexterity + Brawl) and melee (Dexterity + Melee). Unarmed combat includes something as raucous as a barroom fight or as organized as a boxing match. Opposing characters use their bodies to fight, and they must be within reach of each other (one yard). During melee, opponents use hand-held weapons, which may include knives, swords or broken bottles. Maximum fighting distance ranges from one to two yards.

• **Ranged Combat:** This type of armed combat involves projectile weapons (Dexterity + Firearms) such as guns, or thrown objects (Dexterity + Athletics). Range varies based on the weapon, though the target must be in sight.

COMBAT TURNS

Combat scenes can sometimes be extremely confusing because so much goes on at one time. Keeping all the actions and repercussions straight is challenging. Combat almost always progresses through a series of three-second turns. The system for handling combat turns is further divided into three stages: initiative, attack and resolution. This division helps the Storyteller track characters' actions and their results.

STAGE ONE: INITIATIVE

Who goes first? You don't have to resort to going clockwise around the table, unless it works for you. We

suggest the following instead. At the beginning of each turn, all players roll one die and add the result to their characters' *initiative ratings* [Dexterity + Wits]. Your Storyteller rolls for any characters she controls in the scene. The player with the highest result acts first, followed by the others in descending order of result. If two characters tie, the one with the higher initiative rating goes first. If both have the same initiative rating, they act simultaneously. Your character's wound penalties (p. 245) subtract directly from his initiative rating.

Next, all players announce their characters' intended actions. Declare these proposed actions in reverse order of initiative, so that faster characters can decide their actions based on what they hear. A fast character has the opportunity to react to a slower character's actions. During this stage, players announce any multiple actions, teamwork, use of powers or Willpower, or even a delay of action to see what other events unfold. The Storyteller may ask for clarification of your character's action to paint a complete picture.

Three possible exceptions can change the initiative order. If you choose to delay your character's action, you may act at any point *after* your designated place in the initiative queue. Called yielding, this option allows your character to pause and wait, so others can act first. You can even interrupt another, slower character's action. If two players both yield and finally decide to act at the same time, the one with the higher original initiative placement goes first.

Defensive actions may also interrupt the normal stream of initiative (see Aborting Actions on p.240 and Defensive Maneuvers on p. 240). You can have your character defend herself at any time as long as you have an action left and either make a successful reflexive Willpower roll or spend a Willpower point. A defensive action takes place at the same time in the turn as the attack against which your character defends. You trade your normal action for the chance to protect against the attack. Your character may defend herself only (block, dodge, parry), though the Storyteller may decide that your character's defensive action does damage to the attacker.

Finally, any extra actions occur after everyone else has gone, no matter where your character falls in the initiative queue. If both you and another player take multiple actions, you go in order of your initiative ratings. Multiple defensive actions—those taken to defend against multiple attacks—occur at the time that the attacks take place, though.

STAGE TWO: ATTACK

Initiative establishes order, and players announce their characters' intentions prior to the attack stage. The attack stage determines the outcome. Players roll for success one at a time, in order. The Storyteller guides you through this process, decides difficulties, chooses which Attribute-Ability combinations apply

and approves the use of Willpower. If your character doesn't have an appropriate Ability, she can still attempt the attack, but the dice pool is modified as per p. 220.

Most combat falls under one of two categories: close or ranged. For close combat, roll either Dexterity + Brawl (unarmed) or Dexterity + Melee (armed). In the case of ranged combat, roll either Dexterity + Firearms (guns) or Dexterity + Athletics (thrown weapons). Any weapon used may modify your dice pool or difficulty, depending on its special or inhibiting aspects such as a targeting scope, antiquity or rate of fire.

Most attacks call for a default difficulty of 6. Situational modifiers (weather, lighting, range or cramped quarters) may adjust this number. If you fail the roll, your character misses and does no damage. If you botch, your character not only misses, but misery strikes. Perhaps the weapon jams or explodes, the blade breaks, or your character punches a brick wall instead of her opponent.

STAGE THREE: RESOLUTION

Once you determine that the attack hits, calculate the damage your character inflicts on his opponent. The type and amount of damage done depends on the method of attack. All attacks have specific damage ratings that indicate the number of dice (the damage dice pool) you roll to determine how much pain and injury your character causes.

The weapon used influences your damage dice pool, as do other situational factors. Any *additional* successes (i.e., all beyond the first one) gained on an attack roll, add an additional die to the damage dice pool. Your character not only hits his opponent, but he lands the blow with greater accuracy or power. If it's *your* character who's wounded, you may attempt to soak damage, rolling to determine whether her natural constitution offsets any harm. The rest of this chapter offers more detailed information on determining damage.

After you determine the damage your character inflicts upon her target, the Storyteller portrays that damage in descriptive terms, narrating the outcome of the attack. Rather than simply say, "Okay, the guy loses three health levels," the Storyteller makes events interesting. He might announce, "You pump three rounds into the guy's chest. He staggers and falls to the ground… and then gets back to his feet. Steam slowly rises from his wounds, and he grins at you as he raises his shotgun." By being evocative, your Storyteller creates atmosphere, entertaining you and lending a sense of narrative continuity to what would otherwise be a series of dice rolls.

COMBAT SUMMARY

Stage One: Initiative

• Everyone rolls initiative. Declare actions in descending numerical order, including multiple actions, activation of powers or Willpower use. The character with the highest initiative attempts her action first. You may yield your turn until later in the initiative queue. With a successful Willpower roll or the expenditure of a Willpower point, your character can defend against an attack in exchange for her normal action. This defensive action takes place at the same time as the attack, no matter when your established initiative falls.

Stage Two: Attack

• Unarmed close combat, roll Dexterity + Brawl.
• Armed close combat, roll Dexterity + Melee.
• Ranged combat (guns), roll Dexterity + Firearms.
• Ranged combat (thrown weapons), roll Dexterity + Athletics.

Stage Three: Resolution

• You determine the damage inflicted by attacks, based on weapon type or maneuver, adding any extra dice gained from successes on the attack roll to the damage dice pool.

• Targets may attempt to soak damage, if possible.

• The Storyteller describes the attack and wounding in narrative terms.

DAMAGE TYPES

Different types of attacks have different damage ratings that indicate the number of dice you roll to determine how much pain and suffering your character inflicts. Called the damage dice pool, it takes many factors into consideration, including the attacker's Strength or the nature of any weapon used.

Damage rolls are made against a base difficulty of 6. Each success inflicts one health level of damage to the victim. The victim may attempt to resist this damage by making a soak roll (see Soak). Based on the nature of the attack, three different types of damage may result:

• **Bashing:** Your character punches, hits with a blunt instrument or otherwise pummels her victim. This type of damage probably doesn't kill the target instantly, but repeated damage could certainly do so. Use your character's Stamina rating to resist bashing effects. Bashing damage heals fairly quickly (see Bashing Damage, p. 247 for more detail).

• **Lethal:** Gunshots, blades and even falling damage might prove instantly fatal to your character. Normal humans may not use Stamina to resist lethal effects, but the fallen and other supernaturally enhanced beings are able to do so. Lethal injuries take quite a while to heal by normal means.

• **Aggravated:** Some supernatural attacks are exceptionally dangerous to the fallen, and are considered sources of aggravated damage. Aggravated damage may not be soaked *at all*, except in rare circumstances where a power or enhancement may offer some protection. Aggravated damage heals at the same rate as lethal damage.

Your damage dice pool, of whatever type, must always have at least one die, regardless of the modifiers. Even the weakest attack has a chance of inflicting a minor amount of damage. Furthermore, you cannot botch a damage roll. If you roll a botch on a damage roll, it simply indicates that your character gives her victim a weak slap that does no real harm.

SOAK

Your character's natural resilience aids her in resisting damage under certain circumstances so that she can "soak" damage. Your soak dice pool equals your character's Stamina rating. Normal humans can resist only bashing damage, unless they have some form of special protection such as armor. The fallen can protect themselves from lethal damage as well, bolstering their resilience with the strength of their Faith.

During the resolution stage of combat, you may roll your soak dice pool to resist damage that your character incurs from attacks. As a reflexive action, this does not cost an action; it occurs automatically. *Soak rolls use a difficulty number of 6 unless modified by your Storyteller.* Each success you roll removes one from the total damage inflicted. As with damage rolls, you cannot botch a soak roll.

ARMOR

While demons can protect themselves from lethal damage, armor is still a useful tool. It also comes in handy for protecting your thralls from danger. Add armor's rating to your character's Stamina (or Faith) score when determining your soak pool. Armor can help protect against bashing, lethal and aggravated damage.

Attackers may make targeting rolls to hit unprotected portions of a defender and thus ignore armor. The Storyteller modifies the attack's difficulty as per Targeting on p. 240.

No armor is indestructible. If the damage rolled in a single attack equals or exceeds double the armor's rating, the equipment is destroyed.

Armor may hinder mobility, too. It subtracts a number of dice from dice pools related to bodily coordination and agility (most Dexterity-based dice pools). Dice pool penalties are provided on the Armor chart (p. 244).

COMBAT MANEUVERS

The following systems are options that characters may use during combat. If you visualize your character's moves — rather than just roll dice for a generic "attack"

— the story becomes more interesting and the drama more intense. Most of these maneuvers take one action to accomplish.

General Maneuvers

• **Aborting Actions:** At any time during a turn, you can abandon your stated action to block, dodge or parry an incoming attack. You must either make a successful Willpower roll (a reflexive action) using Willpower rating as a dice pool (difficulty 6), or you can spend a Willpower point to be allowed to defend automatically. If your Willpower roll fails, your character may not defend, and she must follow through with her originally declared action on your initiative.

You enact your defense at the moment the attack occurs, even if the attack occurs before your place in initiative comes around. If your character has already acted this turn, she may not defend against the attack. (See Defensive Maneuvers, see below, for descriptions of blocking, dodging and parrying.)

• **Ambush:** To have your character sneak up on or secretly lie in wait for her quarry and get a surprise attack, roll Dexterity + Stealth as a resisted roll against the target's Perception + Alertness. If you score more successes than the victim, your character may stage one free attack against him, and you add any extra successes beyond the first in the ambush roll to your attack dice pool. On a tie, your character still attacks first, but the target may defend with a block, dodge or parry. If the target gets more successes, he sees your character coming and both parties roll initiative normally. Targets already involved in combat cannot be ambushed.

• **Blind Fighting/Fire:** Situational factors — pitch darkness, blindness or physical damage — inhibit vision during combat. Attacking while blinded incurs a +2 difficulty to the roll, and ranged attacks cannot be made accurately at all.

• **Flank and Rear Attacks:** If your character attacks from the flank of his target, add a single attack die to your dice pool. If your character attacks from the rear, add two extra attack dice to your pool.

• **Targeting:** If you want your character to attempt a called shot or to aim for a specific location on the target, the difficulty of the attack roll increases. Your character can bypass armor or cover by doing so, however, or he can inflict extra damage by calling a shot. A successful targeted shot, punch or stab can have dramatic results beyond simply inflicting damage, such as destroying an object, blinding an enemy or disarming an opponent.

Target Size	Difficulty	Damage
Medium (leg, arm, briefcase)	+1	No modifier
Small (hand, head, weapon)	+2	+1
Precise (eye, heart, padlock)	+3	+2

Defensive Maneuvers

When under attack, your character may defend rather than following through on her intended action. As long as your character has not yet acted in this turn, she may attempt to dodge, parry or block an incoming attack. To attempt a defensive maneuver, you must either make a successful Willpower roll versus a difficulty of 6 or spend a Willpower point (see Aborting Actions). If your Willpower roll fails, your character must follow through with her originally declared action on your initiative.

Your character can defend against almost any type of attack by using a dodge, block or parry maneuver. Not all of these options work in all situations, though. Dodging may prove impossible in a confined area. Your character doesn't know to block or parry if she's surprised. The Storyteller decides whether your character may realistically attempt a defensive maneuver.

All defensive maneuvers use the same basic system. Each is treated as a resisted action, and your defense roll is compared to the opponent's attack roll. If the attacker rolls equal or fewer successes, he misses. If the attacker rolls more successes than the defender, he subtracts the defender's successes from his own. Any leftovers are added to his damage dice. In this way, even though the defender does not prevent the attack, he reduces the amount of damage he takes from the hit.

• **Block [Dexterity + Brawl]:** Your character uses her own body to deflect a hand-to-hand bashing attack. Lethal attacks cannot normally be blocked unless the defender can soak lethal damage for some reason. Ranged attacks cannot be blocked.

• **Dodge [Dexterity + Dodge]:** Your character bobs, weaves, ducks or dives to avoid an attack. It's assumed that she has the room to maneuver. If not, the Storyteller may disallow a dodge. In melee or brawl combat, the successful defender ducks out of the way of the attack. During a ranged attack, such as in a firefight, the successful defender moves at least one yard and ends up behind cover or prone on the ground. (For advice on what might happen next, see Cover, p. 243.)

• **Parry [Dexterity + Melee]:** Your character uses a melee weapon to deflect either an unarmed or armed close-combat attack. When your character parries with a weapon that can cause lethal damage, the attacker may actually be injured. If you roll more successes on the resisted action, add the weapon's base damage to the number of extra successes you earn on the defense roll. This total forms your damage dice pool, which you roll to determine how much injury the defender inflicts on the attacker.

Defense Complications

Although characters' actions in a turn follow a particular order based on initiative rolls, it's important to remember that all the combat in one turn occurs over a period of only three seconds, which makes events nearly simultaneous. As a result, your character may defend against attacks that occur later in the initiative queue if you announce that she intends to use

a multiple action to either take both an offensive action and a defensive one or to just defend for the entire turn. This differs from what would happen if you wanted to abort your regularly scheduled action to have your character defend against an earlier attack. In the case of aborting, you give up your regular action and cannot defend against subsequent attacks.

If you perform a multiple action involving both offensive and defensive actions, your character attacks when your place in the initiative queue comes up, then also defends against any attacks thrown at her by characters who follow her in the queue. The multiple-action system applies, though, and each subsequent defensive action becomes more difficult (see Multiple Actions, p. 222).

Note that naming *multiple opponents* to defend against complicates matters further and adds to defense rolls' difficulty numbers (see Multiple Opponents, p. 242).

Rather than attack *and* defend in the same turn, your character can choose to do nothing *but* defend against attacks. As with the preceding system, doing so differs from aborting your turn to defend against an attack that occurs prior to your regularly scheduled action. Instead, you defend against only those attacks that occur simultaneously with or following you in the initiative queue. Your character may not defend against attacks that happen prior to her regular action. If your character does nothing but defend in this manner, do not use the multiple-action system. Rather, you have a full dice pool for the first defensive action and lose one die from it for each subsequent defensive action made in the same turn. When you run out of dice, your character may no longer defend against attacks. It's tough to avoid several incoming attacks.

MANEUVER CHARACTERISTICS

You usually roll combat maneuvers against a difficulty of 6. Certain special combat effects and situational factors modify your attack roll, difficulty number or damage dice pool. The following categories explain maneuver characteristics in this chapter's rules.

• **Traits:** The recommended Attribute + Ability traits used for the maneuver. If your character doesn't have the appropriate Ability, default to the Attribute alone and modify the difficulty as per p. 220.

• **Accuracy:** Some maneuvers add dice to attack rolls. A "+3" adds three dice to the attacker's dice pool for that attack.

• **Difficulty:** Some maneuvers impose modifiers, positive or negative, to an attack's difficulty. Base difficulty is 6, and any modifiers listed add to or subtract from it. A "+2" indicates that the attack's difficulty — initially 6 — increases to 8.

• **Damage:** This category is the damage dice pool.

CLOSE COMBAT MANEUVERS

This is simply a list of the common maneuvers used in close combat. Your character can create his own; the Storyteller determines the appropriate traits, difficulty, accuracy and damage involved.

All brawling combat inflicts bashing damage unless stated otherwise. Weapon type determines the damage inflicted in melee (see the Melee Weapons chart, p. 244). Damage inflicted using a weapon is typically considered lethal, though blunt objects such as clubs or bats inflict bashing damage. Weapons never cause aggravated damage, unless they have some supernatural enhancement. Physical enhancements such as horns or claws might cause any of the three types of damage.

The Storyteller may modify the difficulties and damages of the maneuvers described in this section, depending on the combat style your character uses. Always remember that what works best for drama and the story takes precedence over rules.

• **Clinch:** Your character grapples her target. She applies a clinch with a successful attack roll. Roll Strength damage in the first turn. In subsequent turns, your character and his opponent act in order of placement in the initiative queue. The attacker can attempt to inflict damage automatically by squeezing (Strength); no further attack roll is required. The victim can try to escape the clinch with his action. Neither may perform any other type of action until the victim breaks free or is released. Make resisted Strength + Brawl rolls for the victim to escape a clinch. If the escaping character gets more successes, he breaks free. Otherwise the two continue to grapple.

Traits: Strength + Brawl   **Difficulty:** Normal
Accuracy: Normal **Damage:** Strength

• **Disarm:** A character can knock a weapon out of an opponent's hand by making an attack roll at +1 difficulty (usually for a total of 7). If successful, roll damage dice. If damage successes exceed your opponent's Strength score, your character knocks the weapon free. Your opponent takes no damage, though, since the attack focuses on the weapon rather than the wielder. If you botch, your character may drop her weapon or get in the way of a blow instead.

Traits: Dexterity + Brawl/ Melee   **Difficulty:** +1
Accuracy: Normal **Damage:** Special

• **Hold:** This maneuver resembles a clinch, but without intent to do damage. Your character immobilizes but does not injure the target. If your roll succeeds, your character manages to hold her target until the target's next action. Both players roll resisted Strength + Brawl at that time. If your opponent gets more successes, he is free. If he does not, the victim remains immobilized until his next action — at which point he may try again.

Traits: Strength + Brawl   **Difficulty:** Normal
Accuracy: Normal **Damage:** None

• **Kick:** A simple knock to the shins imposes a +1 modifier to difficulty and inflicts the attacker's Strength +1 in damage. The Storyteller may increase these numbers if your character attempts a spinning martial-arts kick to the head or something equally complex.

Traits: Dexterity + Brawl   **Difficulty:** +1
Accuracy: Normal **Damage:** Strength +1

• **Multiple Opponents:** When fighting multiple opponents, your character suffers attack *and* defense difficulties of +1, cumulative for each opponent after the first, to a maximum of +4.

• **Strike:** Your character simply punches. The base attack is a simple action that inflicts your character's Strength in damage. The Storyteller may wish to increase the difficulty and/ or damage dice if the attack is more complex or targeted at a specific location. Most attacks using physical enhancements (claws, fangs, etc.) are simply variations on a strike.

Traits: Dexterity + Brawl   **Difficulty:** Normal
Accuracy: Normal **Damage:** Strength

• **Sweep:** Your character attempts to knock her opponent off his feet with a sweep of the leg or use of a weapon such as a staff or chain. If your roll proves successful, your character's opponent takes Strength damage and must roll Dexterity + Athletics (difficulty 8) to avoid a knockdown (see Maneuver Complications, p. 243).

Traits: Dexterity + Brawl/ Melee   **Difficulty:** +1
Accuracy: Normal   **Damage:** Strength; knockdown

• **Tackle:** Your character rushes her opponent in an attempt to tackle him to the ground. Your attack roll suffers a +1 difficulty modifier. If successful, Strength + 1 damage is inflicted. *Both* players must roll Dexterity + Athletics (difficulty 7), however, lest their characters suffer a knockdown (see Maneuver Complications, p. 243). Even if your character's target succeeds at his Athletics roll, he is still unbalanced and suffers a +1 difficulty to his actions in the next turn.

Traits: Strength + Brawl   **Difficulty:** +1
Accuracy: Normal **Damage:** Strength +1

• **Weapon Strike:** Your character uses a weapon to slash, thrust or jab in melee. See the Melee Weapons chart, p. 244, for particulars.

Traits: Dexterity + Melee   **Difficulty:** Normal
Accuracy: Normal **Damage:** Per weapon type

RANGED COMBAT MANEUVERS

A number of strategies affect ranged-combat maneuvers. Many physical conflicts involve ranged weapons, and the following systems offer ways to deal with them. Feel free to create your own maneuvers. The Ranged Weapons chart, p. 245, provides more specific information.

• **Aiming:** For each turn that your character aims at her target, add one die to your attack pool. The maximum

number of dice that can be gained this way equals your character's Perception, and your character must have at least one dot in Firearms to perform this maneuver. If the weapon has a scope, add two more dice when your character aims. Your character must focus on aiming during this time and can perform no other actions. Taking an action before shooting, even to defend, cancels the benefits of time spent aiming. Furthermore, your character cannot aim at a target moving faster than a walk.

• **Automatic Fire:** A weapon unloads its entire ammunition clip in one attack against a single target. You make one roll, adding 10 dice to the weapon's accuracy. The difficulty increases by two, however, due to recoil. Extra successes beyond the first add to your damage dice pool, which is still treated as equivalent to that of one bullet. When using automatic fire, your character may not target a particular part of the body or object, and she may attempt the maneuver only if her weapon's clip is at least half-full when she fires.

Traits: Dexterity + Firearms **Difficulty:** +2
Accuracy: +10 **Damage:** Special

• **Cover:** Your character may duck behind a wall, lie flat on the ground or use another character as a shield. All these maneuvers constitute cover. It makes your character more difficult to hit, but it may also make it awkward for your character to attempt other actions. The difficulty to hit a character behind cover increases according to the following chart.

By the same token, the difficulty to fire back from the safety of cover increases, since your character must pop up, fire, then duck down again. If your character fires back from shelter, the difficulty modifier to your roll is one less than the modifier listed on the chart. Therefore, if the listed difficulty is +1, you suffer no increase to your difficulty for firing back.

If both combatants take cover, difficulty modifiers are cumulative. If your character hides behind a car and her target hits the dirt — prone — your attack difficulty is modified by +2 (+1 for firing at a prone target, and +1 for firing from behind a car). Your opponent's difficulty is also modified by +2 (+2 for firing at a target behind a car, though he takes no modifier for firing from a prone position).

Cover Type	Difficulty Increase
Light (lying prone, behind streetlight)	+1
Good (behind car)	+2
Superior (around a corner)	+3

• **Multiple Shots:** Your character can take more than one shot in a turn as a multiple action. The first shot's dice pool decreases by the total number of shots fired, and each subsequent shot's pool drops by an additional die, cumulatively. The weapon's rate of fire limits how many shots your character can get off in a turn.

Traits: Dexterity + Firearms **Difficulty:** Normal
Accuracy: Special **Damage:** Weapon type

• **Range:** The Ranged Weapons chart, p. 245, lists each weapon's short range. All attacks at short range call for a difficulty of 6. A weapon's maximum range is double its short range. Attacks from a range greater than short, but less than maximum, have a difficulty of 8. A target within two meters of the attacker is at point-blank range. Roll point-blank shots versus a difficulty of 4.

• **Reloading:** Your character must spend one full turn to reload her gun. She may reload while doing something else as a part of a multiple action at the Storyteller's discretion.

• **Strafing:** Firing a full-automatic weapon across an area rather than at a specific target adds 10 dice to a standard attack roll and empties the clip. This maneuver, called strafing, covers a maximum of three yards.

Make one attack roll and, if successful, divide your successes evenly among all targets in the designated area. The successes assigned to a particular target are added to your damage dice pool for that specific target, as well. If there is only one target within range or area of effect, only half the successes affect him. If you roll fewer successes than there are targets, you or the Storyteller assign one per target until all have been allocated. (Your Storyteller may prefer to allocate successes randomly; other targets remain unaffected). Dodge rolls versus strafing are at +1 difficulty.

Traits: Dexterity + Firearms **Difficulty:** +2
Accuracy: +10 **Damage:** Special

• **Three-Round Burst:** Your character fires three shots from the weapon's clip at a single target, and you gain two additional dice on your attack roll. Only certain weapons have the capacity to fire this way (see the Ranged Weapons chart). Recoil adds one to the difficulty of your attack roll. As with automatic fire, your damage dice pool is formed as if only one bullet had been fired from the weapon.

Traits: Dexterity + Firearms **Difficulty:** +1
Accuracy: +2 **Damage:** Weapon type

• **Two Weapons:** Your character gains a distinct advantage by firing two weapons at once, although this maneuver has its share of complications. Considered a multiple action, the maneuver imposes the standard reduced dice pools for total shots fired. Recoil modifiers apply as well. Additionally, your attack rolls suffer +1 difficulty for her off hand, unless she's ambidextrous. Your character may fire a number of shots equal to the weapons' rates of fire.

Traits: Dexterity + Firearms **Difficulty:** +1/ off-hand penalty
Accuracy: Special **Damage:** Weapon type

MANEUVER COMPLICATIONS

Combat can be complicated by numerous events, several of which are listed here. Your Storyteller should feel free to come up with others as a situation warrants.

• **Blinded:** If your character acts against a blind opponent, you gain two extra dice on any attack rolls.

On the other hand, blind characters receive a +2 modifier to the difficulty of all actions.

• **Dazed:** If, on any single attack, your damage successes exceed the target's Stamina (for humans) or Stamina +2 (for demons), the victim is dazed. Only successes left over after the defender's soak attempt apply and are compared to the defender's Stamina. A dazed victim loses his next action, and he can neither act nor defend during that time.

• **Immobilization:** When your character attacks an immobilized victim who can still struggle (held by someone, for example), add two dice to your attack roll. All attacks hit automatically if the victim is completely immobilized (tied up or somehow paralyzed).

• **Knockdown:** Your character falls or is forced off his feet. Make a Dexterity + Athletics roll to determine whether he can stand immediately. His initiative decreases by two in the next turn, however. If the roll fails, your character's next action can be to rise. In case of a botch, your character falls hard or at an odd angle and suffers one bashing health level of damage automatically.

Your character may use certain maneuvers such as sweep or tackle to knock an opponent down. Other particularly powerful attacks — a solid punch or a hit with a bashing weapon — may also knock a target flat. Your Storyteller decides if a knockdown occurs in these instances. They happen only when they are cinematic or appropriate to the story.

MELEE WEAPONS

Weapon	Damage	Conceal
Sap	Str +1	P
Club	Str +2	T
Knife	Str +1	J
Sword	Str +2	T
Small Ax	Str +2	T
Large Ax	Str +3	N

Weapon: Your character may use many other items as weapons (meat cleaver, pencil, razor, chair). Apply the listing above that approximates the weapon used.
Concealment: P = Can be hidden in pocket; J = Can be hidden in jacket; T = Can be hidden in trench coat; N = Cannot be concealed at all.

ARMOR

Class	Armor Rating	Penalty
Class One (reinforced clothing)	1	0
Class Two (armor T-shirt)	2	1
Class Three (Kevlar vest)	3	1
Class Four (flak jacket)	4	2
Class Five (full riot gear)	5	3

CLOSE-COMBAT MANEUVERS

Maneuver	Traits	Accuracy	Difficulty	Damage
Block	Dex + Brawl	Special	Normal	(R)
Clinch	Str + Brawl	Normal	Normal	Str (C)
Disarm	Dex + Brawl/ Melee	Normal	+1	Special
Dodge	Dex + Dodge	Special	Normal	(R)
Hold	Str + Brawl	Normal	Normal	(C)
Kick	Dex + Brawl	Normal	+1	Str +1
Parry	Dex + Melee	Special	Normal	(R)
Strike	Dex + Brawl	Normal	Normal	Str
Sweep	Dex + Brawl/ Melee	Normal	+1	Str (K)
Tackle	Str + Brawl	Normal	+1	Str +1 (K)
Weapon Strike	Dex + Melee	Normal	Normal	Weapon

(C): The maneuver carries over into successive turns.
(K): The maneuver causes a knockdown.
(R): The maneuver reduces an opponent's attack successes.

RANGED-COMBAT MANEUVERS

Maneuver	Traits	Accuracy	Difficulty	Damage
Automatic Fire	Dex + Firearms	+10	+2	Weapon
Multiple Shots	Dex + Firearms	Special	Normal	Weapon
Strafing	Dex + Firearms	+10	+2	Weapon
3-Round Burst	Dex + Firearms	+2	+1	Weapon
Two Weapons	Dex + Firearms	Special	+1/ off-hand	Weapon

RANGED WEAPONS

Type	Damage	Range	Rate	Clip	Conceal	Example
Revolver, Lt.	4	12	3	6	P	SW M640 (.38 Special)
Revolver, Hvy.	6	35	2	6	J	Colt Anaconda (.44 Magnum)
Pistol, Lt.	4	20	4	17+1	P	Glock 17 (9mm)
Pistol, Hvy.	5	30	3	7+1	J	Sig P220 (.45 ACP)
Rifle	8	200	1	5+1	N	Remington M-700 (30.06)
SMG, Small*	4	25	3	30+1	J	Ingram Mac-10 (9mm)
SMG, Large*	4	50	3	30+1	T	HK MP-5 (9mm)
Assault Rifle*	7	150	3	42+1	N	Steyr-Aug (5.56mm)
Shotgun	8	20	1	5+1	T	Ithaca M-37 (12-Gauge)
Shotgun, Semi-auto	8	20	3	8+1	T	Fiachi-Law 12 (12-Gauge)

Damage: Indicates the damage dice pool.

Range: This number represents the practical shot range in yards (difficulty 6). Your character may fire at twice this distance, but attacks are considered long range (difficulty 8).

Rate: The maximum number of bullets or three-round bursts a gun can fire in a single turn. This rate does not apply to full-auto or strafing attacks.

Clip: The number of shells a gun can hold — the +1 indicates a bullet can be held in the chamber, ready to fire.

Concealment: P = Can be hidden in pocket; J = Can be hidden in jacket; T = Can be hidden in trench coat; N = Cannot be concealed at all.

*Indicates that the weapon is capable of three-round bursts, full-auto and strafing.

HEALTH

Your character's Health trait represents how healthy or wounded she is. When your character suffers damage, every success removes one level of Health from her. As your character becomes progressively more injured, her wounds affect her ability to perform actions (modifiers are applied to the dice pools of certain tasks). If she's hurt badly enough, she may become incapacitated, need hospitalization or even die. And if she lives, months may pass before she heals fully, unless she benefits from supernatural aid. The following section explains Health in detail.

THE HEALTH CHART

Track your character's current physical condition on the Health chart located on your character sheet. This chart indicates the penalties imposed to your dice pools for each level of injury your character sustains. As he suffers more injuries, his health declines, his actions become more difficult and he may eventually fall unconscious or die.

Every character has seven health levels ranging from Bruised to Incapacitated. If he has no injuries at all — no levels checked off on the sheet — your character is in perfect health. If he falls below Incapacitated, he's dead. Whenever your character's attacker scores a success on a damage roll, mark off one health level on your character's Health chart. Multiple successes deliver multiple levels of damage. For example, if your character's attacker achieves one success on a damage roll (after your soak roll) and your character is currently in perfect health, that damage success reduces him to Bruised. You mark off the first box on your character sheet (Bruised).

The number to the left of the lowest box marked indicates your current dice-pool penalty. The more damage your character takes, the more difficult it becomes for

HEALTH CHART

Health Level	Dice-Pool Penalty	Movement Penalty
Bruised	—	Slightly contused; your character suffers no movement or dice-pool penalties.
Hurt	-1	Superficially hurt; your character suffers no movement penalties.
Injured	-1	Your character's movement is impaired slightly (halve maximum running speed).
Wounded	-2	Significantly hurt; your character may not run, though he may still walk or jog.
Mauled	-2	Badly hurt; your character may hobble no more than three yards per turn.
Crippled	-5	Extremely hurt; your character may crawl no more than one yard per turn.
Incapacitated	—	Direly hurt; possibly unconscious; your character may do nothing, take no actions, and only certain reflexes such as soak may be attempted if he's unconscious.
Dead	—	The end of the road for mortals. Demons, though, may not have to throw in the towel just yet....

him to act at full capacity. Subtract the penalty listed beside your character's current health level from your dice pool for every action your character performs (including initiative rolls, but excluding reflexives such as soak rolls) until the wound heals. These penalties also affect movement, impairing it based on the level of injury.

Incapacitated

When your character's Health drops to Incapacitated, your character may or may not be conscious, at the Storyteller's discretion. He may request that you make a Stamina roll to determine whether your character remains awake. If she's unconscious, she may not perform any reflexives related to her Faith or Willpower, though she may still attempt to soak any further damage. If your character manages to remain conscious, she may continue to perform all reflexives, though she has fallen and can't get up — at least not until some of her wounds have healed. She may also speak, but even that may prove difficult. The Storyteller may request a Willpower roll or expenditure for your conscious character to say anything at all.

Applying Damage

Your character can sustain three different types of damage: bashing, lethal and aggravated. Bashing damage includes any wounds inflicted by blunt instruments, punches, kicks or other similar trauma. Lethal damage comes from knives, bullets or any type of attack that actually pierces or cuts flesh. Aggravated damage is caused by fire or by supernatural sources. All types of injuries are cumulative, and the resulting total determines your character's current health level. Specifics on each type of damage are provided here.

When marking your character's damage on his character sheet, record a slash "/" for bashing damage, an "X" for lethal damage and an asterisk "*" for aggravated damage. These marks go in the boxes beside the different health levels on the Health chart. Mark the top square first and work your way down, filling them in as your character becomes more wounded.

When your character acquires a mixture of damage types, mark the aggravated damage at the top; it pushes any lethal or bashing damage down. Lethal damage is marked next; it pushes any bashing damage down. For example, if you mark that your character has taken a level of bashing damage in the Bruised box, and she then takes a level of lethal damage, mark the Bruised box with an "X" for the lethal damage and move the bashing damage down by putting a "/" in the Hurt box. Any further bashing damage goes in the Injured box and beyond. Any further lethal damage pushes the entire thing down again until all the boxes are marked with either "/", "X" or "*".

Once all the boxes are marked, any further damage, of whatever type, causes existing bashing damage to turn into lethal damage on a one-to-one basis. Once all the boxes are marked, it isn't necessary to continue pushing bashing damage downward. Any further lethal damage simply marks over existing bashing damage.

DEMON: THE FALLEN

Example: *Rebecca is captured by two Earthbound cultists at the temple compound. One of them hits her with a nightstick, causing one level of bashing damage. Adam, her player, marks that on Rebecca's character sheet by putting a "/" in the box next to Bruised. Rebecca manages to knock the guard down, but the other one shoots her at close range, doing two levels of lethal damage. Adam marks this damage with an "X" in the boxes next to Bruised and Hurt, then moves the original bashing damage down by marking a "/" in the box next to Injured. Staggered by her wounds, Rebecca still has enough vigor to draw her shotgun and fire blindly at the guards. They fall back, allowing her the chance to get into her car and drive off.*

BASHING DAMAGE

Any kind of damage that does not pierce the body, but that batters against it, is considered bashing damage. This includes most damage from hand-to-hand combat, punches, kicks, beatings with a blunt instrument and even falling or being thrown into a brick wall. Use a "/" when marking bashing damage on your character sheet.

Once your character falls to Incapacitated, mark any further bashing damage over your existing bashing levels (using "Xs" this time). Skip any boxes already marked with lethal damage and move down to the first that is bashing only. Each level that goes from "/" to "X" due to ongoing bashing trauma is now considered lethal. Once your character goes one level below Incapacitated with lethal damage ("X"), she dies. Your character may therefore die from prolonged bashing attacks, but not nearly as quickly as from lethal damage alone (see Healing Bashing Damage).

If bashing damage injures your character to the level of Incapacitated, she may neither act nor move as dictated by the Incapacitated rules, above.

Example: *Rebecca drives back toward town, pursued by a truckload of cultists. The truck hits the back of her car, slamming her into the steering wheel. She suffers two levels of bashing damage. Adam marks these on her character sheet as slashes next to Wounded and Mauled. The new wounds add to the ones Rebecca has already sustained.*

Seriously injured, Rebecca speeds desperately toward town, hoping to escape her pursuers. Adam fails a crucial Drive roll, however, and Rebecca crashes her car into a tree. The crash inflicts another three levels of bashing damage. Adam marks two of them on Rebecca's Health chart as a "/" in the boxes next to Crippled and Incapacitated. He then marks the last one as an "X" next to Injured. Because the chart is full, he must turn the uppermost bashing damage he's already marked into lethal damage. Any further bashing damage slowly turns those "/" marks into "X" marks. Rebecca lies unconscious in the wreck car, defenseless as the truck pulls up nearby....

LETHAL DAMAGE

Attacks made with piercing or cutting weapons — such as knives or guns — deliver lethal damage. Fire and electricity also cause lethal damage. A mortal character may not usually soak lethal damage at all, but demons may soak lethal damage through the use of their special powers. Mark lethal damage on your character sheet with an "X." Once your character becomes Incapacitated lethally, meaning that you have marked an "X" in the box next to Incapacitated, any further bashing or lethal damage kills your character.

Lethal wounds require medical attention to prevent serious bleeding. If you mark an "X" next to Wounded or beyond on your character's sheet, your character suffers one extra lethal level of damage automatically for each hour that passes without medical attention. One success on an Intelligence/ Wits + Medicine/ Survival roll by a rescuer — or by the character, if she's not Incapacitated — stops the bleeding. Demons also have the ability to stop their bleeding by sheer force of will. Demon characters may spend a point of Faith and make a Willpower roll in this situation. If it succeeds, the bleeding stops.

If you mark an "X" next to Crippled or Incapacitated on the damage track, your character *must* seek more complete medical care, or she will not recover at all. If your character has an "X" next to Incapacitated, he is comatose at worst and delirious at best, and he could still die even if all attacks have stopped. Again, demons are hardier than mortals — they can use their Faith to heal their most grievous injuries.

Example: *Rebecca lies stunned in the crashed car, as the cultists get down from their truck. The mortals open fire, riddling the car with bullets. Most of the gunfire misses Rebecca, but she is hit once.*

She already has three lethal wounds and is Incapacitated from her bashing wounds. The bullet does just one level of lethal damage (it doesn't hit any vital organs). Adam marks the Wounded box with an "X." Because the chart is already full with bashing damage to the level of Incapacitated (as shown in the previous example), he doesn't need to push down the bashing damage.

Weakened by the barrage, the car collapses in on itself, and Rebecca is pinned down by the wreckage. The impact of the collapse inflicts another bashing level on Rebecca. Adam marks through the bashing damage next to the Mauled box, making it lethal. He does so because Rebecca's chart is full, and any further bashing damage marks over what bashing damage is already there.

Rebecca is helpless, badly injured and trapped in the wrecked car. Things look grim — until her fallen allies suddenly appear next to the truck. They use their powers and weapons to quickly eliminate the surprised cultists, before rescuing Rebecca and getting her medical attention.

AGGRAVATED DAMAGE

Attacks from supernatural sources, such as a demon's claws, enchanted or imbued objects and certain evocations deliver aggravated damage. Aggravated damage is even harder to soak than lethal damage. Demons may not soak aggravated damage at *all*, unless they have a power or

enhancement that allows them to do so. Aggravated damage is also much harder to heal than other damage types. Demons may not use Faith or powers to heal aggravated wounds, but must instead heal naturally over time. Mark aggravated damage on your character sheet with an asterisk "*". Apart from these factors, though, aggravated damage is the same as lethal damage.

HEALING TIMES

Human beings heal slowly, and while demons are something other than human, they still retain some of the frailties of their hosts. Although demonic powers can repair damage, demons heal at the same rate as humans, and an injury can remove a character from action for months. Healing may occur during downtime (see p. 219), but only if nothing else of importance occurs during that period.

The following sections explain how characters heal. Every level of damage (whether bashing or lethal) must be recovered individually. Therefore, a character reduced to Incapacitated by bashing damage must spend a full 12 hours at that level before he can even hope to be only Crippled. Once he has healed from Incapacitated to Crippled, he must spend another six hours at Crippled before he heals to Mauled, and so on.

HEALING BASHING DAMAGE

Bashing damage involves injuries that simply bruise the body through a blunt attack such as brawling combat or a fall. Bashing damage does not require medical attention. The wounds eventually heal on their own. Serious injuries, however, may have greater consequences. Your character's vision or hearing may suffer due to concussion. She might also experience excruciating pain from internal bruising or even lose muscle control in a limb. Appropriate medical attention can negate some of these effects, and injuries healed with Faith or powers never leave any lingering consequences or scars.

HEALING TIMES FOR BASHING DAMAGE	
Health Level	**Recovery Time**
Bruised to Wounded	One hour each
Mauled	Three hours
Crippled	Six hours
Incapacitated	12 hours

HEALING LETHAL AND AGGRAVATED DAMAGE

Lethal wounds can kill characters quickly, as being disemboweled, shot or dismembered has disastrous implications. Aggravated damage is even worse. Both types of damage heal at the same rate.

HEALING TIMES FOR LETHAL DAMAGE	
Health Level	**Recovery Time**
Bruised	One day
Hurt	Three days
Injured	One week
Wounded	One month
Mauled	Two months
Crippled	Three months
Incapacitated	Five months

DEMONIC HEALING POWERS

The power of faith transcends the weakness of the flesh. The supernatural vigor of a demon allows him to ignore many of his host's vulnerabilities. All demons have the ability to rebuild their damaged bodies or to cleanse their systems of pain and fatigue, simply by filling their mortal shell with the breath of life.

For a demon to instantly heal his wounds, he needs a moment's concentration to touch the fabric of reality and draw upon its energy. In game terms, this means he needs an entire turn to heal wounds. During this turn, the demon cannot make any other actions — he cannot attack, defend himself or even move. Doing so leaves him sorely vulnerable, so while it is possible to do this in the midst of combat, it's a dangerous tactic indeed. It's often something best done when a battle is over, or if the demon is safely behind cover.

Once the demon finds that moment of calm, he can spend one point of Faith. Doing so instantly heals one level of lethal damage, or *all* levels of bashing damage. Only one point of Faith can be spent thus each turn — if the demon needs to repair multiple levels of lethal damage, it takes multiple turns of concentration.

If the demon is attacked and takes damage while trying to heal himself, the attack breaks his concentration and ruins his effort to heal himself. The attempt is unsuccessful and the demon suffers further damage, although he does not lose any Faith.

STATES OF GRACE

The powers of the Fallen are many and varied, and the impact they have on the running of **Demon** chronicles is considerable. Chapter Seven deals with the details and mechanics of Celestial powers. This chapter looks at systems and methods for implementing those powers and defining how demons interact with the normal world.

These systems are less mechanically strict than many of the other systems in this chapter. Demonic powers have a huge impact on a chronicle's progress and feel, so they can't be determined simply with dice and tables. Much of the work lies with the Storyteller, who should make decisions based on what she feels is best for her story and her chronicle.

FAITH

Faith is the energy of the cosmos, the breath of the Creator and the lifeblood of the damned. Demons use Faith to enhance themselves, or to alter reality using the tools given them by their former Lord.

The irony is that demons cannot generate Faith themselves. Faith is about belief, not knowledge, and demons *know* the truth about the Creator and His grand experiment. For a demon, simply *believing* in God is as effective as regular people *believing* in lawn furniture.

Unable to feel the Faith they require, demons must turn to humans for their belief. By opening a mortal's eyes to the wonders and horrors of the cosmos, a demon can draw out the precious breath of Faith from within that person and use it for their own ends. This isn't an easy task, since most inhabitants of the World of Darkness live a life in which faith and piety are irrelevant fossils. Gaining Faith from a human requires hard work and dedication, but the rewards justify the effort.

There are two ways in which a demon can collect Faith from a mortal. Faith can be *reaped* from a human by forcing him to acknowledge the existence of the demon deep within his soul. A willing mortal can also *offer* Faith in return for promises of wealth, influence or power.

REAPING FAITH

In the World of Darkness, God is considered almost as much a folk legend as Santa Claus. People may pay lip service to a religion, but it's a hollow, meaningless habit for most. Going to church has as much emotional meaning for most people as picking up their dry cleaning. But it's possible to show a human the truth about the cosmos and the Creator, to reawaken his desiccated soul and let the breath of God flow from him. All it takes is an act of transcendent holiness — or mind-blasting depravity.

If a demon can show a human the truth about the world, can show him her Celestial nature, she may be able to harvest some slight power from the mortal's brief

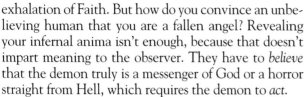

exhalation of Faith. But how do you convince an unbelieving human that you are a fallen angel? Revealing your infernal anima isn't enough, because that doesn't impart meaning to the observer. They have to *believe* that the demon truly is a messenger of God or a horror straight from Hell, which requires the demon to *act*.

Once a demon has decided to target a particular mortal (which could be a spur-of-the-moment decision or part of a slow and intricate plan), she needs to convince him that she truly is a being apart. For low-Torment demons, this might mean an act of kindness or heroism — such as saving a family from a serial killer by appearing as a luminous angelic being. For high-Torment demons, it might be a vicious act of torture — such as appearing as a monstrous creature and slowly flaying a victim with terrible claws. What matters is that the mortal truly *believes* that he is interacting with an angel or a demon. The Storyteller has final say on whether a given person will respond appropriately to a particular act — some Storyteller characters may react in unexpected ways. If the person does respond, the demon has a chance to reap some of his newly found Faith.

Example: *Rebecca decides to attempt to reap some Faith from a homeless man. Summoning a display of lights with an evocation, she appears to the man as a radiant being. Having caught his attention and planted the suggestion that she may be a divine being, she then spends a few hours with the man — buying him a hot meal and talking to him about the love of the Creator and the possibility of divine forgiveness. The Storyteller decides that this is an appropriate reaping attempt — it establishes a relationship between mortal and demon, and it fills the mortal with hope.*

Example: *Ishmael, on the other hand, targets a local fence and drug dealer as a prospect for reaping. Rather than try a positive approach, he'd rather play hardball. After all, the drug dealer's an asshole, and Ishmael's tormented urges are becoming hard to resist. Ishmael kidnaps the man and keeps him bound and gagged in a dark closet for a week, torturing him until the man is driven to madness. When he pulls the man's blindfold off and shows him his demonic visage, the dealer readily believes Ishmael is a demon sent to collect his soul.*

Reaping Faith from a mortal requires a resisted roll. The player decides just how the demon will attempt to reap the mortal's Faith — a conversation about love, an amputation without anesthetic or anything else the player thinks might be appropriate.

The player makes a Willpower roll, with a difficulty of 7. The Storyteller also makes a Willpower roll for the mortal (difficulty 7). Willpower is the trait that measures a character's resistance to stress and suggestion, so a character with a high Willpower is unlikely to have her whole worldview turned around by the demon's acts.

If the demon gains more successes than the mortal, she reaps a small amount of Faith points. In most cases, this is just a single point — reaping is too crude a method, and people's belief is too weak, to gain any real power. The Storyteller may decide, however, that a particular reaping attempt is more effective than usual. If the demon's actions resonate strongly with the mortal's personality, beliefs or personal history, it may draw more Faith out of him. In such a situation, the Storyteller may rule that the demon gains two points of Faith. Demons who rely on reaping for Faith often spend time researching their targets, because if they can tailor the reaping attempt to the mortal's psyche, they have a good chance of better results.

Example: *Rebecca, Adam's character, is reaping Faith from the homeless man. Adam makes a Willpower roll at difficulty 7 — Rebecca's Willpower is 6, so Adam rolls six dice. The homeless man has a Willpower rating of 3, so the Storyteller rolls three dice at difficulty 7. Adam gets a total of three successes. Normally, a successful reaping gains a demon just a single Faith point. In this case, though, the Storyteller rules that Rebecca's approach touches a long-lost core of belief in her subject, and Rebecca gains two points of Faith.*

It's possible to reap Faith from the same mortal more than once, but each new attempt requires a new display of divine or blasphemous power, a separate act of love or hate (and possibly a new Ability used in the reaping process).

It's difficult to gain much Faith through reaping — mortals are slow to believe, and few have the strength of personality to really *commit* to their belief. A far more reliable source of Faith is to collect it from someone who offers it freely.

OFFERED FAITH

When a mortal comes to believe completely in the true nature of a demon and feels an ongoing respect for (or terror of) that demon, then he may become a continuing source of Faith. This is a far more reliable source of Faith than reaping, and demons who want to further their goals need to establish relationships (whether positive or negative) with humans who can offer them Faith.

While the systems and mechanics of offered Faith are simple, it is not a simple thing to groom someone as a source. Entering into a bargain is a momentous and dangerous act, and demons must work hard to find mortals who have the potential for being worth the trouble and effort. This is something that can only be done through roleplaying, not through rules. Responsibility for choosing a worthy mortal and offering him a pact rests with the character (and her player).

To become a source of Faith, a mortal must enter into a *voluntary* agreement with a demon. The demon gives the mortal whatever he desires; in return, the mortal offers her his Faith. Exactly *what* the mortal gains will vary from person to person, of course. It cannot be something mundane, because that lacks the meaning required. The demon must share her power with him in some way, which often means gifting him with one of her evocations or abilities.

When a thrall is empowered through a demonic pact, the exact abilities and gift imparted to the mortal depends upon the strength of her Faith and belief in the demon. The mortal's Faith rating is manipulated by the demon and shaped into a gift. Full details on this process can be found in the section on Empowering Thralls, p. 252.

When shaping the Faith of an appropriate thrall — one the Storyteller has ruled could be a source of offered Faith — the demon can divert some (but *not* all) of the thrall's Faith toward himself. Only a small amount of Faith can be diverted in this way — but the demon receives this gift of Faith *daily*.

As shown in Empowering Thralls (p. 252), thralls have a Faith potential of 1-5. The demon can claim no more than *half* of this Faith (round up) for himself, while the remaining Faith points may be spent on empowering the thrall.

The Storyteller can rule that a particular thrall is not a suitable source of Faith, and that the demon can only use the mortal's Faith to bestow gifts of power. Alternatively, some mortals are suitable sources, but not *perfect* sources. While some of their Faith can be offered to their dark master, it's a smaller amount than the demon might prefer. This decision depends strongly on the nature of the relationship between demon and mortal, and on the mortal's own spirituality. It doesn't really matter if the mortal loves and worships the demon or fears and hates her. What's important is how *close* the bond is between them. If the mortal rarely thinks of the demon or of the gifts she's given him, then he might not be as strong a source as a mortal with the same Faith rating, who thinks of the demon constantly and relies heavily on her infernal gifts.

Example: *Ishmael has found a new thrall, a social worker and former nun whose strong beliefs have been worn down by years of thankless labor. The Storyteller has ruled that the nun would be an appropriate source of offered Faith, so Ishmael's player decides to divert some of the nun's Faith to Ishmael.*

The nun has a Faith potential of 3. Half this potential, rounded up, is 2, so the nun could offer Ishmael two points of Faith per day, leaving one point of Faith to use for empowering the thrall. That's not much to work with, though, so Ishmael's player decides to keep only one point of Faith aside for offering, spending the other 2 on gifts for the new thrall.

Now Ishmael receives a point of Faith from his thrall at the start of every day, for as long as the agreement between them holds. If Ishmael breaks the pact, or if the nun dies, then the daily offering of Faith will end.

Offered Faith is harvested from the source once per day. This occurs at dawn — the breaking of a new morning, the time when the Creator first looked down upon His world. Physical distances are meaningless to Faith, so in the event that the demon and mortal are in different time zones, the Faith still comes to the demon. It is generated when dawn comes to the *mortal*, however (which could make all the difference in an early-morning crisis).

TAKING TOO MUCH

Another advantage of offered Faith over reaped Faith is that the relationship can be abused by the demon, who can draw more and more Faith from their source in a time of crisis. This is not something to enter into lightly, for it causes great mental and physical distress to the source — it can drive the mortal mad or even kill him.

In order for a demon to ravage a source of Faith for more power, she need merely reach out with her will. The mortal doesn't have to be nearby — the demon can draw upon their Faith from the other side of the planet. The source need not be willing either. He need not even be *conscious*. The demon is the instigator here, strip-mining the mortal's soul and lifeforce for power, and the source is helpless to resist. The mortal can try to run away or fight the demon off, but the demon can still draw upon his Faith even while the mortal is hitting her with a baseball bat. The demon can draw upon multiple thralls for Faith simultaneously, allowing her to spread the risks of failure among several followers.

When ravaging a source thus, the demon may add additional dice to her evocation roll up to her permanent Faith score. A demon with a Faith of 4 could add up four extra dice by ravaging sources, but he could not add a fifth die even if further sources were available. The player is not restricted by the number of sources the demon has, or how powerful these sources are. The player can add as many dice as she likes to her pool, up to her limit, as long as the demon has at least one source to ravage.

Once the demon has added as many extra dice as desired, the player makes her evocation roll. A botched roll results in the loss of a Faith point from the character's current Faith pool.

For each bonus die used in this fashion, the ravaged thrall loses a point of Willpower, whether the evocation is successful or not. This loss takes the form of racking pain, hallucinations, waves of terror or other mental trauma. If the source loses all his available points of Willpower in this fashion, he loses his grip on his sanity and gains a mental instability or derangement of some kind. This madness is permanent, unless treated with psychiatric help.

If the demon draws more bonus dice from a thrall than the thrall has Willpower, each die inflicts one level of lethal damage (this damage cannot be soaked). This trauma takes the form of internal injuries, nosebleeds, stigmata or even scarring and burns (if many levels are lost). If he takes enough damage, the thrall will die.

If the source survives this ravaging, he might still never be the same. The demon has violated his soul, left it bleeding. His mind may be shattered, and his body may be wracked with pain from internal injuries. The Storyteller may decide that the mortal becomes a poorer source of Faith for the demon and generates fewer points of Faith each day (perhaps even to the point of no longer generating Faith at all). Similarly, the Storyteller may

rule that the demon's Torment rating increases as a result of her heinous misuse of her follower.

Example: *Ishmael needs to perform a powerful evocation, but his odds of success are slim. He decides to draw more Faith from his sources to increase his chance for a spectacular result. He has three sources to rely upon, so his player can increase his pool by several dice. Ishmael has a Faith rating of 5, so he can draw as many as five extra dice from his sources — the player does so, and rolls a total of eight dice. His thralls must now pay the price for Ishmael's rapaciousness, losing five points of Willpower between them. The player may take all five points from a single hapless mortal or spread the debt over all three sources to mitigate the damage.*

Dealing With Mortals

Many demons expected to return to a world where they could easily control and rule over humans. They didn't plan for a world where faith was all but dead, where six billion people teemed over a haggard planet and where they would have to work in secret to achieve their goals. The demons expected humans to be weak and easily manipulated — and they are — but they are also the key to achieving the plans and schemes of the Celestials. For demons to reach their goals, they *need* humans — as sources of Faith, as tools, as agents. As for the fallen, they have remembered something even more terrible — the urge to protect and even love humanity as they once did long ago.

Empowering Thralls

Demons need servants, and servants need tools in order to do their masters' bidding. It's often very useful to gift a thrall with a portion of your own spiritual power, so that they may better serve you. It's also an excellent bargaining chip — easy to win someone's loyalty when you can promise her eternal beauty or immense power. The biggest limitation on blessing a thrall comes not from the demon, but from the mortal herself. The demon reshapes the mortal's faith and belief into a new configuration, a shape that draws power from the cosmos. The demon can bestow only a weak blessing if the mortal's faith is weak, but if her belief is strong, the demon can fill her with awesome power.

Within certain boundaries, demons can empower their thralls with their own abilities, gifting them with supernatural powers. The system for doing so is fairly simple, but it's not something to enter into lightly. Characters should never rush into empowering their followers or offering pacts to all and sundry. Choosing when to do so is an important moment in the chronicle, and it should be treated as such.

Demons can only impart abilities that they themselves possess — to grant the gift of invisibility, the demon must be able to become invisible himself. The demon can give four kinds of gifts — Attributes, innate abilities, the enhancements of his apocalyptic form and evocations.

Attribute: The demon can increase the thrall's Attribute ratings, making her stronger or smarter. A thrall's Attributes cannot rise above 5, however. Mundane abilities only go so far.

Enhancements: The demon can impart one of the eight enhancements of his apocalyptic form to a thrall, giving her the ability to grow fangs, soak lethal damage and more. Low-Torment demons can impart one of their high-Torment special abilities if desired at the cost of a temporary Torment point.

Evocations: The demon can even imbue a thrall with a weaker version of one of his evocations. The demon must decide on a specific evocation to bestow upon his servant.

Other Abilities: Demons enjoy many special abilities, such as their immunity to possession. The demon can impart one of these advantages to a thrall. Similarly, the demon can bestow a gift of a more general nature, such as the ability to see or walk again.

Once the demon has decided on what abilities to bestow upon the thrall, the two enter into a pact. The demon agrees to imbue the thrall with power, while the mortal agrees to serve in whatever way the two agree upon. At the Storyteller's discretion, the mortal might qualify as a source of offered Faith (see Offered Faith, p. 250), but there are many other ways in which a mortal can help her master.

With the pact finalized, the deal is sealed with the demon's gift. Imparting a gift to a mortal requires nothing more than a turn's concentration. Many demons, however, like to add ritual and ceremony to the procedure in order to impress their new thralls. After concentrating, the demon mentally reshapes the thrall's soul, using the mortal's Faith as a tool. The stronger the thrall's Faith is, the greater the changes the demon can make to her essence, and the more powerful the gifts the demon can bestow upon her.

Faith Potential

Mortals don't have a Faith rating. Instead, they have a Faith *potential*, a measure of how much Faith a demon can use to reconfigure their souls.

The Storyteller decides what Faith potential a mortal possesses. Most humans have a Faith potential of 2. Someone such as a devout priest with strong religious beliefs (no matter how twisted) would have a potential of 3. A Faith potential of 4 is the province of the fanatically religious, such as a fundamentalist preacher or Buddhist monk. Only a handful of people possess the determination, belief and devotion necessary for a potential of 5 — this is the hallmark of the pope, Mother Teresa or the Dalai Lama. Mortals with a potential of 1 are spiritually weak, with no religious beliefs and little ability to believe in the demon's power. Such mortals make poor thralls, but may have other abilities that compensate. People with zero potential exist, but they are rare. Such spiritually dead, deeply skeptical mortals cannot enter into a pact with a demon.

No rolls are needed to reshape the mortal's soul. The mortal's Faith rating is used as a "pool" of points for buying effects and gifts that benefit the thrall, according to the following guidelines:

• A point of Faith can be used to repair chronic injuries or impairments — allowing a paralyzed character to walk or giving sight to a blind thrall. If the mortal is missing lethal health levels as an effect of his condition, they are converted into bashing levels, which can then heal normally.

• A point of Faith can be converted into 10 freebie points (see Character Creation, p. 122). These points can be used to buy or improve traits such as Attributes, Abilities or Willpower. They cannot be used for improving Backgrounds.

• One point of Faith can be used to impart one of the demon's inherent powers, such as immunity to mind-control. The thrall permanently benefits from this power, rolling Willpower (difficulty 7) to activate its effects.

• One or more points of Faith can be used to give the mortal a limited evocation from the demon's lore. This gift costs one to five Faith points, depending on the level of the evocation in question (i.e., a three-dot evocation would cost the mortal three of her Faith points.) To perform the evocation, the thrall must make a Willpower roll (difficulty 8), with the number of successes determining the scope and effect of the evocation.

• One point of Faith bestows one of the enhancements of the demon's apocalyptic form on the thrall. To benefit from the enhancement, the thrall must make a Willpower roll (difficulty 6). Success allows the thrall to use the enhancement for a scene. The demon can bestow more than one enhancement, but he must spend a point of Faith on each.

• Up to half of the thrall's Faith potential can be used to make the mortal a source of offered Faith, if the Storyteller approves (see Offered Faith, p. 250).

Example: *Rebecca has found a thrall, a local police detective named James Wong. Rebecca agrees to improve Wong's health and vitality in return for his service. Most mortals have a Faith potential of just two, but Wong is also a church deacon with a strong core of religious belief, so he has three points of Faith potential. After a short ritual designed to impress Wong, Rebecca concentrates, reaches out with her soul and uses Wong's belief to reshape his essence.*

Adam, Rebecca's player, can spend the three points of Wong's Faith potential to modify the character. The first point is converted into 10 freebie points, and Adam uses them to improve Wong's Stamina and Dexterity by one dot each. The second dot is used to give Wong the Increased Size enhancement of Rebecca's apocalyptic form, which he can assume with a successful Willpower roll. With the final Faith point, Adam gives Wong Rebecca's immunity to mind-control, ensuring that her servant cannot be corrupted by her enemies.

It's possible to give new gifts to a thrall you've already empowered, but it's very difficult to do so. In order to further alter a thrall, the mortal's Faith potential must increase — which only occurs if his belief and dedication to the demon becomes significantly stronger. The Storyteller is the sole judge as to whether a thrall's Faith potential increases. If a thrall's belief grows, the demon can spend the extra point of Faith on new improvements — but doing so requires a new Faustian bargain between demon and thrall.

INVOKING CELESTIAL POWERS

To reveal one's true nature to another is risky for anyone, but far more so for a demon revealing his Celestial self to mortals. For demons, Faith is like air — they need it to survive. Yet modern mortals are cynical and bereft of faith, and exposure to high levels of disbelief makes life very difficult for the fallen. The presence of unbelievers can even disrupt the use of Faith.

It's often more difficult (and expensive) for a demon to invoke her powers around skeptical mortals. Whether a mortal is skeptical enough to disrupt the use of Faith is up to the Storyteller to decide. As a rule of thumb, the "average" mortal doesn't believe in the supernatural, but her disbelief isn't forceful enough to affect the demon. More strong-willed people, or those who have a major problem with the notion of the supernatural (such as a pragmatic scientist) can cause the demon problems.

One observer *might* cause a problem, but a group almost certainly will. Mortals are pack animals, and they draw courage from the presence of their fellows. When a group of mortals witnesses a demon's use of Faith, their resistance is stronger; they back each other up on an unconscious level to reject the outsider. Even if the mortals would not interfere with the demon on their own, they *will* interfere as a group. Only among true believers and worshippers will demons be able to evoke their spiritual powers without interference.

If a demon uses an evocation in the presence of a resisting mortal or wishes to assume her apocalyptic form, the Storyteller makes a Willpower roll for the observer at difficulty 8. Each success on this roll raises the difficulty of the demon's roll by one. For a group of observers, the Storyteller decides on the average Willpower rating of the group's members (usually 3 or 4) and makes the same roll. She adds another die to the roll for every five members of the group, (so for a group of 20 members with Willpower 3, the Storyteller rolls seven dice).

The presence of unbelievers makes life increasingly difficult for demons, which is a good reason for them to work in secret or surround themselves with thralls and worshippers.

REVELATION

Each time a demon uses her Faith, mortal observers can make a Perception + Awareness roll to sense the demon's true nature. The difficulty of the roll is 10 minus the total number of Faith points the character spent (or

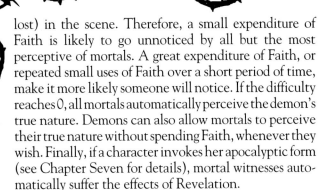

lost) in the scene. Therefore, a small expenditure of Faith is likely to go unnoticed by all but the most perceptive of mortals. A great expenditure of Faith, or repeated small uses of Faith over a short period of time, make it more likely someone will notice. If the difficulty reaches 0, all mortals automatically perceive the demon's true nature. Demons can also allow mortals to perceive their true nature without spending Faith, whenever they wish. Finally, if a character invokes her apocalyptic form (see Chapter Seven for details), mortal witnesses automatically suffer the effects of Revelation.

The mortal's reaction depends on two factors: the character's Torment and the mortal's Willpower. Fallen with a low Torment (less than half their Willpower) are glorious and awesome, shadows of the divine beings they once were. Fallen with high Torment (greater than their Willpower) are living nightmares who are terrible to behold. Those in between may be either or both, depending on the mortal's preconceptions (and the judgment of the Storyteller). Mortals with low Willpower scores are likely to be overwhelmed by the demon's true nature, while those with greater Willpower can overcome the initial shock and deal with the Revelation (although it still comes as a shock, even to the most jaded and confident of mortals).

When a mortal has a Revelation, roll the mortal's Willpower against a difficulty of the demon's permanent Faith. Mortals whose players fail the roll are so awed or horrified by what they see that they are incapable of doing anything but standing and staring raptly. If the demon directly threatens them, they flee as quickly as possible and later rationalize what happened to them. They believe it was a dream or hallucination, or they simply forget about it altogether.

Mortals whose players succeed in the roll are still impressed, but they remain capable of taking rational action (which may still involve fleeing as quickly as possible). They also remember some or all of what happened, although they're not likely to be believed. One success is enough to recall that something extraordinary happened, two successes provide basic details, and three or more successes mean that the mortal recalls exactly what happened (and will probably never forget it).

A botch on the Willpower roll means that the mortal suffers a complete collapse, either fainting dead away or turning into a gibbering mass, overcome with awe or terror. Those with a particularly weak constitution may even suffer a heart attack, stroke or other complication at the Storyteller's whim. Upon recovering, the mortal recalls nothing of the experience, but may still exhibit aftereffects, such as recurring nightmares or hair gone permanently white.

One effect a Revelation does *not* have is to reap Faith from those who witness it. While the witnesses are filled with a momentary awareness of the character's nature, it's an unfocused and impersonal awareness. Reaping Faith requires the demon to form a *relationship* with a mortal, even if only for a short time — not just to flash his horns and forked tongue. While revealing one's revelatory form may certainly *aid* in reaping Faith, it's never enough in and of itself to gather power for a demon.

Faith as a Weapon

Hundreds of years in the past, when religion was a central part of the lives of the everyday person and faith as a whole was stronger and more prevalent, it was possible for religious leaders and their followers to defy and even defeat the legions of Hell with powerful prayers, blessed items and potent exorcisms. Demons in the modern world have little to fear from the local drive-in church or apoplectic televangelist, but it is still possible to encounter people, places or artifacts that are capable of giving even the mightiest demons pause.

Holy Ground

Historically, churches and other holy sites were blessed when their foundations were laid, in order to render them inviolate to the forces of evil. The practice continues today, but the underlying faith that gave the blessing power is no more. Churches, graveyards and other sites constructed within the last 200 years are not considered holy ground *per se*, but older structures — and even a rare few new ones where the worshippers truly believe — can potentially hold a demon at bay.

Like mortals, any place of worship, be it a church, graveyard or roadside shrine, can have a Faith potential based upon the amount of real faith invested by generations of worshippers. Sites can have a Faith potential of 1-5, with the highest potential reserved for truly ancient and venerated sites, such as Manger Square in Bethlehem or the Temple of the Rock in Jerusalem. Demons with a Torment of 4 or more who try to enter such a site suffer a number of levels of lethal damage equal to the site's faith potential each turn they remain. This damage is manifested by seared flesh or stigmata-like wounds to the hands and face. A successful Willpower roll is required each turn to remain on holy ground. If the roll fails, the demon flees the area.

Fallen with a Torment of 3 or less have rejected their demonic nature in favor of their angelic and human essence, and they may enter a holy site without injury. The few demons who have successfully accomplished this are at a loss to explain why they were not burned, but they point to it as proof that redemption is still possible.

Sacred or Blessed Items

Similar to holy ground, it is possible for the truly faithful to infuse an item with holy power sufficient to cause harm to one of the fallen. Such holy items are very rare and are often highly prized artifacts guarded zealously by their worshippers, though it is possible for persons of great faith to bless common items and create powerful weapons, such as holy water. Like holy ground,

a sacred object can have a Faith potential of 1-5, with the highest potential reserved for truly venerated and unique objects. These items inflict a number of levels of lethal damage to a demon equal to their Faith potential each turn they are held against the demon's skin. Fallen with a Torment of 3 or less are unaffected by these items.

Blessed items are more potent examples of these objects, having been venerated with a specific purpose in mind. A mortal with a Faith potential of at least 3 is required to successfully bless an item, and such objects can possess a Faith potential of 1-5 depending on the amount of time and effort spent infusing it. As a rule of thumb, a blessed item gains one point of Faith potential per day of prayer. At the time of creation, the item is blessed to perform the function of a banishment, abjuration or binding prayer. Blessed items only function when used by a mortal with a Faith potential of at least 1. When used, add the Faith potential of the item and the mortal wielder to determine the total dice pool for the resisted roll. Fallen with a Torment of 3 or less are unaffected by these items or the prayers associated with them.

Prayers

Prayers are similar to a demon's evocations, in that they are focused uses of Faith that effect a change in reality — specifically to banish, forbid, bind or exorcise the fallen.

Prayers are performed as a resisted roll between mortal and demon. The mortal's player rolls a number of dice equal to his Faith potential against the demon's Willpower. If the mortal is successful, the effects of the prayer are applied immediately. More than one mortal can combine their Faith potential to add power to a prayer. Four types of prayers can be used against the fallen, and they can be targeted against any demon within the mortal's line of sight:

• **Banishment:** A successful prayer of banishment forces the demon to flee the area. The demon may not return to the site for a number of hours equal to her Torment score.

• **Abjuration:** The prayer of abjuration can be used to bar a demon from entering a given area. The prayer can cover an area in yards equal to the mortal's faith potential (multiple mortals can combine their faith potential to increase this area), and if successful, the demon may not enter for a number of hours equal to her Torment score.

• **Binding:** The prayer of binding roots the demon to the ground, trapping him as long as the mortal continues her prayer. The demon cannot move from the spot by physical or supernatural means of any kind, but he can still perform other evocations, throw things or take other such actions. The demon remains trapped as long as the mortal is able to continue her prayer, and no further rolls are required. Stamina or Willpower rolls may be required if the mortal intends to keep up the prayer for hours, though. Blessed items empowered with this prayer continue to work only as long as the wielder brandishes the item before the demon.

• **Exorcism:** The prayer of exorcism is an ordeal of faith intended to drive a demon from its mortal host. To successfully perform this prayer, the mortal must win a number of resisted rolls greater than the demon's permanent Faith rating. One roll may be performed per hour of game time, so an exorcism performed against a demon with a permanent Faith rating of 5 would require a minimum of 5 hours to complete. If successful, the demon is forced from his mortal host and may not reenter it, forcing him to find another suitable vessel or risk being pulled back into the Abyss. Of course, the demon isn't compelled to remain in the area and be exorcised, so unless the fallen is physically incapacitated, the exorcism is usually performed simultaneously with a prayer of binding.

Dealing with the Damned

In the harsh new mortal world, the only things demons are familiar with are other demons. It's a shame, then, that the damned are at each other's throats constantly — faction against faction, fallen against their former masters, the Earthbound against these new invaders.

Conflict and interaction between demons is a pivotal part of any **Demon** chronicle, and these systems examine the ways in which demons interact — be it in person or through the use of agents and followers.

True Names

Names are important, both to the thing being named and those interacting with it. Names give us identity; names give us the tools we need to interact with others. For demons, names are more than simply labels — they are intrinsic parts of the demons' very nature. While a demon may have many names — his original Celestial Name, the name of his human host, titles and nicknames — he has only one True Name. Originally, this was the name given to him by the Creator; after the Fall, the True Names of all demons altered and mutated to fit their fundamentally changed nature. For the demons now incarnate in human hosts, the potential exists for their True Names to change once more if they can radically redefine themselves and their diabolic nature.

To know a demon's True Name is to have power over her. When a demon's True Name is used as a part of a ritual (see Summoning and Binding, p. 256), the demon falls under the control of the person performing the ritual. She retains her will and sense of self but is compelled to follow the orders of her controller.

Even without such a ritual, knowing a demon's True Name is useful. By speaking a demon's True Name, you instantly gain her attention, no matter where in the world she may be, and you can communicate verbally with her. The Name can also be used as a goad to intimidate or manipulate the demon. If a character knows a demon's True Name, he gains a number of dice (equal to the demon's Faith rating) to use in Mental and Social rolls against that

demon. Actions that would be affected include Intimidation or Subterfuge rolls to control the demon, as well as Research or Investigation rolls to determine her plans or whereabouts. The Storyteller has final say on whether a given action would receive a benefit for knowing a demon's True Name. Physical actions or combat are not affected by knowing an enemy's True Name. (Knowing someone's nature will not protect you from her claws.)

Obviously, learning someone's True Name is an incredibly useful tool against them, and the search to learn True Names plays an important part in **Demon** chronicles. The following systems focus on how to piece together a True Name, as well as what *won't* help in the quest for knowledge.

A True Name is more than simply a collection of letters. It's a configuration of supernatural energy, a footprint on reality itself. In many ways, a demon *is* her True Name, so while that Name has a reflection in the world as a construction of language, it also has a meaning. For a True Name to be used, the wielder must understand the *meaning* of it. Furthermore, the name can only be used if it is spoken, as the user channels the breath of the Creator through his own breath. Therefore, a Name has no power if it is just written down or simply pulled together by accident. You can't set a computer to juggle permutations of letters and try to affect a demon, because the computer has no breath or soul. Only a living (or once-living) being can use a Name, and only if he understands what it is that he is speaking.

This also means, however, that if you can piece together a demon's personality and purpose, you can piece together her True Name. Knowing why a demon does something, you can gain an insight to the meaning of her acts — which gains insight into the meaning of her Name. True Names can be collected slowly — a letter here, a glimpse of meaning there — until the character knows the full Name (or at least, what he *hopes* is the full Name).

If a character knows what he is looking for, his player can attempt to make a series of extended rolls to work out a demon's True Name. Through research and investigation, the character must try to amass a number of successes with various rolls (determined by the Storyteller); once he has those successes, he knows the True Name. The amount of successes required depends on the power of the demon, as stronger demons have more complex Names. Demons of low rank (such as the player's characters) would require 10 successes to establish their True Name; middle-rank demons such as lords or overlords would require as many as 15-20 successes, and the mighty barons or dukes demand 30 successes or more at the Storyteller's discretion.

What kinds of activities can yield clues to a True Name? Here are some examples:

• Looking through occult texts to find names of demons and matching them up with your subject's acts (Intelligence + Occult). Just finding the right books would be a story in itself, though, as tomes of true occult knowledge are rare and jealously guarded by their owners.

• Investigating a crime scene, looking for the subtle touches that betray the criminal's personality. (Perception + Investigation)

• Interrogating the demon's followers, finding out how they address her in their blasphemous rituals. (Manipulation + Intimidation)

• Ransacking the demon's sanctum, finding her personal belongings and seeing what they say about her. (Perception + Empathy)

• Observing the demon's handiwork. Every time a demon performs an invocation, she leaves an imprint in the fabric of reality, similar to a psychic fingerprint. (Perception + Occult)

Players are bound to come up with other ideas for learning fragments of True Names, and Storytellers should decide if an idea is valid and what traits are involved. The difficulty of these rolls is always high — usually 8, possibly 9 if the action is particularly unusual.

The Storyteller should always make the roll, and note down in secret how many successes (if any) have been gathered toward the total. The character never truly *knows* if he has learned the full True Name, though. Eventually, he just has to use what he's learned and hope it's enough.

Incomplete True Names have no power to command or bind a demon — like a password, it either works completely or it doesn't. For game purposes, it isn't necessary to actually spell out a character's True Name, though players are welcome to do so if they want. What is important is the progress the investigators make toward deciphering its meaning, reflected in their accumulation of successes.

Summoning and Binding

Occult history is full of stories of sorcerers summoning demons to them and binding them to their will — or being destroyed by forces they cannot control. There's a lot of truth to some of these stories. Some of those demons pulled from Hell still exist today as the Earthbound.

Armed with the correct summoning rituals, a sorcerer — whether mortal or demon — can summon a demon into his presence. A second ritual can then bind the demon to the summoner's will, forcing her to become his servant.

Of course, doing so isn't easy. In fact, it's very difficult and incredibly dangerous. If the rituals are not followed *exactly*, and if the summoner lacks certain vital data, the summoned demon is free to do whatever she likes — such as punishing the fool who dared try to subjugate her.

In order to summon a demon, the sorcerer needs the correct ritual. There are literally *thousands* of summoning rituals described in various occult tomes, and the vast majority do nothing at all. The remaining few have power, but only if applied to the right demon. A ritual designed to bind an Earthbound will likely have no effect

against a modern fallen. At the very least, the ritual must address the correct demonic House. To summon a Devourer, for instance, you must have a ritual designed to summon an Devourer and not a Malefactor.

Finding the correct ritual is a long and arduous process that could take months (or even years) of occult research. Storytellers can represent this search with an extended Intelligence + Occult roll (difficulty 7), where the summoner needs to accumulate 20 successes. Before the player can even *attempt* the roll, though, the character needs to know something about the demon he means to summon — her name (preferably her True Name) and her House. Most rituals include methods for both summoning and binding a demon (although some only do one or the other).

CREATING RITUALS

If a determined summoner cannot find an appropriate ritual, it's possible to *design* one from scratch — one perfectly tailored to a specific demon. Doing so is even harder than finding the correct ritual, though. A skilled occultist can construct a ritual in less time than it would take to find an equivalent rite, but the process is far riskier. Creating a ritual is an extended Intelligence + Occult roll (difficulty 8). Rolling once per month, the occultist must assemble 25 successes (or more, if the Storyteller so rules). The Storyteller should make this roll in secret. If any of the rolls botch, the ritual is fatally flawed — but the occultist is unaware of the problem. Such flawed rituals will *always* disastrously backfire when used, no matter how well the occultist performs the rite.

Once the occultist has the ritual, he can then attempt to perform it, which is a long process that takes *hours*, not turns. The Storyteller may require the character to have specific props, cast the ritual at a specific place and time or abide by other restrictions on the casting.

Once the ritual is performed, the summoner's player rolls Wits + Occult to summon the demon. The difficulty of this roll is usually 6, but the Storyteller may decide to adjust it upward (if the ritual isn't entirely suitable or the summoner doesn't have the right props) or downward (if the summoner has extra props, such as items associated with the demon). If the roll fails, the ritual doesn't work. On a botch, the mystic energies might backfire in an explosion or summon an unbindable monster.

If the roll is successful, the demon is transported instantly to the site of the ritual, where she appears in her apocalyptic form. For demons incarnate in a human host, such as the fallen, this leaves their mortal bodies in a deathlike coma (possibly leading to complications if she was talking to someone at the time…). Earthbound demons are pulled from their physical vessels. Demons still in Hell are instantly transported to this plane of existence.

The ritual must provide a space for the demon to inhabit — a protective magic circle, square or diagram.

Common wisdom has it that the circle protects the summoner — but the truth is that it protects the *demon*. Demons without physical hosts are normally pulled back into Hell (see Finding a New Host, p. 259), and they cannot speak or interact with living beings. The mystic space within the circle, though, protects the demon from Hell's spiritual gravity and allows her to speak and interact with the summoner. The circle is a shield, not a cage. The demon can move out of it whenever she wishes, but if she does so, she will be caught by the terrible pull of the Abyss, and be far from her host. It behooves most demons, then, to stay within the circle. When the ritual ends or the summoner dismisses the demon, the demon is returned to her body — or, depending on the agreement reached with the summoner, possibly into a new vessel.

Once the demon is summoned, the summoner can interact with her, assuming he is not panicked and overwhelmed by witnessing the demon's apocalyptic form (see Revelation, p. 253). He can converse or attempt to make a voluntary pact with the demon. The demon can choose to listen or simply fume in silence. Most occultists, though, are not summoning demons just for conversation — they instead attempt to bind the demon to their will. Binding a demon requires further use of the ritual. It is *essential* to know the demon's name at this point. At the very least, the summoner must know the demon's Celestial Name, but it's far preferable to know the demon's True Name.

The players of the summoner and the demon make contested Willpower rolls. The summoner has one advantage in this contest — if he has assistants or acolytes participating in the summoning ritual, they can add their will to his. The Storyteller makes a Willpower roll (difficulty 8) for every extra participant in the ritual, and each success adds a die to the summoner's Willpower pool.

If the summoner knows only the demon's Celestial Name, the demon receives bonus dice to this roll equal to her Faith rating. If the summoner knows the demon's True Name, binding the demon is easy. The summoner receives a number of *automatic successes* on the Willpower roll equal to the demon's Torment rating. True Names are potent weapons, and few demons can stand against someone armed with knowledge of their soul.

If the demon gains more successes than the summoner, the binding fails and the demon escapes. If the summoner gains more successes, though, he is able to bind the demon to his will for a limited time.

Each success the summoner gains equates to a command he can give the demon. These commands must be fairly specific and revolve around a particular action. "Protect me from all my enemies" is too wide-ranging a command. "Kill Gideon Wallace" is more appropriate. The summoner could also command the demon to vacate a host, to grant the summoner powers or any other action that can easily be summed up in a few words.

If a demon is bound to follow commands, she must do so to the best of her ability and make the attempt as soon as possible. She cannot act directly against the summoner while bound to even a single command. She can attack him once she completes all the commands, but not until all her tasks are done. She can, however, act indirectly against him — perhaps by persuading someone else to attack him — and she can work to subvert her commands as much as possible. Wise summoners structure their commands to leave few gray areas and protect themselves from their anger of their servants; foolish summoners lie in unmarked graves or worse.

Once the commands expire, the summoner may try to rework the ritual to bind the demon to his will at a later date. Doing so requires subtle modifications to the ritual and is very risky. The Storyteller makes an Intelligence + Occult roll (difficulty 8) on the character's behalf, and must gain more successes than the number of previous binding rituals the summoner has performed with the demon in question (so if the summoner has bound the demon twice before, three successes are required). If the roll is successful, the summoner and demon go through the same summoning and binding process as before. If the roll fails, the binding ritual is ineffective — although the summoner won't know this until he attempts to use it. On a botch, the demon becomes aware that the ritual is now ineffective, and he can feel free to wreak bloody vengeance on the summoner.

DEATH AND LIFE

In the beginning, Celestials knew nothing of death or the dangers of a physical existence. Theirs was a spiritual nature, untouched by mortality. The War changed all that, proving that these beings could still be destroyed. In this new era, the fallen are learning that their mortal forms can be killed and that they still risk final dissolution at the hands of their enemies.

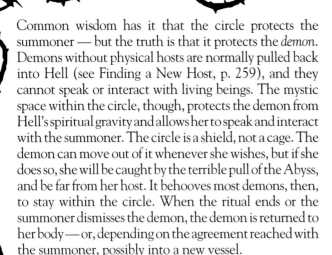

MORTAL SUMMONS

A mortal summoner can breach the barriers around Hell and summon a demon from the Abyss — an *impossible* feat for even the most skilled and strong-willed demon. No one knows exactly why demons are blocked from pulling their brethren from Hell, but the popular theory is that God placed wards within the fabric of Hell to prevent just such an occurrence. Perhaps the Creator knew there was a risk of demons escaping the Abyss at some point, and He ensured that such escapees could not simply pry open the gates of Hell and rescue their fellows. Therefore, only a human occultist can summon demons from Hell — assuming she has access to the right rituals. Of course, there is nothing to prevent a demon from teaching a suitable thrall to enact the summoning rituals — or from summoning and binding demons already loose on Earth.

FINDING A NEW HOST

Death is not the end — not for demons, anyway. In fact, "death" is a concept hard to apply to Celestials. Their mortal shells can be damaged, killed or destroyed, but what does that matter to the immortal spirit inside? A demon can easily survive the death of his host, and travel to a new one, but they must do so quickly. Celestial beings cannot exist long in the physical world, since the rigors of being caught between two worlds weakens the spirit and eventually drags it back screaming into Hell.

When a demon character is reduced below Incapacitated by lethal or aggravated damage, the host body is killed. In the next turn, the demon manifests in his apocalyptic form, hovering above his former body. In this form, the demon cannot be affected in any way (with a few exceptions — see Final Destruction, p. 260). In turn, the demon cannot physically affect anything or evoke the powers of his lore. His perceptions are altered in this state — he can see living beings by their souls, but can perceive inanimate objects only dimly. His form is unaffected by gravity, walls or obstacles — it can move in any direction, flying Willpower + 5 miles each turn.

While the demon is unaffected by the physical world, it is hardly in a good position. The moment the demon is severed from its physical host, it immediately suffers the terrible pull of the Abyss trying to draw it back into its eternal prison. Each turn the demon exists in the physical world without a host, the player must make a Willpower roll (difficulty 6). If he fails this roll, the demon is sucked back into Hell. Willpower points may be spent for automatic successes for this roll as normal.

Example: *Ishmael's search for the Earthbound cult comes to a terrible end when he encounters Atoth-Nagan — a monstrous, powerful Devourer in the cult's service. The two demons clash in a deserted museum, but Ishmael is torn apart by the Devourer's mighty claws. In the next turn, Ishmael materializes above the body in his apocalyptic form, expelled by its dying breath. The Abyss begins to pull at him straightaway, so his player must make a Willpower roll every turn so that Ishmael can stay on this plane. Even with the character's strong Willpower rating of 7, his player will eventually fail the roll. Desperate to stay out of Hell, Ishmael must find a new vessel.*

To survive, the demon must find a new host. Yet doing so is difficult because the same restrictions apply that were imposed on the demon when it escaped from Hell. It must possess a living body, one whose mind or soul is so diminished that they are barely human. If a suitable host body is nearby, the act of possession requires a Willpower roll against a difficulty of 8, though this number drops to 6 if the victim is also one of the demon's thralls. If one of the demon's thralls willingly accepts the demon, no roll is required; possession is automatic. The player and the Storyteller should work together to determine the demon's new traits, possibly re-designing the

character and applying an experience bonus equal to the demon character's earned experience. Most of the time, though, the demon will be hard-pressed to find a suitable host in the short time it has left before dissipating.

There is one other option. It's an unpleasant one, but it beats Hell. A desperate demon may inhabit an inanimate object, becoming one of the Earthbound. Few objects have the right properties to host a demon, though. The Celestial cannot simply inhabit the first elevator or fountain pen it comes across. The object must be discrete — not part of another object — and it must have a certain amount of "resonance" with humanity. This resonance could come from the fact that the object looks human — such as a statue — or because it is used constantly by humans who pay attention to it. No one pays attention to an elevator, even though they use it constantly, but a computer used by a struggling writer to write the Great American Novel would be a suitable host. The Storyteller has final say on whether an object is appropriate.

Whatever vessel the demon chooses, he must try to reconfigure his energies to inhabit it, which requires a Willpower roll (difficulty 9). The difficulty drops to just 6 if the vessel has a close affinity with the demon's personality or House, or has been properly attuned to house a disembodied soul. A Defiler would find it easier to inhabit a boat, given her affinity with the water, while a Malefactor would find it easier to inhabit a finely made watch. If the roll succeeds, the demon can take permanent residence in his new vessel. If it fails, he must keep searching for a new body, and he cannot attempt to occupy this one again. On a botch, the demon loses a point of permanent Willpower. If a possessed object is destroyed, the demon is cast adrift once more and must repeat the process of finding a new host or returning to the Pit.

Example: *Ishmael must find a new body in order to escape Hell. No thralls or other suitable mortals are nearby, so he is forced to attempt to inhabit an object. The Storyteller decides that there is an appropriate object in the scene — a granite statue of a Greek hero, which has been the subject of attention for hundreds of museum patrons. As a Fiend, Ishmael has no connection with such an item — he'd have better luck with something like an old telescope or a statue of a Greek oracle — but beggars can't be choosers. Ishmael's player rolls against a difficulty of 9 to reconfigure Ishmael's energies, but the roll fails. Ishmael cannot occupy the statue, and must keep searching for a new vessel. Atoth-Nagan, though, has other plans...*

Even safe in a new host, the demon is still battered by the experience of being discorporate. The character loses a point from his Faith *rating* and gains a point of *permanent* Torment. If he was inhabiting a human body, the demon must also come to terms with the new memories and personalities left inside the human shell. He must somehow incorporate them into its own psyche. The hours and days after inhabiting a new body

can be very disconcerting, so Storytellers and players will find plenty of potential for stories in this period.

FINAL DESTRUCTION

Nothing is truly immortal. Demons have lived since the very creation of the universe, but even they can be killed. Their energies can be dissipated, cannibalized by their enemies. A light that has shone from the beginning of time finally winks out.

When a demon is in his apocalyptic form, having been expelled from his vessel in some way, he is unaffected by almost all physical or supernatural entities. Yet all demons possess the ability to destroy a discorporate Celestial and consume his energies to make themselves stronger.

To consume a Celestial, the demon needs to breathe in the energies from a victim's revelatory form. Doing so doesn't necessarily require bodily contact, but the two must be within arm's reach. The Celestial can attempt to flee, being unaffected by gravity or obstacles, so the demon must act quickly.

Once the demon is close enough to inhale the Celestial's energies, his player makes a Faith roll. The victim resists with his Faith or Torment rating — whichever is *higher*. If the demon knows his victim's True Name, he adds the victim's Faith rating to his own dice pool.

If the victim wins the contest, he steals a number of Faith points equal to his successes from the aggressor, and he can continue looking for a new vessel. If the aggressor earns more successes than the victim, he consumes the victim and gains strength from its energies. The victim in this case is permanently destroyed.

Example: *Ishmael's host body is destroyed, and he desperately flails about for a new body. Atoth-Nagan is too fast, though, and he moves in to consume Ishmael's discorporate form. Ishmael's Faith rating is 5, and his Torment is 6 — so his player rolls a pool of six dice. Atoth-Nagan has a Faith rating of only 4 — but he knows Ishmael's True Name. The Storyteller adds Ishmael's Faith rating of 5 to Atoth-Nagan's pool, for a total of nine dice. The Storyteller and player both roll. The player rolls three successes for Ishmael, while the Storyteller rolls five for Atoth-Nagan. Ishmael's soul is devoured by the monster, and he is lost forever.*

When a Celestial is devoured, the Storyteller makes a roll using its Faith rating (difficulty 6). For each success on this roll, a portion of the Celestial's energies is converted into a Faith point. Much like using a mortal's Faith potential in an infernal pact (see Empowering Thralls, p. 252), the conquering demon can use these Faith points to empower itself, spending the points in the following ways:

• A Faith point can be converted into five freebie points, and the demon can use those points to improve its traits (see Chapter Six, p. 128). Only Abilities, Attributes and Willpower can be improved in this way, and the demon cannot increase his traits to a level greater than that possessed by the consumed Celestial.

• Each point of Faith can be "converted" into a memory or item of knowledge — the location of a temple, the hiding place of a relic, the True Name of a rival — as long as that information was known to the demon who was devoured. The Storyteller is the final arbiter on what a character might have known and how much information can be gained thus.

• The demon can choose to increase his Faith rating by one by spending *two* Faith points. This increase in Faith allows a corresponding increase in lore — and the demon can actually gain the lore known by the consumed demon. Only the lore of the victim's House may be learned thus. Even if the devoured demon knew other evocations, those powers are not central to its essence.

Example: *Atoth-Nagan has destroyed Ishmael, and the fallen's soul is devoured like a sweetmeat by the demon. Ishmael had a Faith rating of 5, so the Storyteller rolls five dice at difficulty 6 and gets three successes. Atoth-Nagan can gain three points of Faith from his foe. The Storyteller decides that Atoth-Nagan converts one Faith point into plundered memories — the demon learns the location and identities of Ishmael's thralls and fallen allies. The player uses the other two points to increase the Devourer's Faith rating by one, thus allowing an increase in lore. Atoth-Nagan gains a dot in the Lore of Portals, one of Ishmael's House lore paths.*

Rumors persist that there may be rituals that permit *mortals* to destroy discorporate demons and perhaps even store their energies to use for sorcery or to gain power. Such rituals are rare to the point of being mythical, and demons would move mountains to deny humanity such weapons.

STATES OF BEING

For the fallen, reintroduction to the mortal world comes as a shock. Formerly celestial beings unaffected by the hazards of nature and physics, they are now partially mortal beings, with almost all the frailties and vulnerabilities of their hosts.

The following systems present a variety of ways in which characters can suffer physical or mental harm.

DERANGEMENTS

Derangements are behaviors that occur when the mind is forced to confront intolerable or conflicting feelings, such as overwhelming terror or profound guilt. When the mind is faced with impressions or emotions that it cannot reconcile, it attempts to ease the inner turmoil by stimulating behavior such as megalomania, schizophrenia or hysteria to provide an outlet for the tension and stress that the conflict generates. Mortals and especially thralls caught in the grips of the fallen and their Earthbound foes are forced to participate in activities and witness sights that would strain the sanity of the strongest person.

It must be noted that people who are "crazy" are neither funny nor arbitrary in their actions. Insanity is

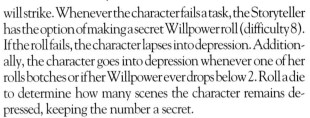

frightening to people who watch someone rage against unseen presences or hoard rotten meat to feed to monsters. Even something as harmless-sounding as talking to an invisible rabbit can be disturbing to observers.

The insane, however, respond to a pattern only they know, stimuli that they perceive in their own minds. To their skewed perceptions, what happens to them is perfectly normal. The character's derangement is there for a reason, whether she saw her own children devoured alive or she begins to believe that humanity must be culled to diminish monsters' feeding stock. What stimuli does her insanity inflict upon her, and how does she react to what happens? Work with the Storyteller to create a pattern of provocations for your character's derangement, then decide how she reacts to such provocation.

Fugue

Victims suffering from fugue experience "blackouts" and loss of memory. When subjected to a particular variety of stress, the character begins a specific, rigid set of behaviors to remove the stressful symptoms. This syndrome differs from multiple personalities in that an individual in the grip of a fugue has no separate personality. Instead, he is on a form of "autopilot" similar to sleepwalking. Decide on the kind of circumstance or exposure that triggers this state, be it the death of a defenseless human, confrontation with a specific sort of creature, confinement or something worse.

Make a Willpower roll when the character is subjected to the appropriate extreme stress or pressure (difficulty 8). If the roll fails, roleplay the character's trancelike state. Otherwise, control of your character passes to the Storyteller for a number of scenes equal to the roll of a die. During this period, the Storyteller may have the character act as she sees fit to remove the source of the stress. At the end of the fugue, your character "regains consciousness" with no memory of her actions.

Hysteria

A person in the grip of hysteria is unable to control her emotions, suffering severe mood swings and violent fits when subjected to stress or anxiety. Decide on a particular circumstance that triggers the character's episode: the presence of children, encountering a monstrous demon or evens something as simple as an open flame.

Make a Willpower roll whenever the character is subjected to this form of stress or pressure. The difficulty of the roll is usually 6, increasing to 8 if the stress is sudden or especially severe.

Manic-Depression

Manic-depressives suffer from severe mood swings, sometimes resulting from severe trauma or anxiety. Victims may be upbeat and confident one moment, then uncontrollably lethargic and pessimistic the next.

Mortals or fallen with this derangement are constantly on a hair trigger, never knowing when the next mood swing will strike. Whenever the character fails a task, the Storyteller has the option of making a secret Willpower roll (difficulty 8). If the roll fails, the character lapses into depression. Additionally, the character goes into depression whenever one of her rolls botches or if her Willpower ever drops below 2. Roll a die to determine how many scenes the character remains depressed, keeping the number a secret.

A mortal or fallen in a depressive state loses a point of Faith (to a minimum of 1) for the duration of the mental episode. Upon emerging from the depressive state, the character is energetic, relentlessly upbeat and active (obsessively so) for a number of scenes proportional to the time spent in depression. When the character is in this manic state, the difficulty of all Willpower rolls decreases by one.

Megalomania

Individuals with this derangement are obsessed with accumulating power and wealth, hoping to salve their insecurities by becoming the most potent individuals in their environment. The character is invariably arrogant and supremely sure of her abilities, convinced of her own inherent superiority. The means of achieving such status can take many forms, from devious conspiracies to outright brutality. Any individual of equal or higher status than such a character is perceived to be "competition."

Mortals or fallen with this derangement struggle constantly to rise to the height of power and influence, by any means necessary. In a megalomaniac's view, there are only two classes of people: those who are weaker and those who do not deserve the power they have and must be made weaker. This belief extends to everyone, including the character's immediate allies. This derangement lends an extra die to all of the victim's Willpower rolls, due to her towering sense of superiority.

Multiple Personalities

The trauma that spawns this derangement fractures the character's personality into one or more additional personas, allowing her to deny her trauma or any actions the trauma causes by placing the blame on "someone else." Each personality is created to respond to certain emotional stimuli. For instance, an abused person might develop a tough-as-nails survivor personality, create a "protector" or even become a murderer to deny the abuse she suffers. In most cases, none of these personalities is aware of the others, and they come and go through the character's mind in response to specific situations or conditions.

Mortals or fallen with multiple personalities can manifest different Abilities or perhaps increased or diminished Faith for each identity, but it is the Storyteller's responsibility to determine the specific details.

Obsessive/Compulsive

The trauma, guilt or inner conflict that causes this derangement forces the character to focus nearly all of his attention and energy on a single repetitive behavior or

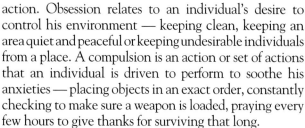

action. Obsession relates to an individual's desire to control his environment — keeping clean, keeping an area quiet and peaceful or keeping undesirable individuals from a place. A compulsion is an action or set of actions that an individual is driven to perform to soothe his anxieties — placing objects in an exact order, constantly checking to make sure a weapon is loaded, praying every few hours to give thanks for surviving that long.

If a character has an obsessive or compulsive derangement, determine a set of specific actions or behaviors that the character follows to the exclusion of all else (even if doing so interferes with his current agenda or endangers his life or others' lives). The effects of obsessive/compulsive behavior can be negated for the course of one scene by spending a temporary Willpower point. If the character is forcibly prevented from adhering to his derangement, he may lose control among enemies or allies and attack either (or both) indiscriminately.

Paranoia

The character believes that her misery and insecurity stem from external persecution and hostility. Paranoids obsess about their persecution complexes, often creating vast and intricate conspiracy theories to explain who torments them and why. Anyone or anything perceived to be "one of them" might be subjected to violence.

A demon or mortal who suffers from paranoia has difficulty with social interaction, and the difficulties of all such dice rolls increase by one. The character is distrustful and wary of everyone, even close friends and family. The slightest hint of suspicious behavior is enough to provoke a Willpower roll to retain control, with the difficulty relative to the degree of the behavior.

Schizophrenia

Conflicting sets of feelings and impulses that he cannot resolve can cause your character to develop schizophrenia, which manifests as a withdrawal from reality, violent changes in behavior and hallucinations. This derangement is the classic sort, causing victims to talk to walls, imagine themselves to be the King of Siam or receive murderous instructions from their pets. Mortals who turn to conventional medicine for help are typically diagnosed as schizophrenic.

Roleplaying this derangement requires careful thought, and the Storyteller must determine a general set of behaviors relevant to the trauma that causes the condition. Hallucinations, bizarre behavior and disembodied voices stem from a terrible inner conflict that the individual cannot resolve. Establish a firm idea of what that conflict is, then rationalize what kind of behavior it causes.

Mortals or fallen with this derangement are unpredictable and dangerous—even more so than usual. In situations that trigger a victim's inner conflict, a point of Willpower can be spent to avoid its effects for the duration of the scene.

Disease

Most mortals rarely fear death from a gunshot or a car bomb or the claws of a monster. The biggest fear for most human beings is disease — be it a contagious disease such as AIDS or cholera, or non-contagious illnesses such as cancer and leukemia.

For the fallen, disease is rarely an issue as their supernatural energies keep their host healthy almost constantly. As long as a demon has even one point of Faith remaining, he is completely immune to any and all diseases. He also does not age as long as he has at least one point of Faith in reserve.

If the demon *does* run out of Faith, his body loses its immunity. It does not suddenly crumble to dust from old age or instantly contract the diseases it "should have" caught before, though. It simply means the character is now just a normal person until he can recoup another point of Faith.

In the rare event that a demon without Faith is exposed to a disease, the Storyteller should allow the character a Stamina roll to resist the contagion (difficulty anywhere from 4 for a minor flu bug to 10 for Ebola). Minor diseases inflict penalties to dice pools; more serious diseases inflict bashing or lethal damage and may even reduce a character's Attributes.

If an infected character regains Faith, the disease is instantly purged from his system. Any penalties vanish, and any damage taken heals back at the normal rate (or faster with supernatural assistance).

Drowning

Unless aided by supernatural powers, the fallen still need to breathe. Your character can drown if he is submerged completely or held underwater, or if a swimming roll botches and the Storyteller is cruel (see Swimming, p. 234). A character can hold her breath as indicated on the following chart:

Willpower can also be spent to continue holding one's breath. Each point grants another 30 seconds if Stamina is 3 or lower or

Stamina	Holding Breath
1	30 seconds
2	One minute
3	Two minutes
4	Four minutes
5	Eight minutes

another full minute if Stamina is 4 or higher.

When your character can no longer hold his breath, he begins to drown or suffocate. A drowning character suffers one lethal health level each turn. When your character reaches Incapacitated, he dies in one minute per point of Stamina.

Electrocution

Electricity does nasty things to humans and their demonic possessors. An electric shock is considered lethal

damage. If your character comes in contact with a source of electricity without appropriate insulation, she takes damage. The Storyteller may ask you to roll Strength (difficulty 9) to determine whether your character can pull away from the current. Armor does not protect from electricity, although an evocation or apocalyptic form may.

The following chart shows the amount of damage delivered based on the source of the electrical shock. Normal humans may suffer permanent damage or Attribute loss if they fall to Incapacitated as a result of electrical shock, but demons do not. Their enhanced constitutions protect them from long-term impairment.

Health Levels/Turn	Electrical Source
One	Minor; wall socket
Two	Major; vehicle battery
Three	Severe; junction box
Four	Fatal; main feed line

Falling

Characters who leap from rooftop to rooftop must be prepared for the consequences. Your character might walk away from a short fall or never walk again after a long one. The following chart lists the number of damage dice your Storyteller rolls. If your character falls 30 feet or less, damage can be diminished by grabbing outcroppings or tumbling upon impact. Make a Dexterity + Athletics roll against the difficulty listed on the chart. Each success on this roll reduces the damage dice pool of the fall by one.

Any remaining damage successes are bashing. If your character falls more than 30 feet, no amount of acrobatics helps, and the damage is lethal. Modifiers may also apply based on where your character lands — concrete hurts a lot more than water, depending on the altitude of the fall. The numbers on the chart assume a hard surface awaits.

Falling Damage

Feet	Save Roll	Difficulty	Damage Dice
10	Dex + Athletics	7	2 (bashing)
20	Dex + Athletics	8	5 (bashing)
30	Dex + Athletics	9	10 (bashing)
40	None	—	10 (lethal)
50	None	—	10 (lethal)
60	None	—	10 (lethal)

Fire

The nature, extent and temperature of a fire all affect how destructive it is to your character's body. The greatest danger arises when his clothes ignite and he continues to take damage even after the initial exposure to flame. Your character takes damage automatically in every turn that he remains in contact with the fire, until he escapes or extinguishes the blaze. No damage dice are rolled for fire. Lethal health levels are simply lost as if

successes had been rolled. Some demons may be protected from fire by their apocalyptic form.

Health Levels/Turn	Size of Fire
One	Clothing or hair on fire; body part exposed to torch or similar small fire
Two	Bonfire; half the body exposed to extensive flames
Three	Inferno; entire body engulfed in raging fire

Poisons and Drugs

Just as the fallen are immune to the rigors of age and disease, so too are they protected from the effects of drugs and poisons. While such substances can still affect them, their superior nature shields them from the worst effects.

There are three types of drug in **Demon**:

• **Depressants:** Drugs that calm, soothe or dull the mind and senses. Alcohol, marijuana and heroin are all depressants. When a character is affected by these drugs, he usually loses a number of dice from his pools due to distraction and lethargy. A mild depressant might remove one die, while a very powerful one might remove three.

• **Stimulants:** Drugs that wake you up and give you energy. Caffeine and cocaine are both stimulants. Most stimulants are too mild to have much game effect, except possibly for adding a die to some Stamina-related pools. Very powerful stimulants might add a die to Strength or Dexterity pools as well. In all cases, there's an inevitable comedown after the boost. Fatigue and lethargy usually take one to three dice from all pools after the rush is over.

• **Poison:** Poisons work like an attack and can be soaked with a Stamina roll. As a general rule, your character takes from one to three levels of bashing damage per scene or even turn (depending on the intensity of the poison). The effects last and damage continues to accrue until the poison wears off or an antidote is provided.

When a character takes a drug or is poisoned, the player makes a Stamina roll (difficulty 7 for most substances). Fallen characters add their Faith rating to this pool as long as they have at least one point of Faith remaining. If the roll is successful, the character is unaffected by the drug or the damage of the poison is reduced.

Temperature Extremes

Extreme heat or cold has an adverse effect on your character. It may reduce his Dexterity, Strength or even affect his mental acuity by reducing Wits. Under the worst conditions, it deals damage. Frostbite, hypothermia or heat exhaustion have dire consequences. The Storyteller can represent extreme weather conditions through reduced dice pools, increased difficulties or lost health levels.

Some fallen characters may be able to weather such conditions without problems if evocations or the enhancements of their apocalyptic forms protect them.

His executive assistant informed him the moment the helicopter landed, but he kept the men from the Pentagon waiting for nearly an hour simply because he could. They were not men in the habit of waiting, certainly not for the likes of a civilian like himself. He reclined in his leather chair not a dozen steps from the lavishly appointed conference room, savoring the sound of their veins constricting as their blood pressure surged like steam in a kettle. He knew with a certainty that only his Master could provide exactly how long he could keep these men waiting before they summoned the outrage to storm out of DynaCom's executive office building. He strode into their presence like a beneficent deity less than a heartbeat from their breaking point.

They leapt to their feet as he entered, these old, burly men with chests full of ribbons, and a thrill resonated through his bones. *This is power*, he thought, resisting the urge to cackle like a madman. The muscles deep in his throat bunched and coiled in anticipation as he strode to the head of the table and waved generals and admirals to take their seats. He made no apology for his rudeness, instead getting directly to business.

"Gentlemen, if you'll open the folders on the table before you, I'll summarize the project thus far. I wouldn't go so far as to call the equipment a mind-control device, but let's just say that we've found a way to make your troops *extremely* persuasive when they want to be."

He leaned back in his chair and launched into the pitch. He had notes but didn't pay them any attention. It wasn't like he needed them. He felt the power coiled like a spring deep in his throat, thrumming like a taut wire with each and every word, molding the brains of these gold-encrusted fools like so much putty. He could have told them to dance naked on the table, and they would have leapt to obey. He could have told them to go home and fuck their daughters, and they wouldn't have blinked an eye. It didn't matter what his company had to sell. They would buy, and pay dearly for the privilege.

The deal was struck in less than an hour. They liked what he had to offer, but then, he expected they would. They would be ready to accept delivery by the end of the summer — a bit longer than he wanted, but he was in a gracious mood, so he let it pass. He dismissed them with a wave of his hand and made his way back to his executive suite.

He'd just closed the door behind him when the Master's presence filled his mind like a dagger of ice. The pressure struck him blind in an instant.

HAVE YOU SERVED ME WELL? It was a howling wind and a sound like bones breaking, and a voice older and crueler than death itself.

"Master," he gasped, falling to his knees. "I have done as you commanded. They will take the devices by the end of the summer."

THAT IS NOT WHAT I WISH, the terrible wind moaned through his mind. IT MUST BE NOW.

He curled into a ball, trembling violently. "Can't... can't be now," he whimpered. "Not... possible... these things take time..."

YOU DISAPPOINT ME, the voice said, and then the pain truly began. He writhed amid his own filth for hours as the Master demonstrated what power truly was.

CHAPTER TEN: STORYTELLING

When, in our whole lives, did we honestly face, in solitude, the one question on which all turned: whether after all the Supernatural might not in fact occur? When did we put up one moment's real resistance to the loss of our faith?
—C. S. Lewis, *The Great Divorce*

In previous chapters, you've been introduced to the world of the fallen — their origins, the failed war against Heaven and their mysterious release from what was believed to be eternal damnation. You've learned about their Houses, factions and powers, as well as the mechanics of creating interesting and evocative characters. Now comes the real challenge: bringing the apocalyptic world of **Demon** to life.

Demon is about faith, temptation and the heroic struggle for redemption in the face of overwhelming odds. The fallen have returned to a cynical, faithless world teetering on the brink of destruction. They are mere shadows of their former glory, clothing themselves in the bodies of men and women, but the untapped faith of six billion souls lies at their fingertips, and they can walk the earth as gods once more if they wish. Power and freedom beckon for the first time in eons. The question is: What will they do with it? Will the fallen heed the call of their infernal masters and pave the way for their return, laying the foundations for hell on earth? Will they turn their backs on the old ways and promote the

beliefs of their faction over the ancient ties of House and lord? Will they reject their past entirely, renounce old loyalties and chart their own path to glory? Can they stand by and watch the corruption of mankind continue, or will they revel in it, hastening the human race to its doom? Do they dare resist the tyranny of the Earthbound, or will they search the world for the lost Morningstar and raise the banner of rebellion once more? Above all, do they resist the corrupting influence of their Torment or trade their nascent humanity for power and become truly demonic? The Storyteller must draw on the characters' backgrounds, hopes and ambitions to create stories that challenge their — and their players' — convictions and beliefs. As a result, taking on the role of a Storyteller in a **Demon** game is very demanding. It requires careful thought and background work to build character-driven chronicles and stories. You must create a world that is a nightmare reflection of our own, enticing and repellent, exhilarating and horrifying. You must evoke the thrill of inhuman power and the temptations that go with it. There is nothing that the

fallen cannot accomplish with enough Faith, but are they willing to pay the price in human misery and the corruption of their souls?

Storytelling sounds like a lot to manage all at once, and it is at first. Fortunately, the Storyteller doesn't have to do it all herself. The secret to successful storytelling is, ironically, the work of the players. Fulfilling the expectations and interests of a chronicle's players is the first trick to creating the game's setting. Then — if the chronicle and its overall story have been carefully developed — the actions of the characters, both good and bad, will have consequences that spawn further stories. Never forget that the more the players are involved with what happens in a chronicle, the less work you, the Storyteller, must take upon yourself. You aren't supposed to do it all alone. A Storyteller should have as much fun with the game as the players, and this chapter details how.

This chapter illustrates the process of creating and running a **Demon** chronicle and offers advice for making the most out of the individual stories that carry the chronicle along. Building a detailed and cohesive background, a world for your players to redeem (or destroy), begins with input from your players and your own ideas for what kind of overall story you would like to tell. Once you have decided on the details of the setting, the next step is creating characters to fill it, again keeping in mind the kind of chronicle you want to tell. After the characters are in place, you can then get to writing the chronicle in earnest, working out the intrigues and events that move the overall story along and draw on each character's goals and motivations. Each step builds upon the next, giving you more and more background to make each story enjoyable and easy to manage. If you have never run a roleplaying game before, don't be intimidated by the big picture. Take it a step at a time, do it for fun, and let your imagination run wild.

Beginnings

Chronicles don't spring fully formed from a Storyteller's head. They usually start from a single idea or a handful of impressions. Reading through the rulebook an image leaps out at you: Demons from disparate Houses and factions unite to protect their hometown against their more monstrous kin, for example, or vow to atone for their past sins by making Earth a paradise once more. The central premise can be grandly epic or gritty and visceral depending on the kinds of stories you want to tell. The question is, how do you turn these nebulous ideas into a well-rounded foundation to build your stories upon?

The first step begins with the players. Before you can really develop the foundation for your chronicle, you must have a strong grasp on what sorts of characters they want to play and how their concepts relate to your ideas. Suppose you are considering a chronicle where the characters are humanity's protectors, guarding their hometown

against the ravages of truly monstrous fallen and creating a haven for other demons in search of redemption. This kind of chronicle suggests stories of heroism and sacrifice as the characters fight against their former comrades and face tough decisions on the price they are willing to pay for the sake of their human charges.

But what if one player has her heart set on playing a member of the nihilistic Ravener faction and another wishes to be a ruthless, manipulative Faustian, neither of which is compatible with your premise? It's never a good idea to force character choices on a player, because you want each player to feel as if he is contributing to the game and playing a character in whom he is really interested. At this point comes some amount of negotiation and compromise. Perhaps you can interest him in your vision of heroism and redemption but shift the focus of the chronicle to center instead on the characters' struggles against the menace of the Earthbound, something that every faction can rally against. The important point is to make sure that your ideas and the players' expectations are in synch before you even begin to develop the chronicle, so that everyone's choices contribute to the concept as a whole instead of trying to pull it in a dozen different directions.

Once everyone agrees on the general direction of the chronicle, the players can begin to create their characters while you shape the world they will live in. It's worthwhile to do this simultaneously, because it allows your ideas and theirs to play off one another, and it might point you in directions that you could have missed otherwise. Suppose, for example, that a player wants to create a character who is fairly young but has some political connections and moderate wealth. Taking these considerations into account, you could suggest that the character is the daughter of a prominent local politician. She's grown up around the movers and shakers of the city, which provides her with useful connections and insight into the city's politics.

This allows you to pose more questions for the player. What is the relationship like between father and daughter? Does she agree with his politics? Is he corrupt or a dedicated public servant? Does his constant struggle for reelection strain his relationships with her and other family members? Does she have siblings, and are they following in their father's footsteps? Ask questions and prompt the player to fill in the blanks. Doing so allows him to further expand and enrich his character background and provide you with a wealth of story suggestions for your chronicle. How does the demon reconcile the feelings of his host against the desire to enthrall her father? What if another demon tries to enthrall him or one of her siblings? How can she use her father's political connections to further her own agenda in the city, and will that bring her into conflict with other fallen or worse, the servants of the Earthbound? Get your players

to go into a lot of detail when creating their characters. Sit in with them during the creation process and brainstorm about their backgrounds, then make the most of the information they come up with. They can provide you with a whole host of characters, situations and conflicts that will be of use to you later.

A character's choice of Backgrounds provides further opportunities to add depth to your chronicle and enrich your stories. Encourage the purchase of thralls, contacts, influence and the like, then brainstorm with the player to flesh them out. Where do a character's resources come from? Is she an heiress? Did she win the lottery? Did she stumble onto a drug deal gone sour and steal the bloodstained cash? What effect do these circumstances have on who the character is and her place in the chronicle? Likewise, thralls or contacts are more than just dots on the character sheet — they are people with their own needs, goals and viewpoints. For instance, suppose a player wants her character to have a midlevel contact in the police department. Who is this contact, and how did the character establish this relationship? The contact might be the character's uncle, a veteran homicide detective who has a habit of asking pointed questions about the character's lifestyle and activities (particularly if he catches her at the scene of a recent murder!).

Each Background is an added dimension to the character concept, containing a wealth of ideas to inspire a Storyteller. How does a demon reconcile his ancient memories with the real and immediate ties of his host's family and friends? Does the character embrace these relationships wholeheartedly, or does he regard them as useful sources of Faith and nothing more? These situations are some of the first dilemmas that the characters must face, and they can influence his actions in many subtle ways. While it is always tempting to just gloss over the particulars of each character's prelude and get on with "being a demon," doing so leaves out a vital dimension in the character's struggle against her Torment. Paying attention to this aspect of character creation provides you with a fertile field from which to draw ideas and supporting characters.

Once you have determined a general direction for your chronicle and incorporated elements of the players' characters, you can then move on to establishing the details of your setting.

a World of Darkness

A setting is more than just a physical location where your stories take place. It's an environment that reflects the themes of the chronicle and supports the kind of stories you want to tell. Consider the bleak urban landscape of *The Crow* and the way it lends strength to the movie's themes of death, love and hope. Would the story have been as powerful if it had been set amid the clean streets of a sunny Colorado town?

• **Faith No More:** The world of **Demon** is a darker, bleaker reflection of our own. As you envision the details of the setting there are some crucial elements to keep in mind: The fallen have returned to a world that has forgotten them. The relentless march of technology and reason has made a mockery of faith, equating belief in the divine with childlike ignorance or the delusions of the mad. People still attend church or pray in the direction of Mecca, but it's only lip service to institutions that let them justify their excesses and vilify those with whom they disagree. Modern churches are made of glass and steel, with high-tech sound systems in place of a choir and their own TV studios to get the call for contributions out to the masses. Centuries of greed, violence and fear have alienated humanity from the divine. Prayers go unanswered, innocents continue to suffer, and acts of

Mortal Limitations

One of the everyday challenges for a **Demon** Storyteller is maintaining a careful balance a character's cosmic knowledge and power with the limitations of her mortal host body. It's tempting for a player to assume that their character is privy to boundless amounts of knowledge based on memories that go back to the beginning of time. Though it's fun to play upon ancient memories and the divine insights of the Celestials to add depth to a **Demon** character, taking advantage of such knowledge could easily upset the balance of your chronicle if taken too far. And who wants to play an all-knowing angel anyway? Where's the challenge in that?

There's nothing wrong with allowing players to make use of their character's ancient memories, especially when doing so helps advance the plot of your chronicle or add to the drama of a story. To keep such access from getting out of hand, though, emphasize to your players that while their characters undoubtedly have a wealth of knowledge at their disposal, accessing it is another matter. For all its complexity, the human mind is not up to the task of containing all of a demon's memories, so recollection is imperfect at best. Calling up details from the War of Wrath would be like you or I trying to remember episodes of our early childhood. We tend to remember a collection of images, some vivid and relevant, others seemingly random, and all of them tinted by personal feelings and perspectives. Because of their mortal limitations, demon characters will remember their past in the same fashion and bring their vast knowledge down to a more manageable level.

generosity and compassion are invitations to be victimized. God, as the famous line once read, is dead in the hearts and minds of humanity.

• **Shades of Gray**: Coupled with the poisoning of human faith is a pervasive cynicism in human nature and the decay of the fabric of society. Violence and despair are endemic. The rich get richer, the poor get poorer, and no one believes that things are going to get any better. Humanity is rotting from within, continuing a sad, slow decline, and symbols of its decay are everywhere in the weathered façades of great Gothic churches and granite office buildings. Amid soulless towers of steel and glass might sit an abandoned cathedral whose stained glass is rich with color and beauty from a time now lost. Such a place serves as a haunting reminder of what might have been or could be again. The world has lost its heroes. They were caught in sex scandals or taking bribes, or perhaps they fell victim to urban violence. There is no strong leadership, no faith in politicians or belief in building a better tomorrow. People know better.

• **The End is Nigh**: The sky is thick with pollutants, and the seas are burial grounds for uncounted tons of chemicals and other wastes. The climate is growing steadily hotter, unleashing brutal droughts and terrible storms, and rising waters threaten coastal cities and islands. The newspapers are full of stories predicting that a terrible catastrophe is looming, and many people cannot shake the dread that humanity is in its final days. As wars and rumors of wars sweep the globe, and the earth writhes and seethes with heat, even the fallen believe that the end of the world is soon at hand.

These points illustrate the essence of the World of Darkness, and they are important because they heighten the dilemmas that your characters face as they fight against their demonic nature. Despair and resignation are all around them; violence and death are common. What is one more killing, one more lie? How much difference can one person, even *an angel*, make? Virtues such as courage and compassion are hard to find and even harder to maintain, but it is the struggle for them that is important. This struggle is the source of the game's triumph and tragedy, and the decisions you make in developing your setting should take this into account. It is important to point out that you don't have to adhere religiously to these concepts, and the degree to which you emphasize them is strictly a matter of personal taste. The only truly important thing to remember is that your environment should be one in which doing the right and honorable thing is difficult and daunting.

There is, of course, no limit to the possible physical locations you can choose for your chronicle. Future **Demon** sourcebooks will focus on the city of Los Angeles as the game's signature setting, but details about its infernal inhabitants and their

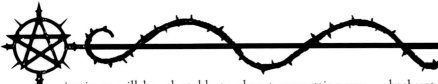

intrigues will be adaptable to almost any setting you choose. If you want to set your chronicle in a large city that you are unfamiliar with, your local library can provide useful information and maps, which you can then reinterpret to suit your purposes. Remember, though, that you aren't constrained to be faithful in every detail. This is the World of Darkness, and you can shape it any way you choose. Consider the preceding guidelines, and adapt the details in favor of your own ideas to build the proper mood. Many Storytellers prefer to set their chronicles in dark reflections of their own hometowns. Drawing on familiar details helps paint a vibrant picture for the players and gives the setting a visceral realism that is difficult to achieve otherwise.

As you map out the length and breadth of your locale, draw ideas from important city features, combining function with symbolism to make interesting images. For instance, an abandoned train station in the center of the city might make an ideal site for a pack of feral Devourers, contrasting their bestial natures with the old structure's faded grandeur. An abandoned cathedral in a decaying section of the city might come to be a haven of sorts to the fallen, its stained glass and graffiti-stained walls providing a poignant reflection of their tragic existence and their search for redemption. A grand old apartment building in the center of the city might appeal to a haughty Devil, holding court in a spacious, gloomy penthouse rich with the style of older, happier times long forgotten. Demons are territorial creatures, and the places they claim invariably mirror their individual character and attitudes. Consider the details of your setting carefully, and create locations that suggest a certain mood or contrast the natures of the people who live there. You don't have to spend hours exhaustively detailing every nook and cranny, though. Instead, concentrate on two or three cool, evocative details that create a memorable image in your mind.

Styles of Play

An important aspect to consider as the details of your chronicle come together is the scope and style of the stories you want to tell. Will the chronicle follow the lofty ambitions of a band of demon lords and span entire continents, or will it focus on the gritty, everyday struggles of a handful of fallen who wrestle with their darker natures as they try to redeem a single, troubled neighborhood? **Demon** supports a broad spectrum of playing styles, from the operatic to the visceral, and it's helpful to determine at the outset what style best complements the scale of your chronicle.

• **Operatic:** Operatic chronicles are epic tales that deal with themes on a grand scale. The actions and ambitions of the characters are larger-than-life, and the consequences of their decisions are momentous. Gritty realism takes a

backseat to bold, dynamic stories in which fallen angels stride the earth like titans and whole nations are prey to their schemes of glory, domination and revenge. Operatic chronicles focus much more on the superior nature of the character instead of her mundane, human aspect. Thralls are merely pawns to be seduced, used and abandoned. Human relationships are few and far between, but they are intense and passionate when they occur. Cities are backdrops for the characters' ancient feuds, forbidden romances and frightening schemes. When they triumph, they save entire cities from ancient evil; when they fail, the world burns around them and their loved ones lie amid the ashes — often slain by the character's own hand. Operatic stories are pure melodrama, but they free the Storyteller to concentrate on telling exciting, action-filled tales that don't require tons of subtlety or attention to mundane details like paying the electric bill.

• **Cinematic:** Cinematic stories fill the middle ground between opera and the visceral. The characters are supernatural creatures with human cares and relationships. In a sense, they exist in two worlds, and their toughest struggles often revolve around keeping them from colliding. Cinematic stories contrast the mundane against the supernatural. The fallen fight dynamic, desperate battles beneath the noses of mankind, retreating to the solace of family and friends to nurse their physical and spiritual wounds. The struggle to balance the two aspects of the character's existence provides a wealth of possibilities for powerful stories that combine realism with wonder.

• **Visceral:** Visceral stories are about human characters with demons lurking beneath their skins. Rather than a world-spanning epic or a chronicle of competing desires, the visceral chronicle is about holding onto the mundane against the pull of the supernatural. The characters may have little to no memory of their time in the Abyss. Indeed, they might not realize that they are demons at all, as they struggle to explain the miraculous yet vaguely sinister events that surround them. These chronicles are less heroic and more horrific, and they work best with a very tight focus and a small scale, centering on the characters' human lives and the effect their true nature has on everyone and everything around them. This mundane focus does not mean that you can't have fun with angelic power and the struggles between ancient, immortal spirits, but the power of the chronicle comes from the characters' struggle to uncover the mystery of their true nature.

Creating the Chronicle

The *chronicle* is the overall story that you want to tell. It is made up of a series of smaller stories in which the

players' characters are the central figures. Think of a chronicle as a collection of books that tells a long, complicated tale. Each book is a story unto itself, which is further broken up into chapters and then into scenes. What happens in each individual story greatly depends on the course of the chronicle as a whole. It's this stage of development that is the most demanding and time-consuming for the Storyteller. **Demon** chronicles work best when they have a definite beginning, middle and end, providing a structure that will increase the power and complexity of your stories. Accordingly, you need to detail this structure in advance, in order to organize your thoughts, indicate when to pick up the pace and provide tension over the course of individual stories. A chronicle loses its focus and energy if there is no real end in sight. After all this work, you want to close things off with a bang, not a whimper, right? Get a journal or disk and set it aside to hold notes and ideas as you outline the course of events in your chronicle. Don't try to keep it all in your head.

At this point, you have a pretty large amount of information to help guide your development of the chronicle. Now you have to flesh out the course the stories will take and blend all of the details into a workable whole. The first step is to choose a governing theme. A theme is the central idea that describes the basic plot of the overall story. Some suitable themes for **Demon** chronicles include:

• **Divided Loyalties**: Although they are free at last from their prison, the fallen are still bound to the service of their infernal masters, who have commanded the characters to prepare the way for their release. Do the characters heed the call of their imprisoned overlords and effectively create hell on earth, or do they risk the wrath of the Princes of Hell by fighting against their release? The risks are terrible indeed, for if the fallen are torn from their mortal shells and returned to the Pit, they will undoubtedly suffer for their disobedience. What is more, for every fallen angel that struggles to keep the monstrous demons in the Abyss, there are ten more who seek just the opposite, sowing corruption and horror at every turn and seeking innocent souls that will make fine vessels for their overlords. This is a classic heroic struggle against fearsome odds that works well with any style of play.

• **The Search for Lucifer**: The disappearance of the Morningstar threw everything the fallen believed into doubt and sowed the seeds of despair that made them into the monsters they are now. What was his fate, and what does it say about the fallen and the future of humanity? Further, what happens when and if Lucifer is found? Will it mean a resumption of the war against Heaven? Is that really even something the characters want? This theme is ideal for chronicles that focus on conspiracy and intrigue, and it works best with a cinematic style of play.

• **A War of Ideals**: The fallen are no longer a single, unified host — they are split into factions whose ideals stand in stark contrast to the rest. Upon their return, these factions gain new vigor, aggressively pursuing their agendas far from the oppressive hand of their overlords. Naturally, this theme works best when all the characters espouse the ideals of the same faction, and such a chronicle provides a great blend of action and intrigue as they fight, ally, conspire and betray their former compatriots. The potential for passionate ideals, forsaken oaths and grand tragedy makes this kind of chronicle idea for operatic or cinematic styles of play.

• **The Greater Evil**: Every one of the fallen has a demon lurking in his heart, but his potential for evil is nothing compared to that of the Earthbound, monstrous demons who never benefited from the counterweight of a mortal host. They are like dark gods, so alien in their madness as to resemble neither angel nor man. Now that these monstrosities have awakened from their long slumber, only the fallen stand between them and their vision for humanity's future. Although the Earthbound themselves are too powerful for the players' characters to face directly, their demonic and mortal servants are another matter. The Earthbound seek to enslave, banish or destroy the newly arrived fallen and complete their nightmarish plans for dominating mankind. This theme places the characters in a situation where they are fighting an undisputed evil but must decide to what lengths they are willing to surrender their humanity in order to stem the tide. Is it worth becoming a monster to save innocent lives from an evil that is greater still? This theme works best with an operatic or cinematic style of play, but it can also work in an intense, visceral chronicle as well.

• **Return to Eden**: The world slouches toward oblivion. Everywhere the characters turn, the indications are clear that the end of this world is at hand. But for beings who witnessed the creation of the universe itself, an end is nothing more than an invitation to begin anew. Do the characters fight to pull mankind back from the brink and restore the world to the paradise it once was, or do they hasten its end in fire and blood, preserving what they must in order to begin a new age, free from the mistakes of the old? Who gets to decide what that new world will be? This theme is ideal for an operatic style of play, but it works equally well with a more humanistic, cinematic style as well.

Themes are important because they let you focus the events and actions along a central idea. They give your chronicle consistency and emotional resonance that you can build to a climactic finale. It is entirely possible to have more than one theme and style of play. You might want to create a chronicle that begins viscerally, with characters seeking answers to explain the strange events in their lives. Then, as they learn more and uncover their true nature as fallen angels, they are confronted with the impending end of the world, which leads the characters

into conflict with other demons and invokes a more cinematic or operatic style of play. Multiple themes can build a rich chronicle for a troupe as a whole, or each character can embody a theme all her own, distinct from her fellows. The only limit is how much effort you, as the Storyteller, wish to devote in developing and smoothly integrating the multiple threads.

Once you have chosen a theme, you can begin to develop the course of events that your chronicle will take, from beginning to end. Like any good story, a chronicle must have a conclusion to be truly effective, and if you know where the chronicle is going, you will have much more confidence in, and control over, your stories. Consider your initial ideas, the characters and the themes you have chosen, then flesh out the details of your chronicle as a rough outline of events.

For example, let's consider the mixed-theme chronicle provided earlier. The characters begin with little or no knowledge of their Celestial nature. They have all experienced strange, even miraculous events, such as awakening from a lengthy coma or surviving a suicide attempt, yet their otherwise normal lives have taken nightmarish turns. It begins with intense and disturbing nightmares of dark, empty landscapes and insistent voices commanding them in a terrible language that they can't understand. Then their lives are plagued by mysterious, even miraculous events. A loved one is diagnosed with a terrible disease, then is completely cured after a visit from the character. A would-be robbery goes awry when the attackers are set upon by a pack of wild dogs. A longtime rival threatens to force the character out of her job but suffers a freak accident that leaves him dead or injured. Before long, the characters begin to wonder if they are the cause of these strange events, and they ultimately question their sanity. Their quest for answers leads them to search newspapers, books and even the Internet for signs that they aren't alone.

Eventually, they discover (or come to the attention of) other demons lurking in the city. These demons try to take advantage of the characters' innocence, using them as pawns in their own schemes, but the characters piece together the truth about themselves over time. Of course, the truth is hardly comforting — in fact, it only makes the characters' lives that much more difficult, as they cannot go back to their "mortal" routine knowing the peril that is growing in humanity's midst. They must drive the demons from the city (or, if you want a more operatic scale, the world), while clinging to the life and love they'd claimed as their own. The stakes grow ever higher as the plot evolves, placing increasing risk on the characters' loved ones, until the final showdown. They must then decide whether to sacrifice their mortal lives and fully embrace the power of their angelic side or cling to their humanity and risk death or worse.

You now have a basic outline of the overall events in your chronicle. In addition to these major points, smaller plot lines will be spawned by the characters' personal goals and backgrounds. These subplots can be tied to the overall plot, or they may be entirely unconnected, contributing to the whole through character development and added conflict. Some ideas for subplots suggest themselves at the beginning of your chronicle, provided by the characters' backgrounds and personalities. Others arise over the course of the game, as relationships and important decisions influence the course of events. Incorporate as many of these subplots into your chronicle as you feel comfortable with, because they provide alternative stories that add dimension to the characters and the chronicle as a whole.

The Devil in the Details

Once you have created your central themes and detailed the course of the chronicle, you are ready to get down to specifics about your setting and the Storyteller characters who exist there. The outline you have developed should give you a guideline as to which characters you need and when they will come into play. For instance, in the previous example, the Storyteller would initially develop the mortal friends, family and loved ones of each character, devoting time and energy to developing their personalities and relationships. As play progresses, the Storyteller can fill in details of the rest of the city's demons, from sympathetic fallen to monstrous demons with their own agenda for the city, as well as other mortals who might play roles in the chronicle. The point is that you, as the Storyteller, should not feel like you have to generate a whole world in a single day. Figure out what you will need for the immediate point in the chronicle, develop those elements in detail, then work ahead to address your future needs.

Demon demands well-crafted Storyteller characters to make the chronicle vivid and emotionally powerful. This is especially true of the characters' thralls, who are both the source of their power and a potent storytelling tool to reinforce the price of power and the peril of the demons' monstrous nature. Thralls have to be well-realized, multi-dimensional characters in their own right, complete with strengths, weaknesses, goals and ambitions. Each time a demon seeks out a human to forge a pact of faith, a relationship is forged as well, and unless you make the players work to create and maintain that bond, they won't think twice before their characters ravage those thralls for power. Paint them in vivid detail and act through them to evoke emotions and ideas in your players.

272

The first Storyteller characters you are likely to create will be those generated by your players' character histories. This is a good place to start, because the players will help you brainstorm their affiliates' lives and characteristics. When creating your first Storyteller characters, work along the following guidelines:

• **Envision the role:** Each character performs a role in your chronicle, even down to the accountant who crosses a dark parking lot and falls prey to a character's hunger. Establish what role the character is to play, then determine what qualities are necessary for the character to fulfill the role effectively. A potential thrall might embody qualities of innocence, ambition, terror or despair. An antagonist, on the other hand, evokes qualities of ruthlessness or cleverness or even brute belligerence. If you are creating a demon character, consider what House the demon is from and how she views her role in the grand scheme of Creation. Is she a Devourer who views herself as a monarch of the animal world, or is she a feral hunter who lives for the thrill of the chase? Is she a Slayer who takes life with regret, or is she a remorseless killer who plucks human souls like weeds? What faction is the character aligned with, and what happened during the war to cause her to make that choice? What are her goals now that she has escaped the Abyss? Does she want to build a petty kingdom on Earth and sate her appetites, or does she want to find a way to storm the ramparts of Heaven and gain justice for her fellow demons?

• **Paint a picture:** Envision what the character looks like, taking into account the qualities you have chosen. Pick out one or two characteristics that make the character interesting to you. If you are envisioning one of the characters' thralls, for instance, the image of a tall, broad-shouldered man with a prominently broken nose offers a memorable picture and suggests both strengths and vulnerabilities that provide hooks for his relationship with the demon in question.

• **Choose a name:** This sounds obvious, but carefully chosen names enhance characters, while poor ones detract from the character image and can even lessen the overall mood of the scenes in which the character appears. If we took the brawler from the last example and named him Poindexter, the players would have a hard time getting past the name, much less appreciating the character and his plight.

• **Age:** How old is the character, and how do those years of life experience affect the way the character looks at the world? Is he young and idealistic, easily swayed by promises of power, or is he the sort of man who's suffered years of success and defeat and has enough fatalism to spare for two grown people?

• **Personality:** Choose one or two words that embody the character's personality. In the beginning, you may wish to fall back on the Natures and Demeanors provided

for character creation, then expand your repertoire of Archetypes as you become more experienced. To make interesting characters, consider choosing personality types that seem to run counter to the "role" that you intend them to play in your chronicle. For example, if you are envisioning a master villain who will haunt the players' characters at every turn, you could challenge the players' expectations and make the character friendly, outgoing, even compassionate. Make him someone who believes that destroying the characters is a regretful necessity that will benefit everyone in the long run. If the character you're creating is one of the fallen, your task is compounded by the fact you are essentially dealing with a demonic personality infused with some of the traits of its mortal host. When you're creating a fallen character, start by defining the demon's personality. How did she view her role in the process of Creation? What motivated her to rebel — love for humanity, resentment of God or loyalty to Lucifer? How did the long war affect her convictions and her perspective on humanity? How did she feel about their defeat and Heaven's eternal punishment? Is she a low-Torment demon or a monstrous one? If she is monstrous, how does her Torment manifest itself? If she is a low-Torment demon, what about her mortal host reawakened her sense of compassion and morality? Once you've answered these questions, then you can move on to what sort of host your demon chose. The temptation is to go with a personality that mirrors that of the demon, and in some cases, that will be the sort of character that would best serve your story, but you can create more striking and memorable characters by creating contrasts between mortal and demon. A Devil who possesses a slick and charismatic politician is effective but somewhat stereotypical, whereas a Devil in the body of a middle-aged soccer mom creates an interesting contrast that accentuates the strengths and limitations of both personalities.

• **Personal History:** Every significant character in your chronicle benefits from some amount of personal history. What conflicts has the character faced? Who has she loved or hated? Are there enemies or former lovers out there who might cross paths with the players' characters at some point? Did the character have a mentor, and how did the relationship affect the character? Establish a character's history in as much detail as you deem relevant to the chronicle. For a demon character, this history is essential. What were her exploits during the war? With whom did she serve? Was she renowned for her heroism or infamous for her mercilessness? Did she commit deeds that she now regrets? Did she make any enemies among the fallen during the struggle? Who is her infernal master, and is she still loyal to him after her escape?

• **Quirks:** Everyone is an individual, and everyone, mortal or fallen, has quirky habits accumulated over time. Whether it's drinking milk right out of the carton or brooding from the top of the highest building

in the city, individual quirks further define characters and make them memorable.

• **Flaws/Weaknesses:** Nobody is perfect. All people have weaknesses or character flaws against which they struggle. This is especially important with regards to major adversaries. Villains who do nothing wrong, make no mistakes and are afraid of nothing are not only discouraging but boring as well. Blind spots or flaws provide chinks in a villain's armor that the characters can exploit, or give an extra level of pathos to a heroic character who must battle not only external demons, but internal ones as well.

• **Statistics/Skills:** Do this last. They're just numbers. Storyteller characters do not have to be constructed along the careful lines of a player's character. You can assign a Storyteller character whatever levels and skills you wish. If the characters aren't unique and interesting, the best set of numbers in the world won't do any good for your chronicle.

The key element to making characters memorable is to avoid stereotypes. It is easy to get lazy and just describe a roving character as a "bestial Devourer," in which case the players fall back on a single well-worn image and set of mannerisms to describe what they encounter. Pretty soon every "bestial Devourer" the characters encounter looks the same, sounds the same, and acts the same. Defy your players' expectations. With a little thought, you can give a character a quirky spin that makes her unique and engages your players' imaginations. Consider the image of a prim, proper socialite possessed by a ravening Devourer, or a Devil in the form of a truck driving, beer-belly redneck. Sometimes stereotypes have value (especially to mislead the players), but for the most part, they should be avoided.

INTO THE FIRE

You've spent time outlining the chronicle you want to tell, as well as building the world and detailing the characters who inhabit it. You have watched your players create their characters, and you've enmeshed their ideas with your own to give the players their own stake in your creation. Now it's time to begin the tale. Here is where all that background work pays off and lets you concentrate on telling your stories in the best way you can.

With your chosen themes and the outline of your chronicle in mind, you need to establish the events that surround the character's prelude, detailing the event that brought about the character's possession and then eventually led him into contact with the other players' characters. This is by no means mandatory, though. In fact, many Storytellers prefer simply to talk over these details, make some assumptions with the players, then get right to the action. Unfortunately doing so means losing an opportunity for some powerful storytelling, as well as a way for both player and Storyteller to explore what might be one of the most significant events in a character's development.

The circumstances of a character's prelude can go a long way toward establishing the often uneasy relationship between the demon's identity and the vicissitudes of her newfound mortal existence. Did the character possess her mortal host in the crushing moment of being laid off or slip through the narrow veins of a strung-out heroin junkie? Who are the mortals she first encounters, and how does she react? How do these experiences affect her perspective on this new and terrible world she has awakened in? Working through each character's prelude provides you and your players with a wealth of insights that you might not otherwise gain.

The best way to explore the fusion of mortal and demon is by first concentrating on the mortal host's life in the hours or even days before possession. Present the player with his character's mortal trials and tribulations, developing his dreams, fears, hopes and needs. Then comes the day when it all falls apart — the sequence of events that strips the mortal of his last vestiges of will. Does he lose his battle against alcoholism, leave his spouse or lose control of his temper for one brutal, irretrievable moment? By building the mortal's past and bringing him to the moment of truth, you and the player can gain a better sense of the emotions and relationships that were paramount in the host's mind at the moment he succumbed to the demon. Thus you can establish the perspectives and feelings that would have the greatest influence in the demon's epiphany.

Example: *Fred creates a character concept around a Slayer who possesses the body of a young man in his early 20s, fresh from college and struggling to make ends meet in the real world. He is married, and his wife has a baby on the way. Money is very tight, and Fred decides the young family lives in a bad section of town because it's the only place with affordable rent. Fred decides that the man works two jobs and rides the bus to get to work, taking him away from home from before dawn until very late at night. He's sleepless, hungry and constantly on edge, worried about how to get through the next month on what little he and his wife bring home. Susan, Fred's Storyteller, picks up the thread from there. She describes a cold night in early winter. Snow and sleet are starting to fall as Fred's family man lurches off the bus and makes his way wearily homeward. Today was payday, and with his wife's birthday coming up, he splurged and bought her a pair of earrings she'd been admiring at the mall. He's so tired and cold that he fails to notice the five figures that step from the shadows of a nearby alley and stalk along in his wake.*

The thieves jump him as he opens the door to his apartment building. Before he knows it, they throw him to the lobby floor and kick him nearly to death. Helpless, he watches the men tear through his pockets, ripping away his money, his wife's present and his keys. Grinning like feral dogs, the thieves climb the stairs to his apartment. The rage, frustration and shame overwhelm him, and Susan and Fred agree that this is the young man's breaking point. His spirit is broken, and into the void rushes Lharael, Fell Knight of the Ebon Legion. Considering the circumstances of the character's prelude, Fred establishes that Lharael is strongly affected by his host's love for his wife and a burning hatred for criminals of any kind, but particularly muggers or thieves. As screams echo down the stairwell, Lharael climbs purposefully to his feet, his body already shrouded with the cloak of mists as the fallen knight rises to take vengeance.*

After the characters have stepped into their mortal lives, it remains to be seen how they are all brought together into a group. Introducing the characters to one another and watching their relationships form over the course of the first story can give the players greater insight into the chemistry

EVOCATIONS AND STORYTELLING

Storytelling a character's first manifestation of her lore is often a challenge, especially in stories where the character is unaware of her true nature. How does the character know to access abilities she doesn't remember having?

There are a number of ways to allow a character insight into her powers indirectly. One method is for an evocation to manifest itself spontaneously in a situation of extreme stress or when in the grip of powerful emotions. A character attacked by a mugger suddenly sprouts claws or deflects a bullet with a gust of wind, or he talks a cop out of giving him a ticket with a degree of charm he never knew he had. While evocations often require words of power to activate them, they don't have to. The character's unconscious need can be enough to make the power manifest itself. Conversely, you can have the character catch himself muttering a stream of indecipherable words that leaves his lips numb and his tongue aching as the evocation unfolds before him. Later, as he struggles to remember what he said, you can build a number of stories around his search for knowledge as he tries to identify and decipher the strange phrases lingering in his mind.

Another method is the dream sequence. The character dreams of flying and wakes to find himself on the roof of his house, or he dreams of calling up a storm and wakes to find his bedroom ankle-deep in water. As he attempts to understand the strange phenomena occurring around him, he slowly uncovers his true nature.

Finally, if the character possesses the Mentor Background, you can create situations in which he is seemingly stalked by a mysterious individual who drops cryptic hints about his true nature and power. This provides lots of opportunity for creepy, nightmarish encounters that should ultimately tempt the character into seeing if the stranger's intimations are true.

of the group and set the stage for possible conflicts. The way in which a group of characters can be brought together depends in part on the type of group that they are to form. The following are some examples:

• **Harbingers of Hell:** The characters are all bound to the same infernal lord, and their return to Earth was coordinated to ensure that they would arrive in the same general time and place. From there, they were to go about the tasks directed by their lord, though the characters may have other plans once they are free from his iron control. This approach is the default method for assembling a group of demons, because they can be of different Houses and factions but still share a common background and history that allows the players to jump right into the chronicle.

• **True Believers:** Similar to the previous method, the characters are all from the same faction and are sent to the same general area by the faction's elders to further the group's agenda.

• **Hounds and the Hunter:** This method thrusts the characters upon one another for mutual survival in a city that is overrun with the Earthbound's demonic and mortal servants. Either the characters are newly arrived and immediately captured, bringing them together and giving them an immediate reason to work together on an escape, or they find one another more or less by accident as their paths cross while being hotly pursued.

• **Return to the Ruins:** The characters are drawn to the site of their former home during the war, and they cross paths with one another in so doing. This setting can be as specific as the ruins of a concealed infernal bastion or as expansive as a broad river valley that in ancient times was part of an undersea trench. This option allows for characters of different Houses and factions, but it provides the opportunity for shared histories that create ready made relationships and rivalries.

• **The Outcasts:** The characters find themselves in a city controlled by a powerful group of monstrous demons, which throws them together in the interests of mutual survival.

Creating Stories

There are several key elements to the storytelling process that you should consider when developing your stories. They are: *plot*, *conflict*, *setting* and *mood*.

The plot is the sequence of events and actions that the characters follow from beginning to end. The first question you should ask yourself when sitting down to design a story is what the plot will be. Like your chronicle, you need to have a clear idea of where the story will go and how you will build the action to a satisfying end. There are two types of plots. Main plots are stories that are integral parts of your chronicle and that move the overall story along. Secondary plots are

unconnected stories that may or may not have anything to do with the chronicle, but which provide entertaining diversions. The best way to run a chronicle is to intersperse secondary plots in between your main plots to give you some breathing room between major events and to allow you to try out interesting ideas without jeopardizing the integrity of your main story.

For your main plots, refer back to your chronicle outline and use it to suggest the next step that your story needs to take. The outline that you created for the chronicle is there to give you guideposts in creating and directing the flow of your main plots.

With secondary plots, anything goes. If your players have been sweating through a series of grim and difficult main plots, maybe it's time to throw in something darkly funny to break the tension. Perhaps they encounter a band of demon-hunters who make up for skill and knowledge with a little reckless enthusiasm and a lot of homemade weapons? If the characters are becoming a little cavalier about their infernal existence, you can create a story involving a mortal family member or lover who has become enthralled by a monstrous demon. Secondary plots are good for experimentation and as transition pieces between major plots.

Any plot should be able to have its central idea summed up in a few short sentences. The following are a few examples:

• A monstrous demon arrives in the city and starts a reign of terror, requiring the characters to take action.

• The characters are approached by a Malefactor who seeks their help in locating a lost artifact of the Age of Wrath.

• The character's city is invaded by a group of Earthbound servants who seek to enslave or destroy any demons they find.

If you cannot explain the main idea of the story in a couple of sentences, you are probably trying to do too much at one time. Focus your ideas into one or two central actions, then develop the course of these events.

It is entirely possible to have a plot within a plot, a side story that runs parallel to the main story you are telling and concerns one or more of the characters. These subplots are good for character development, providing extra conflicts or obstacles that complicate the resolution of the main story. Subplots might include the appearance of a character's former lover, who is in enthralled by the group's main antagonist, or a member of the group might be called upon to act against members of his own House or faction, then must decide where his loyalties lie. If enough detail has been devoted to the creation of the players' characters, many of the stories you create can have additional complications for individual members of the group. Make use of these subplots

whenever possible, as long as they do not detract from the main story as a whole. By working a character's background (or current relationships) into your stories, you further enmesh the player's ideas into the chronicle and actively involve that player in telling the story.

After determining the plot for your story, you then must concentrate on the central conflict. Conflict represents obstacles or opposing forces that the characters must overcome to resolve the plot. Conflict can stem from many sources, both within and beyond the player group. Suppose the characters are confronted by a monstrous demon who is terrorizing their hometown. They could try to face him directly, or better yet, they could undermine his power by striking at his thralls. Characters with low Torment could object to what is essentially a series of cold-blooded assassinations, thus creating conflict within the character group. Whenever possible, Storytellers should encourage this kind of internal dilemma. More than any other kind of conflict, moral conflict presents the characters with an obstacle that they can't simply overcome with brute force. It makes them think, and that is the best kind of challenge there is.

Conflict can be created in any number of combinations. Some obvious sources include:

• **The Clash of Angels:** Fallen and more monstrous demons battle for control over a city, town or region.

• **Factional Strife:** Competing factions struggle to further their agendas at the cost of their rivals.

• **Ancient Feuds:** Two demon lords pit their servants against one another to settle the score of a feud dating back to the War of Wrath.

• **Against the Dark Gods:** The characters embark on a campaign to foil the schemes of one of the Earthbound and its minions.

• **The Church Militant:** The characters are stalked by a group of demon-hunters who seek to exorcise them, or worse, entrap them for future study.

With the plot and its conflicts firmly in mind, you can consider the elements of the setting and mood for your story. Setting is as important a consideration for each story as it is for the chronicle as a whole. Well-chosen details can evoke images and impressions that enhance the impact of the tale you want to tell. Try to make the setting echo the feelings you find to be appropriate to the story. For instance, suppose you wish to have the characters enter the lair of a powerful demon. The way you envision the lair and the creature who lives there, you want the players to feel a sense of helplessness and despair:

The steps of the shelter are crowded, even at midnight. Homeless derelicts sit singly or in small groups, muttering to one another and watching the street with furtive, glassy eyes. Past the weathered wooden doors is a wide hall filled with silent, still forms. Some sleep wrapped in layers of grimy clothes, clutching trash bags filled with their worldly belongings. Others sit on the cots or against the walls, staring into space, their expressions lost, as if struggling to remember who they were and how they came to this cheerless existence. Across the room, past the cold and empty pots of the soup line, lies a dark doorway and the stairs that lead down into the demon's chambers.

Creating the mood for the story goes hand-in-hand with choosing your setting, because it relates again to the kind of atmosphere you want to convey to the players. If the setting consists of evocative surroundings for the story, the mood is the way in which you choose to describe the surroundings and the actions of the characters in them. The secret to evoking a proper mood is to emphasize details that paint the picture you want to convey, while minimizing others. For example:

• **Fear:** To evoke a mood of fear, emphasize images of helplessness, vulnerability and horror. *The children stare at you with eyes that are glassy and round from shock. They scamper away as you approach, whimpering as they retreat into the shadows. All of them avoid the iron door looming at the other end of the cellar.*

• **Anger:** To evoke anger, emphasize details of violence, frustration and outrage. *Someone in the crowd screams, a sound of pure rage, then a bottle smashes against the side of a car. A storefront window shatters, and the sounds of fists and clubs thudding into flesh begin to echo down the street.*

• **Loneliness:** Loneliness is evoked by images of abandonment and solitude. *The theater has once seen days of glory; now its grand marquee is dark, and the windowpanes in the ticket booth are long since broken. Along one wall, yellowed posters linger under grimy glass panes, celebrating the premiere of blockbusters and sultry starlets now lost to time.*

• **Despair:** Despair and angst spring from images of helplessness, dashed hopes and loss of innocence. *They built the boardwalk at the turn of the century for lovers and children, with brightly painted carnival rides and seaside stands selling candy and confections, or offering prizes to tempt an eager suitor. Now the rides are rusted and dull, their skeletons creak in the cold sea air, and the only souls haunting the graffiti-stained shacks are the derelicts, caring for nothing more than a little shelter and a place to drink.*

A carefully chosen setting and details hit the players in the gut, getting under their skin and giving them memorable images that make the gaming experience more tangible and immediate.

Once you have a strong grasp of these elements, you have to put them together into individual scenes that hook the players, set the stage for the action, build the action to a climax, then resolve the story in a way that ties up any loose ends and sets the stage for the next story.

• **The Hook:** The first step in any story is to involve the characters and pique their curiosity and interest. The hook can be a stranger appealing to the characters for help, a sudden summons to the court of a prince or witnessing

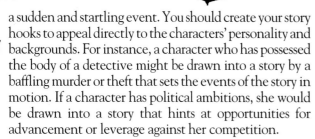

a sudden and startling event. You should create your story hooks to appeal directly to the characters' personality and backgrounds. For instance, a character who has possessed the body of a detective might be drawn into a story by a baffling murder or theft that sets the events of the story in motion. If a character has political ambitions, she would be drawn into a story that hints at opportunities for advancement or leverage against her competition.

• **Setting the Stage:** Once you have the characters interested, you have to draw them into the story and set out the challenges that lie ahead. Don't lay all your cards on the table at once, though. The best way to keep players curious is to give them only a piece of the puzzle at a time. Let them have a sense of what they need to accomplish, an immediate objective toward achieving their goal, and give them hints of what might lie beyond. If the players are smart, they will try to look ahead and figure out where their characters' actions will lead them. If not, they will be open to all sorts of plot twists and complications to make the story interesting.

For example, suppose the characters learn of a child who has been kidnapped by a monstrous demon. The characters might be drawn to save the child for diverse personal reasons. One character might just feel strongly about protecting children. Another might be obsessed with feeding on the child. Still another might want to rescue the child simply to thwart the plans of the kidnapper. In the beginning, all the information they have is the child's identity and accounts describing the kidnapping. From there, they must learn the identity of the kidnapper and the kidnapper's motives, which can add whole new implications to the story. What if the kidnapper is a powerful fallen whose favor the characters have been courting for some time? Do they thwart his plans and forfeit their previous efforts?

• **Building the Action:** As the players progress, the challenges the characters face should become increasingly difficult, with perhaps a few surprises thrown in to complicate things. When you design a story, throw in some hidden complications that the players don't know anything about and can be learned only with a little initiative and forethought. For example, the demon the characters want to confront might have recently invested in several highly paid bodyguards, or the mortal contact who is supposed to be providing the characters with information and assistance might be enthralled to one of their adversaries. Try to pull the rug out from under the characters at least once during the story, but allow them the chance to head off the problem if they use their brains and are resourceful. As the difficulties increase and the tensions mount, you can build the action to a dramatic finale.

• **The Climax:** Your ultimate finale must be worth the effort the characters went through to get there. This is a golden rule of storytelling. Anticlimaxes work fine in books, but not when a group of people have put in hours of effort to reach a goal. The more the players and their characters have to endure, the more dramatic the climax has to be, lest they come away disappointed. An operatic climax should be the stuff of legends — the characters defeat their foes, fighting against overwhelming odds and triumphing through a mixture of skill and personal sacrifice: when all is said and done, they have changed the world. A cinematic climax is less broad in scope but no less intense. The chronicle's events build to a grand, action-packed finale — the characters wrest control of a city from the grip of a usurper or defeat an Earthbound demon and its minions once and for all. A climax to a more visceral chronicle is usually very immediate and personal. The characters face their Torment and overcome it or watch their lives go up in flames. It's more about the decisions the characters make and how their existence is changed as a result.

• **Resolution:** Also known as cause and effect, this is the point in the story where the characters see the effects of their actions and resolve any loose ends or questions that came up along the way. This is a step in the storytelling process where it is easy to put aside any real roleplaying and just have a question-and-answer session with the players. If possible, try to play out the aftermath of a story, letting the players see the effects of their characters' work. If they wrest a school or a church from the grip of a monstrous demon, look for a way to revisit the place later and experience how the characters' actions have changed it for the better — or worse. This denouement helps build the sense of a bigger picture while sustaining players' interest and curiosity.

Sample Stories

The following are a number of story suggestions that illustrate different combinations of conflict, plots and subplots you can use in your chronicles:

• **Lost Souls:** Runaway children are disappearing from the streets around the local bus station, and the police are powerless to catch the perpetrators. Sometimes the bodies of the children are found, clearly victims of ritual mutilation and murder; other times, the victim is never seen again. The perpetrators can be monstrous demons, Earthbound servants seeking a suitable vessel to contain the essence of their master or even a band of misguided demon-hunters attempting to "save" the children of the street from evil.

• **Hail to the Chief:** It's election time, and the media is abuzz with the meteoric rise of a grassroots candidate who has taken the city by storm. Her charisma and charm sway even her staunchest opponents, and her views on even the most controversial issues only serve to increase her standing among the public. Somehow she has remained free from the taint of scandal, though there are rumors that two journalists

investigating her past abruptly abandoned their efforts. (One joined her campaign staff, while the other retired from the media entirely.) Is she a demon, or a mortal in service to one? Should she be stopped before she gains power? If she is exactly what she seems, a natural politician with enormous leadership potential, can the characters protect her from being enthralled?

• **Knocking on Heaven's Door**: There is a church in the worst part of the city that has stood as a bastion of faith in a sea of violence, degradation and despair for years. Now the local priest's campaign against drugs and prostitution has earned the ire of one or more of the local gangs, who have taken a perverse interest in terrorizing the church and its congregation. Such coordination is very unusual among a group of seeming enemies — unless they are being directed by a greater power. Which side do the characters take in the struggle? Do they act to protect the priest from the mysterious demon and his seemingly endless supply of gangbangers, or do they side with the demon and pit themselves against the church? As an interesting twist, what if the priest is in fact the villain of the piece, using his influence to sow discord and corruption among the community, and the demon is fighting against him with the only tools he has available?

• **Bell, Book and Candle**: One or more of the characters is contacted via invocation by a former comrade in arms, a demon who has just recently arrived on Earth and has fallen into the clutches of a group of demon-hunters. The demon is being subjected to rites of exorcism, and is desperate for help, but he can provide only vague clues as to his location. Can the characters track down the demon-hunters and free their comrade before it's too late?

• **Oath of Fealty**: A group of powerful demons has arrived in the city with the aim of subjugating or banishing any fallen they encounter and claiming the city for their own. Do the characters marshal their forces and declare war on the interlopers, or do they choose a more diplomatic course and try to forge advantageous alliances with the invaders? This story can easily be the beginning of a mini-chronicle, as the characters ascertain the strength of their opponents and explore various avenues of diplomacy, intrigue and combat to resolve the situation.

• **Blood Feud**: The characters' infernal masters may still be locked in the Abyss, but they can still reach into the minds of their minions and give them ominous tasks to perform. In this case, one or more of the players' characters (if they share the same master) are contacted and commanded to seek out the vassal of another infernal lord, with whom their master has a long-running feud. They are to sabotage the minion's efforts, whatever they may be, and banish the unfortunate demon back into the Pit. The fallen in question has taken the body of a nurse at a local hospital and is using her powers to nurture and protect the patients there. Do the characters carry out their orders (the master can't force them to obey while still locked in Hell), or do they find some other way of fulfilling their master's wishes?

• **Relics from a Bygone Age**: The characters are approached by a Malefactor who begs for their help in recovering a relic from the estate of a local collector. According to the Malefactor, the relic dates from the War of Wrath and is a powerful device in the hands of someone who knows how to use it, but the demon is evasive on exactly what the device is and what it can do. To make matters more complicated, the collector is himself a thrall in the service of another Malefactor, and he has recently acquired the relic illegally from an archaeological dig in India.

• **The Last Bastion**: Local folklore tells tales of mysterious happenings amid a series of foothills outside town. Strange lights in the dead of night, mysterious apparitions and unexplained disappearances have been recorded in the area for years. Are the stories a collection of simple legends, or do the occurrences point to the existence of an ancient rebel stronghold hidden in the hills? If true, what ancient relics — and timeless dangers — might wait for those bold enough to find the concealed fortress? This story is a good beginning to your chronicle if you want the players to have a safe haven they can take refuge in between stories.

Introducing New Characters

Over the course of any chronicle, the cast of central characters often changes. Demons lose their mortal hosts and are hurled back into the Abyss, become lost to Torment and pass out of the control of the players, or the players themselves sometimes have to drop out of the game and are replaced by newcomers. Introducing new characters into an already established group can be difficult from a story standpoint. How do they find the other characters? What motivation would the other characters have to accept a stranger into their midst? What reason would the group have for trusting this newcomer with their secrets, and vice versa?

One of the easiest ways to bring the new character into the group is to have her literally sent to them via one of the lords still trapped in the Abyss. One way to create a relationship between the newcomer and the group is if the lord in question is also the master of one or more of the established characters. The newcomer is directed to the same locale as the group and given enough information to allow the character to locate the others relatively easily. You can have the character bear a message from her lord to the group by way of introduction, thus creating a convenient basis for acceptance.

Another possibility is a chance encounter brought about by the use of Celestial powers. With their supernatural awareness, the fallen can detect the use of lore or

the expenditure of Faith from a long way away. When a situation arises that causes one or more members of the group to dramatically employ their powers, you can then have the newcomer detect the flare of Faith and use it to track them down, even if it's only for curiosity's sake. If the newcomer arrives in time to contribute to the group's efforts, say by helping turn the tide against a gang of demon-hunters, this creates a reason for the group to look kindly upon the new arrival.

If the chronicle is set in a locale that the characters fought in during the war, it's also possible that the new character was a former comrade in arms who was drawn to the area by the same lure of familiarity as the rest of the group. Past relationships provide excellent ways to smoothly integrate new characters and inspire new stories revolving around past friendships, rivalries or debts of honor.

TELLING THE TALE

It is not enough to design a good story — it must be well told, presented with detail and energy. When you tell your story, strive to make the most of the following qualities:

• **Description:** Make each scene vivid with detail. The quality of your descriptions affects everything from the mood you want to convey to the action of a brutal firefight. Describe people, places and activities in a way that engages all of your players' senses. The more detail you can give, the easier the scene is to envision, and the more alive it becomes.

• **Characterization:** Make your Storyteller characters individuals. This is ten times harder for you than for the players, because they only have one character to concentrate on, while you have an entire world. The amount of attention you can give to each character depends, naturally, on how important she is to your chronicle. Major characters should be treated with all the depth and detail of a player's character. Get inside your characters' heads, use their histories to determine what kind of personality that they might have. Give them hates, fears and hobbies. For minor characters, single out a few distinguishing characteristics. Make them absent-minded or abrasive or neurotic or whatever. Don't be afraid to use little quirks that you might observe about people in everyday life.

• **Dialogue:** This goes hand in hand with characterization, and it is possibly the most important skill a Storyteller must master. When characters talk to one another in the game, whether within the group or with Storyteller characters, act out the conversation. You can bring out more depth to your characters and make the experience more immediate with dialogue, expression and body language. Give each character a distinctive voice and mannerisms appropriate to her personality. Acting out dialogue doesn't come easily — it takes a quick mind and some improvisational skills,

and a little bit of courage if you are self-conscious. Don't get stressed — you're playing a game with friends. Encourage the players to participate, even give an extra experience point at the end of each session for good interplay if you want. Conversation is an art and a skill, and it gets better with practice.

• **Action:** Make your action scenes dynamic and explosive — bones crunch, blood sprays, guns thunder, and objects blow apart under a hail of bullets. Keep the dice rolling in combat scenes to a minimum, interpret the results quickly and then launch into pulse-pounding description. ("The Slayer rises like an ill wind, shrouded in mist and darkness, and fastens its pale hands on Azrael's face. The Devil writhes in pain as the Slayer's touch sucks the life from his mortal form.") The key element is the intensity of the experience. Don't be afraid to fudge results sometimes to keep the action and pace at a fever pitch.

• **Mystery:** Keep the players guessing. Never show them the full picture of what is going on. Nothing in the World of Darkness is quite what it appears to be, and it is good to emphasize this point with plot twists, betrayals and hidden complications to your stories.

• **Influencing Events: Demon** is about telling a good story, which requires careful planning and an idea of where the events of your chronicle are leading. The problem is that sometimes the players will throw you a curve. Perhaps they will miss the obvious clue that will expose the central mystery of the chronicle, or maybe they will go in a totally unexpected direction and stumble onto a part of the story that they weren't supposed to deal with yet. Worse yet, one of them gets a lucky hit in battle and kills off the major villain whom you had planned to be their major adversary for the next 12 stories. There are no easy solutions to these situations, but basically you have two courses of action to choose from. You can either roll with the punches and adapt to the changes, or you can use your godlike powers to avoid the problem entirely. The best rule of thumb is to fudge events directly only if it enhances the game as a whole. If the characters miss a vital piece of data, steer them back toward it. If you would rather see your major villain killed off in a more dramatic way, fudge his soak rolls and let him limp away. Use this sparingly. It is your privilege as the Storyteller, but if you abuse it, you will convince the players that their characters can't really succeed at anything, which ruins the game.

THE COMMANDMENTS

The art of storytelling is a process, like any artistic endeavor, and it might seem like an overwhelming task at first. The main elements to remember, though, can be broken down into five "musts" and five "must-nots."

You Must…

• **Involve the Players Whenever Possible:** Incorporate their ideas and backgrounds into your city and chronicle. Doing so will take some of the burden of world-building off your shoulders and give the players more of a stake in the story you are telling. Ultimately, the players should be the most important — though not necessarily the most powerful — denizens of your chronicle.

• **Accommodate the Players' Expectations:** Remember, it's their game, too. You need to have some idea of what kind of game the players want to play before developing your chronicle.

• **Work Things Out in Advance:** The more information you have worked out before game time, the more attention you will be able to devote to telling the story. If you've taken the time to think through the story's various twists and turns, you will be better able to cope with the inevitable player curve ball.

• **Keep the Story First and the Rules Second:** Do not let the tale you want to tell get held back by the rules. You can make them or break them as you see fit, as long as doing so enhances the story and makes it more enjoyable for the players.

• **Use Description, Dialogue and Action:** Make your world come alive with vibrant description, involving sights, smells, taste and touch. Encourage roleplaying by acting out conversations and using different voices to individualize your characters. Keep the pace and intensity high with dynamic action.

Conversely, You Must Not…

• **Rely on Stereotypes:** Nothing drains the life out of your chronicle faster than an endless parade of identical, cardboard characters.

• **Forget the Payoff:** If the players work hard and make smart decisions, their characters' success must be in proportion to the challenges they have faced. Otherwise, they will feel cheated.

• **Tell The Players Everything:** Much of the challenge in a game is in the mystery, the parts of the story that you hold back for the players and their characters to discover on their own.

• **Abuse Your Power:** You are the final arbiter of events, and your word is law, but you cannot use this authority to beat the characters into doing what you want them to do. It is a game, it's for fun, and everyone should have a good time, whether it follows the script or not.

• **Panic:** If the players pull the rug out from under you, don't be afraid to call a break and take some time to collect your thoughts. It will happen a lot at first, but after a while, you will be able to handle anything they throw at you.

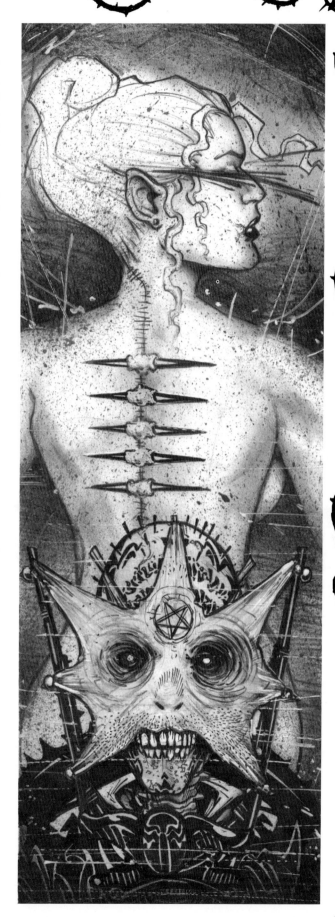

post

The scars the demon gave him made Jack Milton the perfect bait. Sometimes he savored the irony of the situation; other times it made him want to put a bullet in his brain.

The thick, ropy burn scars that twisted the left side of his face and neck ensured that he'd never be one of the Beautiful People, but getting into the club hadn't been a problem once he'd dropped a wad of cash into the doorman's jacket pocket. Finding a table was easy; keeping it to himself was easier still. Since he'd sat down, no less than three people had come over to buy him a drink or introduce themselves, drawn by his expensive clothes and the diamond ring on his little finger. He watched them approach with some interest, curious to see how close they would come before they saw his face. The moment was easy to detect — their expressions were open and friendly one second, then it was like they'd been hit in the gut. Their eyes would widen and their smile would go slack. Being practiced club-goers, each one looked away and walked briskly past.

He was waiting for the one whose expression wouldn't change. The one who would want him for what he was.

Milton never saw her approach. He polished off his fourth vodka tonic, and by the time he'd set the glass down, she was standing at the other side of the table, smiling down at him with eyes the color of a stormy sea. She was *beautiful*. Even knowing what to expect, the sight of her made Jack catch his breath. For a fleeting moment he forgot about his scars and his shriveled lungs and wondered what he'd done to deserve this gorgeous woman's attention.

"It looks like all the other tables are taken," she said in a throaty voice that made him think of whiskey and smoke. "Mind if I join you?"

"Please," he said, ashamed at how eager he sounded. The demon's smile widened as she slid in beside him.

They talked for more than an hour, and she never said a single thing about his face. That would come later, he knew, after she'd wrapped him around those perfect fingers of hers. That's when she'd offer a way to give him his old features back, to make him the man he once was. For a price of course. One he knew all too well.

It was close to three before he got up the courage to ask her to come home with him. Before he knew it, they were crossing the street to his car. The demon eyed the gray Jaguar. "Very nice, Jack." She eyed him appraisingly. "You seem like a man with a lot to offer."

"I'll bet you say that to all the boys," he said. Her laughter was wild and genuine.

He opened the door for her, and after she'd slid into the leather seat, he leaned in and smiled a little nervously. "Did you see my cell phone when we were sitting at the table?"

The demon paused. From the brief look of concern that crossed her face Milton wondered if the creature knew what a cell phone was. "I... don't think so."

"Great. Lost another one. Listen, would you mind if I ran inside and checked? It will only take a minute."

"No problem, Jack," the demon said. "I'm patient."

Jack shut the door and forced himself to jog across the street, the cold air cutting like jagged glass through his ruined lungs. But the pain helped him focus, reminding him of who he was and what he'd come to do.

He couldn't turn back the clock. Nothing would erase that first pact he'd made or all the horror that followed. Nothing would bring back his family or his health. He'd intended to die in the blast that killed the monster who'd enslaved him, but even that mercy had been denied him. Now he could only make the best of his borrowed time.

Milton reached inside his pants pocket for the remote control and hit the button, detonating the twenty sticks of dynamite set carefully beneath the passenger seat. He'd seen how demons could heal themselves of terrible injuries, but he'd yet to see one survive being blown to bits.

He turned back and stared deeply into the flames. The demon was gone, its soul sent screaming back into Hell. "Be seeing you," Jack Milton said.

CHAPTER ELEVEN: ANTAGONISTS

To do aught good never will be our task,
But ever to do ill our sole delight,
As being the contrary to his high will
Whom we resist. If then his Providence
Out of our evil seek to bring forth good,
Our labor must be to pervert that end,
And out of good still find means of evil.
—John Milton, *Paradise Lost*

For all their power, the fallen do not lack for enemies. Monstrous demons, mortal demon-hunters and the twisted servants of the Earthbound are three of the most common types of antagonists that threaten a fallen angel's freedom, not to mention the lives of those mortals who are bound to them.

Storytellers are encouraged to use the following profiles as sources of inspiration to create their own colorful and challenging antagonists. These profiles are only general guidelines, though. You are encouraged to embellish, alter or dismiss any of the details provided to better match the needs of your story.

MONSTROUS DEMONS

Of all the multitudes of fallen who have returned to the world in the wake of the Maelstrom, only a few have had the good fortune to find themselves in the body of a man or a woman that, for all their miseries and faults, still possessed qualities of compassion and humanity that shook the demons from their all-encompassing Torment. The vast majority of the fallen remain as the Abyss made them: anguished, malevolent monsters, eager to reclaim their lost glory and revenge themselves against God and man. Monstrous demons are the primary foes the players' characters will face, whether as predators stalking the souls of a city, rivals for power or the primary agents and shock troops of the Earthbound.

DEVILS

State Senator Edward Carson glared at the man across the wide expanse of his antique desk. "What are you trying to pull?"

William Zobel smiled. "I'm not trying to pull anything."

"But this is political suicide!" Carson said. "If the airport is expanded, hundreds of people will lose their homes. Elkwood

Village would lose a third of its tax base because of the expansion. If my name is attached to this bill, I'll lose the next election!"

Zobel shook his head. "You need to relax."

"Relax?"

"Listen," Zobel replied. "First of all, as I recall, Elkwood's mayor supported your opponent during the last election. I think it's fitting that he should pay for supporting your opponent."

"But I can't let hundreds of people go homeless. I don't care how much money you contribute."

Zobel sighed. "First, I don't think you appreciate your situation. If it weren't for me, you couldn't afford to run for office."

"I—"

"Second, let's not forget about the revealing video of your opponent that was conveniently released days before the election."

Carson's jaw dropped.

"Third," Zobel continued, "you need to see the bigger picture. For businesses to grow, the airport needs to expand. To be blunt, those extra runways mean more jobs."

"And profits for your company," Carson replied.

"Very observant."

"At the cost of—"

"The cost is quite small compared to the greater picture. Sure, you will criticized, but Senator Carson, you strike me as a man of courage—"

"What if I'm not as courageous as you think?"

Zobel chuckled. "Then you should be more afraid of what would happen if you don't cooperate."

"Is that—"

Zobel's cold stare was answer enough.

Concept: High-Torment Devils are ruthless power brokers who prefer to manipulate others into doing their dirty work, whether it's a corporate takeover or the assassination of a potential rival. They collect powerful mortals like a craftsman assembles a set of tools, selecting individuals with specific applications in mind, using and expending them as needed. They are corporate tyrants, crime lords, corrupt politicians or radical revolutionaries.

Personality: High-Torment Devils exude an aura of self-confidence and authority, and thus present the image of a natural leader. They are brilliant, suave and extremely charming, but the polished veneer hides a monster who delights in subverting powerful leaders and crushing the spirit of those who defy them. Architect, Autocrat, Curmudgeon, Director, Fanatic, Traditionalist and Visionary are common Natures.

Attributes: Devils have strong Social Attribute ratings, especially in Charisma and Manipulation. Mental Attributes, especially Wits and Intelligence are also useful in the art of the dark deal.

Abilities: Devils usually have high Subterfuge, Expression and Intuition ratings. Many also find uses for Etiquette and Performance.

Backgrounds: Followers (1-3), Influence (1-3), Resources (1-5)

WILLIAM ZOBEL

Nature: Director

Attributes: Strength 2, Dexterity 2, Stamina 2, Charisma 3, Manipulation 4, Appearance 3, Perception 3, Intelligence 4, Wits 4

Abilities: Alertness 2, Bureaucracy 3, Computer 1, Drive 2, Empathy 2, Etiquette 4, Expression 3, Finance 4, Intimidation 4, Law 3, Leadership 4, Performance 2, Politics 5, Stealth 1, Subterfuge 5

Backgrounds: Followers 3, Influence 3, Resources 4

Willpower: 7

Faith: 6

Torment: 8

Apocalyptic Form: The Visage of Radiance

Lore: Radiance 3, Celestials 2, Humanity 3

SCOURGES

Billy was coughing again, dragging Jessica again from a deep, drug-induced sleep. She winced at the pain in her abdomen as she tried to raise her head. The doctors had cut her open, and it still hurt. Not only that, she had to share a room with Billy, who wasn't very nice.

Jessica wanted to yell, but the pain from her stitches made her think twice. Billy wasn't that sick. He had to be teasing.

Slowly, she turned her head toward Billy's bed. What she saw made her forget about her pain.

Behind the curtain, she saw a large shadow towering over Billy's bed, taller than any adult Jessica had ever seen. As the shadow moved its arms over Billy, his coughing worsened.

Jessica bit her lip, trying not to make a sound. What if it heard her? What was it doing to Billy?

Moving slowly, she reached over and fumbled around for the bed's trouble button. She remembered how Mommy said to push it whenever she was in trouble.

Finally she found it and held the button down. Please God, begged Jessica. Don't let the monster get me!

Suddenly, Billy's curtain parted.

"Jessica," a gravely voice whispered.

Jessica yanked the covers over her head and tried not scream. How did it know her name?

"I know you're awake." The voice said, moving closer.

Jessica remained very still.

"Billy was a bad boy. He has to be punished. You're not going to be a bad girl, are you?"

Concept: High-Torment Scourges are walking nightmares, monstrous creatures that exist to inflict pain and misery on mortal and fallen alike. These demons often justify their actions by claiming to punish the wicked, but these Scourges actually spread their plagues to make humanity suffer as they have suffered.

Personality: Monstrous Scourges are often spiteful and quick to anger, and they take an almost feline delight in tormenting their victims over a long period of time. Bravos and Autocrats are common Natures among these Scourges

Attributes: These Scourges tend to have very low Social Attributes, though some try to develop their Manipulation. They favor Wits and Perception.

Abilities: High-Torment Scourges tend to possess Empathy, Intimidation, Stealth and Medicine at medium to high levels.

Backgrounds: Pacts (1-3), Paragon (1-2)

Robert Lowe

Nature: Bravo

Attributes: Strength 4, Dexterity 3, Stamina 4, Charisma 1, Manipulation 3, Appearance 2, Perception 5, Intelligence 4, Wits 5

Abilities: Alertness 4, Awareness 3, Brawl 2, Dodge 4, Intimidation 5, Medicine 3, Security 3, Stealth 3, Subterfuge 3

Backgrounds: Pacts 2, Paragon 1

Willpower: 5

Faith: 5

Torment: 8

Apocalyptic Form: The Visage of Awakenings

Lore: Awakening 3, Winds 2, Fundament 3

Malefactors

Chris noticed Greg admiring his new sculpture, called Iron Christ.

"So what do you think?" Chris asked.

Greg continued to stare. It was a ten-foot-high cross, made of rust-colored iron beams. The Christ figure was made of black iron rods.

Finally he replied. "It's… very moving."

"Thanks."

"I can't explain it." He wagged his finger. "It's almost as if you've captured Christ's transcendence from the human to the divine."

"Most people just see a statue of Christ," Chris said as he finished his drink. "You see the deeper meaning."

Greg nodded. "I look at it, and I see the empowerment of the cross."

"One of the most powerful symbols in the world," Chris added.

"This is the best depiction of the crucifixion I have ever seen."

"Now, now," Chris replied.

"No, this is it!" Greg insisted.

Chris shrugged.

Greg finally turned toward Chris. "I never thought you'd have it in you. Your early work was so…"

"Modern?"

"Well that, too, I guess," Greg laughed. "Chris, what inspired you?"

Chris set down his glass and looked at his work.

"One day I woke up, and the truth was clear to me. I knew that I had to show the world the truth about God."

Greg smiled. "I think you succeeded. Let me tell you something. I'm so sick of artists making Piss Christs then claiming they're actually being reverent to God."

Chris shook his head. "They don't know how to treat an idol."

Greg nodded. "I want to buy this for my church."

Chris pointed toward a woman standing nearby but affecting disinterest. "You need to speak to Mary."

They talked for a few more minutes, before Greg left. Chris grabbed a drink from a waiter, and raised a toast to his work.

"The best is yet to come," he said.

Concept: High-Torment Malefactors delight in making objects of wonder and desire that ultimately enslave or destroy their owners. Many see this as a source of poetic justice — the earth poisoning mankind for a change. These demons frequently ensnare large numbers of thralls with their creations, consuming them slowly as they siphon off their Faith to create still more cursed items.

Personality: Malefactors revel in their dark works of art. For some, corrupting humans is merely an afterthought to their greater vision. Architects, Bon Vivants, Perfectionists and Visionaries are common Natures among these Malefactors.

Attributes: Malefactors tend to have high Mental Attributes, especially Intelligence and Perception. Many also have strong Social Attributes, especially Charisma and Manipulation.

Abilities: As divine artisans, all Malefactors have high Crafts and Expression ratings. Alertness, Awareness and Dodge are also common.

Backgrounds: Contacts (1-2), Followers (1-2), Pacts (3-4), Resources (1-2)

CHRIS SWANSON

Nature: Visionary

Attributes: Strength 2, Dexterity 3, Stamina 2, Charisma 3, Manipulation 4, Appearance 3, Perception 4, Intelligence 5, Wits 3

Abilities: Academics (Art) 4, Alertness 3, Awareness 4, Brawl 1, Computer 2, Dodge 2, Empathy 3, Etiquette 3, Expression 5, Firearms 1, Intuition 3, Occult 3, Performance 2, Research 2, Stealth 2, Subterfuge 3

Backgrounds: Contacts 1, Followers 1, Pacts 3, Resources 2

Willpower: 8

Faith: 8

Torment: 9

Apocalyptic Form: The Visage of the Forge

Lore: Earth 3, Forge 3, Humanity 2

FIENDS

Even as she sobbed, Professor Emily Habenstein heard the footsteps entering her study.

"Get it out of my mind!" she bawled.

"But you're so close," a frighteningly familiar voice replied.

Emily turned around. Joe, a former student, made his way toward her.

"I can't take this anymore," Emily said. "I can't live with this in my head!"

"But you wanted to know how it all fit together. How the great cloth of truth became a quilt of lies?"

Emily covered her face.

"This is why you became a professor of religion. You wanted to put the pieces together. You wanted to be the ant that saw the whole mountain."

Emily shook her head. "But you gave me this… this thing in my head."

"But it's a glimpse of the whole."

"Get it out!"

"But we had a deal, you see," Joe replied. "You would show me the pieces, and I would show you the whole."

Emily turned away.

"What I need to know is the essence of all of God's religions. I need to know the pieces, I need to know the strength people derive from God's lies."

"But why do you need me? Can't you figure out the fucking pieces yourself?"

Joe chuckled. "Why do it yourself when you can have someone else do it for you?"

"Fuck you!"

Suddenly, Emily screamed. She fell off her chair and started rolling on the floor, screaming, "No! No!"

"Let me tell you something, Emily," Joe replied, shaking his head. "Once I walked amongst the stars. But God took that away from me."

Emily stopped rolling.

"I suffered for aeons because of you. Now it's your turn."

Concept: Fiends with high Torment weave tangled webs of madness and fate that ensnare both mortal and demon alike. Where once they tried to maintain the balance of the Grand Design, now they try to manipulate it to serve their own vision of the future.

Personality: Many Fiends tend to be highly manipulative and very condescending toward humanity. They know full well that humans, and even some fallen, can't even begin to understand the Truth. Architect, Bravo, Conniver, Curmudgeon, Director, Perfectionist and Visionary are common Natures.

Attributes: Most Fiends have high Mental ratings, especially Perception. Many also have strong Manipulation scores.

Abilities: Alertness, Awareness, Empathy and Intuition are usually high, reflecting the Fiends' powers of observation. Some may learn Science (Psychology) to better understand the frail minds of humans.

Backgrounds: Pacts (1-2), Paragon (1-2)

Joe Voss

Nature: Director

Attributes: Strength 2, Dexterity 3, Stamina 2, Charisma 2, Manipulation 5, Appearance 2, Perception 5, Intelligence 4, Wits 4

Abilities: Academics (Theology) 2, Alertness 5, Awareness 4, Brawl 1, Computer 2, Dodge 3, Empathy 4, Etiquette 2, Firearms 1, Intimidation 2, Intuition 4, Investigation 2, Medicine 1, Science (Psychology) 3, Stealth 3, Subterfuge 3

Backgrounds: Pacts 2, Paragon 1

Willpower: 9

Faith: 7

Torment: 7

Apocalyptic Form: The Visage of Patterns

Lore: Light 2, Patterns 3, Portals 3

Defilers

Michael moaned as Helen pulled the straps tighter.

Helen walked in front of Michael, her green eyes showing through her leather mask. She caressed her black whip.

"The word on the street is that you're starting to slip," she said, moving closer.

"Yes, Mistress."

She ran her gloved hand across his chest. "You're losing your grip on the business," she whispered. "Your competitors are cornering the market on—" she pinched one of his nipples "—young, fresh bodies."

No one had ever spoken to him like that, bullshit games or not, thought Michael. Yet he didn't feel angry, which surprised him. He only wanted to please her, and that scared him.

"I've been bad," said Michael, surprised at the sincerity in his voice.

Helen released the nipple. "No, baby. You've been more than bad." Faster than a viper, her hand closed around his throat. "You've been sloppy."

Michael struggled against the leather straps. Her grip strengthened. How could she be so strong?

"You should see the pretty young things Roberto has."

Helen let go of his throat. She leaned closer to his face, her blue eyes staring into his.

Wait a minute, Michael thought. Didn't she have green eyes?

"Your women are used up," she hissed. "I can help you, Michael. You can unload some of them on me."

"But mistress, I can't just—"

The whip cracked beside his head. Searing pain ripped through the flesh of his ear.

"You don't want to be known as a dog keeper, do you?"

"Fuck!" Michael felt warm blood run down his neck. He writhed in the chair, but the straps held him fast.

The whip raked across his back, splitting the skin and scoring into the flesh beneath. Michael howled.

"You like that, don't you, slave?"

NO! he thought, but to his horror he found his head nodding eagerly for more.

"There's so much more you and I can do," she hissed. With a practiced flick of her wrist, the whip snaked out and clipped off his earlobe. Michael screamed, pleasure and pain entwined, and Helen savored it like wine.

Helen walked in front of Michael. Her brown eyes looked into his.

"Won't you help me build my dog house?"

Concept: While some Devourers use violence to strike back at humanity, the deeply anguished Defilers use a more subtle tactic. Industrial society has isolated people. The mass media makes them ashamed of their bodies. Humans want lovers. They want to look beautiful. Defilers play on these desires to enslave humanity, and many desperate people are all too willing to fall into their trap.

Personality: Defilers can have almost any Demeanor, and it's usually quite the opposite of their true Natures. High-Torment Defilers tend to have Conniver, Gallant and Trickster Natures.

Attributes: Charisma and Manipulation Attributes tend to be high. These characters also tend to have good Dexterity and Stamina scores.

Abilities: These Defilers usually have good Alertness, Empathy, Expression, and Intuition Abilities. Etiquette and Performance are secondary in importance, but also valuable.

Backgrounds: Allies (1-3), Contacts (1-2), Followers (1-3), Pacts (1-3)

Helen Tisdale

Nature: Director

Attributes: Strength 2, Dexterity 4, Stamina 3, Charisma 4, Manipulation 5, Appearance 4, Perception 3, Intelligence 3, Wits 3

Abilities: Alertness 4, Athletics 3, Brawl 2, Dodge 3, Empathy 3, Etiquette 2, Expression 3, Firearms 1, Intimidation 4, Intuition 3, Law 3, Leadership 3, Linguistics 2 (Spanish, Portuguese), Melee 2, Occult 2, Performance 4, Politics 2, Stealth 3, Streetwise 4, Subterfuge 4

Backgrounds: Contacts 2, Followers 3, Pacts 3

Willpower: 7

Faith: 7

Torment: 9

Apocalyptic Form: The Visage of Longing

Lore: Longing 3, Storms 2, Humanity 3

Devourers

Tiptakzi sniffed the forest air, and a growl rumbled from his throat. Humans, he thought. And close. Very close.

The demon slipped silently through the trees, rage fueling his lean, powerful limbs. The scent grew stronger, and now

Tiptakzi could hear the sounds of hammering. The demon bared his fangs. This mountain was his. He'd given enough of his blood for humanity during the war, lost enough friends and seen enough of the world ruined in vain. No more.

A few more leaps, and he could see the humans. Dressed in camouflage jackets, they were hammering metal spikes into trees and marking them with flags.

When he escaped from Hell, he couldn't believe the utter devastation humanity had unleashed on the Earth. After everything they'd done for mankind, this was how they were repaid?

From the tall branches, Tiptakzi called to the green life surrounding him, and the wood bent itself to his will. The first logger was snatched from the ground by a braided rope of vines, his liquid screams cut short as a dozen lashing tendrils ripped the man to pieces.

The other man disappeared into the foliage, his cries of terror echoing from the tall trees. It was only a few miles to the old logging road. Tiptakzi would let the man get halfway there before he'd give chase. A good challenge made the kill that much more worthwhile.

Concept: The angels of the Wild who are consumed by their Torment regard humanity as nothing more than objects of sport. They slake their pain in the death agonies of those who fall beneath their talons, and their relatively low status as angels of the Sixth House makes them highly susceptible to influence from monstrous demons of the higher-status Houses. Therefore, these demons are routinely seen as enforcers, hunters and raiders in the service of monstrous demon lords or the Earthbound.

Personality: Autocrat, Bravo, Curmudgeon, Loner and Rebel are common Natures among these Abominations. Usually their Demeanor matches their Nature. They have no need for deception or artifice.

Attributes: Abominations always have high Physical Attributes, even if their original hosts weren't physically fit. Many have high Wits and Perception, Attributes that are useful in the wild. They also tend to have low Appearance and Charisma.

Abilities: All have Alertness, Brawl, Dodge, Intimidation, Stealth, Survival and Animal Ken. Those call the cities their home may also have Streetwise and Melee. Knowledges tend to be limited to what their host knew.

Backgrounds: Pacts (1-3), Paragon (1-2)

TIPTAKZI

Nature: Loner

Attributes: Strength 5, Dexterity 4, Stamina 5, Charisma 1, Manipulation 5, Appearance 1, Perception 5, Intelligence 2, Wits 5

Abilities: Alertness 5, Animal Ken 4, Brawl 4, Dodge 4, Intimidation 4, Investigation 3, Medicine 1, Stealth 4, Survival 4

Backgrounds: Pacts 1, Paragon 3

Willpower: 6

Faith: 8

Torment: 9

Apocalyptic Form: The Visage of the Beast

Lore: Beast 3, Flesh 3, Wild 2

SLAYERS

Apil-Sin caressed the water-stained casket. He could feel the invisible tethers against his fingertips.

"I'm waiting." He whispered. The tethers vibrated.

Apil-Sin extended his senses into the shadow lands. During the war, he helped build the shadow lands to protect the souls of humanity from annihilation (or whatever God intended to do with them). It was supposed to be their separate Eden. Now an endless storm ravaged the Slayers' creation. Over the roaring winds, he could hear the screams of countless souls.

There was one in particular who interested him now. The Slayer focused his will and called out the specter's name.

In the living world, the lights flickered. In the shadow lands, an apparition coalesced out of the storm. Its body was formless, but its eyes glowed a fiery yellow.

"WHO SUMMONS ME?" the wraith howled.

Hundred of mouths appeared across the spirit's corpus, each filled with sharp fangs. It leapt at the demon with a deafening roar. Apil-Sin held up his right hand. The wraith stopped as if it had slammed into a brick wall.

"I don't have time for this, Marvin," Apil-Sin said. "We have work to do."

The wraith struggled vainly against the Slayer's will. "Who are you?"

Apil-Sin smiled. "I would have thought that was obvious by now, Marvin. I am your master."

The demon spoke words of power, and the specter screamed as it was drawn across the Veil and into the recently unearthed coffin.

Apil-Sin returned his senses to the living world. From inside the casket came the sound of hands clawing at the rotted satin.

Concept: High-Torment Slayers no longer revere the sanctity of the souls of mankind. Ghosts are tools to be used by the Halaku, coin to trade with or weapons to be used against their enemies.

Creation is dying. Soon it will all belong to them.

Personality: Slayers possess a wide variety of Natures. Many have Bravo and Director Natures, which they usually direct toward ghosts.

Humanity's attitude toward the afterlife amuses many of these Slayers. How can they be so sure about their fate when even the fallen don't know the truth?

Attributes: Like all Slayers, they tend to have high Mental Attributes, especially Perception. They also have high Manipulation scores. Many also have high Stamina ratings.

Abilities: Alertness, Awareness, Intimidation, Intuition, Stealth and Subterfuge are common Abilities among these Slayers. Many also have good

Investigation skills. Those involved with death cults may also gain access to Occult Knowledge.

Backgrounds: Followers (1-2), Influence (1-2), Pacts (1-3)

Apil-Sin

Nature: Conniver

Attributes: Strength 2, Dexterity 1, Stamina 4, Charisma 3, Manipulation 5, Appearance 2, Perception 5, Intelligence 3, Wits 4

Abilities: Alertness 3, Awareness 4, Brawl 1, Computer 2, Dodge 4, Etiquette 2, Firearms 2, Intimidation 4, Intuition 3, Medicine 4, Occult 3, Politics 1, Research 3, Subterfuge 3, Stealth 3

Backgrounds: Contacts 2, Influence 1, Followers 2, Pacts 2

Willpower: 6

Faith: 8

Torment: 8

Apocalyptic Form: The Visage of the Spirit

Lore: Death 3, Spirit 3, Realms 2

EXORCISTS

Centuries of cynicism and despair have blinded much of humanity to the existence of the divine, but among the world's six billion souls, there are a few who still keep the faith — or learn to accept the truth when there is no other alternative. Of the handful of men and women who witness a demon and see the being for what it truly is, only a fraction of those are courageous (or desperate) enough to fight back against the legions of Hell. These would-be demon-hunters, or exorcists, fight lonely, brutal battles against the fallen, little differentiating between the monstrous or the repentant.

The Cursed Sight

Iowa City Shooter May Have Been Delusional

(Iowa City, IA) The Boat House Club shooter, who killed 5 and injured 15, may have believed that his victims were "feeding" an alien.

Sources close to the investigation claim that the shooter, David Lynn Carpenter, was obsessed with aliens. Investigators found hundreds of UFO books, magazines and photographs in the room he rented. They also found pictures of an unidentified individual that Carpenter appeared to be stalking. Police are attempting to contact the person Carpenter allegedly followed.

Carpenter's co-workers at Chicago BBQ also confirm Carpenter's obsession with UFOs.

"Every day it was aliens this, aliens that," William Osborne said. "He was convinced they were taking over people's bodies. I told him he was nuts, but that just set him off on a tirade."

"David claimed he could sense aliens," said Jill Gilman, another co-worker. "He said he'd get a tingling feeling whenever they were near him."

Gilman later added, "David believed that the aliens had to feed off of us. That's why they didn't try to take over all of humanity. They need us for food. I think he said that each alien needed at least 100 people to sustain it."

A neighbor, who would only identify himself as Jack, claims that Gilman wasn't always obsessed with aliens.

"He used to be a normal guy. He wasn't very social, but then again who is?"

That changed a few months ago, according to Jack.

"I saw him running into his room, and he didn't reply when I asked him what was up? I don't know, maybe he was running away from someone. The next day, I saw him throwing out his stereo and TV. I asked him what was up, and he replied that they were bugged. I stopped talking to him after that. Occasionally, I'd hear him yell, 'Stop spying on me,' or 'You'll never eat my brain!' I was surprised he wasn't locked up."

Witnesses to the shooting also report hearing Carpenter making comments about aliens.

"I was just eating my sandwich when I heard someone yell, 'Stop feeding him! He's an alien brain-sucker,'" said Julie Hoffman. "I was about to laugh, then I heard the gun shots. It seemed like he was shooting at the staff. All the while he kept yelling, 'Stop feeding him! Stop feeding him!'"

Concept: Not every mortal reacts to the fallen in the same way. Most are overcome with hysteria, eventually blocking out the experience or rationalizing it into something their minds can handle. An unlucky few, however, cannot let go of the things they have seen, and they become obsessed with the knowledge that *something* walks the earth beneath mankind's very nose, and if they don't try to stop it, who will?

These zealots, as the Cryptics call them, each have their own interpretation of the revelations they have seen. Some think that the fallen are space aliens disguised as humans. Others believe that the fallen are clones sent by the so-called New World Order to replace ordinary people. A handful believe that they are witnessing the arrival of the Antichrist and his false prophets, and that the end of the world is at hand. None have arrived at the truth behind the fallen. If the facts don't fit their pet theories, they tend to ignore them.

As ordinary humans, the zealots pose no physical threat to the average fallen, nor do they possess any special resistance to a demon's power. They can, however, be a serious threat to mortals and thralls close to a demon, stalking and killing individuals thought to be "infected" or "under alien influence."

Personality: Many suffered from mental illness before encountering the fallen. Others seemed perfectly sane before their fateful encounter. Zealots tend to be loners, but charismatic individuals can and do form groups of

"disciples" that support their activities. Addict, Fanatic and Loner are common Natures among the zealots.

Attributes: Attributes vary among zealots, though many tend to have low Social scores. Their obsession has made them withdraw from other people.

Abilities: Abilities can vary wildly among Zealots. Most have some Stealth and Firearms Ability.

Backgrounds: Zealots tend to have very low Background scores. Rarely do they have more than two dots in Resources.

Faith Potential: 1

Powers: Zealots are not subject to the effects of demonic Revelation. (See page 253 of Chapter Nine for details.)

DAVID LUNN CARPENTER

Nature: Loner

Attributes: Strength 2, Dexterity 3, Stamina 3, Charisma 1, Manipulation 2, Appearance 1, Perception 3, Intelligence 2, Wits 3

Abilities: Alertness 3, Brawl 1, Dodge 2, Firearms 2, Intimidation 3, Melee 1

Backgrounds: Contacts 2, Resources 2

Willpower: 4

Powers: Immunity to Revelation.

GABRIEL'S SWORD

Father Dennis Forbin sat straight as the door to the confessional closed. He prayed that his suspicions about Father Phillips were wrong.

"Bless me, father, for I have sinned," said a woman's nervous voice.

"How long has it been since your last confession?"

"Where's Father Phillips?" the woman asked, slightly confused.

"Please answer my question," the priest tersely replied.

"Maybe I should come back another—"

"Father Phillips cannot be here today," Forbin replied. "I assure you that your words will only be heard by God and myself."

"I don't doubt your word, Father," the woman continued. "It's just that I really needed to talk to him."

"I can relay your message to him if you like."

The woman said nothing.

"How long has it been since your last confession?" the priest asked, this time in a more friendly tone.

"I don't know," she replied.

"What do you wish to confess?"

Silence.

"You can tell me anything."

"Father, have you ever loved anyone?"

"Of course."

"I mean really loved someone," she replied, this time asserting herself. "Loved them as if your only reason for existence was to love that person?"

"It sounds more like an obsession than love."

"You don't understand," she sighed.

"And Father Phillips did?"

"No one can understand, but he tried. He's always tried to help everyone in this parish."

The priest reached inside his robes. "Even if it meant violating the laws of God?"

The woman said nothing.

Forbin continued. "And would he consort with the forces of darkness—"

"How dare you!" the woman replied. This time her voice was lower, and almost masculine in tone. "How dare you judge Father Phillips! He—"

"Made deals with the agents of evil?"

Silence.

"Father," a hissing voice said this time. "How do you know God isn't evil?"

The priest pulled an ornate dagger from his robe. "I have read—"

"How do you know?" the voice hissed again.

"I have faith," he replied.

"You must have a lot of faith if can look at the world and still believe in the goodness of God."

Suddenly the wall shattered, and two arms, covered in fish-like scales, reached for Forbin

"Maybe God will thank you when you see him," the monster hissed as its clawed hands closed about Forbin's throat.

Forbin thrust the dagger into the creature's arm. It let out an inhuman wail, then it was gone in a shower of splintered wood. Forbin staggered to his feet and tried to give chase.

Concept: Since the early days of the Catholic Church, there have been holy orders dedicated to ridding the world of Satan's minions. These orders reached the zenith of their influence and power in medieval times. They campaigned against the obscene

cults of the Earthbound across the breadth of the known world, stamping out the demons' sources of Faith and driving them into hiding.

After the Middle Ages, these holy orders began to wane as infernalism declined in Europe and elsewhere. Many of these orders disbanded as belief in the supernatural faded. A few survived as secret orders, though, unknown to the Church hierarchy.

With the arrival of the fallen, these orders are experiencing a revival. Although their groups tend to be small, the knowledge, holy rituals and weapons they possess make them some of the most dangerous enemies of the fallen.

Personality: Members of these orders tend to have forceful personalities. Autocrat, Bravo, Fanatic, Survivor and Traditionalist are common Natures, though there are Caregiver and Penitent members as well.

Attributes: Members have various Attributes, though most have high Mental Attributes. Those in the field may have good physical scores.

Abilities: All have strong Knowledges. They also possess Alertness, Awareness, and Intuition

Backgrounds: Allies (1-3), Contacts, (1-2), Influence (1), Followers (1-2), Resources (1-2)

Faith Potential: 1-2 (Group leaders may have as high as 3)

Powers: Immunity to Revelation, Blessed Items, Holy Prayers

FATHER DENNIS FORBIN

Nature: Fanatic

Attributes: Strength 2, Dexterity 3, Stamina 2, Charisma 3, Manipulation 4, Appearance 2, Perception 3, Intelligence 4, Wits 4

Abilities: Academics (Theology) 4, Alertness 2, Awareness 1, Dodge 2, Intimidation 2, Leadership 3, Performance 2, Occult 2, Research 4, Subterfuge 3

Backgrounds: Allies 2, Contacts 2, Followers 3

Willpower: 6

Faith Potential: 3

Powers: Immunity to Revelation, Prayers of Binding, Abjuration and Exorcism, Blessed Dagger (Abjuration)

TRUE BELIEVERS

Folsom Maximum Security Prison had strict rules regarding prisoner interviews. The warden allowed Chris only two hours a day to tape, but by the time he and the cameraman got through the searches and the daily paperwork the available time had been cut in half. There wasn't much time for small talk once the guards brought Lance Carter to the interview room.

Chris motioned to the cameraman to start recording. "Lance, I have to ask you this. How did you become involved in the death of Rich Burdett?"

"We saved Rich from the everlasting fires of Hell! I've told everyone that from the beginning. He'd let the Devil into his soul, and we had no other choice if he was to find his way to Heaven. I just wish I could have stopped him before he killed Joe."

Chris and the cameraman glanced at each other.

"You mean Joe Burdett?"

"Yeah." Lance sighed. "Little Joe." He buried his face in his hands.

Chris shook his head. "Lance, Joe isn't dead."

Lance looked up.

"He's very much alive. In fact, he's been instrumental in making this documentary possible. I've even got some audio tapes of our interviews here if you'd like to listen to them."

Lance slammed his fist on the table.

"You're a damned liar! I saw the demon tear Joe's throat out! He's dead!"

"Lance, listen to me."

"No, you listen to me. For years Reverend Steward was right. The Devil is walking among us!"

"Did he tell you that Rich was—"

"Joe suspected it and told me. He said his brother was questioning God."

"College students do that sometimes," replied Chris.

"Damn it! Rich wouldn't do that. So I went to Reverend Steward. He knows about these things."

"Lance, I know about his group. Anything they don't like is the work of the Devil."

"Why don't you talk to Rich's college friends? They'll tell you he was trying to buy their souls."

"Rich offered to help, but—"

"I saw it myself!"

"Then tell me."

Lance stood up. "At the last meeting, Reverend Steward told us to wait and pray for Rich's soul. But some of the students wouldn't listen. Said they had a plan to beat the Devil out of Rich. Just like the Bible says. I helped them. I told them to take Joe along. Maybe Joe would give Rich the strength to fight the Devil."

"What happened then?"

"We went to his place, and… well, we tried talking to him at first. We sat down with him and tried to get him to pray with us, but he called us fools and worse. That's when Joe got in his face and rebuked him in the name of Christ, and…" Lance's face went pale. "That's when the demon showed himself. He tore Joe's throat out with his claws, and we knew we didn't have a choice. Like Reverend Stewart says, we're warriors of the Lord, and sometimes we've got to spill the blood of sinners so that the righteous will prevail."

"And that's when you tied Richard up with electrical cord and beat him to death. Because he was a demon. Not because he'd decided to leave your church."

"I don't remember how it all happened. The last thing I saw was Joe falling down, holding his throat, and the blood… dear God…" Lance's face twisted with pain.

Chris shifted uncomfortably in his chair. "Lance, Joe's throat was badly torn, but the cuts missed the major blood vessels. It took a lot of stitches, but he's okay. He says that Rich had nothing to do with what happened to him. Instead, he says that once you'd finished killing Rich, you turned on him, slashing his neck repeatedly with a kitchen knife. So tell me the truth. What happened?"

"I'm telling you the truth!" Lance cried. "The demon tore his throat out! Unless…" his eyes widened in horror. "Unless he never meant to kill Joe at all. Oh God. God preserve us. Joe didn't die. The Devil left Rich and took him instead. What have I done?"

Concept: For years, many ministers have claimed that the Devil is walking the Earth spreading evil and that true believers must rally together to save mankind before it's too late. These ministers and their followers didn't have a true foe to pit themselves against before, but as the exploits of the fallen find their way into the news, these believers see through the bizarre headlines to grasp the "truth" that lies beneath. They know nothing about the true nature of the fallen, but after a lifetime of fire-and-brimstone sermons, these true believers figure they have all the facts they need.

Some of these erstwhile holy warriors are involved in traveling revival shows, going city to city looking for demons. Others may be part of Internet chat groups, sharing information about sightings and coordinating "crusades" against known locations of demonic activity. Some may be members of college religious groups who suspect that the Devil is taking over their universities.

Many of these members have above-average levels of Faith, which can make them dangerous for the Fallen to confront. Many of these individuals know very little about demons, however, other than what they've read in the Bible or heard from a sermon. They may also have wildly inaccurate information gathered from various religious books.

As a result, these demon-hunters can be fooled by a clever fallen. Worse, they may attack idealist types, thinking that they're under demonic control.

Personality: Believers come from various backgrounds. Some found God after fighting addiction. Others grew up in religious homes and never lost their faith. All are motivated by the desire to serve God. Architect, Autocrat, Fanatic and Traditionalist are common Natures. There are also Penitent and Conformist believers as well.

Attributes: Attributes vary greatly among the believers. The more successful demon-hunters have high Stamina, and high Manipulation ratings.

Abilities: Due to their diverse backgrounds, Abilities vary greatly, though most have a dot or two in Academics.

Backgrounds: Allies (1-2), Contacts (1-2), Followers (1-3), Resources (1-3)

Faith Potential: 1-2

Powers: Immunity to Revelation, Holy Prayers

REVEREND BRIAN STEWART

Nature: Architect

Attributes: Strength 2, Dexterity 2, Stamina 3, Charisma 3, Manipulation 4, Appearance 3, Perception 2, Intelligence 4, Wits 4

Abilities: Academics (Bible-Study) 3, Alertness 2, Awareness 1, Dodge 2, Intimidation 2, Leadership 4, Performance 3, Research 1, Subterfuge 3

Backgrounds: Contacts 2, Followers 3, Resources 2

Willpower: 6

Faith Potential: 2

Powers: Holy Prayers of Binding, Abjuration and Exorcism, Sacred Object (crucifix)

THIEVES OF DARKNESS

Shu-Durul struggled inside the binding circle. Whoever had laid it knew him well. He could just barely feel the spiritual gravity of the Abyss beyond its edges, daring him to cross that fateful threshold.

He could see 20 robed figures staring at him from outside the circle. Even despite his demonic nature, they remained unmoved.

He'd learned about the secret society through one of his thralls. At the time it sounded like fertile ground for a demon such as himself and a way to acquire more powerful

servants. Now he was trapped in a boardroom filled with occult paraphernalia.

"Release me at once!" Shu-Durul shouted.

He thought he heard a chuckle.

Shu-Durul spat a stream of curses that crackled in the air like lightning.

"Silence," spoke a stern voice.

A hooded figure stepped forward.

"Who dares—"

The figure tossed salt toward Shu-Durul, and every nerve in the demon's mortal shell erupted in pain. He howled.

"I dare to do this to you, Mr. Ryan," the leader said. "But I know that isn't your real name. For now, you can know me as the leader of this society. An ancient society dedicated to studying the servants of the Morningstar."

Shu-Durul fell to the ground, convulsing in pain.

"Our scholars speak of epic struggles with others like you. It has been a while since we tried to capture one of your kind. I expected a challenge." He chuckled. "You disappointed us. Perhaps you are just a minor being. A mere servant of a true demon, perhaps?"

The pain vanished. "Why are doing this when I can give you anything you want?"

The leader laughed. "No I don't think you would give me what I want." The leader snapped his fingers. One person began to chant. "We don't want any gifts from you. Gifts from your kind always have strings attached." He snapped his fingers. Another person began to chant. "We want the source of your gifts." Another snap. Another person chanting. "We want your essence, Mr. Ryan. We want your power." Another snap. Another chant. "We want to become divine."

Shu-Durul charged at the leader. The barrier pushed him to the ground. Shu-Durul laughed as he slowly stood up.

"Your prison is weakening," laughed Shu-Durul. "When I get out—"

"We'll be done with you long before the shell breaks." He snapped his fingers. Shu-Durul screamed.

Concept: Not all demon-hunters fight on behalf of God. Some seek out demons to steal their power. Why bargain with a demon for a few measly favors when you can become as powerful as a demon yourself?

Since ancient times, magical societies sought to exploit the demons they summoned. Some wished to enslave them. Others sought to drain them of their essence to fuel their rituals.

As superstitious belief faded in the world, these societies declined as it became harder to summon demons. The few that survived did so by seeking out the Earthbound, or they dedicated themselves to preserving their arcane arts.

The arrival of the fallen has revived these societies. They now seek out all demons, fallen and Earthbound alike, for their rituals. Some will pose as potential thralls in hopes of luring a demon to its doom.

Personality: Exploiting demons is the ultimate power trip. Many Autocrats, Bravos and Directors are attracted to these societies. Addicts who are addicted to the danger and excitement are also represented, as are Bon Vivants and Fanatics.

Attributes: Most have high Mental ratings, usually with three or more dots in Intelligence and Perception. Many also have high Manipulation scores.

Abilities: All members have 3 or higher in Occult and Research Knowledges. Many also have high Academics, Science, Politics or Finance Knowledges, depending on their "normal" profession.

Backgrounds: Contacts (1-2), Influence (1-2), Followers (1-3), Resources (1-2)

Faith Potential: 1 (Group leaders can have as high as 2)

Powers: Immunity to Revelation, Summoning and Binding Rituals, Blessed Items

WILLIAM EMERSON (FIRST PRECEPTOR OF THE STAR CATCHERS)

Nature: Bon Vivant

Attributes: Strength 1, Dexterity 2, Stamina 2, Charisma 4, Manipulation 4, Appearance 2, Perception 4, Intelligence 4, Wits 4

Abilities: Alertness 4, Awareness 5, Computer 2, Dodge 3, Empathy 3, Etiquette 3, Expression, 3, Finance 4, Intimidation 4, Investigation 3, Leadership 4, Occult 5, Politics 2, Research 4, Subterfuge 3, Technology 2

Backgrounds: Contacts 2, Followers 3, Resources 2

Willpower: 8

Faith Potential: 2

Powers: Immunity to Revelation, Summoning and Binding Rituals

SERVANTS OF THE EARTHBOUND

Unlike the fallen, the Earthbound are demons who escaped Hell's clutches hundreds, even thousands of years ago and have tormented the human race ever since in the guise of dark and terrible gods. Though finally driven into hiding with the rise of Christianity and the supplanting of faith with reason as the cornerstone of humanity's perceptions, the return of the fallen has stirred the Earthbound from their long slumber to complete their obscene subversion of the human race.

Individually the Earthbound are several orders of magnitude more powerful than the most potent fallen, having had ages to hone their powers and adapt to the world as it is today. This very strength is also their weakness, though. Their spirits are too powerful to possess human bodies, much like the spirits of the great barons and overlords still bound in the Abyss. Therefore, for the time being, they must work through the efforts of their agents: ever-growing cults of worshippers drawn from the decadent and the disaffected and the willing (or unwilling) fealty of monstrous demons who have every reason to hate humanity as much as the Earthbound themselves. These servants of the Earthbound are found in nearly every major city across the globe, hunting and enslaving the fallen wherever they are found or perpetrating acts of violence and corruption designed to further poison humanity's collective soul.

THE THUG

OFFICAL POLICE REPORT, COUNTY OF SAN BERNADINO

NO PHOTOCOPIES TO BE MADE WITHOUT PERMISSION

CONTENTS: *INITIAL STATEMENT OF GERARD "JERRY" BROWNLOW, CONCERNING GUNFIGHT AT "HELL BENDERS" CYCLE GANG CLUBHOUSE.*

(Note: interviewee under emergency medical treatment at time statement was made)

It was about one, one-thirty in the morning, something like that. There were about 10 of us, just hanging out at the clubhouse. You know, shooting pool, drinking, that sort of thing.

Then there's this massive fucking crash, and Leo Daschell drives right through the fucking plate glass windows on his hog. Just right through 'em. Glass everywhere, people yelling.

Anyway, it's fucking Leo, who we told to leave and never come back last week. Guy was a headcase, you know? Tried to kick the shit out of Joe Jaffee's old lady for no fucking reason. So we told him to fuck off.

But here he is, through the fucking window. With a shotgun in one hand. And when his bike hit the ground, he just started shooting. He's driving around the club — which is only four rooms, you know, not exactly spacious — just blowing people away.

Well, we all throw down on him and start shooting. I mean, self-defense, right? We got a right to protect ourselves. I took cover behind the Coke machine and gave it my best shot, and I know I hit the son of a bitch. I saw plenty of people hit him, but he wouldn't go down.

It's got to be Kevlar, right? Fucker had to be wearing a bulletproof vest. I thought I saw someone hit him in the head, but I must've been wrong.

Anyway, we're shooting the son of a bitch, but he's not feeling it, and he's just going off with that shotgun, taking us out. When he ran out of ammo, he pulled a fucking Desert Eagle out of his jacket and kept going. When he got me in the shoulder, I went down and didn't move. I figured I'd play dead, try not to get shot anymore.

All of us, taken out in about two minutes. Then he pulls the key to the safe off Joe's body, unlocks it and gets out that weird box Joe bought in Mexico. I mean, what the fuck? All that for some fucking silver box?

Then he got back on his hog and pulled out. You joes showed up about five minutes later. Thanks for all the fucking help.

Concept: Thugs are thralls with a simple purpose — to fight and to kill the enemies of the Earthbound. They are not meant to be subtle or to work behind the scenes — they exist to shoot an opponent in the face, or to beat a meddling occultist to death with a lead pipe. Thugs are usually violent, dangerous people even before becoming thralls of the Earthbound. A thug might be an ex-soldier, a gangbanger, a neo-Nazi militia member or a corrupt police officer.

Pact: Thugs usually have a burning hatred or serious grudge against some individual or group, for reasons real or imaginary. The Earthbound will offer them the power to kill their enemies in return for their service. Since that service involves the violence thugs are already attracted to, the mortal rarely balks at the offer.

Personality: Sane, well-adjusted people don't voluntarily enter lives of extreme violence. Thugs are generally attracted to inflicting pain, and they see other mortals as weaklings or soulless toys for them to victimize. Thugs often have Addict, Bravo, Fanatic, Rebel or Survivor Natures.

Attributes: Thugs tend to emphasize the Physical Attributes, of course, making them more dangerous as fighters. Despite the title, thugs aren't necessarily stupid. A thug might have good Mental Attributes, but still tend toward physical action.

Abilities: The combat Abilities — Brawl, Dodge, Firearms and Melee — are of paramount importance to

thugs. Also useful are Abilities that help them find targets and get into position. Thugs usually have good ratings in Athletics, Drive, Intimidation and Stealth.

Backgrounds: Allies (1-2), Mentor (1-5)

Powers: The Earthbound will usually improve the physical capabilities of their thugs. This might be as simple as improving their Physical Attributes or as complex as giving them a physical enhancement such as claws or armored skin. Two useful enhancements are the power to inflict lethal damage barehanded and the ability to soak lethal damage. Thugs are rarely gifted with more complex demonic powers.

LEO DASCHELL

Nature: Bravo

Attributes: Strength 5, Dexterity 3, Stamina 5, Charisma 2, Manipulation 2, Appearance 2, Perception 2, Intelligence 2, Wits 3

Abilities: Athletics 2, Brawl 4, Dodge 1, Drive 3, Firearms 3, Intimidation 3, Melee 1, Stealth 1, Streetwise 2, Survival 1, Technology 1

Backgrounds: Allies 1, Mentor 3

Willpower: 5

Gifts: Daschell's Strength and Stamina have been enhanced. By spending a point of Willpower, he can soak lethal damage with his Stamina for a number of turns equal to his Stamina rating. Once per scene, he can spend a turn concentrating, then spend a point of Willpower in order to heal one level of lethal or bashing damage.

THE IDEALIST

Dear Mom,

Sorry about not writing for a few months. Things have been pretty CRAZY here. Between classes and trying to get something worthwhile done, I haven't had time for a social life — let alone long enough to write to you.

So how am I doing? Well, the bad news is that my grades could be better. I'm trying, I really am, but there's so MUCH I have to get done. I'm falling behind on my classes. I promise I'll do better after Spring Break. The good news is that I'm doing a LOT with the Action Group and we're really getting things accomplished. It's more than just protests and demonstrations, we're really DOING things. And I have YOU to thank for it.

A lot of students here are anti-globalization, but they don't really have much of a background in resistance. I mean, it's GREAT that they want to make a difference, don't get me wrong. But they're not coming from fifteen years on a commune, they don't have ROOTS in the movement. So a few of them starting looking to me to be an organizer and co-ordinator, because it feels natural to me.

But leadership and experience isn't enough to make a difference. We were getting together, we had

collective meetings, we arranged marches, but it doesn't have any effect. The WTO and their cronies don't care what the people WANT, they hold us off with their shocktroops and decide our futures anyway. So I started getting really frustrated.

That's when I started having the DREAMS. And again, that's why I have you to thank for things. You taught me to accept my own spirituality, to reach out for the Higher Powers that are there to guide and nurture us. Well, these dreams… they came from a spirit, a Power of some kind. A being of light that wants to help us protect the peoples of the world.

Over the last month or so, I've been doing a lot of meditation, a lot of communing with the Benefactor — that's what I call Her, the Power that's touched me. The first thing She did was send us good fortune in the form of funding grants from college administration. Now I've TRIED to get funds from them in the past, so believe me, having it come through like this was a MIRACLE. The Benefactor also showed me who to contact for getting things like vans, equipment and medical supplies at little or no cost.

The most AMAZING part, though, is that She shows me how to spy on the globalists and learn their plans! Mom, you wouldn't believe it. I just walk into Fat Cat Central, into banks and government buildings and whatever, and no one sees me!

The stuff I've learned… Mom, it's so HORRIBLE. They won't stop at ANYTHING for profits. And I'm starting to realize how far we have to go to make a difference and do the right thing in this world.

I'm going to drop out of sight for a while during spring break. I need to meet other organizers and compare notes. With the help of my Benefactor, I know how to take these BASTARDS down, no matter how many water cannons and Presidents they have on their side.

If it all goes well, then I'll get so much done that I'll have lots more time for school. If it doesn't, burn this letter. And don't tell ANYONE you heard from me.

Gotta go save the world now. Lotsa love,
Cloud.

Concept: Not every thrall comes to the Earthbound seeking power or glory. Some have more altruistic motives; others stumble across the demon's secret by chance. Idealists have little or no connection to the occult, violence or the world of the powerful. They're people who stumble across veterans of the war and make the terrible mistake of thinking that struggle can be used for a good purpose. An idealist might be a student activist, a crusader for morality, a struggling artist or a well-meaning cop.

Pact: An idealist isn't looking for power to benefit himself, he needs it to help others or to fix a situation he feels is wrong. The Earthbound offers tools and advantages to aid in the "good fight," all the while

working to corrupt the idealist and use her for its own unspeakable purposes.

Personality: Unlike other thralls, idealists are generally normal, well-adjusted people. Their weakness is usually strong feelings about a certain cause, which drives them to accept an Earthbound's offer of aid. Typical Natures are Architect, Bon Vivant, Penitent, Rebel or Visionary.

Attributes: Idealists come from all walks of life and vary wildly in their abilities. Most, though, are involved in some kind of activism and tend to have good Social Attributes to aid their cause.

Abilities: Again, it's hard to make general statements about idealists because they're so varied. Most, however, tend to emphasize Abilities such as Bureaucracy, Empathy, Etiquette, Expression, Leadership or Performance. This social aptitude is what makes them attractive thralls. They can communicate well with others, without seeming false or power-hungry.

Backgrounds: Contacts (1-2), Mentor (1-5), Resources (1-3)

Gifts: Idealists generally want aid in their cause, and that's what the Earthbound provides. This aid might be something as simple as resources, followers or other real-world assistance. The Earthbound might also grant more metaphysical gifts such as improved Attributes or demonic powers, but it is less likely to gift someone with grotesque physical enhancements.

Cloud Brannigan

Nature: Visionary

Attributes: Strength 2, Dexterity 3, Stamina 2, Charisma 5, Manipulation 3, Appearance 3, Perception 3, Intelligence 3, Wits 3

Abilities: Academics 2, Athletics 2, Bureaucracy 3, Computer 3, Empathy 4, Expression 2, Firearms 1, Intuition 2, Investigation 2, Research 2, Security 3, Stealth 3 Technology 2

Backgrounds: Allies 2, Mentor 3, Resources 1

Willpower: 5

Powers: Cloud's Charisma has been enhanced by her "benefactor." By spending a point of Willpower, Cloud can become invisible for a number of minutes equal to her successes on a Manipulation + Stealth roll (difficulty 6). She can also see in complete darkness for a scene by spending a point of Willpower.

The Occultist

Not for the first time, Father Sean Riordan considered the fact that he was damned.

Once that had mattered to him, but now it was nothing but an irritating stray thought, a distraction. He had more important things to worry about — like how to get the Liber Malictorium *out of the library. It would have been so much* easier back when the book had been written. Then he could have just hidden the book under his cassock and walked out.

But this wasn't the Dark Ages, and the library at Notre Dame Seminary had extremely good security. Magnetic sensors, computerized records, video cameras. Plus, he was wearing a sweatshirt, not a cassock. Even late at night, when there were probably only three people in the whole building, this was going to be difficult.

Riordan stood by the bookshelf, thinking. The Malictorium *was part of the sealed collection, and it had taken him too much money and effort just to gain access for him to give up now. He had to get it out — and if that meant going to extreme lengths, that's what had to be done. He caught the eye of the night custodian and beckoned the man over.*

A few minutes later, a gunshot rang out through the library, and the security guards bolted for the upper stacks. In the shadows, Riordan waited for them to pass. He knew what they'd find — the custodian dead by his own hand, having blown his brains out to silence the terrifying commands Riordan whispered into his ears. Tugging the hood of the sweatshirt over his head, Father Sean ran for the exit, jumping over the checkout counter to avoid the magnetic readers. A few moments of sprinting, and he was clear of the building.

Not for the first time, Father Sean Riordan reflected that he was damned. But as he inspected the tome of blasphemous knowledge his master required and thought of the terrible wisdom he could learn from the book of demonology, he decided he didn't give a fuck about his damnation.

Not when he had the chance to gain power instead.

Concept: People who learn occult secrets are often seized by the desire to learn more, without thought of the consequences. Occultists already have a strong backing in mysticism and secrets before falling prey to the Earthbound. An occultist might be a New Age mystic, a priest, a historical scholar or a dabbler in black magic.

Pact: Occultists thirst for hidden knowledge, believing that knowing secrets makes them better than other people. The Earthbound are the ultimate prize for these people, and the promise of further knowledge and mystical power is all they need to seal the pact.

Personality: For many occultists, knowing a secret is more important than using it. They tend to combine the intellectualism of scholars with the rapacious greed of a thief. Natures such as Curmudgeon, Director, Pedagogue, Traditionalist and Visionary are all appropriate.

Attributes: Naturally, occultists emphasize the Mental Attributes, especially Intelligence. Those who use their knowledge as a way of influencing others — such as a mystic with an entourage of students — may have good ratings in Manipulation or Charisma.

Abilities: Occultists focus on Knowledges, primarily Occult and Research, but possibly also Academics, Computer, Investigation and Linguistics. Depending on how they go about obtaining their hidden secrets, occultists might also have good ratings in Awareness, Intuition, Security, Streetwise and Subterfuge.

Backgrounds: Contacts (1-3), Followers (1-3), Mentor (1-5), Resources (1-3)

Gifts: The Earthbound usually offer occultists gifts that enhance their ability to learn secrets. Enhanced Mental or Social Attributes are one possibility, as are the offers of demonic powers. Earthbound might also teach Occultists summoning or binding rituals, or even the True Names of their enemies.

Father Sean Riordan

Nature: Traditionalist

Attributes: Strength 2, Dexterity 2, Stamina 2, Charisma 3, Manipulation 4, Appearance 2, Perception 3, Intelligence 4, Wits 5

Abilities: Academics 2, Awareness 3, Empathy 2, Expression 1, Intuition 3, Law 2, Medicine 2, Occult 4, Research 4, Stealth 1, Subterfuge 2

Backgrounds: Contacts: 1, Followers: 2, Resources: 1

Willpower: 7

Gifts: Riordan's Manipulation and Wits Attributes have been improved by his master. He possesses limited versions of the high-Torment evocations Lamp of Faith and Find the Faithful, which are activated by spending a point of Willpower for each use. He knows the basic structure of binding rituals and can attempt to modify them to fit a given demon.

The Power Broker

COUNCILOR MENENDES WITHDRAWS FROM ELECTION

Councilor Sandler offers sympathy to former rival.

In a statement today, Chicago city councilor Herman Menendes announced his withdrawal from the upcoming mayoral election. He cited overwork and a desire to spend more time with his family as his main reasons for withdrawing and stated that he was planning on focusing on local and borough issues over citywide issues for the foreseeable future.

Councilor Irene Sandler held a press conference shortly after Councilor Menendes's statement, offering sympathy and condolences to her former rival in the election. She wished him all the best in his future endeavors and expressed regret that Councilor Menendes would no longer be present at next week's debate.

The sentiments were a far cry from the often vicious disagreements between the two councilors during the previous weeks of the election campaign. Readers may recall councilor Menendes's allegations of financial irregularities

and vote-rigging in the Sandler campaign — allegations he was forced to withdraw and apologize for after he failed to present promised evidence.

With the withdrawal of Councilor Menendes and the death of independent candidate Geoff Skellams last month in a car accident, voters are faced with only three candidates for the position of mayor. Councilor Sandler is currently considered to be the favorite and is expected to win the election by a narrow but comfortable margin.

Councilor Menendes refused to comment further on his withdrawal from the election. He is expected to spend the next few weeks on vacation with his family and should return to active duties after the election.

Concept: A power broker was always someone with a lust for power, even before encountering their demonic master. Successful power brokers already had a measure of power, but desire more; less successful ones have nothing but their craving to be important. A power broker might be a businessperson, a city councilor, a media magnate or a bureaucrat.

Pact: Power, wealth, prestige, fame — these are the things a power broker wants more than air. The Earthbound are only too happy to provide their thralls with power as long as the power broker uses his newfound advantages to increase the power and dominance of his master at the same time.

Personality: Power brokers are controllers and leaders trying to amass their own personal empire. Typical Natures include Architect, Autocrat, Conniver, Director or Perfectionist.

Attributes: Social Attributes are the primary focus of power brokers, giving them the ability to command and use others. Many also have strong Mental Attributes, particularly Wits.

Abilities: Power brokers are social animals and are skilled in controlling/ interacting with others. They tend to have high ratings in Bureaucracy, Etiquette, Finance, Leadership, Politics and Subterfuge.

Backgrounds: Contacts (1-3), Influence (1-3), Mentor (1-5), Resources (1-4)

Gifts: To get power, you need power. The most obvious gift for a power broker is real-world advantages — money, resources, followers, connections and so on. Another useful gift is enhancing the thrall's Social Attributes or possibly bestowing powers that influence the minds of others. Power brokers rarely receive physical enhancements.

Councillor Irene Sandler

Nature: Autocrat

Attributes: Strength 2, Dexterity 2, Stamina 2, Charisma 5, Manipulation 5, Appearance 3, Perception 2, Intelligence 4, Wits 4

Abilities: Alertness 2, Bureaucracy 4, Empathy 2, Etiquette 3, Finance 1, Leadership 4, Politics 4, Subterfuge 4

Backgrounds: Contacts 3, Influence 2, Mentor 3, Resources 3

Willpower: 8

Gifts: Sandler's Manipulation and Charisma have been increased by her master. She also possesses a version of the high-Torment evocation Engage. Several of her staff members are also thralls, and two of them are dangerous thugs.

THE DESTROYER

"Finnegan," Rochelle whined, "it's almost one in the morning. I want to go out."

"Patience, petal," Finnegan said from his bedroom. "I'm just getting my happy face on. You don't want me to go out with my shitty face on, do you?"

"I just want to go now," she complained. "That E's starting to kick, and I want to dance."

"Alright, lovey, alright. Just give me a second." In the bedroom, Finnegan adjusted his jacket in the mirror and rubbed a little coke into his gums. I do indeed look mighty fine, he thought. Now if only that bitch would shut the fuck up. He bent down, reached under the bed, and pulled out a plastic jerry can of gasoline. Bit of stress relief tonight, he thought as he put the can into a camera case and zipped it shut.

"You're not taking photos, are you? We finished the shoot already."

"No, sweetie, not tonight. But I always need me tools now, don't I? Now say thanks to Finnegan for the lovely drugs."

"Thank you," she pouted.

"Close enough. Let's go."

❖　　　❖　　　❖

It took the London Fire Department three hours to put out the blaze. Finnegan watched from the window of the nightclub across the street, in between selling the rest of his supply of E. The club bored him, Rochelle bored him. Just more stupid, brainless fashion monkeys, who don't give a fuck about anything but labels and cocaine prices.

But fire was different. Fire fascinated; fire lured. Fire was beautiful in ways that none of the models he photographed could ever approach. Nothing took the edge off the week or distracted him from the stupid puling masses of London like setting a fire and watching it burn.

Too loud in here. I need air. I need to smell the smoke. Finnegan got to his feet, wandered downstairs to the street. He bought a coffee, joined the rubberneckers around the still smoldering wreck of the empty hotel.

One of these days, I'll end up burning someplace that's still occupied. Won't that be a fucking tragedy.

He was standing there, drinking coffee and dreaming about holocausts, when the fire spoke to him, when it whispered in his mind. And as the fire made him an offer too tempting to refuse, Finnegan felt himself grinning.

He felt himself looking forward to tomorrow's Vogue shoot.

Concept: Destroyers are even more dangerous than thugs, but without the same urge for physical violence. They are often sociopaths who channel their lust for blasphemy and violation into careers that let them inflict anguish and pain on others. A destroyer might be a drug-dealer, an arsonist, a spy or a terrorist.

Pact: The Earthbound look for agents to spread misery and destruction; a destroyer wants the power to take his activities to a new level of horror — the two are made for each other. In many cases, all the Earthbound has to do is give the destroyer a little power, then sit back and watch him naturally do all his master could desire.

Personality: Destroyers are usually bastards, through and through — the kind of sociopaths that poison a neighborhood dog just because its barking annoys them. Typical Natures include Bravo, Conniver, Curmudgeon, Fanatic and Rogue.

Attributes: While thugs concentrate on the physical, destroyers are likely to emphasize Mental Attributes. They may also have good Social Attributes, particularly Manipulation.

Abilities: Destroyers focus much less on straightforward combat Abilities, and more on Abilities that cause massive destruction quickly. They tend to have high ratings in Bureaucracy, Demolitions, Security, Subterfuge and Technology.

Backgrounds: Contacts (1-2), Mentor (1-5), Resources (1-2)

Gifts: Destroyers look for advantages that allow them better opportunities for destruction. This might mean enhanced Mental or Physical Attributes, immunity to fire or increased soak, or powers that allow access to targets, such as invisibility or mind-control. Destroyers are also likely to possess physical enhancements, since they run the risk of encountering armed opposition to their schemes.

KELLY FINNEGAN

Nature: Conniver

Attributes: Strength 2, Dexterity 3, Stamina 4, Charisma 3, Manipulation 4, Appearance 3, Perception 2, Intelligence 3, Wits 4

Abilities: Athletics 2, Awareness 2, Brawl 2, Computer 1, Demolitions 3, Drive 2, Expression 3, Melee 1, Stealth 2, Streetwise 3, Subterfuge 3, Technology 1

Backgrounds: Contacts (1), Mentor (3), Resources (2)

Willpower: 7

Gifts: Finnegan's Stamina and Wits have been enhanced by his master. He can spend a point of

Willpower to soak fire damage with his Stamina for a scene. He also possesses a limited form of the high-Torment evocation Fuel.

HUNTING PARTIES

For the Earthbound, the sudden influx of new demons into the waking world is both a blessing and a curse. These newcomers are poised to interfere with plans and schemes that have been developed over centuries, and that cannot be borne. But in this faith-starved world, the fallen represent something more than just obstacles. They are sources of precious energy, ones that must be exploited to lend the Earthbound the power they need to survive and prosper.

Sending a single thrall, though, is a waste of resources. No thrall, no matter how enhanced, can measure up to the sheer power of a demon. What's needed is a hunting party — a group of thralls handpicked by their master to effectively take down fallen targets.

The exact nature and style of a hunting party depends entirely on the Earthbound that controls it and the thralls that comprise it. The following material is meant as a guideline to help Storytellers design hunting parties that fit the needs of their chronicle.

Storytellers should ask the following questions about a hunting party:

What is its purpose? Parties are usually either kill squads — sent to destroy a threat to the Earthbound quickly and decisively — or capture squads — sent to imprison a fallen target so that the Earthbound can use him as a source of Faith.

How does it operate? Subtle parties spend a lot of time and energy pinpointing a target in secret, then operating without leaving evidence. Overt parties are more likely to make sudden, noisy attacks on their target, then clean up any evidence and witnesses afterward.

What tools does the team use? Does the party focus on occult tools such as rituals and artifacts? Do they use heavy firepower and high-tech equipment? Does it prefer to work at a remove, using other agents and mundane groups like the police as their puppets?

How many are there in the group? A small group must be careful and make clever use of limited resources. A large group can afford to take bigger risks, and it can survive the loss of a few members.

The Storyteller characters in a hunting party usually fall into one of four categories:

Thinkers: The people who plan the attacks, organize the other thralls and make sure everything works.

Hitters: The thralls who actually fight the demons, whether with guns, bombs or supernatural powers.

Talkers: Because hunting parties operate in secret, they need members who can fool the police, fast-talk their way past neighbors and generally smooth the way for the rest of the group.

Support: Drivers, medics, occultists with binding rituals — any thrall who's charged with assisting the project is classed as support.

A "typical" kill squad would consist mainly of hitters, with a thinker in charge and perhaps a few support people for backup. A capture squad might have only one hitter, relying instead on talkers and support personnel.

INDEX

INDEX

INDEX

DEMON
the fallen

NAME: _____ NATURE: _____ HOUSE: _____
PLAYER: _____ DEMEANOR: _____ FACTION: _____
CHRONICLE: _____ CONCEPT: _____ VISAGE: _____

ATTRIBUTES

PHYSICAL
Strength_____●OOOO
Dexterity_____●OOOO
Stamina_____●OOOO

SOCIAL
Charisma_____●OOOO
Manipulation_____●OOOO
Appearance_____●OOOO

MENTAL
Perception_____●OOOO
Intelligence_____●OOOO
Wits_____●OOOO

ABILITIES

TALENTS
Alertness_____OOOOO
Athletics_____OOOOO
Awareness_____OOOOO
Brawl_____OOOOO
Dodge_____OOOOO
Empathy_____OOOOO
Expression_____OOOOO
Intimidation_____OOOOO
Intuition_____OOOOO
Leadership_____OOOOO
Streetwise_____OOOOO
Subterfuge_____OOOOO

SKILLS
Animal Ken_____OOOOO
Crafts_____OOOOO
Demolitions_____OOOOO
Drive_____OOOOO
Etiquette_____OOOOO
Firearms_____OOOOO
Melee_____OOOOO
Performance_____OOOOO
Security_____OOOOO
Stealth_____OOOOO
Survival_____OOOOO
Technology_____OOOOO

KNOWLEDGES
Academics_____OOOOO
Computer_____OOOOO
Finance_____OOOOO
Investigation_____OOOOO
Law_____OOOOO
Linguistics_____OOOOO
Medicine_____OOOOO
Occult_____OOOOO
Politics_____OOOOO
Religion_____OOOOO
Research_____OOOOO
Science_____OOOOO

ADVANTAGES

BACKGROUNDS
_____OOOOO
_____OOOOO
_____OOOOO
_____OOOOO
_____OOOOO

LORE
_____OOOOO
_____OOOOO
_____OOOOO
_____OOOOO
_____OOOOO

VIRTUES
Conscience_____●OOOO
Conviction_____●OOOO
Courage_____●OOOO

APOCALYPTIC FORM
_____
_____
_____
_____
_____
_____
_____
_____

FAITH
O O O O O O O O O O
☐ ☐ ☐ ☐ ☐ ☐ ☐ ☐ ☐ ☐

TORMENT
Permanent
O O O O O O O O O O
Temporary
O O O O O O O O O O

WILLPOWER
O O O O O O O O O O
☐ ☐ ☐ ☐ ☐ ☐ ☐ ☐ ☐ ☐

HEALTH
Bruised ___ ☐
Hurt −1 ☐
Injured −1 ☐
Wounded −2 ☐
Mauled −2 ☐
Crippled −5 ☐
Incapacitated ☐

EXPERIENCE
[   ]

Camera obscura

Floruit

Nocti

Quod erat demonstrandum

memento mori